Elements of Fluid Mechanics

Elements of
Fluid Mechanics

Dennis G. Shepherd

CORNELL UNIVERSITY

HARCOURT, BRACE & WORLD, INC. / NEW YORK · CHICAGO · BURLINGAME

ENDPAPERS *Front*. The flow pattern around a cylinder with circulation. From Professor F. N. M. Brown, Department of Aero-Space Engineering, University of Notre Dame. *Back*. The flow pattern in a diffuser, showing separation from one wall. From the film *Flow Visualization* by the National Committee for Fluid Mechanics Films and Educational Services Inc.

DRAWINGS BY FELIX COOPER

Library of Congress Catalog Card Number: 65-17741

Printed in the United States of America

Preface

Beginning texts in fluid mechanics cannot by their nature claim to present original material. Therefore, the reason for a new book must lie in the method of presentation, together with the choice of subject matter and the emphasis given to various topics. This volume, the outcome of many years' experience in teaching students of mechanical engineering, originated as supplementary material designed to augment the standard texts, most of which were oriented toward either hydraulics or aerodynamics. My aim was to stress compressible flow by introducing it as early as possible and integrating it with the other topics rather than dealing with it separately. The material was expanded and revised many times during its development into this text.

The level of presentation is suitable for third-year students with today's customary background in mathematics and mechanics. A knowledge of elementary thermodynamics is also assumed, so that compressible flow can be introduced without delay. It is intended that the text be supplemented by a book of gas tables giving, as a minimum, the isentropic-flow, Fanno, Rayleigh, and normal-shock functions. Considerable use is made of the second law of thermodynamics and the concept of entropy for interpretation of the phenomena of gas dynamics. In particular, the application of fluid mechanics to turbomachinery includes compressible-flow machines, such as compressors, steam turbines, and gas turbines, as well as hydraulic machines. The inclusion of such topics and the extended discussion of others have necessitated the trimming or omission of some material. Thus fluid statics is treated lightly, and open-channel flow not at all.

All ten chapters may be covered in a year of study comprising about seventy class sessions. Chapters 1 through 8, i.e., everything except the chapters on propulsion and turbomachinery, make up a four-hour one-semester course, whereas everything except the gas-dynamic relationships following nozzle flow in Chapter 7, the two-dimensional gas-flow developments of Chapter 8, and Chapters 9 and 10 makes up a standard three-hour one-semester course.

I endeavor to make clear not only the steps in an analysis but also the reasons for them, in the hope that the student may learn how to proceed independently. Accordingly, certain topics are treated in a rather detailed manner, and several analyses are performed for general, three-dimensional unsteady flow, even though subsequent discussion is limited to one- or two-dimensional steady flow. It seems to me preferable initially to envisage the general case and then to simplify it, rather than to have the student confronted at some later time with the more difficult extensions of theory when he is unfamiliar with the general formulation. Vector treatment is used to a degree, as vectors are now commonly taught in earlier studies; however, an appendix is provided for a quick review of or, if necessary, an introduction to the vector essentials needed for the text. Although some results are expressed in terms of vector operators for the benefit of the more mathematically sophisticated student, the developments never assume a knowledge of them. Rigor and depth stop short of the development of the Navier-Stokes equations, which nevertheless are quoted in a final or working form for comparison with certain other results. In my opinion, such development is too complicated and time-consuming at this stage and leaves all but the most exceptional student with insufficient real understanding to make it worthwhile.

Almost no examples are given; when they do appear, they are usually expressed in symbols rather than numerically. I do not subscribe to the current practice of providing worked problems in the text, for I believe that the first attempt by the student to apply a theory to a numerical problem, even if initially unsuccessful, is the essential step in learning; too often a worked example leads to solution by substitution rather than by understanding. I readily agree that some guidance is often desirable but prefer to leave the degree of such guidance to the individual instructor.

A word of explanation about the units used is in order. As discussed in Chapter 1, the units selected are pounds mass and pounds force, together with the dimensional constant, g_c, in pounds mass per pound force per foot per second squared, or $(\mathrm{lb}_m/\mathrm{lb}_f)/(\mathrm{ft/sec}^2)$. The use of the slug for mass is now fashionable and certainly produces neater-looking formulations, but I find it desirable to adhere to the pound mass and to emphasize the difference between the variable quantity g (the acceleration) and the constant g_c. Those who prefer the slug can simply ignore the g_c symbol. All final forms of relationships, i.e., the working equations, include g_c where necessary; however, in some of the developments the constant is omitted in order to avoid repetition.

I am indebted to many people who have contributed in different ways to this volume and express my gratitude for their help. Since the text is an introduction to fluid dynamics, I have borrowed much from earlier writers whose contributions have become a common heritage. Most of the problems are new; but again many must resemble those originated by others, and I ask forgiveness if, over the years, I have appropriated them as my own. Many of my past and present colleagues have contributed their ideas and experience, notably Professors B. Gebhart, J. F. Barrows, R. E. Mates, and G. P. Francis, all of whom have taught some of the material in this text.

Above all, however, my thanks are due to my colleague Professor F. J. Pierce, who has been associated since its inception with the course based on this material. He has made invaluable suggestions not only regarding details but also regarding the concept and form of the manuscript as a whole. In addition, he has worked on the final manuscript and proofs, and his painstaking efforts amount to collaboration in several of the major developments.

Finally, I am grateful to Mrs. Leora Decker for preparing innumerable editions of the mimeographed notes, invariably under pressure of time, and to the distaff side of my family for typing the final manuscript.

DENNIS G. SHEPHERD

Ithaca, New York
February, 1965

Contents

Fluid Properties and Flow Characteristics

1.1 *Definition of a fluid*

We all have a general idea of what a fluid is—"a substance that flows"—but a more precise definition is needed for a detailed study. We take as our definition of a real fluid that it is a substance which moves continuously under the action of a *shear* force, no matter how small that force may be. This immediately differentiates it from an elastic solid, which undergoes a finite displacement (strain) up to a given limit of stress and then breaks. There are substances that exhibit properties of an intermediate nature, that behave as elastic solids up to certain values of stress and then act as fluids. These are called *plastic* materials or materials in a plastic state.

An important aspect of a fluid is that in most cases it is treated as a *continuum*. We know that materials consist of individual particles separated in space. In particular, the kinetic theory of gases is built upon the concept of elastic molecules in continuous motion and collision. However, the particles are so small and so numerous that the macroscopic effect which we observe is that of a continuous medium. This situation may be expressed by the idea that the density ρ, as the ratio of mass M to volume V, exists at a point in the fluid, i.e., in the limit.

$$\rho = \lim_{\Delta V \to 0} \frac{\Delta M}{\Delta V}$$

We commonly distinguish two forms of a fluid, one a *liquid* and one a *gas*. Again our everyday experience makes the distinction clear, although from thermodynamics we know that at or near the critical state our ordinary sensory criteria are in doubt. A liquid appears to have a definite volume, and whereas it deforms to take the shape of its container, it has a *free surface* as one boundary if its volume is less than that of the container. A gas always expands to fill its container, no matter how large, and its volume is always indefinite unless the pressure and temperature are fixed. A liquid was said to "appear" to have a definite volume because large changes of pressure and temperature are required before any effect is noticeable. The change in volume due to pressure becomes important in such applications as diesel-engine fuel injection, where the pressure may be in thousands of pounds per square inch. The change in volume due to temperature is remarked in the admonition not to fill completely the gasoline tank of a car in summertime, as the expansion due to a change from the underground storage temperature of, say, 50°F to the ambient temperature of, say, 90°F may lead to spillage.

Since the volume of a liquid is considered constant in most flow situations, a liquid is said to be *incompressible*. Although this term implies strictly that there is no change in volume with pressure, it is usually taken to mean *constant density*, with changes due to temperature being regarded as negligible. For small changes of pressure, the density change of a gas is very small, so that frequently it is a simplification to think of the gas as incompressible. With a gas, however, it is possible to change the density substantially by a change of temperature, with little or no change of pressure, and here it is necessary to distinguish carefully between the terms "incompressible" and "constant density." In general, the terms are interchangeable unless changes due to temperature are obvious or specifically stated.

The behavior of an incompressible fluid is so much easier to analyze than that of a compressible fluid that many relationships are developed for constant density. Such relationships are valid for liquid flow (except in extreme cases) and for many cases of gas flow, so that the restriction of incompressibility is not unrealistic. For gas flow with significant change of pressure, a different approach must be made. Here the problem is usually simplified if the gas is considered as ideal, i.e., as obeying the simple equation of state for a gas, $pv = RT$, or $p = \rho RT$. In thermodynamics sometimes a distinction is made between a vapor and a gas, with the former being a gas in a state near saturation or below the critical temperature. For some common fluids, e.g., steam and refrigerants, which do not obey the ideal equation of state sufficiently accurately for some work, tables of properties are available, but generalized relationships are too cumbersome to be worthwhile.

For a gas at extremes of pressure and temperature, the problem becomes very complicated owing to nonideal-gas behavior. At very low pressures the continuum concept is no longer tenable, as the mean free path of the molecules becomes comparable with the size of a body immersed in the fluid (e.g., at 60 miles altitude the mean free path is of the order of a foot). At high pressures the intermolecular forces and actual molecular dimensions relative to the mean free path require an involved equation of state like that of van der Waals or Beattie-Bridgman. At high temperatures, such as those encountered in missile and space-vehicle technology, the gas dissociates and ionizes so that it becomes what is called a *plasma*, exhibiting complex chemical, electrical, and magnetic properties. Such phenomena are not discussed here. The simpler relationships, which are valid for the more usual condition of a gas, are a starting point for the analysis of more extreme conditions.

1.2   *Units in fluid mechanics*

Before examining the particular properties of fluids that manifest themselves in this initial study of fluid mechanics, we must discuss the problem of systems of units for measuring them. The difficulty arises from the usage of force, mass, and weight as both primary and derived concepts and through the consequent terminology. The issue is a very vexed one, because the broad field of fluid mechanics includes several developed technologies that employ units of measurement best suited to their own somewhat circumscribed areas. Hydraulics, since it deals largely with a single, incompressible fluid, uses the pound as a unit of force or of quantity of matter without discrimination. Aerodynamics uses the pound as the unit of force and the slug as the unit of mass. Thermodynamics, primarily concerned with the quantity of matter or mass, uses the pound as its measure. A brief review of these units is given to establish a consistent system for this text. It is best for the reader to realize that there is no single, accepted "correct" system at the present time and that the only thing to do is to understand the basic ideas so as to be able to convert from one system to another as necessary.

With Newton's law, which states that force is proportional to the product of mass and acceleration, $\mathbf{F} \propto M\mathbf{a}$, as an equation, a proportionality factor, k, must be introduced, so that

$$\mathbf{F} = kM\mathbf{a}$$

It is through the numerical and dimensional value of k that the multiplicity of units, and oftentimes confusion, enters.

A desirable treatment is to make the constant k equal to unity, so that $\mathbf{F} = M\mathbf{a}$. Then with *unit acceleration*, 1 ft/sec^2, $\mathbf{F}$ and M have a fixed relationship. With the unit of a *pound* for *mass*, the unit of *force* is a *poundal;* this system is not now used in the U.S.A. With the unit of a *pound* for *force*, the unit of *mass* is a *slug*, used in the field of aerodynamics. Either of these systems dispenses with any numerical factor but requires a "special" unit for force or mass. The word "special" arises because the use of the pound for both force and mass has the longest historical background in engineering and is current in engineering generally. In everyday terms, the pound is used to measure both the quantity of a substance (its *mass*) and its *weight*, which is a *force*. When a substance is said to have a weight of 1 pound, what is really meant is that the force of gravitation, acting between the substance and the earth, has a value of 1 pound. Since this force is constant within small limits on the surface of the earth, it measures the quantity of the substance. The gravitational force, as weight in pounds, thus is the unit for measuring force generally. However, the gravitational force on a body gives rise to an acceleration not of unity but, in the customary units, of about 32.2 ft/sec². Therefore, in the equation $\mathbf{F} = kM\mathbf{a}$, with force and mass in pounds, k can no longer be unity but must have the numerical value of 1/32.2, as well as units of seconds squared per foot, the reciprocal of acceleration. It is given the symbol $1/g$ in technologies that do not distinguish between the pound of force and the pound of mass; hence, $\mathbf{F} = M\mathbf{a}/g$. The gravitational acceleration does vary from place to place on the earth's surface, and so although a quantity of material or mass does not vary, its weight changes. In other words, the pound of force varies with location. To overcome this inconsistency, we define a *standard* pound of force as the force that gives a mass of 1 pound a standard acceleration, g_0, namely, 32.1739 ft/sec². The standard pound of mass is defined in terms of a quantity of platinum kept under conditions that, as far as is now known, are absolutely constant with respect to any possible change due to chemical or physical effects.

The relationship of force and mass in pound units is then fixed, with k having the numerical value of 1/32.1739 and the symbol $1/g_c$. The units of force and mass may be kept distinct by means of the terms *pound force* and *pound mass*, abbreviated lb_f and lb_m, respectively. Thus the equation $\mathbf{F} = kM\mathbf{a}$ becomes

$$\mathbf{F} = \frac{M\mathbf{a}}{g_c}$$

With lb_f, lb_m, and ft/sec², the units of g_c are $\dfrac{\mathrm{lb}_m}{\mathrm{lb}_f}\dfrac{\mathrm{ft}}{\mathrm{sec}^2}$, or

$$g_c = 32.1739 \frac{\mathrm{lb}_m}{\mathrm{lb}_f}\frac{\mathrm{ft}}{\mathrm{sec}^2} \qquad [1.1]$$

If the force on a body is the gravitational attraction, i.e., its weight, $\mathbf{W}$, the acceleration $\mathbf{a}$ is then $\mathbf{g}$, the *local* acceleration of gravity; hence

$$\mathbf{W} = M\frac{\mathbf{g}}{g_c} = \mathrm{lb}_m\left(\frac{\mathrm{ft}}{\mathrm{sec}^2}\right)\left(\frac{\mathrm{lb}_f\;\mathrm{sec}^2}{\mathrm{lb}_m\;\mathrm{ft}}\right) = \mathrm{lb}_f$$

For most engineering purposes at or near the surface of the earth, the local scalar value of **g** is taken as the standard value, g_0 (and both g and g_0 are taken as 32.2 for slide-rule calculation). Hence numerically $g = g_0 = g_c$, but dimensionally g/g_c has the units lb_f/lb_m. Thus in fluid flow the external force in pounds force required to give a certain acceleration, **a**, in any arbitrary direction is $M\mathbf{a}/g_c$; at the same time, the force of gravity may be acting significantly on the fluid, and this force in pounds force is $M\mathbf{g}/g_c$.

When we consider weight, we shall express it in pounds force as Mg/g_c, retaining the g/g_c term even though it usually has a practical value of unity. This procedure will allow a simple and convenient use of units throughout. It is sometimes argued that as g is usually numerically equal to g_c and therefore inconsiderable in calculation, the distinction between pound force and pound mass is purely academic. In certain branches of technology, this may be so, but where the fields of hydraulics, aerodynamics, and thermodynamics mingle, the use of the pound without discrimination can lead to chaos, both in principle and practice. Furthermore, the present focusing of attention on space travel, essentially a problem in fluids engineering, requires a very active concern with the value of g, the local acceleration due to gravity, and the meaning of g_c, the dimensional relationship of force and mass.

The use of the pound for the unit of force only and the slug for the unit of mass is attractive in that it obviates the need for any numerical proportionality factor. However, it requires the numerical value of any variable involving mass to be in slug units. As most engineering data are available in pound units, a conversion must be made initially. Aerodynamic data are very often given in slug units—e.g., the National Advisory Committee for Aeronautics (N.A.C.A.) standard atmosphere for use in aeronautical-performance work gives density at any altitude in slugs per cubic foot—but thermodynamic data are invariably in pound units. The pound force and pound mass units are used in this text for the following reasons:

1. Most of the data required for calculations are in pound units.

2. The inclusion of the pound mass unit and the g_c proportionality factor makes any correct physical equation *explicitly* dimensionally homogeneous; i.e., the insertion of the appropriate dimensions gives the same final dimensional quantity on each side. (Use of the slug unit requires the replacement of slug by pounds force-seconds per square foot, lb_f-sec/ft^2, for explicit homogeneity.)

There is really very little difference in usage, and those who prefer slugs can ignore the g_c term and enter all mass units as slugs, with 1 slug = 32.174 lb_m. The subscripts f and m will be applied where thought necessary but will be dropped in general, because it should become automatic to distinguish between pound force and pound mass in use.

Table 1.1 shows the force, mass, and acceleration relations for several systems, including the metric system.

Table 1.1

FORGE	MASS	ACCELERATION	$g_c = 1/k$	DESCRIPTION
lb_f	slug	ft/sec²	$1\,\dfrac{slug}{lb_f}\dfrac{ft}{sec^2}$	technical, English
poundal	lb_m	ft/sec²	$1\,\dfrac{lb_m}{pdl}\dfrac{ft}{sec^2}$	absolute, English
lb_f	lb_m	ft/sec²	$32.1739\,\dfrac{lb_m}{lb_f}\dfrac{ft}{sec^2}$	engineering, English
dyne	g_m	cm/sec²	$1\,\dfrac{g_m}{dyne}\dfrac{cm}{sec^2}$	absolute, metric, cgs
g_f	g_m	cm/sec²	$980.665\,\dfrac{g_m}{g_f}\dfrac{cm}{sec^2}$	engineering, metric
newton	kg_m	m/sec²	$1\,\dfrac{kg_m}{new}\dfrac{m}{sec^2}$	absolute, metric, mks

1.3   *Forces acting on a fluid*

The forces that may act on an element of fluid are conveniently divided into *body* forces and *surface* forces. The former act on the element as a whole and depend on the quantity of fluid, i.e., its mass or volume. Direct contact in the usual sense is not needed, and the force may act at a distance. Examples of body forces are gravitational force (weight), electric force, and magnetic force. Usually the body force may be regarded as acting at the centroid of a finite body of fluid, as, e.g., the weight.

Surface forces act directly on the boundary of a fluid element and thus are contact forces proportional to the surface area. For any plane element of area A within a fluid, as in Fig. 1.1, then in general there is a resultant force, $\mathbf{F}$, in some direction. The force $\mathbf{F}$ may be resolved into a normal component, $\mathbf{F}_n$, and a plane or tangential component, $\mathbf{F}_t$. The *average stress, f*, on the area A is F/A. As the area becomes smaller, with a corresponding decrease in $\mathbf{F}$, f becomes $\Delta F/\Delta A$; and in the limit as $\Delta A \rightarrow 0$, the stress at any point

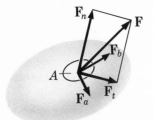

Figure 1.1

becomes dF/dA. The fact that we may consider stress at a point is a consequence of the continuum hypothesis. The tangential component $\mathbf{F}_t$ may be resolved into two components, $\mathbf{F}_a$ and $\mathbf{F}_b$, along any two convenient coordinates in the plane of A, and thus the stress on A may be described in terms of three components. Now we shall see how these normal and tangential components conform generally to pressure and viscosity, respectively, taking up the latter first.

1.4   *Viscosity of a fluid*

It is a common observation that a fluid exhibits resistance to motion other than that due to inertia and furthermore that because a spacewise variation of velocity is possible in a body of fluid, there is a sliding of one layer of fluid over another and hence some sort of internal friction. Yet in a fluid flowing past a solid surface, the fluid movement is imperceptible very close to the surface. This situation is formalized in the *no-slip* condition, which means that there is no relative velocity at the common boundary of a fluid and a solid surface.

The property of internal friction of a fluid is called *viscosity*, or *viscous action*, and there is a very simple relation by which it can be defined. In Fig. 1.2 PQ represents a rigid surface bounding a stationary fluid, and RS represents a flat plate parallel to PQ and distance h from it, moving with uniform velocity, U, in the x direction. In the steady state, with the no-slip condition at both the fixed and moving surfaces, the velocity distribution is linear, varying from zero along PQ to U along RS, and there is a *shear stress*, τ, on the plate RS in the negative x direction proportional to the velocity U and inversely proportional to the distance h; i.e.,

$$\tau \propto \frac{U}{h}$$

With a proportionality factor, μ, this becomes

$$\tau = \mu \frac{U}{h} \qquad\qquad [\mathbf{1.2}]$$

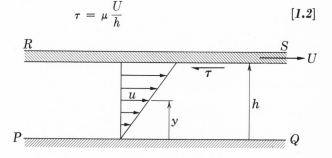

Figure 1.2

For the situation described, the *velocity gradient*, or rate of change of velocity, in the y direction is constant, and with u the velocity at distance y, then

$$\frac{U}{h} = \frac{du}{dy}$$

The shear stress is the same across the fluid from one surface to the other, and thus we may write

$$\tau = \mu \frac{du}{dy} \qquad [1.3]$$

which is the defining equation for the coefficient of absolute viscosity.

A very great number of fluids, including water and most of the common liquids and all gases except at very low pressures, exhibit this relationship, which is known as *Newton's law of viscosity*. Such fluids are called *Newtonian*, and the proportionality factor μ is called the *coefficient of absolute viscosity*, sometimes *dynamic viscosity*, and quite generally simply *viscosity*.

Eq. 1.3 may be applied anywhere in a moving fluid. Departing from the rather hypothetical case of Fig. 1.2, a fluid may be moving over a surface as shown in Fig. 1.3, with zero velocity at the boundary and varying velocity outward into the body of fluid. Across an infinitesimal thickness of fluid, dy, normal to the flow direction and distance y from the surface, there is a relative velocity du. The shear stress at the plane distance y from the surface is $\tau = \mu \, (du/dy)$. As du/dy is not constant in this case, the shear stress varies, but it may be calculated if the velocity distribution is known. Note the difference between the relationships for shear stress in an elastic solid and in a Newtonian fluid. In the solid, $\tau = G\gamma$, where G is the shear modulus and γ is the angular strain, i.e., $\Delta x/\Delta y$. In the fluid, the shear is proportional to the *rate* of strain, $(\Delta x/\Delta t)/\Delta y$, where t is time, because by definition a fluid cannot sustain a shear stress without relative motion.

The coefficient of absolute viscosity, μ, is a property of a Newtonian fluid in a given state. It depends on pressure and temperature, but the effect of pressure is so small that it may be neglected except at extremely high pressures. The effect of temperature, however, is considerable, particularly for liquids, for which the viscosity *decreases* as the temperature increases. Thus the viscosity of water is halved with a rise in temperature from 60 to

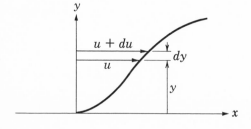

Figure 1.3

120°F. For gases, viscosity increases as the temperature increases. Air, for instance, exhibits an increase in viscosity of 8.7% between 60 and 120°F. The change in viscosity with temperature for liquids, in which the molecules are relatively tightly packed, is interpreted as due to a loosening of the forces of attraction between the molecules, which enables them to slip by one another with increased ease, producing decreased stress for a given rate of strain. For gases, in which the molecules are far apart, the kinetic theory interprets an increase in temperature as an increase in random molecular velocity and accordingly in the exchange of momentum across a given plane; the momentum flux produces a shear stress when the fluid is in motion, and as the momentum flux changes, the viscosity changes.

The units of viscosity can be obtained from Eq. 1.3. Then

$$\mu_f = \frac{\tau}{du/dy} \equiv \frac{\text{lb}_f/\text{ft}^2}{(\text{ft/sec})/\text{ft}} \equiv \frac{\text{lb}_f\text{-sec}}{\text{ft}^2} \qquad [1.4]$$

It is often very convenient to express μ in terms of mass, as it is frequently associated with the density, ρ. With mass expressed in pounds, μ_m is defined as $g_c\mu_f$. The units of μ_m are then given by

$$\mu_m = g_c\mu_f = \left(\frac{\text{lb}_m}{\text{lb}_f}\frac{\text{ft}}{\text{sec}^2}\right)\left(\frac{\text{lb}_f\text{-sec}}{\text{ft}^2}\right) \equiv \frac{\text{lb}_m}{\text{ft-sec}} \qquad [1.5]$$

Thus μ_f and μ_m represent the coefficient of viscosity in force units, as pounds force-seconds per square foot (lb_f-sec/ft^2), and in mass units, as pounds mass per foot-second (lb_m/ft-sec), respectively.

These are the usual engineering units in the U.S.A., but in the scientific field and in countries using the metric system, the basic unit is the *poise*, defined as 1 g_m/cm-sec, corresponding to μ_m. Since the poise (named after Jean Louis Poiseuille, 1799–1869, a French scientist who did pioneer work in the field of viscous flow) is a rather large unit, the centipoise, $\frac{1}{100}$ poise, is often used instead. Another common unit in the field of lubrication is the *reyn* (named after Osborne Reynolds, 1842–1912, a British scientist and engineer responsible for many advances in the field of fluid flow generally), defined as 1 lb_f-sec/in.^{2}, i.e., corresponding to $\frac{1}{144}\mu_f$.

We shall find that the ratio of absolute viscosity, μ, to density, ρ, occurs very frequently, as both are properties of a fluid. This ratio is termed the *kinematic* viscosity and given the symbol ν.

$$\nu = \frac{\mu}{\rho} \qquad [1.6]$$

With ρ in lb_m/ft^3, μ must be μ_m in lb_m/ft-sec; thus

$$\nu = \frac{\mu_m}{\rho} \equiv \frac{\text{lb}_m}{\text{ft-sec}}\frac{\text{ft}^3}{\text{lb}_m} \equiv \frac{\text{ft}^2}{\text{sec}} \qquad [1.7]$$

This is independent of force and mass, hence the name kinematic. Note that the units must be similar with pounds force and slugs; i.e., $\nu = \mu_f/\rho \equiv$ [(lb$_f$-sec)/ft^2]/(slug/ft^3) $\equiv$ ft-lb$_f$-sec/slug $\equiv$ ft-lb$_f$-sec/(lb$_f$-sec^2/ft) $\equiv$ ft^2/sec.

The metric unit for ν is the poise per gram-cubic centimeter (poise/g-cm^3) $\equiv$ square centimeters per second (cm^2/sec), called the *stoke* (named after Sir George Stokes, 1819–1903, a British mathematician who was one of the founders of what is now called classical hydrodynamics), again divided into centistokes for convenience. Some charts of viscosity vs. temperature for air, water, and a number of fluids of interest are given at the end of the chapter.

Viscosity is difficult to measure directly from shear stress and velocity gradient. In industry a number of simple types of apparatus are used that determine the time in seconds for a liquid to flow out of a container of prescribed shape and dimensions. In the U.S.A. the Saybolt viscometer measures ν in *Saybolt seconds*, whereas in Great Britain measurements are in *Redwood seconds*. The values are empirical and thus require empirical conversion to standard units.

Although most fluids, including those most frequently encountered, are Newtonian, other fluids with differing behavior are important in many instances. *Non-Newtonian* fluids do not exhibit the direct proportionality of shear stress and rate of strain given in Eq. 1.3. There are many different classes of such fluids (and some are not classifiable), and the study of them is a branch of rheology (the science of deformation and flow). For steady-state flow, an expression similar to Eq. 1.3 may be applicable.

$$\tau = \eta \frac{du}{dy} + k \qquad [1.8]$$

where η is not a simple proportionality factor like μ, but may itself be a function of shear stress or rate of strain, and k is a constant. Because a mathematical expression is needed in the analysis of flow of non-Newtonian fluids, many formulations are possible. These are sometimes mathematical models that reproduce the stress–rate of strain characteristics of a particular fluid but do not necessarily represent the actual physical behavior. We shall limit the discussion here simply to a graphic representation of a few of the more common classes of fluids.

Fig. 1.4 shows the general behavior on a diagram with shear stress as the ordinate and rate of strain as the abscissa. The boundary behavior is indicated by the ordinate for an elastic solid and by the abscissa for an ideal or nonviscous fluid ($\mu = 0$). Curve A is for a Newtonian fluid, having a constant slope because μ is constant for a given state. Curve B is for an ideal or Bingham plastic, showing that a certain stress level is required before deformation occurs, following which the fluid behaves in Newtonian fashion. (This can be represented by Eq. 1.8, with $\eta = \mu$ and $k = \tau_0$, the initial stress.) Curve C is for a *pseudoplastic* fluid, in which the apparent viscosity, η, decreases with increasing rate of strain. Suspensions of clay or paper pulp

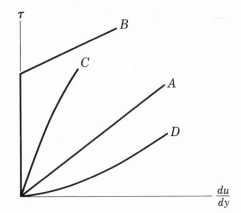

Figure 1.4

in water are examples of pseudoplastic substances. Curve D is for a dilatant fluid, in which η increases with increasing rate of strain.

In another class of non-Newtonian fluids, called *viscoelastic*, the rate of strain is dependent on both the shear stress and the amount of strain. Some fluids show a time-dependent property; i.e., the strain rate is a function of stress and of duration of stress. In one class of this type, called *thixotropic*, there is a decrease in apparent viscosity or in shear stress with time. Most pigment suspensions, such as paint, are thixotropic, capable of being stirred and applied in a workable condition but settling down and not continuing to run after stress is removed.

We shall consider only Newtonian fluids hereafter, but we have drawn attention to non-Newtonian fluids in order to emphasize that the ordinary laws of fluid motion must not be applied indiscriminately without regard to fluid type. The analysis of flow of non-Newtonian fluids is becoming increasingly important because of the need for closer control of processes in, e.g., the food and paint industries. In certain advanced technologies, precise analysis may be critical. In one kind of nuclear reactor a slurry (a mixture of solid particles in a liquid) containing radioactive material is used, and in the aerospace field high-energy fuels consisting of liquid hydrocarbons with powdered metal suspensions may be advantageous. However, a knowledge of Newtonian-flow behavior is necessary as a background for developing new knowledge.

1.5   *The ideal fluid*

In the previous section we have treated that very significant property of a *real* fluid, its viscosity. In paradoxical fashion we shall now define an *ideal* fluid as nonviscous or inviscid and proceed in later chapters to develop for it in some detail a number of relationships. The major reason is that the assumption of an ideal fluid greatly simplifies analysis. In fact, in many instances it is very difficult to obtain an exact answer if viscosity is introduced. Simplicity would not be a valid reason if it did not provide clues to a workable answer. On the one hand, it leads to relationships that are true in their main characteristics but that have to be modified by empirical coefficients to a greater or less degree; on the other, it allows us to divide a problem into two parts and, by patching together an ideal flow and a simplified viscous flow, obtain an answer.

Ideal flow may be likened to the reversible process in thermodynamics, unattainable in practice but providing a basis for a rational analysis that illuminates the actual process.

1.6   *Pressure*

For a fluid without viscous stress, the normal stress is due only to pressure. The condition of no viscous stress can, by the relation $\tau = \mu \, du/dy$, be met either by $\mu = 0$, a fluid of zero viscosity (ideal fluid), or by $du/dy = 0$, which implies either no motion (static fluid) or no velocity gradient (uniform velocity). For a real fluid in motion with a velocity gradient, the viscous forces may produce a normal stress component due to the resistance of the fluid to elongation. In the first instance we shall consider only the case of a fluid at rest.

The normal stress, f_n, in Fig. 1.1 theoretically may act in either direction, and it does so in a solid. A fluid, however, can in general not support a *tensile* stress, i.e., one directed outward from the surface A. (It has been found that an almost completely pure liquid, with no dissolved gas or solid present to act as nuclei for a discontinuity, can support a surprisingly high tensile stress, but such fluids are seldom encountered.) The stress is therefore *compressive* and directed toward the surface. This stress is called the *pressure* (occasionally the *pressure intensity*) and in the units of this text is measured in pounds per square inch (lb/in.² or psi) or pounds per square foot (lb/ft² or psf).

Now let us examine the relationship among the normal stresses due to pressure alone on a number of interfaces in different planes at a point in a fluid. We can take a very small element of fluid, analyze the force balance, and then shrink the volume to an infinitesimal proportion to find the result for a point.

Fig. 1.5(a) shows such an element, with a constant triangular cross section, ABC, in the xy plane. The element is in equilibrium, as the fluid is at rest. The forces acting on it are thus body forces, in this case only the

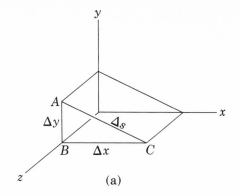

(a)

Figure 1.5

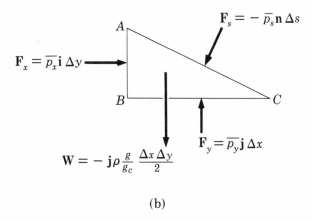

(b)

gravitational force or weight, and surface forces, in this case the normal forces due to pressure. We shall consider equilibrium only in the xy plane, because the analysis can be repeated in similar fashion for any plane. We can then make a two-dimensional analysis, as in Fig. 1.5(b).

The normal forces are due to average pressures $\overline{p_x}$, $\overline{p_y}$, and $\overline{p_s}$ acting on the surfaces Δy, Δx, and Δs, respectively (length in the z direction is taken as unity). Note that F_x and F_y are positive because they act in the same directions as the positive directions of unit vectors $\mathbf{i}$ and $\mathbf{j}$. On the other hand, F_s is negative because unit vector $\mathbf{n}$ is defined as positive outward from surface Δs (see Appendix). Likewise, W, the weight, is negative because it is oppositely directed to $\mathbf{j}$. With the equilibrium condition that $\Sigma \mathbf{F} = 0$, these vertical and horizontal components result: For the y direction

$$\Sigma F_y = \overline{p_y}\,\Delta x + (-\,\overline{p_s}\,\Delta s\,\mathbf{n}\cdot\mathbf{j}) - \rho\,\frac{g}{g_c}\frac{\Delta x\,\Delta y}{2}$$

$$= \overline{p_y}\,\Delta x - \overline{p_s}\,\Delta x - \rho\,\frac{g}{g_c}\frac{\Delta x\,\Delta y}{2} = 0$$

On division through by Δx and rearrangement,

$$\overline{p_y} = \overline{p_s} + \rho \frac{g}{g_c} \frac{\Delta y}{2}$$

In the limit, as the element is shrunk to infinitesimal proportions, $\Delta y \to 0$ (along with Δx and Δs), and the average pressure, $\overline{p}$, over a finite area becomes the pressure at a point, p. Thus

$$p_y = p_s$$

For the x direction

$$\Sigma F_x = \overline{p_x} \Delta y + (- \overline{p_s} \Delta s \, \mathbf{n} \cdot \mathbf{i})$$
$$= \overline{p_x} \Delta y - \overline{p_s} \Delta y = 0$$

Thence, as before, in the limit

$$p_x = p_s$$

Finally then we have

$$p_x = p_y = p_s = p \qquad\qquad [1.9]$$

Since surface Δs was arbitrarily chosen, we may conclude that the pressure at a point in a fluid at rest is independent of orientation. Thus it is confirmed that pressure is a scalar quantity, although the forces produced by it on a surface with a given orientation are vectors, being normal to the surface and directed toward it.

This development of the scalar nature of pressure is valid only for a fluid at rest and depends on the absence of shear stresses for the force equilibrium. By extension, the argument may be made to apply to fluids with uniform velocity, because with $du/dy = 0$, the shear stress is zero. Likewise, it may be extended to cover nonviscous or ideal fluids in which the velocity is not uniform, because even with $du/dy \neq 0$, $\tau = 0$ since $\mu = 0$. In this case there may be an acceleration, but, as with the gravitational body force, this is proportional to the mass and hence volume of the body or to the linear dimension cubed. The surface force due to pressure is proportional to the linear dimension squared, and so in going to the limit, the inertia vanishes.

In the case of a real, viscous fluid with nonuniform velocity, the shear forces must be considered, and the problem becomes complex. We shall not attempt an analysis here but shall merely state that it can be shown that the *sum* of the compressive stresses in three mutually perpendicular directions at a point has a unique value regardless of the absolute orientation. The average value of these stresses is called the bulk stress and is generally treated as the pressure.

1.7 *Density, specific weight, and specific gravity*

The density of a substance is its mass per unit volume, or specific mass, measured in pounds mass per cubic foot (lb_m/ft^3) and given the symbol ρ. The *specific weight* of a substance is its weight per unit volume, measured in pounds force per cubic foot (lb_f/ft^3) and given the symbol γ. At the surface of the earth where $g \approx g_c$, the values of ρ and γ may be taken as the same numerically, but the units are different. Thus

$$\rho = \frac{M}{V}$$

$$\gamma = \frac{W}{V} = \frac{Mg/g_c}{V}$$

and hence
$$\gamma = \rho \frac{g}{g_c} \qquad\qquad [\textit{1.10}]$$

The *specific gravity* of a substance is the ratio of its mass to the mass of an equal volume of water or the ratio of densities of the substance and water. However, the density of water varies slightly with pressure and sufficiently with temperature to require the designation of a standard temperature in giving a specific gravity. For scientific work a temperature of 4°C (at which water has its maximum density) is specified, but in engineering 60°F is commonly used. It is also necessary to state the temperature of the liquid in question if it differs from the standard water temperature. Quite often the variation of density of a liquid with temperature is inconsiderable in comparison with other uncertainties in an engineering problem. It will be so considered in this text. Thus a specific gravity (sp gr) here may be taken as the ratio of the density of a liquid at its own temperature to that of water at 60°F, which is 62.37 lb/ft³ (62.4 for simplicity). For gases, specific gravity has no meaning unless pressure and temperature are known and is little used except in comparing a number of gases, when the standard is sometimes air with an arbitrary density of unity.

In the petroleum industry, hydrometers are calibrated to a special gravity scale for convenience. The American Petroleum Institute (A.P.I.) defines specific gravity as

$$\text{A.P.I. gravity, degrees} = \frac{141.5}{\text{sp gr } 60/60°F} - 131.5 \qquad [\textit{1.11}]$$

where sp gr 60/60°F means the ratio of densities of fluid at 60°F and water at 60°F. (The A.P.I. scale replaces an earlier scale sometimes found in the literature, degrees Beaumé, only slightly different numerically.)

The inverse of density is *specific volume*, $v = 1/\rho$, expressed in cubic feet per pound mass (ft^3/lb_m) and commonly used in thermodynamics. The inverse of specific weight has no name although sometimes erroneously called "specific volume."

1.8 *Compressibility, elasticity, and coefficient of expansion*

All fluids change volume with change of pressure and temperature—liquids very slightly, gases very markedly.

A given volume of fluid, V, at pressure p suffers a change of volume ΔV when the pressure changes by Δp. The *mean compressibility*, $\bar\beta$, is defined as the fractional change in volume per unit change in pressure, so that for a given mass of fluid, i.e., of specific volume v,

$$\bar\beta = -\frac{\Delta v/v}{\Delta p}$$

with the minus sign indicating that an increase of pressure results in a decrease of volume and thus in a positive value of $\bar\beta$. Since temperature may change at the same time, the value of $\bar\beta$ is not completely determined; for it to have a fixed value, the particular process must be known. Usually two processes are singled out, the isothermal and the reversible adiabatic (isentropic). In the limit, as the changes become infinitesimal, we can define the *compressibility*, β, as follows (using subscript T for the isothermal and subscript s for the reversible adiabatic):

$$\beta_T = -\frac{1}{v}\left(\frac{\partial v}{\partial p}\right)_T \qquad [\textbf{1.12}]$$

$$\beta_s = -\frac{1}{v}\left(\frac{\partial v}{\partial p}\right)_s \qquad [\textbf{1.13}]$$

It can be shown from thermodynamics that for a pure substance

$$\frac{\beta_T}{\beta_s} = \frac{c_p}{c_v} = k$$

where k is the ratio of the specific heat at constant pressure, c_p to that at constant volume, c_v.

For liquids, where there is only a very small change of temperature due to pressure in a reversible adiabatic process, the isothermal value β_T is usually taken as the compressibility, but it must be stated at a given temperature. The true compressibility as given by the partial derivative varies with the pressure level, and thus if the pressure is changed over a wide range, a step-by-step calculation or integration may be necessary.

Although compressibility is used in thermodynamic analysis, it is customary in engineering to use *elasticity*, which is the reciprocal of the compressibility, as is done for solids. The defining parameter is then the *bulk modulus of elasticity*, *E*, with

$$E = -\frac{dp}{dv/v} = \frac{1}{\beta_T} \qquad [1.14]$$

where the partial derivative has been replaced by the exact derivative with the assumption that the temperature is constant. The units of E are generally pounds per square inch (psi).

For water at normal pressure and temperature E may be taken as 315,000 psi. It increases about 30% when the pressure is 15,000 psi and varies with temperature level, yielding a maximum value at 120°F. With E as 315,000 psi, a 1% reduction of volume requires a pressure of 3150 psi, so that ordinarily water is assumed incompressible. Compressibility is, however, an important property when the propagation of elastic waves is being considered and when the fluid pressure is very high, e.g., in diesel-engine fuel injection and at considerable depths in the ocean.

For gases, compressibility is not usually regarded as a specific property except for thermodynamic analysis, as changes in volume are calculated directly from an equation of state, generally that for an ideal gas, $pv = RT$. For an ideal gas, the isothermal compressibility is simply the reciprocal of the pressure, $1/p$. From $pv = RT$,

$$p\,dv + v\,dp = R\,dT = 0 \qquad \text{(for constant } T)$$

$$\frac{dv}{dp} = -\frac{v}{p}$$

Therefore, $$\beta_T = -\frac{1}{v}\frac{dv}{dp} = -\frac{1}{v}\left(-\frac{v}{p}\right) = \frac{1}{p} \qquad [1.15]$$

or $$E_T = p \qquad [1.16]$$

It may be noted that at atmospheric pressure, 14.7 psi absolute, the ratio of the isothermal compressibilities of air and water is $315{,}000/14.7 \approx 21{,}400$. The compressibility ratio of steel, with a bulk modulus of elasticity of 24,000,000 psi, to water is $(3.15 \times 10^5)/(2.4 \times 10^7) \approx 0.013$. From the statement that $\beta_T/\beta_s = k$, then for a perfect gas, $\beta_s = 1/kp$, and $E_s = kp$.

The change of volume with temperature is defined in similar fashion, leading to the *coefficient of thermal expansion* at constant pressure, α_p.

$$\alpha_p = \frac{1}{v}\left(\frac{\partial v}{\partial T}\right)_p \qquad [1.17]$$

For water, α_p is variable with temperature, but a value of 0.00011 per degree Rankine may be taken for normal temperatures. For gases, again from the ideal equation of state, $pv = RT$,

$$\left(\frac{\partial v}{\partial T}\right)_p = \frac{R}{p}$$

Therefore, $$\alpha_p = \frac{R}{pv} = \frac{R}{RT} = \frac{1}{T}$$ [1.18]

1.9   *Cohesion, adhesion, surface tension, and capillarity*

All liquids exhibit the effects of *cohesion,* or attraction force of the molecules one to another, and of *adhesion,* or attraction force of the molecules to those of another liquid or solid in contact with them. It is the cohesive effect that provides the interface between two immiscible liquids and the free surface in a liquid-gas combination. Because the molecules at an interface are subject to attraction from like molecules on one side only, there is excess potential energy at the surface tending to resist separation, resulting in a force tangential to the surface and normal to any line in the surface. This force is called *surface tension,* and given the symbol σ. As energy per unit area, it has units of foot-pounds force per square foot (ft-lb$_f$/ft^2), usually reduced to

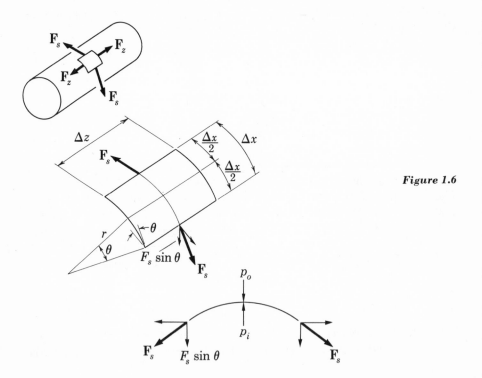

Figure 1.6

pounds force per foot (lb_f/ft). It is this property of surface tension that gives rise to such phenomena as soap films, bubbles, drops in a liquid spray, and the movement of moisture in soil. Any particular manifestation of surface tension is the result of the relative effects of cohesion and adhesion (a consequence of the molecular structure) and the linear dimension involved (a consequence of the mechanical equilibrium). The general principle may be seen in a very simple illustration.

Fig. 1.6 shows a segment of a cylindrical surface of liquid of length Δz, arc length Δx, and radius of curvature r. It is acted upon by surface tension forces on all four edges, but the longitudinal forces, $\mathbf{F}_z$, are collateral and cancel out each other. The side forces, $\mathbf{F}_s$, are tangential, with the x components canceling out but with a y component from each edge of $F_s \sin \theta$ being additive. With the liquid in equilibrium, this must be balanced by a differential pressure, $p_i - p_o = \Delta p$, with $p_i > p_o$. Again the x components of the pressure force cancel out each other, but there is a residual y component of $\Delta p \, \Delta x \, \Delta z$. The force balance for equilibrium is then

$$2F_s \sin \theta = \Delta p \, \Delta x \, \Delta z$$

From the geometry, $\sin \theta = \Delta x / 2r$; hence

$$F_s = r \, \Delta p \, \Delta z$$

With the surface-tension force $F_s = \sigma \, \Delta z$,

$$\sigma \, \Delta z = r \, \Delta p \, \Delta z$$

and
$$\Delta p = \frac{\sigma}{r} \qquad\qquad [\textbf{1.19}]$$

The increase of pressure is inversely proportional to the radius of curvature. This special result for a simple cylinder is qualitatively true for all curved surfaces. (For water, $\sigma = 0.005$ lb/ft, and with $r = 0.020$ in., $\Delta p \approx 0.02$ psi.) Thus we may generalize and say that the effects of surface-tension forces become important in relation to other forces only when the radius of curvature is very small.

When a liquid is in contact with a solid surface, the relative forces of adhesion and cohesion determine whether the surface becomes "wetted." Fig. 1.7 shows a solid surface in contact with water (a) and with mercury (b).

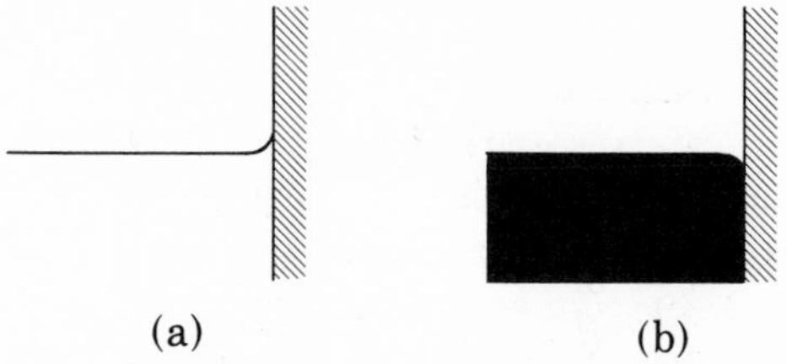

Figure 1.7

(a)   (b)

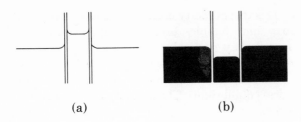

Figure 1.8

(a)   (b)

The adhesive effect causes the water to "climb up" the surface, whereas the cohesive effect forces the mercury downward and away from the surface. With water the adhesive effect causes wetting of the surface, whereas with mercury the cohesive effect is greater and the surface is not wetted. The curvature near the solid surface is called a *meniscus*, and it is significant in small-bore tubes, as shown in Fig. 1.8, where the difference of pressure across the curved free surface inside the tube causes the liquid level to be raised (water) or depressed (mercury). The height of a column of liquid can be used to measure pressure (Chapter 2), but care must be taken that the surface tension effect does not lead to error in measurement. The possibility can be minimized by using large-diameter tubes, in accordance with the principle enunciated in $\Delta p \propto 1/r$.

The *capillary* effect is the reason for "sponge" action, e.g., the upward movement of water in tightly packed soil and the flow of melted wax up the wick of a candle. The pores are very small, and the action is similar to that in the tube of Fig. 1.8. The wetting or nonwetting of a surface can also be important in engineering. For instance, the use of mercury and other liquid metals in a Rankine-cycle heat engine or in a nuclear reactor has many advantages, but the liquids must wet the surface to have good heat-transfer characteristics. Sometimes it is necessary to treat the metal surface containing the liquid to obtain wetting.

1.10   *Thermodynamic properties*

Since a knowledge of elementary thermodynamics is presupposed of the reader, we shall limit the discussion here to a statement of the properties referred to hereinafter, for the purpose of review and to establish nomenclature.

Temperature is used in the usual sense, with the Fahrenheit scale for units, °F standing for degrees Fahrenheit and °R for degrees Fahrenheit absolute or degrees Rankine.

Specific heat is denoted by c_p at constant pressure and c_v at constant volume, units being British thermal units per pound-degree Rankine

(Btu/lb-°R). For liquids, the distinction is normally unnecessary. The ratio of specific heats, c_p/c_i, is denoted by k and is dimensionless.

Enthalpy, H, is the sum of internal energy, U, and pV product, or, as specific enthalpy,

$$h = u + pv \qquad [1.20]$$

the units being British thermal units per pound (Btu/lb) or foot-pounds force per pound mass (ft-lb$_f$/lb$_m$).* For a perfect gas, $u = c_v T$, and $h = c_p T$.

The concept of *entropy* is encountered repeatedly, and it must be assumed that its meaning is already clear. The symbol for specific entropy is s, with units of British thermal units per pound-degree Rankine (Btu/lb-°R). A change of entropy between end states 1 and 2 can be calculated by $\int_1^2 dQ/T$, where Q represents heat, for any *reversible* process or processes between the end states. Qualitative use will be made of entropy as, for instance, via a statement of the second law of thermodynamics that in an isolated system (no energy crosses its boundaries) no process is possible that would result in a decrease in the entropy of the system. For analysis, use will be made of the relationship

$$T \, ds = du + p \, dv = dh - v \, dp \qquad [1.21]$$

A *reversible adiabatic* process is in general referred to in these terms rather than as an isentropic process. An *adiabatic* process can then be either reversible or irreversible.

The *vapor pressure* of a fluid, p_v, is the pressure exerted by the saturated vapor or liquid. It varies markedly with temperature and when the temperature is such that the vapor pressure is equal to the surrounding or ambient pressure, the fluid is said to boil.

1.11   *Laminar flow, turbulent flow, and the Reynolds number*

The existence of two regimes of flow was recognized in the middle nineteenth century. In one regime, an element of fluid tends to travel in an unbroken line, curving round an obstacle if necessary but preserving its separate identity throughout. This is now called *laminar* or *streamline* flow. It is characterized by low velocity, small linear dimension, and high viscosity. In the other regime, an individual fluid element is almost immediately merged with surrounding elements even when the flow as a whole is proceeding smoothly, even linearly. This is called *turbulent* flow and is characterized by high velocity, large linear dimension, and low viscosity.

---

* The symbols h and H will also be used for linear height and head, but the context should be sufficient to prevent confusion.

A change from one regime to the other can be observed in a given apparatus once a certain velocity is reached, e.g., in simple pipe flow. The change, although not instantaneous, occurs sufficiently suddenly for a value of so-called "critical velocity" to be measured. However, this value varies with the size of the apparatus and the particular fluid being used. Although several workers had been close to a general understanding of the factors contributing to this change of flow character at some critical condition, it was Osborne Reynolds who in the 1880's formulated the criterion as a particular value of the parameter $\rho V d/\mu$, where d is some linear dimension characteristic of the flow field. The parameter $\rho V d/\mu$ or $V d/\nu$ allows for the nature of a fluid by virtue of its kinematic viscosity, the flow condition by virtue of the velocity of flow, and the particular arrangement by virtue of a characteristic dimension. It is called the *Reynolds number* and is of outstanding importance in characterizing flow phenomena. It does far more than signify a change in flow regime, and its exact value is used quantitatively. It will be the subject of later chapters.

Although we are still far from able to handle analytically the details of turbulent flow, we know that in this regime particles of fluid, each extremely small but nevertheless containing a very large number of molecules, may be in motion in any direction regardless of the direction of the bulk velocity. Thus, even in such directed flow as that in a pipe, there is an apparently disordered motion of the particles superimposed on the unidirectional main flow. This small-scale motion is called *turbulence* and is present in most, but not all, fluid flows of engineering significance. Because the word turbulence in everyday speech expresses a disordered or eddying motion, such as that of a stream over a rocky bed, it must be kept in mind that in fluid mechanics it has the connotation of very *small-scale* motion detectable only by special measurement techniques or by its effect of rapid diffusion, e.g., of dye. We shall study turbulence and turbulent flow.

Formulation of the Reynolds number was a tremendous step forward in unifying a great deal of experimental data hitherto uncorrelated, but there still remained serious discrepancies between analytical results and experimental evidence.

The burgeoning in the nineteenth century of the theory of the incompressible flow of an ideal fluid, now commonly termed "classical hydrodynamics," was almost wholly mathematical in character and produced a large body of elegant solutions. Although much of this work was useful, it was frustrating to engineers because actual flow in many cases seemed to be so very different from theoretical flow. Thus the ideal-flow postulate leads to the conclusion of zero resistance or drag for an immersed body or for flow in a duct, whereas the calculation of this resistance is one of the most important problems in practice. The bridging of this gap was made by the hypothesis of the *boundary layer*, introduced by Prandtl in 1904 and developed rapidly by his group and others elsewhere. This concept envisages shear strain as originating only at solid surfaces and being limited to a relatively small distance outward from the surface, constituting a boundary layer in which viscous effects are confined, the remainder of the flow being ideal. On meeting the leading edge of an aircraft wing, e.g., air close to the surface is retarded by viscous action, having zero velocity at the surface (no slip) with increasing velocity outward. This boundary layer of air is very thin, although increasing in thickness along the wing toward the trailing edge. Because the boundary layer is thin, simplifying approximations can be made that permit calculation of the retarding effect. Since the flow regime outside the boundary layer is regarded as ideal, velocity and pressure distributions can be calculated as due simply to the presence of the wing as a disturbing effect on the uniform air flow. The division of flow into two parts thus allows analysis yielding results near enough to experimentally determined results that untested cases can be predicted with confidence. In some situations the boundary layer becomes detached from the surface, and a confused eddying motion ensues, e.g., the flow over a rocky stream bed. Although such motion has not yet been completely analyzed, the concept of the boundary layer clearly shows the underlying reason for it, and the rift between theory and practice is understood, even if not always susceptible to exact calculation.

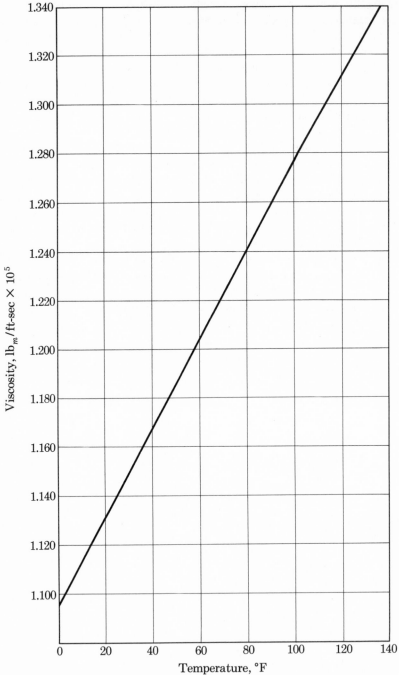

Absolute viscosity of dry air.

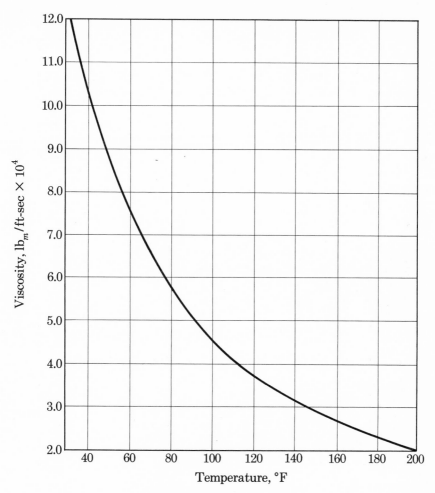

Absolute viscosity of water.

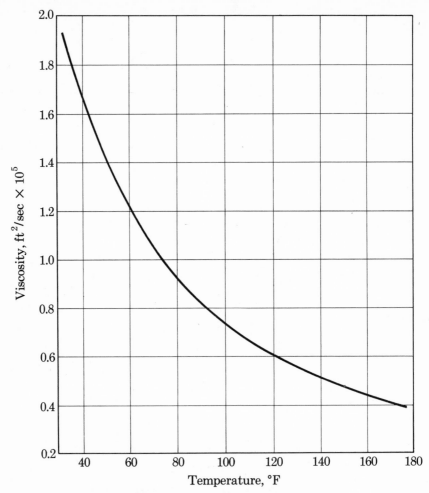

Kinematic viscosity of water.

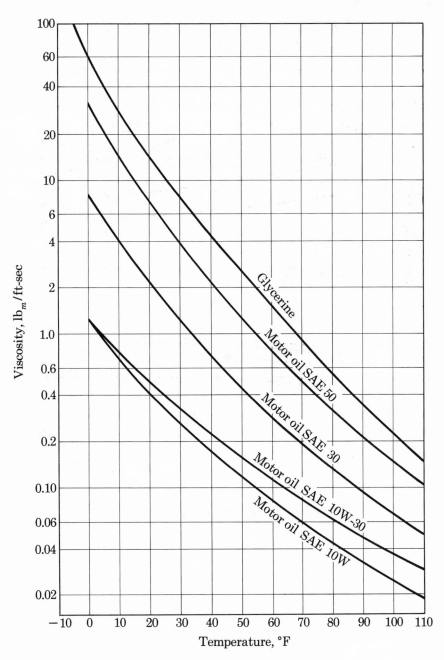

Absolute viscosities of various fluids.

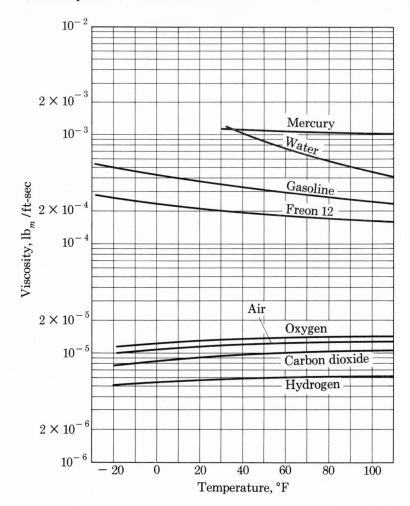

Absolute viscosities of various fluids (cont.).

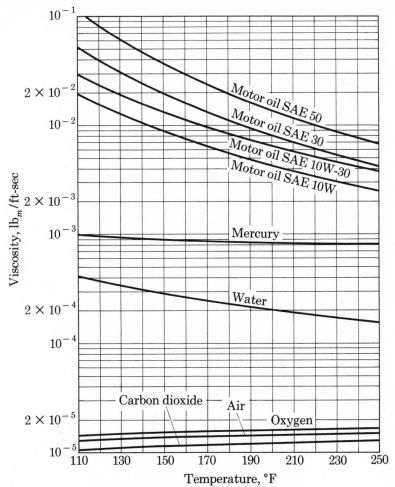

Absolute viscosities of various fluids (cont.).

Problems

1.1. If the gas constant, R, for air has a value of 53.3 ft-lb$_f$/lb$_m$-°R, express its value in (a) ft-lb$_f$/slug-°R, (b) ft-pdl/lb$_m$-°R, (c) ft-pdl/slug-°R, and (d) ft/°R.

1.2. The mass of a body is 100 lb at the surface of the earth, which is at a radius of 4000 miles from the earth's center. The acceleration due to gravity is 32.2 ft/sec^2 at the earth's surface and varies inversely as the square of the distance from the center of the earth. At a height, h, of 250 miles above the earth, express the mass of the body in (a) lb and (b) slugs, and (c) find the weight of the body in lb.

1.3. For air at 44°F,
    a. Calculate the absolute viscosity in lb-sec/ft^2 and in centipoises.
    b. Calculate the kinematic viscosity in ft^2/sec and in centistokes if the pressure is 28.7 psia.

1.4. For the parabolic velocity distribution shown in the diagram,
    a. Find the velocity gradient at the plane 3 in. from the wall.
    b. Find the shear stress at this plane if the fluid is air with a viscosity of 5 × 10^{-7} lb-sec/ft^2.

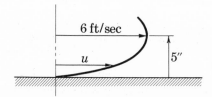

    c. Find the shear stress at this plane for water with a viscosity of 1.9 lb/hr-ft.
    d. Find the shear stress at the plane 5 in. from the wall for air and for water.

1.5. A plate 6 ft long × 3 in. wide slides horizontally over another plate. The gap between the plates is 0.01 in. across and is filled with oil of sp gr 0.9 and kinematic viscosity 1.05 × 10^{-3} ft^2/sec. Find the force required to slide the top plate at a constant velocity of 0.2 ft/sec.

1.6. A horizontal circular plate of 18 in. diameter rotates over a fixed bottom plate, with a gap of 0.009 in. between filled with SAE 30 motor oil. If the steady running temperature of the oil is 85°F when the plate rotates at 90 rpm, find the torque required. Neglect the centrifugal effect.

1.7. The specific weight of alcohol is given as 43.5 lb/ft³. Determine the density, specific volume, and specific gravity of the fluid.

1.8. A certain liquid has a density of 1.5 slug/ft³. Determine the specific weight, the specific volume, and the specific gravity of the liquid on the earth and on the moon. The gravitational acceleration on the moon is 5.47 ft/sec². What is the density of the liquid on the moon in lb/ft³?

1.9. If a fluid is called incompressible when its change of density with pressure at constant temperature is less than 0.2%,
  a. Find the maximum pressure change possible for water to be called incompressible.
  b. Repeat for air originally at atmospheric pressure (14.7 psia).
  c. What is the ratio of compressibility of air and water under these conditions?

1.10. One of the deepest ocean depths discovered to date is about 7 miles. Assuming a depth of 36,000 ft, with a corresponding pressure of 16,000 psi, find the density of sea water if its specific gravity at sea level is 1.026. Take a constant average modulus of elasticity of 350,000 psi.

1.11. A very long, rigid pipe of 1 ft diameter is used in pumping a liquid cross country. The pipe becomes plugged at some unknown point so that no fluid can flow. A piston is inserted in one end of the pipe and slides without leakage. It is forced a distance of 24 in. along the pipe and increases the pressure of the liquid in the pipe by 20 psi. The bulk modulus of the liquid is known to be 200,000 psi. How far down the pipe would you recommend that one look for the obstruction?

1.12. From the definition of compressibility and the relationship $pv^k = $ constant, show that the bulk modulus of elasticity, E, of an ideal gas under reversible adiabatic conditions is kp.

1.13. What must be the radius of a cylindrical jet of water in the atmosphere for the pressure inside the jet to be 0.1% greater than atmospheric pressure?

Statics of Fluids

2.1 *Scope of fluid statics*

Fluid statics deals with the phenomena associated with fluids at rest. Hence there are no tangential forces, and only the normal surface force due to pressure and any body forces are present. Analyses are then made for the condition of equilibrium, when the summation of forces in every direction is zero. The only body force considered will be that due to gravitation, i.e., weight. The relationships for a static fluid also apply to a fluid moving with constant velocity, because there is again no shear stress and no additional body force on the fluid. By a further extension they apply to a fluid with constant acceleration; in this case, each fluid element is acted upon by the same forces so that there is no relative motion and thus no shear stress.

2.2 *Pressure distribution*

Fig. 2.1 shows a cubic element of fluid of sides Δx, Δy, and Δz, with fluid pressure p at point x, y, z at the center of the cube. The z axis is in the vertical direction with gravity acting downward, and the x and y axes are in the horizontal plane. The element is in equilibrium under the action of the forces owing to pressure on all six surfaces and to gravity, which acts at the center as weight $\Delta \mathbf{W}$.

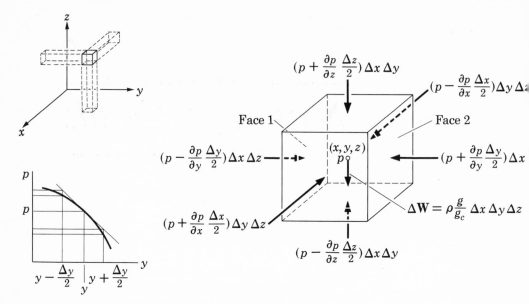

Figure 2.1

If a variation of pressure occurs in all three directions, i.e., $p = f(x, y, z)$, the rates of change of pressure in the three coordinate directions are $\partial p/\partial x$, $\partial p/\partial y$, and $\partial p/\partial z$. We may then express the pressure as a Taylor series expansion in the immediate neighborhood of x, y, z. Using the y direction as an example and expanding from y to $y \pm \Delta y/2$, we have

$$p\left(y \pm \frac{\Delta y}{2}\right) = p(y) \pm \frac{\partial p}{\partial y}\frac{\Delta y}{2} \pm \frac{\partial^2 p}{\partial y^2}\left(\frac{\Delta y}{2}\right)^2 \frac{1}{2!} \pm \cdots$$

With only first-order differentials, this is equivalent to assuming a linear variation of pressure in the immediate neighborhood of x, y, z, as shown graphically in the figure, with an arbitrary curve of $p(y)$ and the tangent to the curve at $y = y$ illustrating the linearization. In the limit as $\Delta y \to dy$, the expression becomes exact. Similar forms may be written for the x and z directions. With this assumption of linear variation of pressure, the pressure on any face may be taken as that at the center of the face. Then for face 1, the increment of pressure from point x, y, z is dependent only on y and is given by $(\partial p/\partial y)(-\Delta y/2)$. Similarly for face 2 the increment is $(\partial p/\partial y)(\Delta y/2)$. In this manner the pressure on all six faces may be obtained. The result is equivalent to a Taylor expansion at point x, y, z, with all terms of higher order than the first dropped. The analysis has been made in some detail, because this method of formulating a relation for fluid conditions at a point is used again in subsequent chapters for different conditions.

The forces on each face are as indicated in the figure, with $\Delta W = -(\rho g/g_c)\,\Delta x\,\Delta y\,\Delta z$. For equilibrium, $\Sigma \mathbf{F} = 0$, or, in scalar form, $\Sigma F_x = \Sigma F_y = \Sigma F_z = 0$, yielding

$$\Sigma F_x = \left(p - \frac{\partial p}{\partial x}\frac{\Delta x}{2}\right)\Delta y\,\Delta z - \left(p + \frac{\partial p}{\partial x}\frac{\Delta x}{2}\right)\Delta y\,\Delta z = 0$$

$$\Sigma F_y = \left(p - \frac{\partial p}{\partial y}\frac{\Delta y}{2}\right)\Delta x\,\Delta z - \left(p + \frac{\partial p}{\partial y}\frac{\Delta y}{2}\right)\Delta x\,\Delta z = 0$$

$$\Sigma F_z = \left(p - \frac{\partial p}{\partial z}\frac{\Delta z}{2}\right)\Delta x\,\Delta y - \left(p + \frac{\partial p}{\partial z}\frac{\Delta z}{2}\right)\Delta x\,\Delta y - \rho\frac{g}{g_c}\Delta x\,\Delta y\,\Delta z = 0$$

With the x direction as an example, this reduces to

$$-\frac{\partial p}{\partial x}\,\Delta x\,\Delta y\,\Delta z = 0$$

Passing to the limit as Δx, Δy, and $\Delta z \to 0$ and dividing through by the volume $dx\,dy\,dz$, we have $-\partial p/\partial x = 0$. Reducing the other expressions similarly, we obtain

$$\frac{\partial p}{\partial x} = 0 \qquad \frac{\partial p}{\partial y} = 0 \qquad \frac{\partial p}{\partial z} + \rho\frac{g}{g_c} = 0$$

These results can be conveniently expressed in vector form as

$$\mathrm{grad}\ p + \mathbf{k}\rho\frac{g}{g_c} = 0$$

In scalar form we see that both $\partial p/\partial x$ and $\partial p/\partial y = 0$, so that p is constant in the xy plane. Thus the pressure has a *constant* value in a horizontal plane anywhere in a stationary fluid. For the third equation, the vertical or z direction, we can pass from the partial to the ordinary derivative, as p is not a function of x and y, and obtain

$$\frac{dp}{dz} + \rho\frac{g}{g_c} = 0 \qquad\qquad [2.1a]$$

or

$$dp + \rho\frac{g}{g_c}\,dz = 0 \qquad\qquad [2.1b]$$

Eqs. 2.1 express the basic relationship of fluid statics (the *hydrostatic equation*), that the pressure gradient in a fluid at rest is directly proportional to the density. With z positive upward, the pressure increases with depth or increases downward from a horizontal plane. If g is taken as the constant in a given body of fluid, there are three variables, p, ρ, and z, and some relation between two of them must be known before Eqs. 2.1 can be integrated. The simplest, but at the same time a most useful, relation is that for constant density. This is valid for liquids and will now be analyzed.

2.3   *Pressure distribution in a liquid*

With constant density, integration of Eq. 2.1b between any two points 1 and 2 yields

$$p_1 - p_2 + \rho \frac{g}{g_c} (z_1 - z_2) = 0 \qquad [2.2a]$$

or

$$p_1 - p_2 = \rho \frac{g}{g_c} (z_2 - z_1) \qquad [2.2b]$$

Thus the pressure difference is directly proportional to the height difference. Because both quantities are differences, any arbitrary datum may be used for calculation. Fig. 2.2(a) shows a liquid in a container, with an arbitrary elevation datum $z = 0$. Since $z_2 - z_1$ is negative, $p_1 - p_2$ is negative, indicating that p_2 is greater than p_1. Suppose that we want the total pressure at point 1 (Fig. 2.2(b)), this pressure being the sum of that due to depth in the liquid and that due to any pressure p_s acting on the surface. Then from Eq. 2.2b

$$p_1 = p_s + \rho \frac{g}{g_c} (z_s - z_1)$$

Because the free surface is a convenient datum, we may put $z_s - z_1 = h$, where h is simply the depth below the free surface. In general, p_s may be any pressure; e.g., the liquid may be in a closed container with a gas under pressure in the volume above the free surface. For the very common case in

Figure 2.2

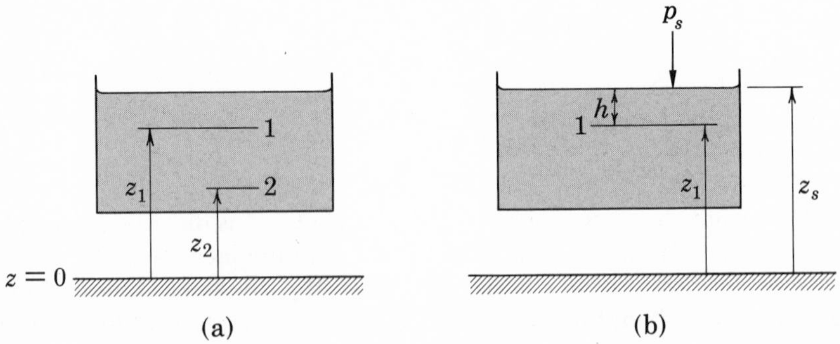

(a)   (b)

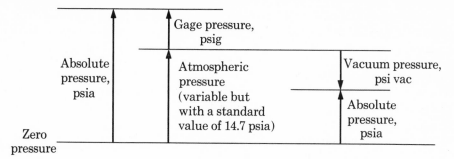

Figure 2.3

which p_s is the atmospheric pressure, p_a, the total pressure at point 1 is $p_a + \rho(g/g_c)h$. Now unless the fluid system is completely closed, atmospheric pressure acts on that part of the fluid in contact with the atmosphere and is transmitted to all points of the fluid; i.e., the fluid everywhere has a component of pressure p_a. Most instruments used to measure pressure measure it as a difference between the total pressure in the fluid and the atmospheric pressure. Thus it is convenient to call p_a the datum pressure where $p = 0$ and to call $p_1 = \rho g h/g_c$ the *gage* pressure. The sum of the gage pressure and the atmospheric pressure is called the *absolute* pressure. It is customary to quote pressures as gage values, in pounds per square inch (psi or lb/in.²), but p_a must be added when the problem requires absolute pressure (e.g., as in all thermodynamic work). For actual test data the exact atmospheric pressure must be known (via a barometer), but for general design use 14.7 psi represents p_a. To avoid ambiguity, gage pressure may be given as psig or lb/in.² gage, but normally it is expressed only as psi. If the pressure is specified as absolute, it is given as psia or lb/in.² abs.

A pressure below atmospheric pressure is a negative gage pressure, usually called a *vacuum* pressure, i.e., psi vac. Fig. 2.3 shows the relationship of gage, absolute, and vacuum pressures.

Because pressure in a fluid is proportional to a linear dimension or the depth of fluid, it is often called *head*. Thus we speak of "a 20 ft head" of water, for instance, meaning a pressure corresponding to a column of water 20 ft high. Eq. 2.1 can be expressed as head in feet if Eq. 2.1b is divided through by $\rho g/g_c$ to give Eq. 2.1c.

$$\frac{dp}{\rho g/g_c} + dz = 0$$

or

$$\frac{dp}{\gamma} + dz = 0 \qquad\qquad [\textbf{2.1c}]$$

where $\gamma = \rho g/g_c$ is the specific weight, commonly used in hydraulics.

2.4   *Measurement of pressure—manometry*

The basic pressure-density-height relationship of Eq. 2.2 provides a primary standard for measuring pressure by the height of a column of liquid of known density. The instruments used for this purpose are called *manometers*. Because they are so frequently employed in experimentation, it is essential that their working be thoroughly understood.

The U-tube manometer in Fig. 2.4 consists of a bent transparent tube partially filled with a liquid, having one side connected to the vessel containing the fluid whose pressure is required and the other side open to the atmosphere. From the fact that the pressure is the same at all points in a horizontal plane within a *continuous* volume of the *same* fluid, the pressure at x is equal to the pressure at y. The absolute pressure at y is equal to the sum of the atmospheric pressure and that due to the height of the manometer liquid between y and z. Thus

$$p_x = p_y = p_a + \rho_m \frac{g}{g_c} (z_z - z_y) = p_a + \rho_m \frac{g}{g_c} h$$

p_x is then the absolute pressure, the gage pressure being simply $\rho_m gh/g_c$ (or $\gamma_m h$). Note that with ρ_m or γ_m in pounds per cubic foot (lb/ft³), h must be in feet and p in pounds per square foot (psf).

This illustration is simple and obvious, but actual manometer installa-

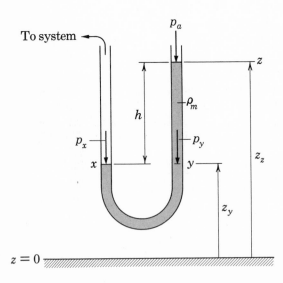

Figure 2.4

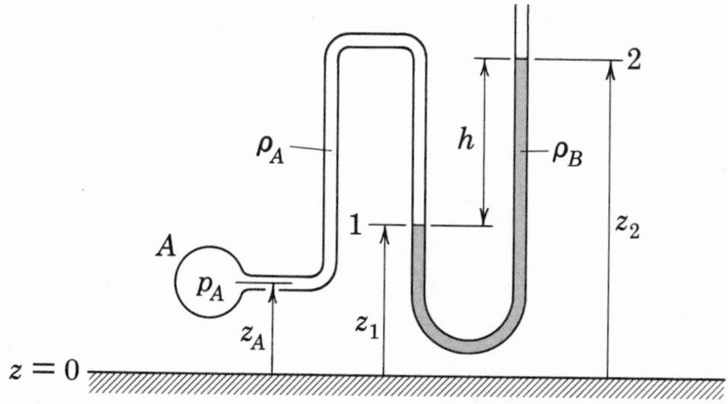

Figure 2.5

tions may require considerable care in analysis for the correct determination of a required pressure. Particular attention is necessary when both the actual fluid and the manometer fluid are liquids. An example of the method of calculation follows.

Fig. 2.5 shows a vessel, A, containing a fluid of density ρ_A whose pressure, p_A, is required. The manometer contains a liquid of density ρ_B. We proceed to apply the basic equation around the system from point to point in the *same* fluid. Thus from point A to point 1,

$$p_A - p_1 = \rho_A \frac{g}{g_c} (z_1 - z_A)$$

From point 1 to point 2,

$$p_1 - p_2 = \rho_B \frac{g}{g_c} (z_2 - z_1)$$

Therefore, $$p_1 = p_2 + \rho_B \frac{g}{g_c} (z_2 - z_1)$$

With this value of p_1 substituted in the first relationship,

$$p_A - p_2 - \rho_B \frac{g}{g_c} (z_2 - z_1) = \rho_A \frac{g}{g_c} (z_1 - z_A)$$

and $$p_A = p_2 + \rho_B \frac{g}{g_c} (z_2 - z_1) + \rho_A \frac{g}{g_c} (z_1 - z_A)$$

Again this is p_A as absolute pressure. If $p_2 = p_a$, then putting $p_2 = 0$ gives p_A as gage pressure. If fluids A and B are both liquids, their densities are of the same order, and the pressure due to the column of measured fluid $(z_1 - z_A)$ must be taken into account. If fluid A is a gas, however, the pressure due to $z_1 - z_A$ can usually be neglected. For instance, suppose that the density of the air at just above atmospheric pressure is taken as 0.08 lb/ft^3, while the density of water is 62.4 lb/ft³. The ratio of ρ_B to ρ_A in this case is then $62.4/0.08 \approx 780$. The height $z_1 - z_A$ can be neglected, and pressure p_A reduces to

$$p_A = \rho_B \frac{g}{g_c} (z_2 - z_1) = \rho_B \frac{g}{g_c} h$$

Now that we have shown the application of the hydrostatic equation in basic fashion to a manometer problem, we shall demonstrate a more rapid method, but one that depends on a good understanding of the pressure-height relationship. For the system of Fig. 2.5, we can see that gage pressure, p_A, is equal to the sum of the pressures due to the head of measured fluid, $z_1 - z_A$, and the head of manometer fluid, h. Hence we may write directly

$$p_A = \rho_A \frac{g}{g_c} (z_1 - z_A) + \rho_B \frac{g}{g_c} h$$

Due care must be taken with the relative levels of the reference points. Thus in Fig. 2.6 the manometer is below the level of vessel A, and in this case the pressure due to the column of liquid, $z_A - z_1$, must be subtracted; i.e.,

$$p_A = - \rho_A \frac{g}{g_c} (z_A - z_1) + \rho_B \frac{g}{g_c} h$$

In measuring gas pressure, oil of sp gr ≈ 0.8 and water are used for the lower ranges, and carbon tetrachloride, CCl_4 (sp gr ≈ 1.6) and mercury, Hg (sp gr ≈ 13.56), are used for the higher ranges. There is a practical upper limit to the pressure measurable by a manometer, even with mercury, owing to awkwardness of manometer height and danger of breakage of glass tubing. The limit is of the order of about 100 in. of mercury, equivalent to a pressure of about 50 psi.

It is valuable for calculation to keep in mind a few equivalents of pres-

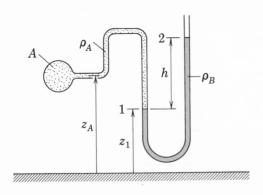

Figure 2.6

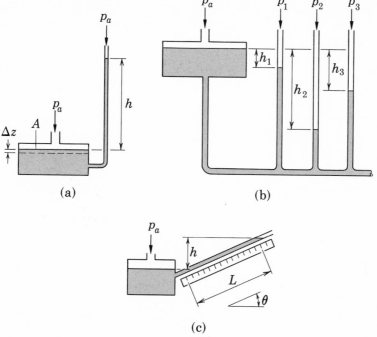

(a)

(b)

(c)

Figure 2.7

sure and liquid height.* These should be verified by means of Eq. 2.2. Atmospheric pressure of 14.7 psi is equivalent to 33.9 ft of water (H_2O) or 29.92 in. of mercury (Hg). Thus 1 psi is equivalent to 2.31 ft H_2O or 2.04 in. Hg. Conversely, 1 ft H_2O is equivalent to 0.433 psi, and 1 in. Hg is equivalent to 0.491 psi.

The U-tube may be used as a *differential* manometer, e.g., in measuring pressure drop along a pipe, if each leg is connected to a pressure source. Sometimes it is convenient to use a *single-limb* manometer, which consists of a U-tube with one leg expanded to a large area so that it is in effect a reservoir (Fig. 2.7(a)). Applying pressure to the reservoir causes a negligible change of elevation of the fluid in it, and so the whole measurement is made by the single remaining leg, although a zero reading must be taken initially. When many pressures are to be measured simultaneously, a *multilimb* manometer may be used (Fig. 2.7(b)). Note that for accuracy the area of the reservoir must be many times the combined area of the tubes. To demonstrate this, suppose that in Fig. 2.7(a) the cross-sectional areas of reservoir and tube are A and a, respectively. The levels are originally the same, but

---

* These are quoted with some misgiving, as they are liable to be used blindly without understanding the basic relationship, but nevertheless they are commonly employed.

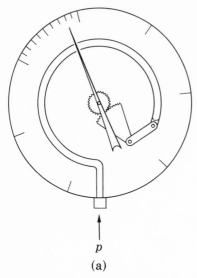

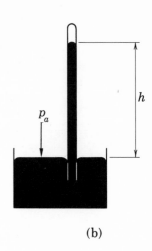

(a)

(b)

Figure 2.8

application of pressure on the reservoir causes a lowering of its level by Δz and a rise of manometer level by h. As the volume of liquid is constant, then $A\,\Delta z = ah$, and $\Delta z = ah/A$. The true manometer relationship is thus

$$p = \rho\,\frac{g}{g_c}\,(h + \Delta z) = \rho\,\frac{g}{g_c}\left(h + \frac{a}{A}\,h\right) = \rho\,\frac{g}{g_c}\,h\left(1 + \frac{a}{A}\right)$$

If just the height, h, from the zero-pressure level is considered, for accuracy within 1% A must be at least 100 times a.

For measuring small pressures, the *inclined* manometer, shown in Fig. 2.7(c), can be used. The actual vertical displacement, h, is read as a magnified value, L, on the inclined scale, with $h = L \sin \theta$. When used for the fractional air pressures in furnaces, the inclined manometer is known as a *draft gage*. For measuring small pressures with great precision, many special micromanometers are available, but these will not be described here.

For higher pressures for which manometers are unsuitable, the *Bourdon* pressure gage is used. The fluid under pressure is admitted into a closed, bent tube, fixed at the end through which the fluid enters and having a lightweight mechanism at the closed end that converts a small movement of the closed end into a larger circumferential movement. Increase of internal pressure causes the tube to attempt to straighten out, thus moving the pivoted arm over a dial (Fig. 2.8(a)). Although the Bourdon gage can be precise, it requires calibration because it is a *secondary* instrument (as opposed to a manometer, which is a *primary* instrument dependent only on the basic law of fluid pressure).

The *barometer* is used for measuring atmospheric pressure, which is absolute pressure. The single tube, Fig. 2.8(b), closed at one end, is filled with mercury and inverted in a reservoir. The pressure at the top is due only to the vapor pressure of the mercury, and the height h thus measures the atmospheric pressure.

2.5 *Pressure relationships for compressible fluids*

For compressible fluids the density is not constant, and integration of Eq. 2.1 requires a relationship between two of the three variables p, ρ, and z. No general relationships can be established, but some special ones are useful, mostly in connection with the atmosphere.

Such a relationship exists for a gas at constant temperature, i.e., the isothermal case. From the ideal equation of state, $\rho = p/RT$, and, with T constant, this may be substituted in Eq. 2.1 and the equation integrated. Thus

$$dp = - \rho \frac{g}{g_c} dz = - \frac{p}{RT} \frac{g}{g_c} dz$$

$$\frac{dp}{p} = - \frac{1}{RT} \frac{g}{g_c} dz$$

Integration between states 1 and 2, with g constant, yields

$$\ln \frac{p_1}{p_2} = \frac{1}{RT} \frac{g}{g_c} (z_2 - z_1) \qquad [2.3a]$$

or

$$\frac{p_1}{p_2} = e^{(g/g_c)[(z_2-z_1)/RT]} \qquad [2.3b]$$

The atmosphere, as we know only too well, is highly variable in temperature and pressure. However, there are defined trends, and for many purposes, particularly aeronautical ones, it is desirable to specify a *model* atmosphere, i.e., one having standard values that by and large represent average conditions.

The atmosphere changes its character markedly with altitude, always decreasing in pressure but fluctuating in temperature. Several different zones may be distinguished, but their boundaries are not precise. Their nomenclature varies according to whether temperature, composition, or some other condition is used for differentiation. From the surface of the earth up to a height of about 7 miles lies the *troposphere*, which is the domain

Table 2.1

ALTITUDE, FT	TEMPERATURE, °R	PRESSURE, PSFA	PRESSURE, PSIA
0	518.67	2116.2	14.696
5,000	500.84	1760.9	12.23
10,000	483.03	1455.6	10.11
20,000	447.42	973.3	6.759
30,000	411.84	629.7	4.373
36,152	389.97	472.7	3.283
40,000	389.97	393.1	2.730
50,000	389.97	243.6	1.692
60,000	389.97	151.0	1.049
65,840	389.97	114.3	0.793
70,000	392.25	93.73	0.651
80,000	397.69	58.51	0.406
90,000	403.14	36.78	0.255
100,000	408.57	23.72	0.162

For reference, note that at the tropopause the pressure is just under 3.3 psia and at the stratopause it is only about 22 in. H_2O (aircraft with air-breathing engines have been flown at about 100,000 ft).

of "weather." Above this is the *stratosphere*, extending (on a basis of temperature) to about 15 miles. Farther out there is considerable ionization, and the zone from the stratosphere up to about 250 miles is known as the *ionosphere*. For ordinary fluid mechanics only the region up to about 20 miles is of concern, this being the region in which the air, although rarefied, behaves similarly to air at ground level as we know it.

There are several model atmospheres, but the international standard is the International Civil Aviation Organization (I.C.A.O.) standard atmosphere, which is defined up to a height of about 65,000 ft (20 km); beyond this there are several extensions. The figures given here are those of the U.S. Standard Atmosphere, 1962* (Table 2.1). It should be recognized that the figures for beyond the stratosphere are subject to continual revision, as very high-altitude balloons and sounding rockets that enable data to be accumulated have been developed only lately and much work is needed before definite figures can be agreed upon.

In the troposphere the model atmosphere assumes a linear rate of temperature decrease or *lapse rate* of 3.56°F/1000 ft, with sea-level temperature fixed at 59°F (518.7°R), extending to an altitude of 36,000 ft,† at which the

* U.S. Government Printing Office, Washington 25, D.C.
† The exact figure is 36,152 ft. This seemingly incongruously precise figure results from (1) the I.C.A.O. atmosphere's being in metric units, with the round figure of 11,000 m as the geopotential tropopause, and (2) the difference between geometric height

temperature becomes constant at $-69°F$ or $390°R$. This altitude is called the *tropopause*, or isothermal altitude. With a fixed lapse rate, the pressure can be calculated if, at the same time, the values of g, the gravitational acceleration, and R, the gas constant for air, are kept constant. The value of g varies as $1/r^2$, where r is the distance from the center of the earth. If the earth's radius is taken as 4000 miles, then at an altitude of 20 miles the decrease in g from its standard value, g_c, is about 1%, which can be significant. Likewise, the composition of air varies with altitude, changing the value of R. However, for the purposes of analysis, here both g and R will be considered constant at the sea-level standard values.

For the model atmosphere with a constant lapse rate, we can call this lapse rate λ, with units of degrees Fahrenheit per foot (°F/ft), and substitute it in the hydrostatic equation. Thus, from Eq. 2.1,

$$dp = - \rho \frac{g}{g_c} dz$$

and with

$$\lambda = - \frac{dT}{dz}$$

$$dp = \rho \frac{g}{g_c} \frac{dT}{\lambda}$$

Eliminating ρ by the equation of state, $\rho = p/RT$, we have

$$\frac{dp}{p} = \frac{g}{g_c} \frac{1}{\lambda R} \frac{dT}{T}$$

Integrating between a datum state where $p = p_1$ and $T = T_1$ to any state where $p = p$ and $T = T$ gives us

$$\ln \frac{p}{p_1} = \frac{g}{g_c} \frac{1}{\lambda R} \ln \frac{T}{T_1}$$

or

$$\frac{p}{p_1} = \left(\frac{T}{T_1} \right)^{g/g_c \lambda R}$$

[2.4]

Within the limits of altitude for which the lapse rate is valid, $g = g_c$, and so g/g_c cancels out numerically.

An equation relating pressure directly to height can be obtained by integration of the lapse rate–definitional equation; i.e.,

$$T = T_1 - \lambda z$$

and geopotential height. The latter term takes account of variation of gravitational force with altitude.

whence

$$\frac{p}{p_1} = \left(1 - \frac{\lambda z}{T_1}\right)^{g/g_c \lambda R} \qquad [2.5]$$

From the tropopause upward to about 66,000 ft (20 km), the temperature is constant, and thus pressure varies according to the isothermal relations of Eq. 2.3. Above this level, which is called the *stratopause*, the temperature increases up to about 27°F at 155,000 ft. From then on there is a succession of changes, which are beyond our scope.

There are many other model atmospheres, such as Arctic Summer, Arctic Winter, and Tropical, used largely for providing standards for aircraft performance. Of interest in meteorology is an atmosphere with an *adiabatic* lapse rate, for large bodies of air may behave adiabatically over a period of time. The relations governing this condition will be found in a problem at the end of the chapter.

2.6 *Pressure relationships for accelerating fluid systems*

When a mass of fluid is in accelerated motion but with no *relative* motion between particles and thus no shear stresses, a static analysis may be made if the additional inertia forces are taken into account. Two cases will be examined, one for linear motion with constant acceleration and one for rotational motion with uniform angular velocity.

For linear acceleration, consider a rectangular element of sides Δx, Δy, and Δz anywhere within the body of fluid being subjected to constant acceleration **a** in the xz plane (Fig. 2.9(a)). This is a two-dimensional case, with no inertia forces arising in the y direction. It can be generalized to three dimensions if necessary. By Newton's second law, $\Sigma \mathbf{F} = M\mathbf{a}/g_c$, and the forces acting in the x and z directions are shown in Fig. 2.9(b). The pressure at the center of the element is p. The acceleration **a** may be separated into two components, a_x and a_z. In the x direction, $\Sigma F_x = M a_x/g_c$; hence, following the same arguments as in Sect. 2.2,

$$\left(p - \frac{\partial p}{\partial x}\frac{\Delta x}{2}\right)\Delta y\,\Delta z - \left(p + \frac{\partial p}{\partial x}\frac{\Delta x}{2}\right)\Delta y\,\Delta z = \frac{M a_x}{g_c} = \frac{\rho}{g_c}\Delta x\,\Delta y\,\Delta z\,a_x$$

which reduces to

$$\frac{\partial p}{\partial x} = -\frac{\rho}{g_c}a_x$$

Although this is in partial derivative form, we may integrate it if we allow

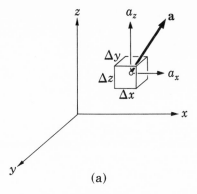

(a)

Figure 2.9

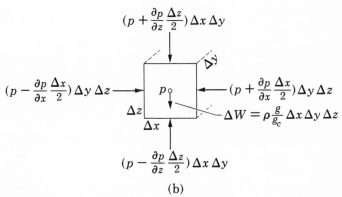

(b)

for some unknown function of z, thus:

$$p = -\frac{\rho}{g_c} a_x x + f_1(z) + C_1 \qquad [2.6]$$

where C is a constant. For the z direction,

$$\left(p - \frac{\partial p}{\partial z}\frac{\Delta z}{2}\right)\Delta x\,\Delta y - \left(p + \frac{\partial p}{\partial z}\frac{\Delta z}{2}\right)\Delta x\,\Delta y - \rho\frac{g}{g_c}\Delta x\,\Delta y\,\Delta z = \frac{M a_z}{g_c}$$

$$= \frac{\rho}{g_c}\Delta x\,\Delta y\,\Delta z\,a_z$$

which reduces to

$$\frac{\partial p}{\partial z} = -\frac{\rho}{g_c}(a_z + g)$$

Integrating with $f_2(x)$, an unknown function of x, gives

$$p = -\frac{\rho}{g_c}(a_z + g)z + f_2(x) + C_2 \qquad [2.7]$$

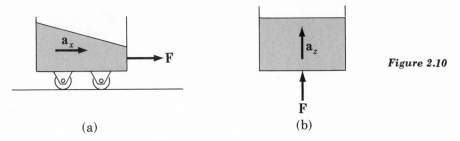

Figure 2.10

(a)   (b)

Since the pressure at a point has been shown to be the same regardless of direction, the values of p in Eqs. 2.6 and 2.7 may be equated, giving

$$-\frac{\rho}{g_c} a_x x + f_1(z) + C_1 = -\frac{\rho}{g_c} (a_z + g)z + f_2(x) + C_2$$

Hence $f_1(z) = -\rho(a_z + g)z/g_c$, and $f_2(x) = -\rho a_x x/g_c$, and the pressure may be written as

$$p = -\frac{\rho}{g_c} [a_x x + (a_z + g)z] + C \qquad [2.8]$$

Alternatively, with $p = f(x, y, z)$, then $dp = (\partial p/\partial x)\, dx + (\partial p/\partial z)\, dz$. Substituting the appropriate partial derivatives and integrating yields Eq. 2.8.

For a line of constant pressure, Eq. 2.8 may be differentiated to obtain dz/dx; hence

$$\frac{dz}{dx} = -\frac{a_x}{a_z + g} \qquad [2.9]$$

If there is a free surface, it is a line of constant pressure, as Eq. 2.9 indicates. Lines of constant pressure in the body of the fluid are parallel to the free surface. The resultant acceleration is normal to the constant-pressure lines.

Two special applications are of interest because they are quite common, namely, horizontal acceleration only and vertical acceleration only. For the former, the slope of a free surface is $-a_x/g$, and so it appears as in Fig. 2.10(a), with the surface sloping backward from the direction of motion. With $a_z = 0$, Eq. 2.8 becomes

$$p = -\frac{\rho}{g_c} (a_x x + gz) + C$$

At any fixed value of x,

$$\frac{dp}{dz} = -\frac{\rho}{g_c} (g) = -\rho \frac{g}{g_c}$$

showing that the vertical pressure distribution is that of the static case. Horizontal acceleration occurs in the fuel tanks of all moving vehicles, such as automobiles and airplanes, and in tank cars on road and rail. The pressure distribution and the position of the free surface must be taken into account in design to eliminate stress and to locate to best advantage pipe connections and vents.

For vertical acceleration, the slope of the free surface is zero, i.e., horizontal (Fig. 2.10(b)). With $a_x = 0$, then

$$p = -\frac{\rho}{g_c}(a_z + g)z + C$$

and

$$\frac{dp}{dz} = -\frac{\rho}{g_c}(a_z + g)$$

i.e., the normal static pressure distribution is increased proportionately to the vertical acceleration. Note that a_z is considered as positive when upward, so that upward acceleration increases the pressure at the bottom of a vessel containing liquid and downward acceleration decreases it. When a_z is downward and numerically equal to g, i.e., $a_z = -g$, the fluid exerts no pressure and is said to be "weightless." The effects of vertical acceleration are experienced in high-speed elevators and again must be taken into account in design when a_z is large, as it may be in rocket launching.

For rotational motion, it is convenient to use a cylindrical coordinate system of r, θ, and z, as shown in Fig. 2.11(a). A small segmental element of fluid at radius r, with sides Δr and Δz and subtending an angle $\Delta\theta$, rotates at a constant angular velocity, ω. Fig. 2.11(b) gives the pressure forces on the element in the $r\theta$ plane, varying with r but not with θ, as there is circumferential symmetry. The element has a normal or centrifugal acceleration, a_r, directed radially inward by virtue of the rotational motion, the force then being Ma_r/g_c. The normal acceleration toward the center is, from mechanics, $\omega^2 r$. The element is in equilibrium under the action of these forces.

The forces due to pressure on the arc sides of the element should be clear from the diagram, but the side force needs some explanation. In the first instance, as the pressure varies radially, the pressure acting on the side is taken as the average of that at r and that at $r + \Delta r$, i.e., p. The force is normal to the face and has components normal to and along the radius through the center of the element. The normal components cancel out, but the radial components are additive, both being directed outward. By geometry, the angle between the component normal to the face and the radius through the center is $\Delta\theta/2$; the radial component is thus the force normal to the face times $\sin(\Delta\theta/2)$. As $\Delta\theta \to 0$, $\sin(\Delta\theta/2) \to \Delta\theta/2$, which is the value used in the force balance.

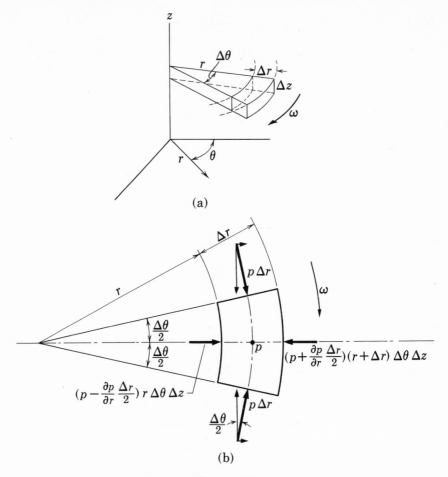

(a)

(b)

Figure 2.11

We then have $\Sigma F = Ma_r/g_c$. Hence, with the positive direction as outward from the axis,

$$\left(p - \frac{\partial p}{\partial r}\frac{\Delta r}{2}\right) r\,\Delta\theta\,\Delta z + 2p\,\Delta r\,\Delta z\,\frac{\Delta\theta}{2} - \left(p + \frac{\partial p}{\partial r}\frac{\Delta r}{2}\right)(r + \Delta r)\,\Delta\theta\,\Delta z = \frac{Ma_r}{g_c}$$

$$= -\frac{\rho}{g_c}\,\pi[(r + \Delta r)^2 - r^2]\frac{\Delta\theta}{2\pi}\,\Delta z\,\omega^2 r$$

where $\Delta\theta/2\pi$ is the fraction of the circular area of the segment subtended by $\Delta\theta$. Expanding the terms, reducing, and dividing through by the volume $r\,\Delta\theta\,\Delta r\,\Delta z$ yield

$$-\frac{\partial p}{\partial r} - \frac{\partial p}{\partial r}\frac{\Delta r}{r} = -\frac{\rho}{g_c}\left(r + \frac{\Delta r}{2}\right)\omega^2$$

As $\Delta r \rightarrow 0$, this reduces to

$$\frac{\partial p}{\partial r} = \frac{\rho}{g_c}\omega^2 r \qquad\qquad [2.10]$$

After integration, again allowing for $f_1(z)$,

$$p = \frac{\rho\omega^2 r^2}{2g_c} + f_1(z) + C_1$$

In the z direction, there is no acceleration, and thus the simple static Eq. 2.1 applies.

$$\frac{\partial p}{\partial z} = -\rho\frac{g}{g_c} \qquad\qquad [2.1]$$

Therefore,
$$p = -\frac{\rho g z}{g_c} + f_2(r) + C_2$$

With p independent of direction, as before,

$$p = \frac{\rho}{g_c}\left(\frac{\omega^2 r^2}{2} - gz\right) + C \qquad\qquad [2.11]$$

For a line of constant pressure,

$$\frac{dz}{dr} = \frac{\omega^2 r}{g}$$

and
$$z = \frac{\omega^2 r^2}{2g} + C \qquad\qquad [2.12]$$

which is the equation of a parabola symmetrical about the z axis. Since a free surface is one of constant pressure, this is a paraboloid, as shown in Fig. 2.12. At any radius, r, from Eq. 2.11,

$$\frac{\partial p}{\partial z} = -\rho\frac{g}{g_c}$$

which is the static pressure distribution. At constant elevation z,

$$\frac{\partial p}{\partial r} = \frac{\rho}{g_c}\omega^2 r$$

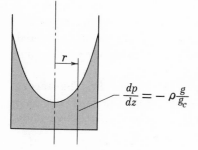

$$-\frac{dp}{dz} = -\rho\frac{g}{g_c}$$

Figure 2.12

giving a pressure gradient increasing linearly with increase of radius.

Rotation of fluid with a constant angular velocity, and accordingly with a pressure distribution and free surface as just demonstrated, is usually termed a *forced vortex*. It is so named because it requires a torque and hence input energy in order to act in this manner, in contrast to a *free vortex*, which is a natural rotational motion not requiring input energy (and which we shall study later). The nomenclature is perhaps unfortunate in that any rotational motion other than a free vortex requires energy and is thus "forced"; the case described is merely the particular one of constant angular velocity of the whole fluid. It is thus better termed as *solid-body* or *wheel* rotation, to which it is analogous. It should be noted that up to Eq. 2.10 the analysis applies to any element of fluid at radius r with angular velocity ω. In the subsequent integration, ω is considered constant with respect to r, but other types of vortex have $\omega = f(r)$. If the function is known, then the integration may be made, resulting in a different final rotation from that given.

A forced vortex of the solid-rotation type develops when a cylindrical vessel is spun on its axis, the steady-state uniform angular velocity being produced by shear forces starting at the wall and being diffused radially inward with time. Note that although viscous action is necessary to attain the motion, once a steady state has been reached, there is no relative motion of fluid particles, and thus the preceding analysis based on pressure forces alone is possible.

The pressure distribution, giving pressure proportional to the square of the radius, Eq. 2.11, is used in centrifugal pumps, compressors, and turbines, and we shall return to it when we study turbomachinery.

2.7   *Forces on plane surfaces*

Eq. 2.1 allows us to calculate the pressure at any point in a fluid. If there is a solid surface in the fluid, then at each element of area on the surface there is a force due to the pressure directed normally to the surface. Only liquids of constant density are dealt with here, as forces due to depth of gas are normally negligible in this situation. Furthermore, the surface is considered to be exposed to liquid on the upper side only, and therefore we are concerned only with the pressure on this upper surface.

Fig. 2.13 shows such a *plane* surface, CD, with trace $C'D'$. The trace is extended to cut the free surface at O, Ox being along the line of intersection of the free surface and the plane of the immersed surface, with Oy being any arbitrary axis perpendicular to it.

The total force, **F**, on the surface is $\Sigma\ \Delta\mathbf{F}$, and ΔF is the product of the pressure, p, due to the column of liquid, h, and the area, ΔA. Thus

$$F = \Sigma\ \Delta F = \Sigma p\ \Delta A = \sum \rho\frac{g}{g_c} h\ \Delta A$$

With infinitesimal areas, then

$$F = \int_A \rho\frac{g}{g_c} h\ dA$$

and in terms of y, with $h = y \sin\theta$,

$$F = \rho\frac{g}{g_c}\sin\theta \int_A y\ dA \qquad [\boldsymbol{2.13}]$$

Now from statics $\int y\ dA$ is the first moment of the area about Ox, with $\int y\ dA = y_c A$, where y_c is the distance of the centroid, G, of the area from Ox. Thus

$$F = \rho\frac{g}{g_c}\sin\theta\ y_c A$$

and with $y_c \sin\theta = h_c$,

$$F = \rho\frac{g}{g_c} h_c A = p_c A \qquad [\boldsymbol{2.14}]$$

The conclusion is that the magnitude of the force on a submerged plane surface is equal to the product of the area and the pressure at the centroid of the area. As shown, the pressure is due only to the column of liquid and is

Figure 2.13

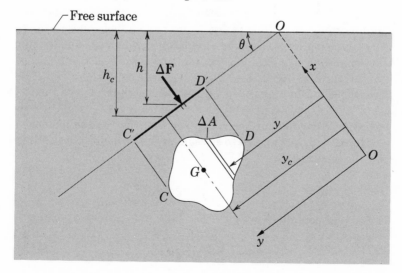

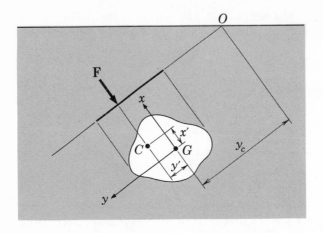

Figure 2.14

thus gage pressure. If the liquid is subject to an additional uniform pressure everywhere, this pressure must be added to that due to h. (It can be visualized as an additional height of liquid above the free surface.) Eq. 2.14 is a considerable simplification; it is possible because the centroid of an irregular area, which can be calculated directly only by a complex integration, can be obtained with ease if the area is broken down into a number of smaller, regular areas with known or readily determined centroids.

Although the force may be calculated from the position of the centroid, its line of action is elsewhere, as the elementary forces $\Delta \mathbf{F}$ have moments proportional to their distances from a pair of axes. A *center of pressure* may be defined as the point of application of the resultant force, i.e., the point where a single equal and opposite force to the resultant force must be situated in order to obtain equilibrium. For an irregular area, moments must be taken about two perpendicular axes. As we have found the centroid to be a convenient location from which to calculate the magnitude of the force, let us place the axes for the position analysis through the centroid and parallel to the x and y axes of Fig. 2.13. In Fig. 2.14, the axes are Gx and Gy, and C is the unknown center of pressure located at distance y' from the x axis and at distance x' from the y axis.

Taking moments about the x axis, we have Fy' as the moment of the resultant force. This is set equal to the sum of the moments of the elementary areas for the whole surface; i.e.,

$$Fy' = \int_A yp\, dA$$

and for the new coordinates

$$p = \rho \frac{g}{g_c} (y_c + y) \sin \theta$$

Thus

$$Fy' = \rho \frac{g}{g_c} \sin \theta \int_A (y + y_c)y \, dA = \rho \frac{g}{g_c} \sin \theta \int_A y^2 \, dA + \rho \frac{g}{g_c} \sin \theta \int_A y_c y \, dA$$

The last term is zero, because $\int y_c y \, dA = y_c \int y \, dA$, and for the origin at G, $\int y \, dA = 0$. From Eq. 2.13,

$$F = \rho \frac{g}{g_c} \sin \theta \int_A (y + y_c) \, dA$$

and with $\int y \, dA = 0$,

$$F = \rho \frac{g}{g_c} \sin \theta \, y_c \int_A dA = \rho \frac{g}{g_c} \sin \theta \, y_c A$$

From the moment equation we then have

$$Fy' = \rho \frac{g}{g_c} \sin \theta \int_A y^2 \, dA$$

Substituting for F from the force equation yields

$$y' = \frac{\int y^2 \, dA}{y_c A}$$

$\int y^2 \, dA$ is the second moment of area, commonly known as the *moment of inertia*, I; in this case, where it refers to the x axis through the centroid, it is designated as I_{xx}. Therefore,

$$y' = \frac{I_{xx}}{y_c A} \qquad [\mathbf{2.15}]$$

Since I_{xx} is always positive, then y' must be positive and, from Fig. 2.14, below the centroid G, i.e., at a greater depth than the centroid.

   Taking moments about the y axis, we have

$$Fx' = \int_A xp \, dA = \rho \frac{g}{g_c} \sin \theta \int_A x(y + y_c) \, dA = \rho \frac{g}{g_c} \sin \theta \int_A xy \, dA$$
$$+ \rho \frac{g}{g_c} \sin \theta \int_A xy_c \, dA$$

and for the origin at G, $y_c \int x \, dA = 0$. Substituting for F as before yields

$$x' = \frac{\int_A xy \, dA}{y_c A}$$

$\int xy \, dA$ is the product of inertia with respect to the x and y axes through the centroid, designated as I_{xy}. Thus

$$x' = \frac{I_{xy}}{y_c A}$$

I_{xy} may be positive or negative, i.e., on either side of Gy in Fig. 2.14. It has a value of zero when either axis is an axis of symmetry of the surface. A considerable number of the surfaces encountered in practice are symmetrical, and with them only y' need be calculated. When a surface is not symmetrical, it can often be divided up into regular areas. Then separate values can be calculated, a resultant position can be determined by means of moments according to the laws governing parallel forces in elementary statics.

2.8   *Forces on curved surfaces*

On a curved surface, as in Fig. 2.15(a), the preceding analysis cannot be used directly because the forces on elementary areas are not parallel. However, resultant horizontal and vertical components may be found, together with their points of action, whence moments may be taken for equilibrium.

Consider an infinitesimal area dA at any point, inclined in the direction θ of the tangent to the surface at that point. Areas in general are characterized by normal outward components; hence, with the representation in Fig. 2.15(b), $dA_x = - dA \cdot \mathbf{i}$, and $dA_z = dA \cdot \mathbf{k}$. The force on the surface is due to pressure and acts toward the surface; thus $d\mathbf{F} = - p\, d\mathbf{A}$. The components of the force, dF_x and dF_z, are then equal to the pressure times the projection of the area on planes normal to the x and z axes, respectively. Therefore,

$$dF_x = - p(- dA \cdot \mathbf{i}) = p\, dA_x = p\, dA \sin \theta$$
$$dF_z = - p\, d\mathbf{A} \cdot \mathbf{k} = - p\, dA_z = - p\, dA \cos \theta$$

The total forces in the x and z directions are then

$$F_x = \int p\, dA_y$$
$$F_z = - \int p\, dA_z$$

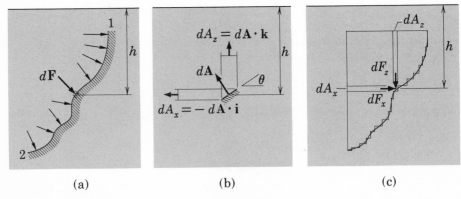

(a)   (b)   (c)

Figure 2.15

The process is equivalent to summing separately the forces on infinitesimal areas dA_x and dA_z as shown in Fig. 2.15(c).

The pressure at any point is due to the depth of fluid, h, measured from the free surface; i.e., $p = \rho gh/g_c$. Hence, over the whole surface,

$$F_x = \rho \frac{g}{g_c} \int h \, dA_x$$

$$F_z = - \rho \frac{g}{g_c} \int h \, dA_z$$

The horizontal force is that due to pressure on the projection of the curved surface in a vertical plane and can be found, together with its line of application, by the methods for plane surfaces. The vertical force is seen to be the weight of the fluid vertically above the surface, as $\int h \, dA$ is the volume of the fluid directly above the surface. Its line of application must extend vertically through the centroid of the volume.

2.9   *Buoyancy*

Consider a body completely immersed in a fluid of constant density, ρ_f, as shown in Fig. 2.16. From elementary physics we recall Archimedes' principle, that the body experiences a *buoyant* force vertically upward equal to the weight of the fluid displaced by the body. This may be demonstrated from the laws of fluid statics just discussed.

Figure 2.16

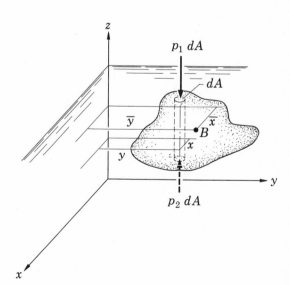

On an elementary vertical prism of cross-sectional area dA, there is a net upward force, dF_z, due to the pressure difference $(p_2 - p_1)\, dA$. With $p = \rho g h / g_c$, then

$$dF_z = \rho_f \frac{g}{g_c} (h_2 - h_1)\, dA$$

Summation of all the elementary prisms constituting the whole body yields

$$F_z = \rho_f \frac{g}{g_c} \int (h_2 - h_1)\, dA = \rho_f \frac{g}{g_c} \int dV = \rho \frac{g}{g_c} V$$

where V is the volume of the body. The term $\rho_f g V / g_c$ represents the weight of the fluid displaced by the body, and thus $F_z = W_f$. With an elementary horizontal prism, the pressures on each end are equal, so that there is no net force. Hence $F_z = F_B$, the buoyant force, and this is equal to the weight of displaced fluid, W_f.

The position where the buoyant force may be considered to act is called the *center of buoyancy*. To determine its location, we take moments about the x and y axes. According to the diagram, the buoyant force F_B acts at B, distance $\bar{y}$ from the xz plane. Taking moments about the x axis and using the earlier result that $F_B = F_z = \rho_f g / g_c \, dV$, we obtain

$$F_B \bar{y} = \rho_f \frac{g}{g_c} \int y\, dV$$

and
$$\bar{y} = \frac{\rho_f (g/g_c) \int y\, dV}{\rho_f (g/g_c) \int dV} = \frac{\int y\, dV}{\int dV}$$

In similar fashion, taking moments about the y axis, we obtain

$$\bar{x} = \frac{\int x\, dV}{\int dV}$$

$\bar{x}$ and $\bar{y}$ are the components of the position of the centroid of the volume; so the center of buoyancy must be at the centroid of the displaced fluid.

The weight of the body is $\rho_b g V / g_c$. Thus if $\rho_b < \rho_f$, the body will ascend in the fluid, and if $\rho_b > \rho_f$, it will descend. In the atmosphere a balloon filled with gas of density lower than that of the surrounding air remains in equilibrium if the buoyancy force is equal to the weight of the gas plus the weight of the balloon structure and payload. If the balloon material is non-rigid, its volume varies with the pressure and temperature of the ambient air and hence with altitude. The net lifting force varies with altitude and requires control by regulation of the mass of gas in the container and by ballast.

When a body is in equilibrium at a fluid interface, i.e., partially submerged in two immiscible fluids. the resultant buoyant force must be separately calculated for each fluid. The line of action of the resultant force

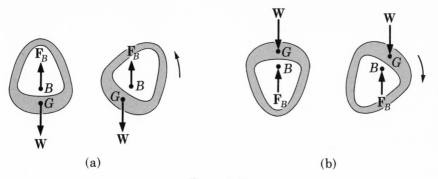

Figure 2.17

must be determined from moments of each component force. This situation is infrequent except when one fluid is air, in which case the buoyancy force due to the air submergence is usually negligible compared to that due to the liquid submergence. However, problems arise in the *stability* of floating bodies.

A completely submerged body is stable only if its center of gravity is below the center of buoyancy. Fig. 2.17(a) shows that any angular displacement will produce a couple tending to restore the system to its initial *stable* equilibrium. On the other hand, Fig. 2.17(b) shows that, although the system may have equilibrium, it is *unstable*, since the slightest disturbance will produce a couple tending to overturn it.

Figure 2.18

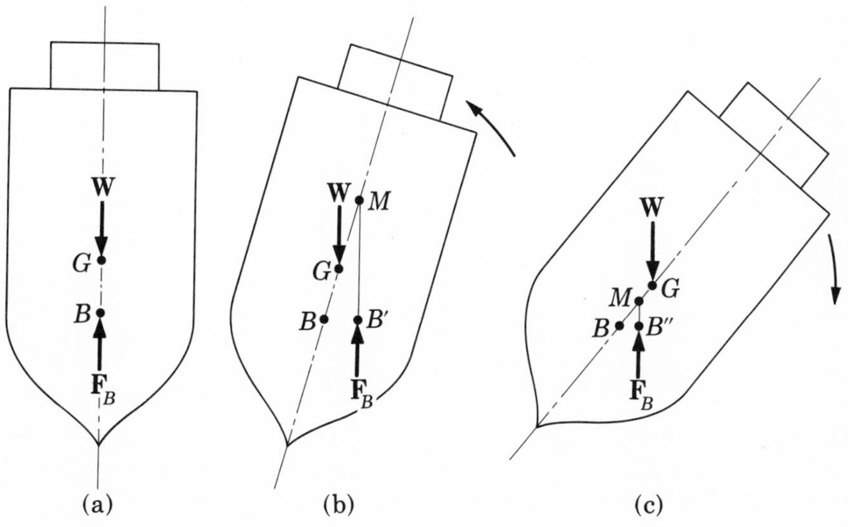

(a)   (b)   (c)

A floating body, however, may be in stable equilibrium even if its center of gravity is above its center of buoyancy. Fig. 2.18(a) shows a vessel on an even keel, with center of gravity G and center of buoyancy B on the vertical line of symmetry producing no couple. If the vessel is tipped or "rolls" to the position in Fig. 2.18(b), there is a counterclockwise restoring couple, because the center of buoyancy, B', has moved to the right of the axis of symmetry so that its line of action, $B'M$, intersects this axis above G. Further tipping may have the effect shown in Fig. 2.18(c), where, although the center of buoyancy, B'', has again moved to the right, the distance is insufficient for stability, as $B''M$ now cuts the axis of symmetry below G, producing a clockwise couple.

The distance GM is known as the *metacentric height*. A ship necessarily has its center of gravity above its center of buoyancy, even though its center of gravity is made as low as possible by installation of the propulsion machinery at the bottom level. A proper regard for metacentric height allows a considerable roll to occur while stable equilibrium is maintained, but too great an angle of heel inevitably causes overturning.

Problems

2.1. Express the pressure p in in. H_2O (a) if fluid A is air and fluid B is water, (b) if fluid A is air and fluid B is oil of sp gr 0.83, and (c) if fluid A is water and fluid B is mercury.

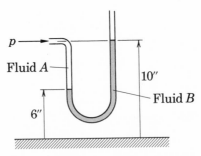

2.2. For the draft gage shown, which has oil of sp gr 0.83 as the fluid,
    a. Find the gage pressure in in. H_2O for the situation shown.
    b. Find the absolute pressure if the barometer stands at 29.32 in. Hg.

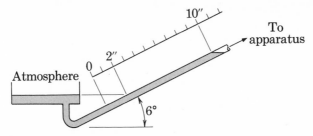

2.3. The two vessels have the same base area and the same height of liquid. The pressure on the base is the same for both by virtue of the hydrostatic equation, and yet the weight of liquid in each vessel differs. Explain this so-called "hydrostatic paradox."

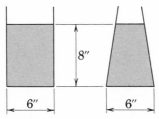

2.4. The pressure in the pipe is indicated by the manometer. The diameters of the right and left legs of the manometer are different and are to be taken as d_1 and d_2, respectively, with z_0 the elevation at which the levels in the two legs become equal.

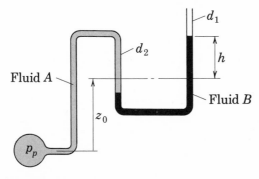

a. Show that the gage pressure in the pipe, p_p, is given by

$$p_p = \rho_A \frac{g}{g_c} z_0 + \frac{g}{g_c} h \left[\rho_B + (\rho_B - \rho_A) \left(\frac{d_1}{d_2}\right)^2 \right]$$

b. If fluid B is mercury and fluid A is oil of sp gr 0.83, find p_p for $h = 4$ ft and $z_0 = 3$ ft for a manometer having both legs of the same diameter.

c. What would be the practical advantage of making d_2 much greater than d_1?

d. If $d_1 = d_2$, derive the expression for p_p directly from the hydrostatic equation.

2.5. If both pipes contain water and the pressure in A is 40 psi and that in B is 20 psi, find the manometer reading, h, in in. Hg.

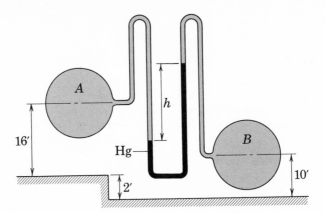

2.6. Find the reading of the pressure gage, A, in psig.

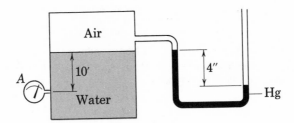

2.7. For an adiabatic atmosphere, show that

$$\frac{g}{g_c}(z - z_1) = RT_1 \frac{k}{k-1}\left[1 - \left(\frac{p}{p_1}\right)^{(k-1)/k}\right]$$

where subscript 1 indicates the reference state, k is the ratio of specific heats, and the other symbols are as in the text.

2.8. Calculate the pressure of the standard atmosphere at an altitude of 50,000 ft, assuming that the lapse rate is 3.56°F per 1000 ft and that the isothermal height (altitude above which the temperature is constant) is reached when the temperature becomes -67.7°F. Sea-level conditions are 14.7 psia and 59°F.

2.9. A barometer reads 24.89 in. Hg at the base of a mountain where the altitude is 5000 ft and the temperature is 55°F. At the peak the barometer reads 17.53 in. Hg, and the temperature is 15°F. Assuming a constant lapse rate from base to summit, estimate the height of the mountain.

2.10. The tank car shown has atmospheric vents at A and B and is accelerated uniformly to the right.

    a. If it contains oil of sp gr 0.83 to a depth of 6 ft when stationary, find the maximum acceleration for no spillage when A is open and B is shut.

b. Find the pressure at C if the acceleration is 4 ft/sec² when A is shut and B is open.

c. If the car is just filled when stationary and both A and B are closed, find the pressure at D during a uniform deceleration from 30 mph to rest in a distance of 88 ft.

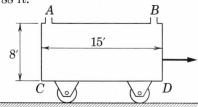

2.11. A simple accelerometer consists of a U-tube containing a liquid mounted in a fore-and-aft position in a vehicle. Show that the acceleration, a, of the vehicle can be given by the expression $a = gh/L$. State the assumptions made. Calculate the differential height for $L = 3$ in. if the vehicle is accelerated uniformly from rest to a speed of 60 mph in 12 sec.

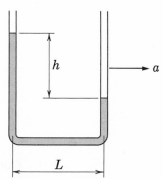

2.12. The cylindrical fuel tanks of a rocket are thin-walled stainless steel cylinders of 8 ft diameter and 10 ft height. They are parallel to the main axis of the rocket, which is to be fired vertically with an initial acceleration of 32.2 ft/sec². The liquid-fuel density is 25 lb/ft³. The fuel tanks are initially full.

a. Find the fluid pressure at the bottom of the tank immediately after firing.

b. Compute the necessary thickness of the tank walls if a design tensile stress of 80,000 lb/in.² is permitted, based upon circumferential (or hoop) stress in the walls due to fluid pressure.

c. If the net force accelerating the rocket remains constant, will this computed thickness be adequate at a later time when 60% of the fuel is expended and the total mass of the rocket is 50% of its initial value?

2.13. A circular cylinder closed at the bottom and open at the top has a diameter of 4 in. and a height of 12 in. When stationary, it is filled with water to a depth of 6 in. If the cylinder is rotated on a vertical axis,

a. Find the maximum rpm possible for the water to be retained.

b. Find the pressure at the base at the circumference and at the axis for this condition.

2.14. At take-off, the rocket shown is subjected to a uniform, vertical, upward acceleration of $3g$ (three times gravitational acceleration). An internal propellant tank is pressurized to 2000 psig, the propellant having a specific gravity of 0.85. Compute the pressure at the bottom of the tank when the depth of fluid is 12 ft.

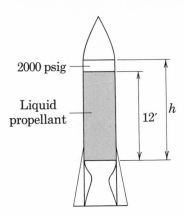

2.15. A rectangular tank is 12 ft long, 6 ft wide, and 8 ft deep. If the tank is filled with water, what are the magnitude and the location of the resultant force on the 6×8 wall?

2.16. A cylindrical tank 6 ft in diameter, with a horizontal axis, has hemispherical ends. The tank is filled with oil of sp gr 0.93, and a pressure gage at the top reads 6 psi. If the mass of the tank is negligible, what is the magnitude of the force tending to pull one of the ends from the cylindrical part (a) in a horizontal direction, and (b) in a vertical direction?

2.17. A circular pipe is 5 ft in diameter. The pipe is horizontal, with a vertical flat plate over one end. Determine the force on the flat plate if the pipe is filled with water to a depth of 3 ft and the remaining space is filled with air at 1 atm pressure.

2.18. The flat gate shown weighs 200 lb and measures 3 ft by 4 ft. It is pivoted 1 ft from one edge. Find the force that the gate exerts upon its supports and the moment that must be applied to hold it in the position shown. Neglect the thickness of the gate.

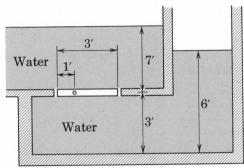

2.19. The 2 ft thick square gate shown weighs 3000 lb and is pivoted at A. The area of the opening it covers is 4 ft by 4 ft. Both fluids are water. Find the force, F, necessary to open the gate.

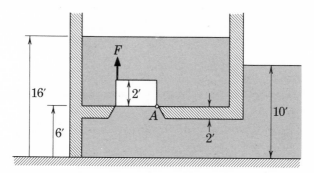

2.20. Calculate the resultant force per unit width on the dam shown.

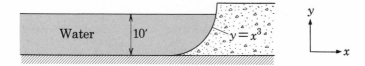

2.21. The gate is 20 ft wide and is pivoted at point P. Find the force required at point A to hold the gate in place.

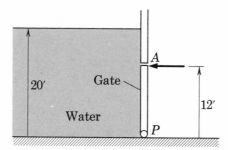

2.22. A cylindrical pine log 1 ft in diameter and 12 ft long is floating horizontally in water. If the pine is of sp gr 0.50, how deep is the log submerged in the water?

2.23. A helium-filled balloon has a structure weight of 3500 lb. When moored on the ground at sea level, the tension in the cable is 450 lb.
    a. Find the volume and mass of helium in the balloon when moored.
    b. If the balloon is released and hovers at an altitude of 9 miles, find the mass of helium that must be released during the ascent and the volume of the bag at that altitude. Assume that the pressure and temperature of the helium are at all times the same as those of the ambient atmosphere, which is taken as I.C.A.O. standard.

2.24. A hydrometer uses the principle of buoyancy to measure specific gravities of liquids. It consists of a constant-area stem with a bulb weighted so that it is always in stable equilibrium. Different lengths of stem are exposed in liquids of different densities. If a hydrometer is calibrated for a liquid of sp gr 1 with a mark at the

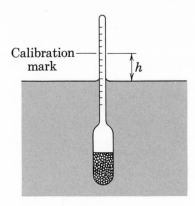

Calibration mark — h

point shown, show that the distance h when the hydrometer is placed in another liquid is given by

$$h = \frac{V}{A}\frac{S-1}{S}$$

where V is the volume submerged for liquid of sp gr 1, A is the cross-sectional area of the stem, and S is the specific gravity of the liquid. From this, show how degrees A.P.I. are directly proportional to distance h.

Kinematics of Fluid Flow

In this chapter we shall discuss the flow of fluids without reference to the dynamics of the motion, i.e., only in terms of velocity and flow rate without consideration of the forces that either produce or are produced by the motion.

3.1 *Description of a flow field*

A flow *field* is a region in which flow is defined in terms of space and time coordinates. If the flow at a given location is constant with respect to time, then it is called *steady* flow. If it is variable with respect to time, it is called *unsteady* flow. Steady flow usually includes flow with the small-scale local velocity fluctuations known as turbulence, provided that the time-average flow is constant. If the velocity at a given time is everywhere the same throughout a field, it is said to be *uniform*. Uniform velocity usually characterizes flow having a constant velocity distribution in a passage of constant shape and area, e.g., flow in a pipe at a considerable distance from the entry, where the effect of the entry has disappeared and the velocity at a given radius remains constant although it may vary with radius.

Position in the field and direction of flow are specified by a coordinate

67

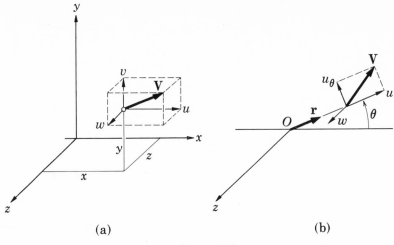

(a)   (b)

Figure 3.1

system that may be designated for convenience. *Cartesian* coordinates are commonly used, with directions in three dimensions given by x, y, and z. Velocity components in these directions are denoted by u, v, and w, as shown in Fig. 3.1(a), with $V = \sqrt{u^2 + v^2 + w^2}$; u, v, and w may all vary with position and time—i.e., they may be functions of x, y, z, and t, so that in general $u = u(x, y, z, t)$, $v = v(x, y, z, t)$, and $w = w(x, y, z, t)$.

However, when the flow pattern has some element of circular symmetry, it is often more convenient to use *cylindrical* or *spherical* coordinates. For our purposes, we shall restrict ourselves to the former, with the three dimensions denoted by a position vector, **r**, positive outward from the origin, O; an angle, θ, positive counterclockwise from the horizontal line through O; and a longitudinal dimension, z, as shown in Fig. 3.1(b). The corresponding velocity components are u_r, u_θ, and w, with $V = \sqrt{u_r^2 + u_\theta^2 + w^2}$. Here u_θ is a *linear* velocity perpendicular to the radius vector and given by $r\, d\theta/dt$. In two dimensions, cylindrical coordinates reduce to plane-*polar* coordinates, denoted by r and θ, with velocity components u_r and u_θ.

It is desirable on occasion to transform one coordinate system to the other, the corresponding relationships being

$$x = r \cos \theta \qquad y = r \sin \theta \qquad z = z$$

Fig. 3.2 illustrates the velocity transformations from the Cartesian system to the polar system, which yield

$$u_r = v \sin \theta + u \cos \theta \qquad\qquad [3.1a]$$
$$u_\theta = v \cos \theta - u \sin \theta \qquad\qquad [3.1b]$$

Eqs. 3.1a and 3.1b can also be obtained analytically as follows:

$$r^2 = x^2 + y^2$$

Therefore,
$$r \, dr = x \, dx + y \, dy$$

Consequently,
$$\frac{dr}{dt} = \frac{x}{r}\frac{dx}{dt} + \frac{y}{r}\frac{dy}{dt}$$

Substituting $x = r \cos \theta$ and $y = r \sin \theta$ gives us

$$u_r = u \cos \theta + v \sin \theta$$

For u_θ, $\theta = \tan^{-1} y/x$. Thus

$$d\theta = \left(\frac{1}{1 + y^2/x}\right)\left(\frac{x \, dy - y \, dx}{x^2}\right) = \frac{x \, dy - y \, dx}{x^2 + y^2} = \frac{r \cos \theta \, dy - r \sin \theta \, dx}{r^2}$$

Hence
$$r\frac{d\theta}{dt} = \cos \theta \frac{dy}{dt} - \sin \theta \frac{dx}{dt}$$

and
$$u_\theta = v \cos \theta - u \sin \theta$$

Alternatively, for transformation from the cylindrical system to the Cartesian system, it can be shown that

$$u = u_r \cos \theta - u_\theta \sin \theta \qquad [3.2a]$$
$$v = u_r \sin \theta + u_\theta \cos \theta \qquad [3.2b]$$

A complete description of a flow pattern may require the coordinates x, y, z, and t, i.e., be three-dimensional, unsteady flow. Most of our problems will be those of steady flow, in which time as an independent variable is not involved. However, some derivations will be carried out in full, because although it is easy to reduce expressions to the steady-flow case by the

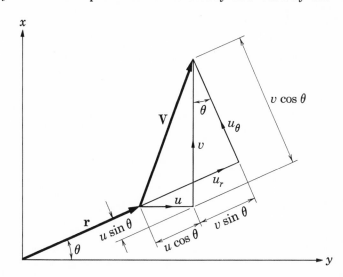

Figure 3.2

omission of time-dependent terms, it is difficult to introduce such terms into a steady-flow relationship without returning to a basic analysis.

Nearly all real flow problems require a three-dimensional analysis for complete solution, but this is extremely complicated and oftentimes impossible. Furthermore, a great many problems require only a simpler analysis to yield useful results sufficiently accurate for most engineering purposes. Again, the major performance characteristics can often be obtained by a still simpler analysis, with the omitted factors needing only a small empirical correction. Hence a flow is often analyzed as *one-dimensional* or *two-dimensional*, even though it is *three-dimensional*. Obviously precise application of these definitions is not always easy, but generally it depends on the number of space coordinates necessary to describe a flow.

Because of the no-slip condition at a solid boundary in real flow, there is always a velocity gradient normal to the flow direction. Therefore, every real flow must be at least two-dimensional, even if it is the same in parallel planes. However, if the flow can be characterized by an *average* velocity in the flow direction at any plane normal to the flow direction, as, e.g., in developed flow in a duct, a one-dimensional analysis may be made. Flow over a body of constant cross section immersed in a uniform stream can be analyzed as two-dimensional if the span (transverse dimension) is infinite, as then the flow in parallel planes is the same. If of finite span, then the flow is necessarily three-dimensional. The examples given in Fig. 3.3 may be helpful.

Fig. 3.3(a) represents *ideal* uniform flow in a duct or between parallel plates. At A and B the flow is truly one-dimensional, and it may be considered so in the varying-area section at C, for although there is a y component of velocity, the state of the fluid may be expressed in terms of an average through-flow velocity, $V = Q/A$, where Q is the volume rate of flow. Fig. 3.3(b) shows *real* fluid flow in the same situation, with a variation of velocity, or velocity distribution, in the y direction. Owing to the viscosity of the fluid, pressure decreases in the flow direction, and thus the flow is two-dimensional, with velocity varying in the y direction and pressure varying in the x direction. However, a one-dimensional analysis may be made in terms of an average velocity in the flow direction. Fig. 3.3(c) represents a flat plate of infinite span in a uniform stream of a real fluid. The viscous effect of the fluid requires zero velocity at the surface of the plate, with velocity increasing outward until it reaches the freestream value, i.e., the velocity beyond any influence of the surface. The retarded region of the fluid increases in size in the y direction at successive planes in the x direction, and thus this case must be treated as two-dimensional. Finally in Fig. 3.3(d), flow over a wing, the flow is strictly three-dimensional, as the finite length of the wing means that the tip must exert an influence on the flow. However, if the wing span is large compared with its width (*chord*), then except near

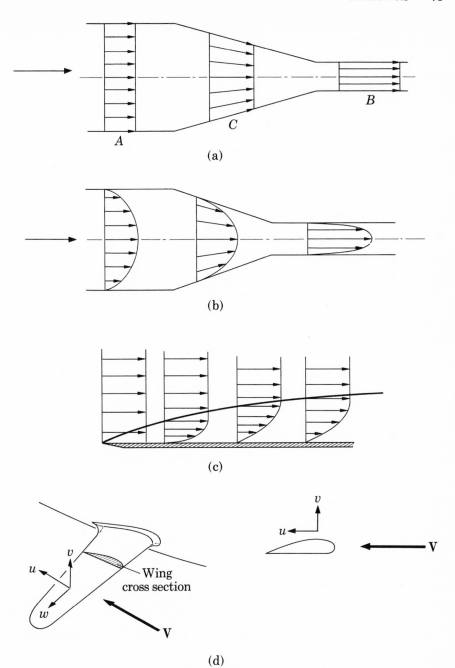

Figure 3.3

the tip itself the flow can be regarded as two-dimensional and analyzed as two-dimensional flow over a shape of infinite transverse dimension. The main characteristics of the wing are given by a two-dimensional analysis, the three-dimensional effect being secondary except near the tip itself. A circular duct has circular symmetry, and the flow in it is treated as one-dimensional. A body of revolution also has circular symmetry, but the flow around it is two-dimensional. These two special cases are quite common, and their flow patterns are termed *axisymmetric.*

A flow analysis requires the determination of fluid properties, such as velocity, pressure, and temperature at any point in the field. For the time being we are concerned only with the velocity, as pressure involves dynamic principles and temperature involves thermodynamic principles. Simple observation of a flowing fluid reveals that a solid particle immersed in it is carried along in a more or less continuous line, not necessarily straight but generally sinuous. At sharp changes of cross section or beyond obstacles in the stream, the pattern is confused, but by and large it may be conceived as one of "streamlines." This word has passed into popular usage as connoting almost any smooth curved shape, but in fluid mechanics it has a precise meaning and may be very different from the path of a particle in a fluid. Three kinds of flow lines are defined—pathlines, streamlines, and streaklines.

3.2   *Flow lines*

A *pathline* shows the course of a *particular* particle of fluid over a given time *interval.* It was described in the instance just cited, and hydraulic engineers make use of it in flow models of rivers, harbors, etc. They take a photographic exposure of a small light floating on a cork, thus obtaining a permanent record of a pathline.

A *streamline* is a line that shows the direction of the *velocity vector* at a given instant of time. By definition, the tangent to a streamline at any point along it gives the direction of the velocity at that point. Thus no fluid crosses a streamline. A streamline, then, shows the direction of an infinite *number* of particles of fluid at a given *instant* of time. An approximation to a streamline can be made visual by a very brief exposure of a large number of illuminated particles in a flow field. Each individual track is actually a pathline, but if the time interval of the exposure is sufficiently short, the tracks indicate the *direction* of the velocity, which in the limit indicates the streamline. A series of short time-exposures of aluminum powder scattered on the free surface of a liquid and suitably illuminated is used to indicate the streamlines in flow around a model shape, such as a wing or blade.

A *streakline* shows the position at a given *instant* of time of a *succession* of particles that have all passed through the same point at an earlier time. Thus dye injected at a point in the flow forms a filament, marking out a streakline (unless the flow is very turbulent, in which case the particles of dye are quickly dispersed laterally over too large an area to give a clear picture).

A streamline is of most interest for the analysis of fluid flow, because it shows the direction of flow at any instant, which is of course constant in steady flow. If a streamline can be expressed in mathematical terms, then the flow direction at any point can be found as the slope at that point of the curve representing a streamline.

In the general case of unsteady flow, pathlines, streamlines, and streaklines are all different, and it is necessary to understand what each implies for visual interpretation, although it is not often necessary to make a complete analysis. In steady flow all three kinds of lines are coincident; thus either the movement of a single particle may be followed (pathline) or fluid may be injected at a given point (streakline) to determine a streamline.

Fig. 3.4(a) shows a body moving at constant velocity **U** through a stationary fluid. To an observer on the body, the fluid appears to follow the paths labeled *streamlines*. To a stationary observer, an individual element of

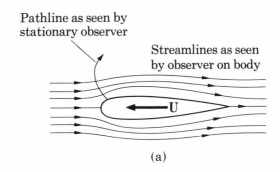

(a)

Figure 3.4

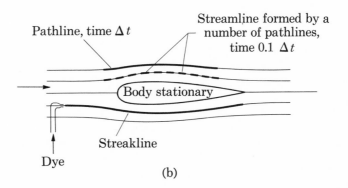

(b)

fluid appears to be pushed away and to the side, marking out a *pathline* and eventually being left behind the moving body. Again from the viewpoint of a stationary observer, successive fluid elements passing through a fixed point in the fluid apparently follow different pathlines, forming a *streakline*. To the observer on the body, the flow appears steady. To the stationary observer, it appears unsteady. If the body is fixed and the observer stationary, then for the case of smooth flow over the same body, the streamlines, pathlines, and streaklines are identical. Fig. 3.4(b) shows how photographs would look for (1) an exposure time Δt of a single particle, (2) a shorter exposure time, say, $0.1\ \Delta t$, of a number of separated particles, and (3) a short or long exposure time of a filament of dye continuously emitted from an upstream source.

3.3   *Relative velocity and velocity triangles*

In the discussion so far, it has usually been assumed implicitly that all velocities are represented with respect to a fixed frame of reference or coordinate system. The velocity of one body relative to that of another is the vector difference between their velocities as measured from the same datum. Thus Fig. 3.5 shows a rotor rotating with uniform angular velocity, ω, and having absolute linear velocity, $\mathbf{U}$, at the periphery, where "absolute" means with respect to the observer, who is stationary. Fluid is directed at an angle α to the tangential direction with absolute velocity $\mathbf{V}$. The velocity, $\mathbf{V}_r$, of the fluid flowing into the rotor *relative* to the rotor is then

$$\mathbf{V}_r = \mathbf{V} - \mathbf{U}$$

The resulting velocity diagram, with magnitude and direction of $\mathbf{V}_r$, appears to the right of the figure.

Now consider the same sort of rotor traveling in the opposite direction and with fluid flowing out of the rotor with velocity $\mathbf{V}_r$ *relative* to the rotor,

Figure 3.5

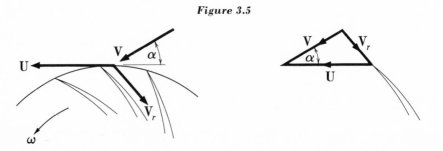

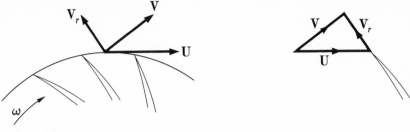

Figure 3.6

as shown in Fig. 3.6. The absolute velocity, **V**, of the fluid is then

$$\mathbf{V} = \mathbf{U} + \mathbf{V}_r$$

as indicated on the right-hand side of the figure. In both cases $\mathbf{V}_r$ is the velocity of the fluid as seen by an observer traveling on the rotor.

The analysis of many flow problems is often simplified if the frame of reference is changed from fixed surroundings to the moving body. Consider the airfoil section designated by A in Fig. 3.7 moving linearly at constant velocity, **U**, through a fluid that is at rest except as disturbed locally by A. At a given instant of time, fluid at point P has an absolute velocity **V** caused by the passage of the body. Its velocity relative to A is $\mathbf{V}_r = \mathbf{V} - \mathbf{U}$. Now at some time, Δt, later (Fig. 3.7(b)), the body has moved a distance $s = U\,\Delta t$, and again at the same point, P, the fluid velocity relative to A is **V**. To a stationary observer the flow pattern is *unsteady* as it moves with the body. To an observer traveling with A, the flow pattern is always the same; i.e., the motion at P is constant for him, and it appears that the fluid is traveling with velocity $\mathbf{V}_r$. Thus the motion is *steady* with respect to A and is most conveniently studied from A. If we superpose a velocity $-\mathbf{U}$ on the whole field, the body becomes stationary, and the fluid has a velocity **U**

Figure 3.7

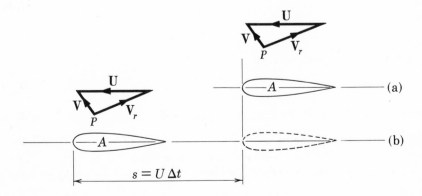

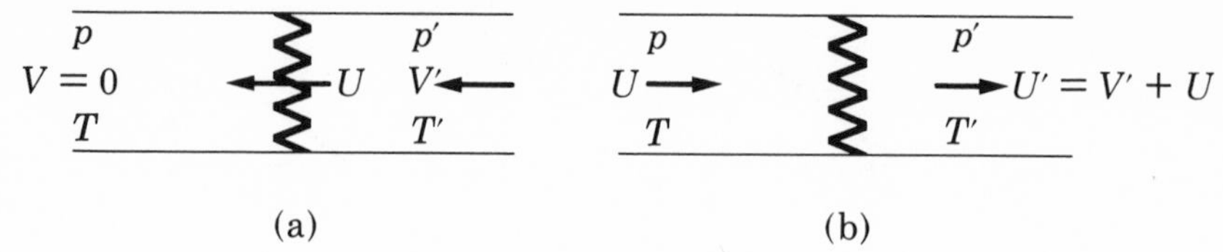

(a)   (b)

Figure 3.8

from left to right except as disturbed by the presence of A. The flow pattern then becomes one of the steady state. Thus instead of having to ride with the body through the fluid, as in an airplane, in order to take measurements of the flow pattern we can investigate it by causing the fluid to travel over the stationary airplane, as in a wind tunnel.

As another example, an important fluid-dynamic effect is a discontinuity of state known as a *shock wave*. A shock wave can be made to propagate along a duct, so that the air has a different pressure and temperature in the region through which it has traveled from that in the undisturbed region ahead of it. For the purposes of analysis, it is sometimes more convenient to superpose a velocity equal in magnitude but opposite in direction to that of the shock wave upon the whole system. Then the shock wave will be stationary, and the air will approach it with the given velocity and suffer a change of state after passing through it (Fig. 3.8).

3.4   *The equation of a streamline*

A streamline by definition is tangential to the velocity vector at all points and at all times. In Fig. 3.9 V is the velocity at a point on the streamline in a two-dimensional flow field, with components u and v, and the slope of the streamline at the same point is dy/dx; hence

$$\frac{dy}{dx} = \frac{v}{u} \qquad\qquad [3.3a]$$

or
$$u\,dy - v\,dx = 0 \qquad\qquad [3.3b]$$

In polar coordinates,

$$\frac{r\,d\theta}{dr} = \frac{u_\theta}{u_r} \qquad\qquad [3.4a]$$

or
$$u_r r\,d\theta - u_\theta\,dr = 0 \qquad\qquad [3.4b]$$

If the velocity components are known as functions of the field coordinates, Eqs. 3.3 or 3.4 may be integrated to give the equations of the streamlines. Sometimes, for simple flow fields, the form of the streamlines may be known

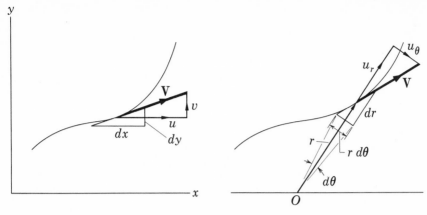

Figure 3.9

(e.g., linear or circular), together with the magnitude of the velocity **V** as a function of the coordinates, from which the streamline equation can be obtained.

Sometimes it is desirable to deal with a finite stream of fluid rather than an individual streamline. A *streamtube* is composed of all the streamlines passing through a finite cross-sectional flow area. It is bounded by streamlines, and thus no fluid crosses its boundaries except at its entry or exit.

3.5 *Conservation of mass and the equation of continuity*

The principle of conservation of mass states that matter can be neither created nor destroyed. (We are not considering the special circumstances of the conversion of mass and energy, as in nuclear reactions.) With fluids we are seldom concerned with an individual element of material but with the flow of material across an area of surface or in or out of a volume.

Fig. 3.10 shows how the conservation of mass applies to fluid flow in a fixed *control volume* or *region*, R, with its surface the *control surface*, S. Suppose that a mass of fluid is flowing out of the surface element $d\mathbf{A}$ with velocity **V** at an angle θ with $d\mathbf{A}$. Then the *volume* rate of flow is given by $\mathbf{V} \cdot d\mathbf{A} = V \cos \theta \, dA$, and the *mass* rate of flow by $\rho\mathbf{V} \cdot d\mathbf{A} = \rho V \cos \theta \, dA$. Over the whole surface, the total mass rate of flow is given by

$$\iint_S \rho\mathbf{V} \cdot d\mathbf{A}$$

where ρ and **V** may be different everywhere over S; i.e., they are functions

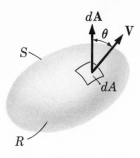

Figure 3.10

of position, or field values. The mass of fluid within R must be decreasing at a rate equal to the efflux through S according to the conservation principle. This rate of mass decrease with respect to time is

$$- \frac{\partial}{\partial t} \iiint_R \rho \, dR$$

Hence

$$\iint_S \rho \mathbf{V} \cdot d\mathbf{A} = - \frac{\partial}{\partial t} \iiint_R \rho \, dR$$

or

$$\iint_S \rho \mathbf{V} \cdot d\mathbf{A} + \frac{\partial}{\partial t} \iiint_R \rho \, dR = 0 \qquad [3.5]$$

This equation of conservation of mass states that the sum of the mass flow rate across the surface of a region and the time rate of change of mass within the region is zero, due regard being paid to the sign of each quantity.

For steady flow the second term is zero; hence

$$\iint_S \rho \mathbf{V} \cdot d\mathbf{A} = 0$$

so that for steady flow through a control volume, mass influx is equal to mass efflux. For the simple but common case of steady flow in which the velocity and density are uniform across finite areas at the entry and exit of a given region, although having different values at entry and exit (Fig. 3.11), then with $\mathbf{V}$ perpendicular to A,

$$\rho_2 V_2 A_2 - \rho_1 V_1 A_1 = 0 \qquad [3.6]$$

From Eq. 3.5 it may be seen that for constant-density (incompressible) unsteady flow as well the second term is zero, for with ρ constant it may be written as

$$\rho \frac{\partial}{\partial t} \iiint_R dR$$

and, as the region is invariant with time, the derivative is zero, and the whole term disappears.

Eq. 3.5 applies to a region and is in terms of velocity normal to the

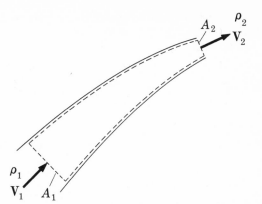

Figure 3.11

surface at every point. Now let us apply it to a very small region by means of Cartesian coordinates and allow the region to shrink to zero, thus obtaining a relationship for conservation of mass at any point in the field.

Fig. 3.12 shows a cubic element of sides Δx, Δy, and Δz aligned with the sides parallel to the coordinate planes. This shape is convenient to use with Cartesian coordinates and does not affect the result, as the region shrinks to a point. At the center point of the element, the density is ρ, and the velocity components are u, v, and w. The mass flow rate into or out of any face is given by the product of density, velocity, and area, the first two variables evaluated as averages over the whole area at a distance $\Delta x/2$, $\Delta y/2$, or $\Delta z/2$ from the center. It should be observed that the analysis is made at a single instant of time, so that although the mass inside the volume is changing

Figure 3.12

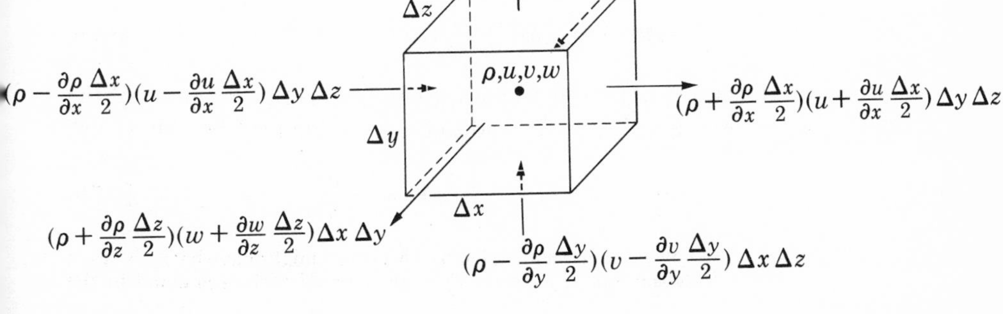

$$\left(\rho + \frac{\partial\rho}{\partial y}\frac{\Delta y}{2}\right)\left(v + \frac{\partial v}{\partial y}\frac{\Delta y}{2}\right)\Delta x\,\Delta z \qquad \left(\rho - \frac{\partial\rho}{\partial z}\frac{\Delta z}{2}\right)\left(w - \frac{\partial w}{\partial z}\frac{\Delta z}{2}\right)\Delta x\,\Delta y$$

$$\left(\rho - \frac{\partial\rho}{\partial x}\frac{\Delta x}{2}\right)\left(u - \frac{\partial u}{\partial x}\frac{\Delta x}{2}\right)\Delta y\,\Delta z$$

$$\rho, u, v, w$$

$$\left(\rho + \frac{\partial\rho}{\partial x}\frac{\Delta x}{2}\right)\left(u + \frac{\partial u}{\partial x}\frac{\Delta x}{2}\right)\Delta y\,\Delta z$$

$$\left(\rho + \frac{\partial\rho}{\partial z}\frac{\Delta z}{2}\right)\left(w + \frac{\partial w}{\partial z}\frac{\Delta z}{2}\right)\Delta x\,\Delta y$$

$$\left(\rho - \frac{\partial\rho}{\partial y}\frac{\Delta y}{2}\right)\left(v - \frac{\partial v}{\partial y}\frac{\Delta y}{2}\right)\Delta x\,\Delta z$$

(i.e., is a function of time), the density and velocity components are instantaneous values. For flow in the x direction, for instance, the net efflux of mass is given by the difference in mass flow rate across yz planes of the element between $+ \Delta x$ and $- \Delta x$; i.e.,

$$\left(\rho + \frac{\partial \rho}{\partial x} \frac{\Delta x}{2} \right) \left(u + \frac{\partial u}{\partial x} \frac{\Delta x}{2} \right) \Delta y \, \Delta z - \left(\rho - \frac{\partial \rho}{\partial x} \frac{\Delta x}{2} \right) \left(u - \frac{\partial u}{\partial x} \frac{\Delta x}{2} \right) \Delta y \, \Delta z$$

which may be reduced to

$$\left(\rho \frac{\partial u}{\partial x} \Delta x + u \frac{\partial \rho}{\partial x} \Delta x \right) \Delta y \, \Delta z = \left(\rho \frac{\partial u}{\partial x} + u \frac{\partial \rho}{\partial x} \right) \Delta x \, \Delta y \, \Delta z = \frac{\partial}{\partial x} (\rho u) \, \Delta x \, \Delta y \, \Delta z$$

The results for the y and z directions are obtained similarly, and so the over-all net efflux of mass is

$$\iint_S \rho \mathbf{V} \cdot d\mathbf{A} = \left[\frac{\partial}{\partial x} (\rho u) + \frac{\partial}{\partial y} (\rho v) + \frac{\partial}{\partial z} (\rho w) \right] \Delta x \, \Delta y \, \Delta z$$

Within the element, the rate of increase of mass with respect to time is

$$\frac{\partial}{\partial t} \iiint_R \rho \, dR$$

and with $\rho \, dR = \rho \, \Delta x \, \Delta y \, \Delta z$, then

$$\frac{\partial}{\partial t} \iiint_R \rho \, dR = \frac{\partial}{\partial t} (\rho \, \Delta x \, \Delta y \, \Delta z)$$

which, since the length elements are not dependent on time, may be written as

$$\frac{\partial \rho}{\partial t} \Delta x \, \Delta y \, \Delta z$$

From the conservation of mass principle, Eq. 3.5,

$$\left[\frac{\partial}{\partial x} (\rho u) + \frac{\partial}{\partial y} (\rho v) + \frac{\partial}{\partial z} (\rho w) \right] \Delta x \, \Delta y \, \Delta z + \frac{\partial \rho}{\partial t} \Delta x \, \Delta y \, \Delta z = 0$$

Shrinking the element, so that in the limit this expression becomes exact with respect to the incremental changes, and dividing by the volume yield

$$\frac{\partial}{\partial x} (\rho u) + \frac{\partial}{\partial y} (\rho v) + \frac{\partial}{\partial z} (\rho w) = - \frac{\partial \rho}{\partial t} \qquad \textbf{[3.7a]}$$

In vector form, the left-hand side of the equation is the *divergence* of the quantity $\rho \mathbf{V}$ (see Appendix, Sect. 8), and so the equation may be written as*

$$\text{div } \rho \mathbf{V} \qquad \text{or} \qquad \nabla \cdot \rho \mathbf{V} = - \frac{\partial \rho}{\partial t} \qquad \textbf{[3.7b]}$$

---

* For those with a knowledge of vector calculus, this result might have been obtained with Gauss' theorem that the flux of a vector through a closed surface is equal to the

This is the *general equation of continuity*, expressing the principle of conservation of mass in terms of the field properties at any point in the field and valid for three-dimensional compressible flow, variant with time.

Simplifications may be made for various particular conditions. In the first place, for steady flow the properties are not functions of time, and hence Eq. 3.7a reduces to

$$\frac{\partial}{\partial x}(\rho u) + \frac{\partial}{\partial y}(\rho v) + \frac{\partial}{\partial z}(\rho w) = 0 \qquad [3.8]$$

or

$$u\frac{\partial \rho}{\partial x} + v\frac{\partial \rho}{\partial y} + w\frac{\partial \rho}{\partial z} + \rho\left(\frac{\partial u}{\partial x} + \frac{\partial v}{\partial y} + \frac{\partial w}{\partial z}\right) = 0$$

For incompressible flow, ρ is constant with both location and time, and therefore Eq. 3.7a becomes

$$\frac{\partial u}{\partial x} + \frac{\partial v}{\partial y} + \frac{\partial w}{\partial z} = \text{div } \mathbf{V} = 0 \qquad [3.9]$$

which is then true for *both* steady and unsteady incompressible flow. For one-dimensional incompressible flow, say, in the x direction,

$$\frac{\partial u}{\partial x} = \frac{du}{dx} = 0$$

and therefore $u = $ constant.

In polar coordinates, a similar analysis using an element as shown in Fig. 3.13 yields for the continuity equation for two-dimensional incom-

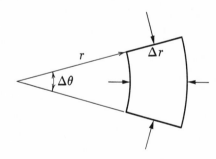

Figure 3.13

---

volume integral of the divergence of this vector taken over the surface of the enclosed volume, i.e.,

$$\iint_{S} \rho \mathbf{V} \cdot d\mathbf{A} = \iiint_{R} \text{div } \rho \mathbf{V} \, dR = \iiint_{R} \mathbf{\nabla} \cdot \rho \mathbf{V} \, dR$$

$$\frac{\partial}{\partial t} \iiint_{R} \rho \, dR = \iiint_{R} \frac{\partial \rho}{\partial t} \, dR$$

Therefore,

$$\iiint_{R} \mathbf{\nabla} \cdot \rho \mathbf{V} \, dR = - \iiint_{R} \frac{\partial \rho}{\partial t} \, dR$$

This equation is valid regardless of the region over which the integration is taken; hence the integrands must be equal. Thus Eq. 3.7b follows.

pressible flow

$$\frac{\partial}{\partial r}\,(u_r r) + \frac{\partial u_\theta}{\partial \theta} = 0 \qquad\qquad [3.10]$$

All physically possible flows must obey the principle of continuity, and therefore the equation of continuity in the appropriate form is a governing condition, applicable to every flow, regardless of whether the fluid is ideal or real. It is used as a building block in constructing a relationship for a flow problem, or it may be used as a test to find out whether an assumed flow is physically realizable.

3.6   *The stream function*

We have seen that a flow pattern can be determined by the streamline equation and a relationship for the velocity. These, together with a statement of the boundary conditions, allow a particular flow pattern to be described but not in a concise fashion. For two-dimensional steady flow, the principle of continuity permits the introduction of a new function, the *stream function*, ψ, which is extremely useful since its definition includes most of the essentials for description of a flow pattern. The existence of the stream function can be demonstrated from solely mathematical considerations, but it is more comprehensible at this stage to define it from a consideration of the physical principle of conservation of mass and then to analyze it further to show how it yields valuable information.

Fig. 3.14(a) shows two streamlines, A and B, of an arbitrary pattern of two-dimensional, incompressible, steady flow in a Cartesian-coordinate system. By virtue of the definition of a streamline, no fluid can cross the

Figure 3.14

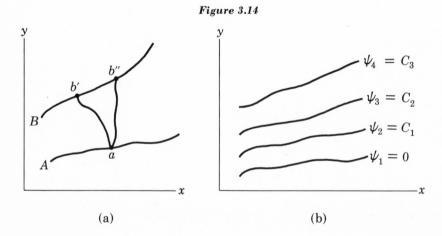

(a)   (b)

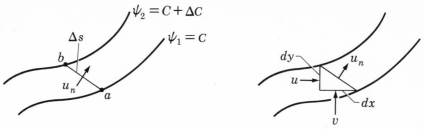

Figure 3.15

streamlines, and by virtue of the principle of conservation of mass, all the fluid crossing the line ab' must also cross the line ab''. Thus the mass rate of flow between any two streamlines remains constant anywhere in the flow field, and if a particular streamline is selected as a datum, then any other streamline can be represented by the addition of the mass rate of flow between it and the datum streamline. If streamlines are given by the function $\psi = f(x, y)$, curves in which ψ = constant are streamlines with a constant rate of flow between any two adjacent ones. For incompressible flow, ρ = constant, and the mass rate of flow may be expressed in terms of the volume rate of flow; accordingly, the function ψ is interpreted in terms of volume rate of flow. Fig. 3.14(b) shows lines of constant ψ, with $\psi_1 = 0$ being the datum.

The velocity components of the flow may be found in the following manner. In Fig. 3.15, ψ_1 and ψ_2 are streamlines a small distance apart, and line ab is any straight-line segment crossing ψ_1 and ψ_2. Without reference to any particular coordinate system, and with unit depth taken as normal to the plane of the diagram, the volume rate of flow, $\Delta\psi = \psi_2 - \psi_1$, is equal to the product of Δs, the length of ab, and the velocity normal to ab, u_n, thus:

$$\psi_2 - \psi_1 = \Delta\psi = u_n \, \Delta s$$

or

$$u_n = \frac{\Delta\psi}{\Delta s}$$

and in the limit,

$$u_n = \frac{d\psi}{ds}$$

In Cartesian coordinates, with $\psi = f(x, y)$,

$$u = \frac{\partial\psi}{\partial y} \quad \text{and} \quad v = -\frac{\partial\psi}{\partial x} \qquad [3.11]$$

The negative sign for v can be explained as follows: If $\psi = f(x, y)$ = constant,

$$d\psi = \frac{\partial\psi}{\partial x} \, dx + \frac{\partial\psi}{\partial y} \, dy = 0 \qquad [3.12]$$

along a streamline. But also, from the streamline equation,

$$u\,dy - v\,dx = 0 \qquad\qquad [3.13]$$

Consequently, $u = \partial\psi/\partial y$ and $-v = \partial\psi/\partial x$.

Similarly, for polar coordinates, with $\psi = f(r, \theta)$,

$$d\psi = \frac{\partial\psi}{\partial r}\,dr + \frac{\partial\psi}{\partial\theta}\,d\theta = 0 \qquad\qquad [3.14]$$

and

$$u_r\,r\,d\theta - u_\theta\,dr = 0$$

Therefore,
$$u_r = \frac{1}{r}\frac{\partial\psi}{\partial\theta} \qquad \text{and} \qquad u_\theta = -\frac{\partial\psi}{\partial r} \qquad\qquad [3.15]$$

As the datum streamline is arbitrary, it is often taken as one of the boundaries of a solid body immersed in a freestream. Representation of a boundary by a streamline implies a flow discontinuity, since the boundary is stationary with respect to the fluid immediately adjacent, and is applicable only to an ideal fluid. A real fluid with viscosity has zero velocity at the boundary (no slip).

To summarize, the stream function of a flow pattern has the following characteristics in two-dimensional flow: (1) $\psi = C$ is the general equation of a streamline, different values of C giving different streamlines; (2) $\psi_2 - \psi_1$ gives the volume rate of flow between two streamlines ψ_1 and ψ_2, and since $\psi_1 = C_1$ and $\psi_2 = C_2$, $\psi_2 - \psi_1 = C_2 - C_1 = \Delta C$; (3) differentiation of ψ with respect to coordinates of the field yields the velocity components, in accordance with Eqs. 3.11 and 3.15; (4) the existence of ψ implies continuity, or, conversely, continuity implies the existence of ψ. Every physically possible two-dimensional steady flow must have a stream function, regardless of any other conditions, and thus ψ exists for possible real flows as well as for ideal flows.

3.7   *Motion and deformation*

A body of fluid in motion in general suffers bodily displacement and change of shape. Fig. 3.16, illustrating a two-dimensional case for simplicity, shows a small element originally of square shape with sides Δx and Δy and velocity components u and v at its center. The parts of the figure show possible changes in position and shape that may make up a general change occurring in a small time interval, Δt.

The element may retain its shape and its orientation in the coordinate system, undergoing only linear displacement or *translation* (Fig. 3.16(a)). It may change its shape while its sides retain their orientation, undergoing pure strain or *linear deformation* (Fig. 3.16(b)). It may change its shape

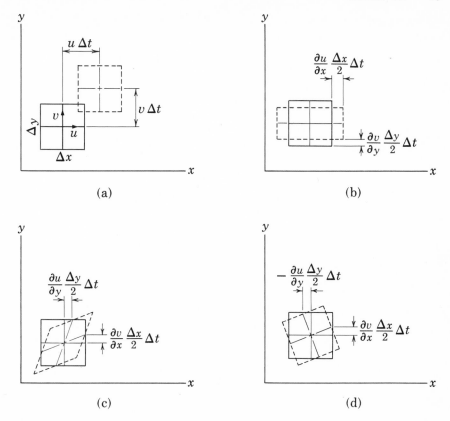

Figure 3.16

with angular strain or *angular deformation* (Fig. 3.16(c)), or it may undergo *rotation* without change of shape (Fig. 3.16(d)).

The rate of translation corresponds to the velocity components u and v. The rate of linear deformation, or the rate at which corresponding sides move apart or toward each other, is measured by the rate of change of a velocity component *in the direction* of that component, i.e., $(\partial u/\partial x)\,\Delta x$ and $(\partial u/\partial y)\,\Delta y$. Note that the rate of linear deformation must conform to the continuity relationship. Angular deformation and rotation, on the other hand, are measured by the rates of change of a velocity component *normal* to the direction of that component, i.e., $(\partial u/\partial y)\,\Delta y$ and $(\partial v/\partial x)\,\Delta x$. The derivative $\partial u/\partial y$ indicates that a fluid has a varying x component of velocity in the y direction; $\partial v/\partial x$ has an analogous interpretation. This situation suggests a shear stress caused by the relative motions of adjacent fluid laminae, and the corresponding derivatives are called *shear derivatives*.

Having observed these relationships graphically, let us formalize them in mathematical terms. Given a velocity, **V**, of an element of fluid, with components u and v both functions of x and y, the components of the differential velocity, $d\mathbf{V}$, are

$$du = \frac{\partial u}{\partial x}\,dx + \frac{\partial u}{\partial y}\,dy \qquad\qquad [3.16]$$

and

$$dv = \frac{\partial v}{\partial x}\,dx + \frac{\partial v}{\partial y}\,dy \qquad\qquad [3.17]$$

This mathematical statement, which may be obtained by a Taylor expansion in the immediate neighborhood of the point x, y, should contain the information obtained by graphic analysis.

Translation is obviously expressed by the components u and v of the given velocity **V**, since $\mathbf{V} = \mathbf{i}u + \mathbf{j}v$, and linear deformation by the terms $\partial u/\partial x$ and $\partial v/\partial y$. The components of angular deformation and rotation may be obtained by expansion of the shear derivatives as follows:

$$\frac{\partial u}{\partial y}\,dy = \frac{1}{2}\frac{\partial u}{\partial y}\,dy + \frac{1}{2}\frac{\partial u}{\partial y}\,dy + \frac{1}{2}\frac{\partial v}{\partial x}\,dy - \frac{1}{2}\frac{\partial v}{\partial x}\,dy$$

and

$$\frac{\partial v}{\partial x}\,dx = \frac{1}{2}\frac{\partial v}{\partial x}\,dx + \frac{1}{2}\frac{\partial v}{\partial x}\,dx + \frac{1}{2}\frac{\partial u}{\partial y}\,dx - \frac{1}{2}\frac{\partial u}{\partial y}\,dx$$

Hence Eqs. 3.16 and 3.17 become

$$du = \frac{\partial u}{\partial x}\,dx + \frac{1}{2}\left(\frac{\partial u}{\partial y} - \frac{\partial v}{\partial x}\right)dy + \frac{1}{2}\left(\frac{\partial u}{\partial y} + \frac{\partial v}{\partial x}\right)dy \qquad [3.18]$$

$$dv = \frac{\partial v}{\partial y}\,dy + \frac{1}{2}\left(\frac{\partial v}{\partial x} - \frac{\partial u}{\partial y}\right)dx + \frac{1}{2}\left(\frac{\partial v}{\partial x} + \frac{\partial u}{\partial y}\right)dy \qquad [3.19]$$

The middle term in each equation gives the shear effect associated with rotation, and the last term gives that associated with angular deformation.

The rotational term is of great importance because it represents the kinematic condition due to the action of shear forces. In particular, the condition of zero rotation, or *irrotation*, is given by the relation $\partial v/\partial x - \partial u/\partial y = 0$. An ideal fluid of zero viscosity cannot support a shear stress, and so, if no rotation is present initially, its flow field has zero rotation throughout and is said to be *irrotational*. However, if the flow field of an ideal fluid exhibits a degree of rotation initially, it retains this rotation throughout subsequent motion, as no shear stresses are possible to cause any change. Knowledge of this behavior of an ideal fluid has considerable consequences, as it permits simplification of mathematical analysis, and the concept of irrotational flow leads to the introduction of another useful function of the field coordinates.

Rotation, then, is defined as the average angular velocity of any two mutually perpendicular line elements in the plane of the flow. For the xy plane, rotation is around the z axis and is denoted by ω_z; for the yz plane it

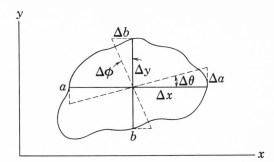

Figure 3.17

is denoted by ω_x, and for the xz plane by ω_y. Rotation is described as *positive* when counterclockwise. From Fig. 3.17, the angular velocity, ω_a, of the line a is

$$\omega_a = \lim_{\Delta t \to 0} \frac{\Delta \theta}{\Delta t} = \lim_{\Delta t \to 0} \frac{\Delta a/\Delta x}{\Delta t} = \lim_{\Delta t \to 0} \frac{[(\partial v/\partial x)\,\Delta x\,\Delta t]/\Delta x}{\Delta t} = \frac{\partial v}{\partial x}$$

Similarly,

$$\omega_b = \lim_{\Delta t \to 0} \frac{\Delta \phi}{\Delta t} = \lim_{\Delta t \to 0} \frac{\Delta b/\Delta y}{\Delta t} = \lim_{\Delta t \to 0} \frac{-\,[(\partial u/\partial y)\,\Delta y\,\Delta t]/\Delta y}{\Delta t} = -\frac{\partial u}{\partial y}$$

Thus

$$\omega_z = \tfrac{1}{2}(\omega_a + \omega_b) = \frac{1}{2}\left(\frac{\partial v}{\partial x} - \frac{\partial u}{\partial y}\right) \qquad [\textbf{3.20a}]$$

which is, of course, the same result as that obtained by the preceding analysis.

For three-dimensional flow, rotation is generally defined in vector form (see Appendix, Sect. 8) as

$$\boldsymbol{\omega} = \tfrac{1}{2}(\mathbf{i}\omega_x + \mathbf{j}\omega_y + \mathbf{k}\omega_z) = \tfrac{1}{2}\boldsymbol{\nabla} \times \mathbf{V} \equiv \tfrac{1}{2}\,\text{curl } \mathbf{V} \qquad [\textbf{3.20b}]$$

Curl **V**, the *vorticity vector*, may be expressed in any coordinate system. For Cartesian coordinates,

$$\omega_x = \frac{\partial w}{\partial y} - \frac{\partial v}{\partial z}$$

$$\omega_y = \frac{\partial u}{\partial z} - \frac{\partial w}{\partial x}$$

$$\omega_z = \frac{\partial v}{\partial x} - \frac{\partial u}{\partial y}$$

where ω_x, ω_y, and ω_z (often given the symbols ξ, η, and ζ in the literature) are the components of curl **V**. Vorticity and rotation have similar meanings but differ in magnitude; thus the vorticity is $2\boldsymbol{\omega}$, twice the rotation.

It must be carefully noted that rotation or irrotation as used in this connection for individual fluid elements does not necessarily apply to the

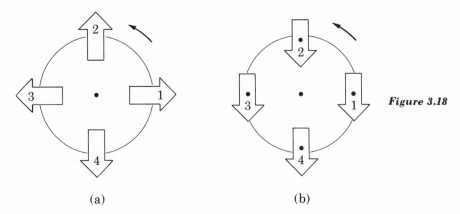

(a)   (b)

Figure 3.18

motion of a fluid as a whole. An ideal fluid can be rotating in the sense that streamlines are curved but still be irrotational according to Eq. 3.20. A helpful analogy compares solid-body rotation, Fig. 3.18(a), and rotation as in a Ferris wheel, Fig. 3.18(b). Applied to a fluid, both motions have circular streamlines, but the first is rotational, and the second is irrotational.

The expression for rotation in cylindrical (polar) coordinates, given here without proof, is

$$\omega_z = \frac{1}{2}\left[\frac{\partial u_\theta}{\partial r} + \frac{1}{r}\left(u_\theta - \frac{\partial u_r}{\partial \theta}\right)\right] = \frac{1}{2}\left\{\frac{1}{r}\left[\frac{\partial}{\partial r}\,(ru_\theta) - \frac{\partial u_r}{\partial \theta}\right]\right\} \qquad [3.21]$$

3.8   *The velocity potential*

Irrotational flow has particular significance in the analysis of fluid motion. In general, curl $\mathbf{V} = 0$ for irrotational motion. For two-dimensional flow, when $\omega_z = 0$, then by Eq. 3.20

$$\frac{\partial u}{\partial y} = \frac{\partial v}{\partial x} \qquad [3.22]$$

Now from the calculus we have the theorem that if $\partial M/\partial y = \partial N/\partial x$, $M\,dx + N\,dy$ is an exact differential of some function of x and y. Designating this function by ϕ, then with $M = u$ and $N = v$ we have

$$d\phi = u\,dx + v\,dy \qquad [3.23]$$

But also

$$d\phi = \frac{\partial \phi}{\partial x}\,dx + \frac{\partial \phi}{\partial y}\,dy \qquad [3.24]$$

and therefore

$$u = \frac{\partial \phi}{\partial x} \quad \text{and} \quad v = \frac{\partial \phi}{\partial y} \qquad [3.25]$$

The function ϕ is a *potential* function, here associated with velocity and called the *velocity potential*. It has the very useful property that its derivative with respect to x is the velocity component in the x direction, u, and its derivative with respect to y is the velocity component in the y direction, v. In vector form (see Appendix, Sect. 8), grad $\phi = \nabla\phi = \mathbf{i}u + \mathbf{j}v + \mathbf{k}w = \mathbf{V}$. The velocity potential is analogous to temperature in a thermal field, where the flow of heat is proportional to the temperature gradient, or to electric potential in an electric field, where the current flow is proportional to the potential gradient. It is difficult to give any closer physical interpretation of velocity potential at this stage, other than to say that its gradient is flow velocity. The derivation of ϕ presented here is not rigorous but is understandable in terms of elementary calculus. It arises from the definition of irrotational flow, just as the stream function arose from the idea of continuity. Although demonstrated for two-dimensional flow, ϕ also exists for three-dimensional flow.

The utility of the velocity potential stems from Eq. 3.25. If ϕ is known, the velocity components can be found. The existence of ϕ implies irrotational flow. On the other hand, if the velocity components are known, the application of Eq. 3.22 will answer the question of whether or not the flow is irrotational; if it is, the velocity potential can be found by integration. Suppose, e.g., that $u = f(x, y)$ and $v = g(x, y)$. Then, if the flow is irrotational,

$$u = \frac{\partial\phi}{\partial x} = f(x, y) \qquad \text{and} \qquad v = \frac{\partial\phi}{\partial y} = g(x, y)$$

From these relations $\phi = \smallint f(x, y)\, dx + h(y) + C_1$

and $\phi = \smallint g(x, y)\, dy + k(x) + C_2$

When these two values of ϕ are equated, $h(y)$ and $k(x)$ can be determined.

In polar coordinates, from the definition of the velocity potential as the function whose rate of change in a given direction is the velocity in that direction,

$$u_r = \frac{\partial\phi}{\partial r} \qquad \text{and} \qquad u = \frac{1}{r}\frac{\partial\phi}{\partial\theta} \qquad\qquad [\textbf{3.26}]$$

3.9   *The stream function and the velocity potential*

From the discussion of stream function, Sect. 3.6,

$$u = \frac{\partial\psi}{\partial y} \qquad \text{and} \qquad v = -\frac{\partial\psi}{\partial x}$$

From the discussion of velocity potential, Sect. 3.8,

$$u = \frac{\partial \phi}{\partial x} \quad \text{and} \quad v = \frac{\partial \phi}{\partial y}$$

Therefore,

$$\frac{\partial \psi}{\partial y} = \frac{\partial \phi}{\partial x} \quad \text{and} \quad -\frac{\partial \psi}{\partial x} = \frac{\partial \phi}{\partial y}$$

Differentiation of these equations with respect to x and y yields

$$\frac{\partial^2 \psi}{\partial y\, \partial x} = \frac{\partial^2 \phi}{\partial x^2} \quad \text{and} \quad -\frac{\partial^2 \psi}{\partial x\, \partial y} = \frac{\partial^2 \phi}{\partial y^2}$$

But for functions with continuous derivatives, the order of differentiation is immaterial; i.e., $\partial^2/\partial y\, \partial x = \partial^2/\partial x\, \partial y$, and hence

$$\frac{\partial^2 \phi}{\partial x^2} = -\frac{\partial^2 \phi}{\partial y^2}$$

or

$$\frac{\partial^2 \phi}{\partial x^2} + \frac{\partial^2 \phi}{\partial y^2} = \nabla^2 \phi = 0 \qquad [3.27a]$$

Similarly,

$$\frac{\partial^2 \psi}{\partial x^2} + \frac{\partial^2 \psi}{\partial y^2} = \nabla^2 \psi = 0 \qquad [3.27b]$$

Eqs. 3.27 are forms of the *Laplace equation*, which is encountered in many branches of physical science. They may be derived from a slightly different viewpoint by the substitution of $u = \partial \phi/\partial x$ and $v = \partial \phi/\partial y$ into the condition for continuity, $\partial u/\partial x + \partial v/\partial y = 0$, yielding Eq. 3.27a, and by the substitution of $u = \partial \phi/\partial y$ and $v = -\partial \phi/\partial x$ into the condition for irrotational flow, $\partial v/\partial x - \partial u/\partial y = 0$, yielding Eq. 3.27b. The Laplace equation must be satisfied for two-dimensional, incompressible, irrotational flow. Alternatively, a function of ψ or ϕ that satisfies the Laplace equation represents a possible two-dimensional, incompressible, irrotational flow. Since there are an infinite number of such functions, a particular solution requires that the boundary conditions be met.

The Laplace equation is *linear;* i.e., it is an equation of the first *degree*, although of the second *order*. The degree of an equation is indicated by the highest power of the highest order, with order being the highest differential coefficient in the equation. A characteristic of a linear differential equation is that solutions are additive; i.e., the combined flow, ψ, of two flows, ψ_1 and ψ_2, is simply $\psi_1 + \psi_2$. Similarly, $\phi = \phi_1 + \phi_2$. This principle of *superposition* is of great importance in obtaining mathematical expressions for fluid flows, because complicated flow regimes can be built up by the addition of two or more simple flows.

Another important relation is the *orthogonality* of lines of constant stream function ψ and of constant velocity potential ϕ. Lines of constant

ψ were previously shown to be streamlines, so that

$$\frac{dy}{dx} = \frac{v}{u}$$

Lines of constant ϕ, for which $d\phi = 0$, yield, from Eq. 3.23,

$$\frac{dy}{dx} = -\frac{u}{v}$$

Thus the slope of the ϕ-line at any point is the negative reciprocal of the slope of the ψ-line at that point; i.e., at any point the ψ- and ϕ-lines are normal to each other or *orthogonal*.

3.10 *Solution of flow problems*

The most usual types of flow pattern are those associated with flow through a channel or flow around a body or bodies completely immersed in a fluid. For instance, a very common situation in engineering involves uniform flow across a cylinder (e.g., a pipe); we are often interested in estimating the resistance to the flow offered by the cylinder or the heat transfer between the fluid and the cylinder. Of course, if there is resistance, it implies a real fluid with viscous shear forces, which are excluded by the assumption of ideal flow. However, the use of the ideal-flow solution rests on the concept of the boundary layer, namely, that the major characteristics of the flow outside the boundary layer are well approximated by ideal or potential flow. Thus it gives us a starting point for analysis.

Combinations of simple flows, as represented by simple ψ- and ϕ-functions, yield flow patterns of practical interest. Any ψ-line may be chosen as a solid boundary, since by definition no fluid crosses a streamline. A combination of simple flows that yields one streamline forming a closed curve can be interpreted as flow around a body of shape similar to the closed curve. This particular curve is most conveniently found by equating to zero the expression for stream function in its appropriate coordinates; i.e., $\psi(x, y)$ or $\psi(r, \theta) = 0$. A considerable number of useful flow patterns can be constructed from relatively few simple flow patterns. Some of the elementary "building blocks" will be analyzed first here, and then the results of superposing them will be studied. The functions of ψ and ϕ may be put into either Cartesian or polar coordinates, as desired. Any flow pattern with some aspect of circular symmetry is generally best handled in polar coordinates. Sometimes analysis is facilitated by the use of both forms. It should be remembered that any coordinate system is theoretically possible and that the choice is dictated by convenience.

3.11   *Simple patterns of flow*

UNIFORM   FLOW

Uniform, steady flow inclined to the x axis (Fig. 3.19) is represented by

$$u = V \cos \alpha = \frac{\partial \psi}{\partial y} = \frac{\partial \phi}{\partial x}$$

$$v = V \sin \alpha = -\frac{\partial \psi}{\partial x} = \frac{\partial \phi}{\partial y}$$

By the method of Sect. 3.8,

$$\psi = V(y \cos \alpha - x \sin \alpha) + C_1 \qquad [3.28a]$$
$$\phi = V(x \cos \alpha + y \sin \alpha) + C_2 \qquad [3.28b]$$

(Note that from now on the constant of integration, C, may be omitted, as it is only an additive constant identifying a given streamline with no effect on the flow pattern itself.)

For the common case of uniform velocity parallel to the x axis, Eqs. 3.28 reduce to

$$\psi = \pm Uy \qquad [3.29a]$$
$$\phi = \pm Ux \qquad [3.29b]$$

with the positive sign for flow in the positive x direction, the negative sign for flow in the negative x direction, and U representing the numerical value of the velocity.

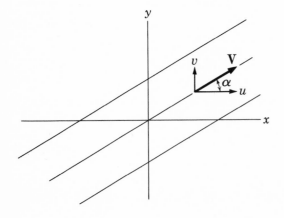

Figure 3.19

In polar coordinates, Eqs. 3.29 become

$$\psi = \pm \ Ur \sin \theta \qquad\qquad [\textbf{3.30a}]$$
$$\phi = \pm \ Ur \cos \theta \qquad\qquad [\textbf{3.30b}]$$

SOURCE OR SINK FLOW

Source flow is conceived as flow radially outward from a point (Fig. 3.20(a)). In two-dimensional flow the radial streamlines are perpendicular to a line through the source origin normal to the xy plane. *Sink* flow is the opposite of source flow; i.e., it is directed radially inward toward a point (Fig. 3.20(b)).

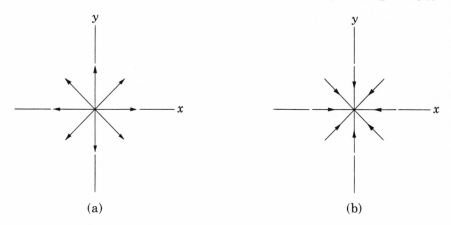

(a)   (b)

Figure 3.20

As source flow is along radial lines, the tangential velocity is zero. Therefore, from continuity,

$$u_r = \frac{Q}{A} = \frac{Q}{2\pi r}$$
$$u_\theta = 0$$

where Q is the volume rate of flow per unit depth normal to the flow plane and is called the *strength* of the source. Thus

$$u_r = \frac{Q}{2\pi r} = \frac{1}{r}\frac{\partial \psi}{\partial \theta} = \frac{\partial \phi}{\partial r}$$

Hence

$$\psi = \frac{Q}{2\pi}\theta \qquad\qquad [\textbf{3.31a}]$$

and

$$\phi = \frac{Q}{2\pi}\ln r \qquad\qquad [\textbf{3.31b}]$$

Streamlines, then, are radial lines from the source origin, and equipotential lines are circles concentric with the source origin (Fig. 3.21). Velocity is

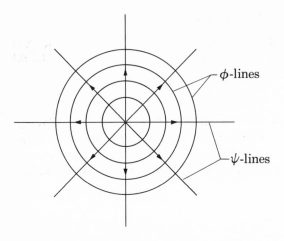

Figure 3.21

inversely proportional to distance from the origin and is purely radial. Note that the source or sink origin is a singular point and that the relationships break down at this point because as $r \rightarrow 0$, $u_r \rightarrow \infty$.

VORTEX FLOW

Vortex flow in general is defined by concentric streamlines along each of which the velocity is constant, although the velocities along different streamlines may have different values. However, in the hydrodynamic sense, vortex flow has the restriction that it must be irrotational throughout the flow field except for possible singular points. Referring back to the expression for rotation in polar coordinates, Eq. 3.21, and setting it equal to zero for the condition of irrotation, we obtain

$$\frac{1}{2}\left[\frac{\partial u_\theta}{\partial r} + \frac{1}{r}\left(u_\theta - \frac{\partial u_r}{\partial \theta}\right)\right] = 0$$

which, with $u_r = 0$ for concentric streamlines, yields

$$\frac{\partial u_\theta}{\partial r} + \frac{u_\theta}{r} = 0 \qquad [3.32]$$

The partial derivative becomes an ordinary derivative because u_θ is not a function of θ, and then integration of Eq. 3.32 gives

$$u_\theta r = \text{constant} = k$$

or
$$u_\theta = \frac{k}{r} \qquad [3.33]$$

The constant is called the *strength* of the vortex and is denoted by $\Gamma/2\pi$.

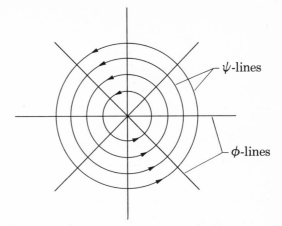

Figure 3.22

ψ-lines

ϕ-lines

Thus the velocity components are

$$u_\theta = \frac{\Gamma}{2\pi r} = -\frac{\partial \psi}{\partial r} = \frac{1}{r}\frac{\partial \phi}{\partial \theta}$$

and $u_r = 0$

Hence, by integration,

$$\psi = -\frac{\Gamma}{2\pi}\ln r \qquad\qquad [\textit{3.34a}]$$

$$\phi = \frac{\Gamma}{2\pi}\theta \qquad\qquad [\textit{3.34b}]$$

A vortex may rotate in either direction, and in accordance with the convention adopted here, a positive value of k or Γ yields a positive value of u_θ, i.e., a counterclockwise vortex.

It is apparent from Figs. 3.21 and 3.22 that the stream and potential functions of a source are interchanged for a vortex. In a vortex as in a source, the center is a singular point, because for zero radius, Eq. 3.33 requires infinite velocity.

3.12   *Circulation*

Vortex flow, which has closed curves for streamlines, introduces the idea of *circulation* in a fluid field. Circulation is defined as the summation over the whole length of a given closed path of the products of the velocity in the direction of the path and the length of an infinitesimal portion of the path. In mathematical terms,

$$\text{circulation} = \oint \mathbf{V} \cdot d\mathbf{s} \qquad \text{or} \qquad \oint V \cos \alpha \, ds \qquad [\textit{3.35}]$$

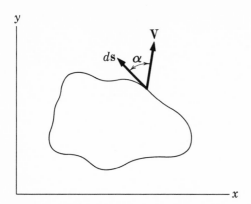

Figure 3.23

where α is the angle between the velocity and the tangent to the path at any point and ds is the infinitesimal path length. In other words, $V \cos \alpha$ is the projected velocity in the direction of the path at any point (Fig. 3.23). This is the *line integral* of the velocity component in the direction of the path around a closed curve. Conventionally the line integral is evaluated in a counterclockwise direction, as indicated by the arrow on the circle on the integral sign.

Because the product of velocity and distance has no familiar physical significance, circulation is a rather tenuous concept at first. Some feeling for it may be obtained through analogy with other line integrals. Thus the line integral of a force component and distance gives us work, $\int_a^b \mathbf{F} \cdot d\mathbf{s} = \int_a^b F \cos \alpha \, ds = W_{ab}$. In an electric field, the line integral of intensity and distance yields electric potential.

In two-dimensional Cartesian coordinates, $\mathbf{V} \cdot d\mathbf{s} = (\mathbf{i}u + \mathbf{j}v) \cdot (\mathbf{i}\,dx + \mathbf{j}\,dy) = u\,dx + v\,dy$; hence

$$\int_1^2 \mathbf{V} \cdot d\mathbf{s} = \int_1^2 u\,dx + v\,dy$$

For irrotational flow the velocity components may be replaced by the potential gradients.

$$\int_1^2 \mathbf{V} \cdot d\mathbf{s} = \int_1^2 \left(\frac{\partial \phi}{\partial x}\,dx + \frac{\partial \phi}{\partial y}\,dy \right) = \int_1^2 d\phi$$

Since $d\phi$ is an exact differential, i.e., is a point function, $\int_1^2 d\phi$ is independent of path, so that, from Fig. 3.24,

$$_A\!\int_1^2 d\phi = {}_B\!\int_1^2 d\phi = \phi_2 - \phi_1$$

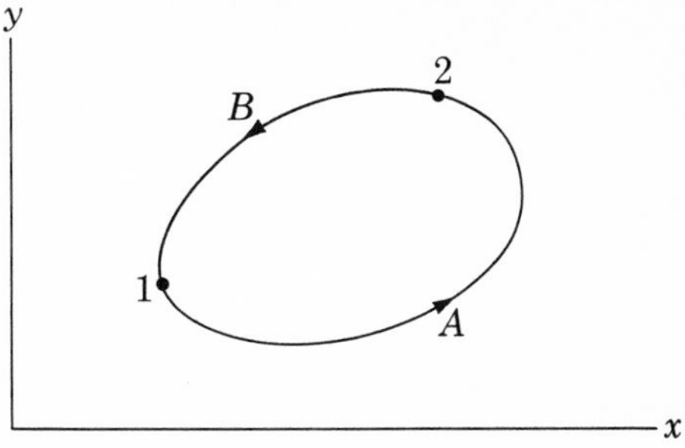

Figure 3.24

Around the closed path 1–A–2–B–1,

$$_A\!\int_1^2 d\phi + {}_B\!\int_1^2 d\phi = (\phi_2 - \phi_1) + (\phi_1 - \phi_2) = 0$$

But $_A\!\int_1^2 d\phi + {}_B\!\int_1^2 d\phi = \int_1^2 \mathbf{V} \cdot d\mathbf{s} + \int_1^2 \mathbf{V} \cdot d\mathbf{s} = \oint \mathbf{V} \cdot d\mathbf{s} = 0$

i.e., for *irrotational* flow, the *circulation is zero*. However, we must be sure that the flow is irrotational at every point inside the region formed by the closed path used in obtaining the line integral and that there are no singularities within the region.

Returning to vortex flow, let us examine it from the viewpoint of circulation. Fig. 3.25(a) shows a vortex with its center located at the origin. The circulation is independent of the path, provided the whole region is irrotational, because the circulation is $\int \mathbf{V} \cdot d\mathbf{s}$ and $\mathbf{V} = \text{grad } \phi$, with ϕ a potential function. Hence the path selected for the line integral may be

Figure 3.25

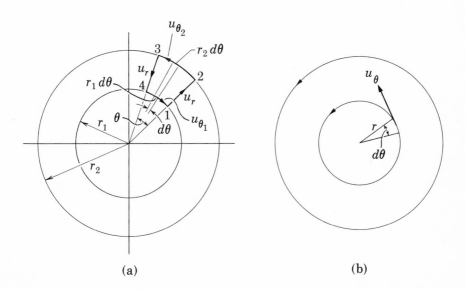

(a)   (b)

chosen for convenience. Let it be 1–2–3–4. Then

$$\text{circulation} = \oint \mathbf{V} \cdot d\mathbf{s} = \int_1^2 \mathbf{V} \cdot d\mathbf{s} + \int_2^3 \mathbf{V} \cdot d\mathbf{s} + \int_3^4 \mathbf{V} \cdot d\mathbf{s} + \int_4^1 \mathbf{V} \cdot d\mathbf{s}$$

The line integrals along 1–2 and 3–4 are zero because they are radial paths, $u_r = 0$, and u_θ is everywhere normal to the path. For 2–3,

$$\int_2^3 \mathbf{V} \cdot d\mathbf{s} = \int_2^3 u_{\theta_2} r_2 \, d\theta$$

and with $u_{\theta_2} = k/r_2$ from Eq. 3.33,

$$\int_2^3 u_{\theta_2} r_2 \, d\theta = k \int_2^3 d\theta = k\theta$$

Similarly, $\displaystyle \int_4^1 \mathbf{V} \cdot d\mathbf{s} = -\int_1^4 \mathbf{V} \cdot d\mathbf{s} = -\int_1^4 u_{\theta_1} r_1 \, d\theta = -k\theta$

Therefore, $\text{circulation} = 0 + k\theta + 0 - k\theta = 0$

as it should be from the preceding general analysis.

Now, however, let us take a path along a circular streamline enclosing the origin, as shown in Fig. 3.25(b).

$$\oint \mathbf{V} \cdot d\mathbf{s} = \int_0^{2\pi} u_\theta r \, d\theta = \int_0^{2\pi} k \, d\theta = 2\pi k = \Gamma \qquad [3.36]$$

The circulation has a finite constant value, Γ, and is independent of radius; consequently, it has the same value for all paths enclosing the origin. The reason for a finite value in this instance is not that the field is rotational but that the closed path includes a singular point, the origin, where $r = 0$ and $u_\theta = \infty$. Thus the circulation is zero everywhere for a region not enclosing the origin, as it should be for irrotational flow, but has a finite constant value if the region includes the origin. The latter case must then contain some rotation, and this is located at the origin itself, which, as was noted, is a singular point.

Circulation is a useful device in the synthesis of flow fields, since it accounts for the lift force of airfoils in ideal flows, as will be seen later. The vortex flow pattern provides a simple means of introducing circulation into an otherwise irrotational flow field.

3.13   *Superposition of flows*

We learned previously that because the Laplace equation was linear, solutions were additive. Thus two or more patterns of flow may be combined or superposed to give a new pattern, which is the vector sum of its com-

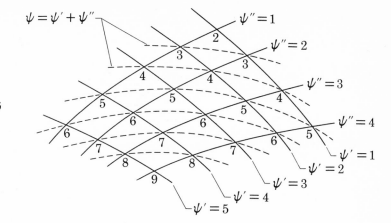

Figure 3.26

ponents. Hence we may write

$$\psi = \psi_1 + \psi_2 + \psi_3 + \cdots + \psi_n$$

Some examples will be analyzed shortly, showing how exact, quantitative results may be obtained. First, however, let us demonstrate a graphic method producing a qualitative picture that aids in the interpretation of a mathematical result.

Fig. 3.26 shows two sets of ψ-lines, a ψ' set and a ψ'' set. Each ψ-line has the value of some constant, in this case, 1, 2, 3, 4, etc. Because $\psi = \psi' + \psi''$, the points of intersection of ψ' and ψ'' may be regarded as points on the combined ψ-line. If these points are numbered with the sums of the values of the component lines, a line (dashed) joining the points having the same number represents the combined ψ-value. Although this graphic method is cumbersome if a small grid is chosen for a large area, seldom is a complete picture required. The method furnishes a good general idea of the flow pattern.

3.14 *Source-sink pair*

The first example of superposition is that of a source and a sink. Fig. 3.27(a) shows a source of strength $Q = 2\pi m$ at $-a, 0$ and a sink of equal strength, $-2\pi m$, at $a, 0$. The combined stream function, ψ, is then

$$\psi = \psi_1 + \psi_2 = - m\theta_1 + m\theta_2 = - m(\theta_1 - \theta_2) \qquad [\textbf{3.37}]$$

P_1 is any point in the field, located by r_1, θ_1 and r_2, θ_2. The streamline through

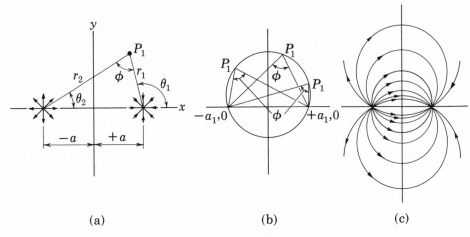

Figure 3.27

P_1 is given by $\psi_{P_1} = $ constant $= C_1$. Hence

$$\psi_{P_1} = - \ m(\theta_1 - \theta_2) = C_1$$

and
$$\theta_1 - \theta_2 = - \ \frac{C_1}{m}$$

According to Fig. 3.27(a), $\theta_1 = \theta_2 + \phi$, and therefore $\phi = \theta_1 - \theta_2 = -C_1/m$. Thus ψ_{P_1} is given by the locus of points P_1 such that ϕ is constant. From geometry we have the theorem that this locus is a circle passing through P_1 and the source and sink origins, $-a, 0$ and $a, 0$. This is shown in Fig. 3.27(b). For any other point P, we have a like angle, $\phi = $ constant, and so the ψ-lines are a series of circles, with centers on the y axis, passing through the source and sink origins. They are shown in Fig. 3.27(c).

3.15   Doublet

A *doublet* is defined as the limiting case of a source-sink pair of equal strengths, Q, whose centers approach each other with the condition that the product of their strength parameter, $Q/2\pi$, and the distance between centers remains constant; e.g., for a source-sink pair of strength $2\pi m$ at $-a, 0$ and $a, 0$, $m(2a) = \mu$, a constant called the *strength* of the doublet.

In order to obtain the stream function of a doublet, it is convenient to express that of a source-sink pair in another manner.

From Sect. 3.14,

$$\psi = -m(\theta_1 - \theta_2) \tag{3.37}$$

and so

$$\tan\left(-\frac{\psi}{m}\right) = \tan(\theta_1 - \theta_2) = \frac{\tan\theta_1 - \tan\theta_2}{1 + \tan\theta_1 \tan\theta_2} \tag{3.38}$$

From Fig. 3.28(a),

$$\tan\theta_1 = \frac{r\sin\theta}{r\cos\theta - a} \tag{3.39a}$$

and

$$\tan\theta_2 = \frac{r\sin\theta}{r\cos\theta + a} \tag{3.39b}$$

Substituting Eqs. 3.39 into Eq. 3.38 and reducing give us

$$\tan\left(-\frac{\psi}{m}\right) = \frac{2ar\sin\theta}{r^2 - a^2}$$

$$\psi = -m\tan^{-1}\left(\frac{2ar\sin\theta}{r^2 - a^2}\right)$$

As a becomes small, the value of the tangent approaches the value of the angle, and so we may write

$$\psi = -m\frac{2ar\sin\theta}{r^2 - a^2}$$

Substituting the doublet condition, $\mu = 2am$, we have

$$\psi = -\frac{\mu}{2a}\frac{2ar\sin\theta}{r^2 - a^2} = -\frac{\mu r\sin\theta}{r^2 - a^2}$$

Figure 3.28

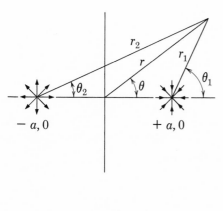

$-a, 0$

$+a, 0$

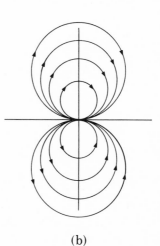

(a)

(b)

Going to the limit, $a \rightarrow 0$, then

$$\psi = -\frac{\mu \sin \theta}{r} \qquad\qquad [3.40]$$

which is the expression for the stream function of a doublet. In the limiting case the streamlines become circles tangent to the x axis, with centers on the y axis, as shown in Fig. 3.28(b). The doublet is a useful flow pattern when combined with uniform flow, as will be seen shortly.

3.16   *Source, sink, and uniform flow*

If uniform flow parallel to the x axis and in the positive x direction is superposed on a source-sink pair at $-a, 0$ and $a, 0$, the combined stream function is

$$\psi = Ur \sin \theta - m(\theta_1 - \theta_2) \qquad\qquad [3.41]$$

By the method of graphic representation, a pattern like that of Fig. 3.29 may be obtained, the exact form being dependent on the relative strengths of the elements and the source-sink distance. One streamline of the combined flow is a closed curve (heavy line) together with the x axis. Along the x axis it divides, forming a loop and recombining at the downstream end. This flow pattern may represent that of an oval-shaped body in uniform flow, as no fluid crosses the boundary of the streamline. It is defined as flow

Figure 3.29

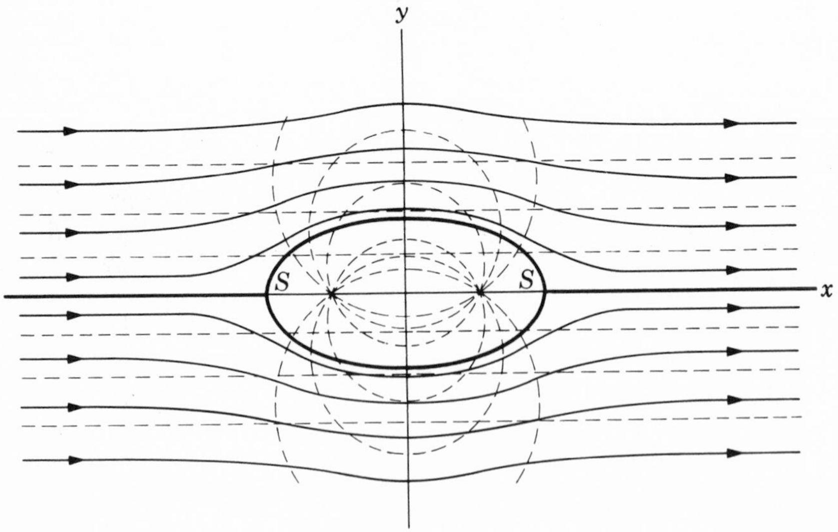

around a *Rankine* body (in this case two-dimensional only). Points S at the ends of the body are called *stagnation* points, because in this ideal picture the flow along the streamline on the x axis is brought to rest there. At the stagnation points the velocity is zero.

By suitable selection of the constants, any oval-shaped body may be produced, and by the distribution of several sources and sinks of different strengths at varying locations, elongated bodies approximating airfoil shapes may be depicted (subject to the restriction that the net strengths of sources and sinks equal zero, in order to satisfy continuity).

3.17   *Doublet and uniform flow (flow around a circular cylinder)*

Our particular interest in the flow around a Rankine body is in the limiting case where a source-sink pair forms a doublet. It can be perceived readily that as the source-sink pair approach each other, the body becomes more nearly circular and in the limit becomes a circle, so that a combination of uniform flow and a doublet yields the pattern of flow around a circular cylinder. This is shown in Fig. 3.30.

The combined stream function of uniform flow and a doublet is

$$\psi = Ur \sin \theta - \frac{\mu \sin \theta}{r} = \sin \theta \left(Ur - \frac{\mu}{r} \right) \qquad [3.42]$$

Figure 3.30

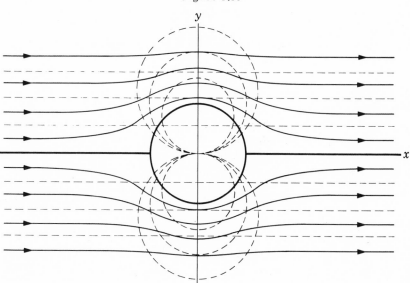

The streamline $\psi = 0$ gives the body shape, and hence

$$\sin \theta \left(Ur - \frac{\mu}{r} \right) = 0$$

Solutions are $\theta = 0$, $\theta = \pi$, and $\mu = Ur^2$. If a particular value of $r = a$ is taken, then the $\psi = 0$ streamline consists of the x axis ($\theta = 0$ or π) and a circle of radius a. Thus, on substitution of $\mu = Ua^2$,

$$\psi = U \sin \theta \left(r - \frac{a^2}{r} \right) \tag{3.43}$$

The velocity at any point is given by

$$V = \sqrt{u_r^2 + u_\theta^2}$$

with

$$u_r = \frac{1}{r} \frac{\partial \psi}{\partial \theta} = U \cos \theta \left(1 - \frac{a^2}{r^2} \right)$$

and

$$u_\theta = -\frac{\partial \psi}{\partial r} = - U \sin \theta \left(1 + \frac{a^2}{r^2} \right)$$

For the surface of the cylinder, $u_r = 0$, and hence

$$V = u_\theta = - U \sin \theta \left(1 + \frac{a^2}{r^2} \right)$$

and with $r = a$,

$$u_\theta = - 2U \sin \theta \tag{3.44}$$

For the stagnation points S, $u = 0$, because $\theta = 0$ and π. The maximum velocity is for $\sin \theta = \pi/2$ and $3\pi/2$, and so $u = -2U$. (Note that a minus sign results because the positive value of u is counterclockwise. The absolute velocity, V, may have a positive sign.)

3.18   *Doublet, uniform flow, and vortex flow (flow around a cylinder with circulation)*

The combination of uniform flow, a doublet, and a vortex yields

$$\psi = Ur \sin \theta - \frac{\mu \sin \theta}{r} + \frac{\Gamma}{2\pi} \ln r \tag{3.45}$$

with a plus sign for the vortex because the circulation is in a clockwise direction. The vortex, having clockwise flow, increases the velocity above the x axis and reduces it below the x axis, producing the general flow pattern of Fig. 3.31. The stagnation points, S, are displaced from the axis. With

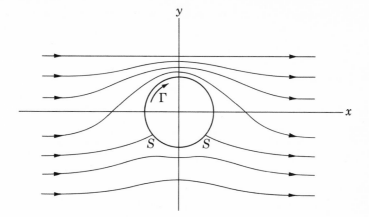

Figure 3.31

only the tangential velocity at the surface of the cylinder, where $r = a$,

$$u_\theta = -\frac{\partial \psi}{\partial r} = -2U \sin \theta - \frac{\Gamma}{2\pi a}$$

and for the stagnation points,

$$-2U \sin \theta - \frac{\Gamma}{2a} = 0$$

and

$$\sin \theta = -\frac{\Gamma}{4\pi U a}$$

For $\Gamma = 0$ (no vortex), the stagnation points are at $\theta = 0$ and π, as found earlier for the simple cylinder. As Eq. 3.45 allows for clockwise circulation, i.e., $\psi = (\Gamma/2\pi) \ln r$, Γ is positive. For the values of Γ given in Fig. 3.32, the stagnation points are lower; e.g., in Fig. 3.32(b), with $\Gamma = 2\sqrt{2}\,\pi U a$, they are at $\theta = -\pi/4$ and $5\pi/4$, and they move downward until at $\theta = -\pi/2$ and $3\pi/2$ they coincide at the bottom as shown in Fig. 3.32(c). For $\Gamma > 4\pi U a$, the stagnation points leave the surface and are located out in the flow, in a pattern of no practical interest (Fig. 3.32(d)).

Figure 3.32

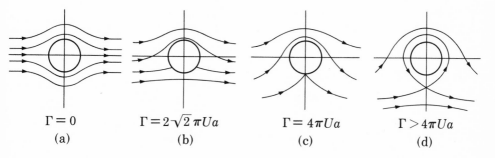

$\Gamma = 0$	$\Gamma = 2\sqrt{2}\,\pi U a$	$\Gamma = 4\pi U a$	$\Gamma > 4\pi U a$
(a)	(b)	(c)	(d)

With an unsymmetrical flow pattern, we should expect some unbalanced force on the body; this situation will be examined in detail following analysis of the dynamics of flow.

3.19   *Alternative methods of solution of flow patterns*

The preceding sections have outlined the basic analytical method of obtaining solutions to particular flow patterns by the combination of ψ functions of simple flows. This method is very useful for some of the more important but still relatively simple flow patterns, particularly as it allows pictures, both graphic and mental, of the flow regimes to be readily assimilated. However, more involved flow patterns rapidly become complex and cumbersome problems, involving many elements. The analysis can be carried out to cover a tremendous number of flow patterns by the introduction of the complex variable, but this requires mathematical operations beyond our scope here.* Even intricate mathematical techniques, however, are inadequate or too time-consuming for some problems, especially those concerned with patterns of a highly unsymmetrical nature. For such cases, and for simpler cases for which a range of variable parameters is essential, there are several approximate numerical methods and experimental analogies available. They are approximate only in that a "closed solution" is not given and the accuracy of the final answer is dependent not on the premises but on the time and effort allocated to successive iterations or on the degree of experimental precision. Three methods will be summarized: one graphic, the *flow net;* one numerical, the *relaxation technique;* and one experimental, the *electrical analogy.*

3.20   *The flow net*

The flow-net method is a graphic one consisting of the sketching of streamlines and equipotential lines in accordance with the flow principles established. Thus we have the velocity at a point,

$$V = \frac{d\phi}{ds} = \frac{d\psi}{dn}$$

where s is distance along the streamline and n is distance normal to the

---

* See, e.g., L. M. Milne-Thomson, *Theoretical Hydrodynamics*, 4th ed., Macmillan, New York, 1960; and H. R. Vallentyne, *Applied Hydrodynamics*, Butterworths, London, 1959.

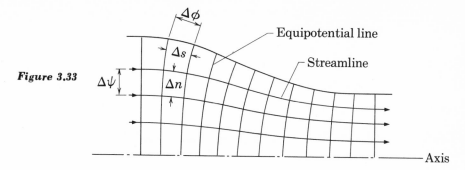

Figure 3.33

streamline through the given point. The differential quantities are replaced by finite, but small, quantities, so that

$$V = \frac{\Delta\phi}{\Delta s} = \frac{\Delta\psi}{\Delta n}$$

If the intervals between streamlines and equipotential lines are made equal, $\Delta\phi = \Delta\psi$, then $\Delta s = \Delta n$, and the pattern becomes a network of curvilinear squares, as shown in Fig. 3.33. This figure illustrates flow in a convergent nozzle, only one-half being necessary for the flow net because of symmetry. In the entry zone, and likewise in the exit zone, the flow may be considered as parallel. The entry zone is divided into a number of equally spaced streamlines—in this example, four. Because of continuity the exit region is divided into four equal units, and estimated streamlines are sketched in between. Then equipotential lines are drawn, crossing the streamlines at right angles and spaced to make equal intervals with the streamlines. A considerable amount of trial and error may be required initially, but practice increases skill.

3.21   *The relaxation technique*

The relaxation or iteration technique consists in more or less arbitrarily allocating numerical values of a particular variable to the intersections of a grid covering the flow field and then using the relevant relationships governing the flow to "relax" or correct these values successively until a sufficient degree of accuracy has been obtained.

Fig. 3.34(a) shows part of a flow field in a nozzle, with nominal streamlines indicated by dashed lines and a square grid of solid lines superposed. Each intersection of the grid lines is given an arbitrary value of ψ. Fig. 3.34(b) shows an enlarged portion of one section of the grid to demonstrate

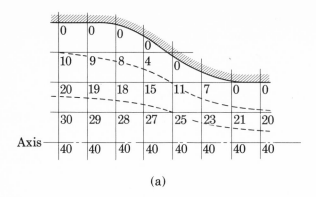

(a)

Figure 3.34

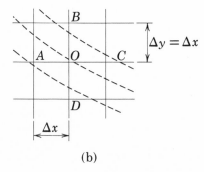

(b)

the method at one point. The condition to be met for physically possible, irrotational flow is that the Laplace equation must be satisfied,

$$\frac{\partial^2 \psi}{\partial x^2} + \frac{\partial^2 \psi}{\partial y^2} = 0$$

The relaxation method replaces the differential form with finite differences. From Fig. 3.34(b), the first derivative at point O in the x direction may be approximated by

$$\frac{\partial \psi}{\partial x} \approx \frac{(\Delta_{AO}\psi/\Delta x) + (\Delta_{OC}\psi/\Delta x)}{2} = \frac{(\psi_O - \psi_A) + (\psi_C - \psi_O)}{2\,\Delta x} = \frac{\psi_C - \psi_A}{2\,\Delta x}$$

where $\Delta_{AO}\psi$ is the change of ψ between O and A, etc. The second derivative is approximated by

$$\frac{\partial^2 \psi}{\partial x^2} \approx \frac{(\Delta_{OC}\psi/\Delta x) - (\Delta_{AO}\psi/\Delta x)}{\Delta x} = \frac{\Delta_{OC}\psi - \Delta_{AO}\psi}{\Delta x^2} = \frac{(\psi_C - \psi_O) - (\psi_O - \psi_A)}{\Delta x^2}$$
$$= \frac{\psi_C + \psi_A - 2\psi_O}{\Delta x^2}$$

Similarly, the second derivative at point O in the y direction may be given by

$$\frac{\partial^2 \psi}{\partial y^2} \approx \frac{\psi_B + \psi_D - 2\psi_O}{\Delta y^2} = \frac{\psi_B + \psi_D - 2\psi_O}{\Delta x^2}$$

for the square grid with $\Delta x = \Delta y$. Then

$$\frac{\partial^2 \psi}{\partial x^2} + \frac{\partial^2 \psi}{\partial y^2} \approx \frac{\psi_C + \psi_A - 2\psi_O}{\Delta x^2} + \frac{\psi_B + \psi_D - 2\psi_O}{\Delta x^2}$$

$$= \frac{\psi_A + \psi_B + \psi_C + \psi_D - 4\psi_O}{\Delta x^2} = 0$$

Therefore,
$$\psi_O = \frac{\psi_A + \psi_B + \psi_C + \psi_D}{4}$$

This is the condition that must be satisfied by adjustment of the initial values of ψ. Thus the first step is to calculate the *residuals*, or imbalances, obtained from the initial estimates. The value at ψ_O is then relaxed to make its residual zero, so that the necessary condition is fulfilled at point O. But this new value upsets those of its neighbors, and so they have to be recalculated. By continual relaxation the residuals are successively decreased. The procedure is repeated until the desired level of accuracy is reached. For irregularly shaped bodies, some portions of the grid covering the flow area will not be rectangular. Therefore, either special relations must be developed in a similar manner to that demonstrated, or the irregular areas must be subdivided by smaller grids to yield better approximations. When final values of ψ have been obtained at all intersections, lines of constant ψ may be drawn, producing a streamline picture. Any desired level of accuracy may be attained through adjustment of the size of the grid and the order of the final residuals.

The relaxation technique is commonly applied in a number of fields. Only the outline necessary for establishing its use in fluid flow has been presented here.*

3.22   *The electrical analogy*

In earlier paragraphs the similarity between an ideal-flow field and an electrostatic field has been mentioned. The analogy is exact, and the electrostatic field must satisfy the Laplace equation,

$$\frac{\partial^2 V}{\partial x^2} + \frac{\partial^2 V}{\partial y^2} = 0$$

where V is the electric potential. We may, therefore, set up an electrical

* For a detailed study, see D. N. de G. Allen, *Relaxation Methods*, McGraw-Hill, New York, 1954.

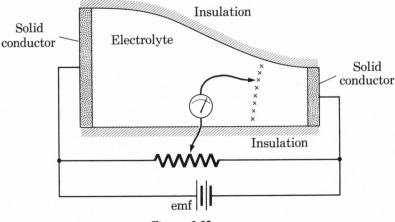

Figure 3.35

system geometrically similar to the flow system and measure directly the value of potential at any point.

In Fig. 3.35 the insulated boundaries of the flow model in question are connected by an electrolyte or conducting material, and an emf is supplied across the inlet and outlet sections. The voltage drop across the flow is measured by voltmeter or potentiometer, and thus the potential field is established. The streamlines can be drawn by the flow-net method once the equipotential lines have been mapped out, or else the emf can be applied across the boundaries with conductors and insulators interchanged, giving the ψ-lines directly.

A three-dimensional system can be explored in this manner, and a two-dimensional one by means of a shallow bath of electrolyte. In the latter case, it is also convenient to replace the electrolyte bath with a sheet of conducting paper, which is readily shaped to the desired boundaries. This system is very useful for rapid determination of a flow pattern.

Problems

3.1. A two-dimensional velocity field is described by

$$u = x$$
$$v = -y$$

Write the general equation of the streamlines and the equation for the streamline passing through point 2, 3.

3.2. The absolute value of the velocity and the equation of the streamlines in a velocity field are given by

$$V = \sqrt{x^2 + y^2}$$

and
$$x^2 - y^2 = \text{constant}$$

Find u and v.

3.3. Derive Eq. 3.10, namely, the continuity equation for incompressible flow in polar coordinates.

$$\frac{\partial}{\partial r}(u_r r) + \frac{\partial u_\theta}{\partial \theta} = 0$$

3.4. Determine which of these velocities satisfy continuity:

a. $u = Kx$
   $v = -Ky$
b. $u = Kx$
   $v = Kx$

c. $u = K(x^2 + xy - y^2)$
   $v = K(y^2 + x^2)$
d. $u = A \ln xy$
   $v = \dfrac{Ay}{x}$

3.5. The stream function of a two-dimensional incompressible flow is given by

$$\psi = x^2 + 2y$$

a. Find the magnitude and direction of the velocity at point 2, 3.
b. Find the magnitude of the velocity component at 2, 3 that forms an angle of 30° with the positive x axis.

3.6. Find which of the following flow fields satisfy continuity and whether they are rotational or irrotational:

a. $u = x^2 y + y^2$
   $v = x^2 - y^2 x$
b. $u = x^3 \sin y$
   $v = 3x^2 \cos y$
c. $u = x^2 + 2xy$
   $v = y^2 + 2xy$
d. $u = k$
   $v = 0$

e. $u = ky$
   $v = kx$
f. $u_r = 2r \sin \theta \cos \theta$
   $u = 2r \sin^2 \theta$
   (continuity only)
g. $u = \dfrac{x}{x^2 + y^2}$
   $v = \dfrac{y}{x^2 + y^2}$

3.7. Determine which of the following velocity fields could represent irrotational flow:

a. $u = A$
   $v = B$
b. $u = Kx$
   $v = Ky$

c. $u = Ax^2 + Bx^3$
   $v = Ay + B \sin y$
d. $u = A \ln xy$
   $v = -\dfrac{Ay}{x}$

3.8. Which of the following stream functions are possible irrotational flow fields?

a. $\psi = 2Axy$

b. $\psi = Ax + By$

c. $\psi = A \ln xy^2$

3.9. Calculate the velocity components for the potentials

a. $\phi = Axy$

b. $\phi = A \sin \dfrac{\pi x}{L} + B \sin \dfrac{\pi y}{L}$

3.10. Determine the flow velocity (in magnitude and direction) given by

$$\phi = 2x + 3y$$

3.11. A two-dimensional incompressible flow is described by the velocity components

$$u = 2x$$
$$v = -6x - 2y$$

Does a stream function exist? If so, find it. Does a potential function exist? If so, find it.

3.12. A two-dimensional velocity field is described by

$$u = x^2 - y^2 + x$$
$$v = -(2xy + y)$$

Show that this field satisfies continuity and is also irrotational. Find the potential.

3.13. Show that the two fields described below are identical:

$$\psi = 2xy + y$$
$$\phi = x^2 + x - y^2$$

3.14. Draw the streamlines for the field represented by $\psi = xy$ for values of $\psi = 0, 1, 2, 3$. Find the corresponding potential, ϕ, if one exists, and draw the equipotential lines. Show that the ψ- and ϕ-lines are orthogonal. What actual flow pattern might this represent?

3.15. Find the circulation of a forced-vortex motion (solid rotation) with concentric streamlines given by the velocity relation $V = \omega r$, where ω is the constant angular velocity, (a) for a segment of angle θ bounded by radii r_1 and r_2, and (b) for a circular path enclosing the origin. Discuss the results.

3.16. Analyze the flow obtained by the combination of a source of strength 4π and a vortex of strength 2 located at the origin, and sketch the resulting flow pattern.

3.17. Show that the flow pattern produced by the superposition of the two flows $\psi = 2\theta$ and $\psi = -5y$ represents uniform rectilinear flow over a blunt-nosed body. Show that the limiting width of the body is $4\pi/5$.

4

Dynamics of Fluid Flow

In this chapter we are concerned with the forces and energies associated with fluid flow. With respect to forces and the motion produced by them, the basic relation is Newton's second law, as in solid-body mechanics, although some adaptation is needed for dealing with a continuous flow of material rather than a single element of mass. With respect to energy, the basic relation is the conservation of energy principle, probably familiar in the form of the steady-flow energy equation of thermodynamics. The continuity relation established in Chapter 3, the force-momentum relation of the second law, and the energy equation are the triumvirate of conservation laws (mass, momentum, and energy) by which all fluid-dynamics problems are analyzed. Again and again in the following work, particular relationships will be developed by the use of these fundamental laws in various combinations and in conjunction with other relations valid for individual cases. This fact is emphasized here in order that the underlying unity of pattern in the derivation of useful forms may be recognized, regardless of the apparent multiplicity of special relationships that will be developed.

We have a choice of two methods in describing a fluid-flow field. The first is to follow each individual particle initially having a position vector $\mathbf{r}_0$ at time t_0, i.e., to determine the history of each particle. This is called the *Lagrangian* method and is the method of solid-body mechanics. The second is to examine what is happening at a given point in space, with this point being occupied continuously and successively by different particles. This is the *Eulerian* method. Although the Lagrangian method is valuable in some problems, it is generally more difficult to obtain solutions throughout the field with it, and so the Eulerian method is commonly used. We shall have occasion to analyze the behavior of a particle or element of a fluid, but from the Eulerian viewpoint; i.e., the particle will be *any* particle at a certain location in space, which we are free to choose. In solid-body mechanics we have to identify a particle and stay with it. Here we shall not be concerned with what happens to that *particular* particle at a later time or at a different location. A knowledge of velocity, acceleration, pressure, temperature, etc., at a given point in the field at a given time is the object of our analysis.

4.1   *Acceleration*

Acceleration defined as the rate of change of velocity with time is familiar but as applied to fluid flow, it must be expressed in terms covering all locations at each instant of time, i.e., in terms of field values. At a given point in space at a given instant of time, an element of fluid may be accelerating owing to change of velocity with *distance* in the vicinity of the point and, at that point, owing to change of velocity with *time*. This may be expressed mathematically by saying that the velocity is a function of distance and time, i.e.,

$$\mathbf{V} = \mathbf{V}(s, t)$$

where the distance, s, is general and can be resolved into components of any coordinate system. A differential increment of velocity is then given by

$$d\mathbf{V} = \frac{\partial \mathbf{V}}{\partial s}\, ds + \frac{\partial \mathbf{V}}{\partial t}\, dt$$

With acceleration defined by $\mathbf{a} = d\mathbf{V}/dt$, then

$$\mathbf{a} = \frac{d\mathbf{V}}{dt} = \frac{\partial \mathbf{V}}{\partial s}\frac{ds}{dt} + \frac{\partial \mathbf{V}}{\partial t}\frac{dt}{dt}$$

or, with the notation $d\mathbf{V}/dt = D\mathbf{V}/Dt$ and the substitution of $\mathbf{V} = ds/dt$, then

$$\frac{D\mathbf{V}}{Dt} = \mathbf{V}\frac{\partial \mathbf{V}}{\partial s} + \frac{\partial \mathbf{V}}{\partial t} \qquad [\mathit{4.1}]$$

The relation $\mathbf{V}\dfrac{\partial}{\partial s} + \dfrac{\partial}{\partial t} = \dfrac{d}{dt}$ appears so often in fluid mechanics that it has a special name, *particle*, or *total*, *derivative*, and a special notation, D/Dt. It gives the rate of change of a property with distance, s, in the flow direction, $\mathbf{V}$, plus its rate of change with time, t, at a given space coordinate. Thus it is the total rate of change of a property of a particle as it moves in space and time—hence the designation "particle derivative."

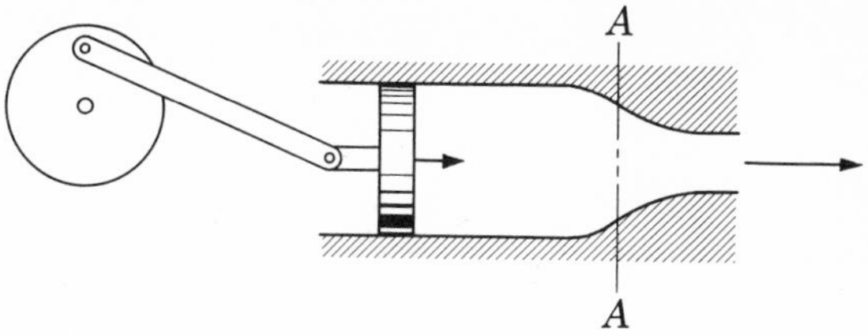

Figure 4.1

Here in Eq. 4.1, the left-hand term, DV/Dt, is called the *total* or *substantial* acceleration and consists of two components. The first component, $V \, \partial V/\partial s$, is that due to position at a given time and is called the *convective* acceleration, i.e., that carried with or conveyed from point to point. The second component, $\partial V/\partial t$, is that due to time at a given position and is called the *local* or *temporal* acceleration. These values of acceleration may be envisaged in Fig. 4.1, which shows fluid being forced through a nozzle into a pipe by a reciprocating piston. The fluid crossing section AA at any instant is accelerating owing to the change of area of the nozzle. At the same time, the whole body of fluid is accelerating owing to the varying speed of the piston. The acceleration in the first case is the convective acceleration, and that in the second case is the local acceleration, their sum being the total acceleration. In steady flow, $\partial V/\partial t = 0$, and the acceleration is wholly convective, $V \, \partial V/\partial s$.

As V is in general a three-dimensional velocity, in Cartesian coordinates the three components are $u = u(x, y, z, t)$, $v = v(x, y, z, t)$, and $w = w(x, y, z, t)$. Then, from the previous development, the acceleration components are

$$\frac{Du}{Dt} = u \frac{\partial u}{\partial x} + v \frac{\partial u}{\partial y} + w \frac{\partial u}{\partial z} + \frac{\partial u}{\partial t} \qquad [\textbf{4.2a}]$$

$$\frac{Dv}{Dt} = u \frac{\partial v}{\partial x} + v \frac{\partial v}{\partial y} + w \frac{\partial v}{\partial z} + \frac{\partial v}{\partial t} \qquad [\textbf{4.2b}]$$

$$\frac{Dw}{Dt} = u \frac{\partial w}{\partial x} + v \frac{\partial w}{\partial y} + w \frac{\partial w}{\partial z} + \frac{\partial w}{\partial t} \qquad [\textbf{4.2c}]$$

It is sometimes convenient, particularly with circular motion, to use the natural coordinates of fluid motion. For two-dimensional flow these would be in the direction of the streamline and in the direction of the radius of curvature of the streamline (i.e., normal to the streamline in the direction of the center of curvature). For three-dimensional flow the third coordinate would be normal to the plane containing the first two. In an analysis restricted to two-dimensional flow, the symbol s denotes the streamline direction, and the symbol n the radial direction. Fig. 4.2(a) shows fluid with velocity V at point P and at time t_0. An instant of time later the fluid has traveled an infinitesimal distance ds to point Q along the streamline. The

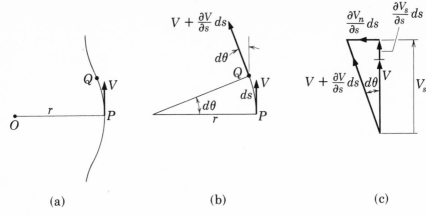

Figure 4.2

fluid has changed direction by $d\theta$, so that $ds = r\, d\theta$, where r is the radius of curvature at P (Fig. 4.2(b)). The velocity has changed by the amount $(\partial V/\partial s)\, ds$. Components of velocity increment are shown in Fig. 4.2(c), $(\partial V_s/\partial s)\, ds$ being the increment in the direction of the streamline at P (by definition tangent to the streamline at P) and $(\partial V_n/\partial s)\, ds$ being the increment in the normal direction.

Recognizing that in general, including the unsteady-flow situation, both V_s and V_n are functions of time t as well as distance s, we have

$$a_s = \frac{DV_s}{Dt} = \frac{\partial V_s}{\partial s}\frac{ds}{dt} + \frac{\partial V_s}{\partial t}\frac{dt}{dt} = V\frac{\partial V_s}{\partial s} + \frac{\partial V_s}{\partial t} \qquad [4.3a]$$

$$a_n = \frac{DV_n}{Dt} = \frac{\partial V_n}{\partial s}\frac{ds}{dt} + \frac{\partial V_n}{\partial t}\frac{dt}{dt} = V\frac{\partial V_n}{\partial s} + \frac{\partial V_n}{\partial t} \qquad [4.3b]$$

For the convective component of a_s, we see from Fig. 4.2(c) that

$$V_s = V + \frac{\partial V_s}{\partial s}\, ds = \left(V + \frac{\partial V}{\partial s}\, ds\right)\cos d\theta$$

With $d\theta$ infinitesimal, $\cos d\theta \to 1$, and thus in the limit

$$\frac{\partial V_s}{\partial s} = \frac{\partial V}{\partial s} \qquad [4.4]$$

For the local component of a_s,

$$\frac{\partial V_s}{\partial t} = \frac{\partial}{\partial t}\left(V + \frac{\partial V}{\partial s}\, ds\right) = \frac{\partial V}{\partial t} \qquad [4.5]$$

with the second-order differential neglected.

Substituting Eqs. 4.4 and 4.5 in Eq. 4.3a gives us

$$a_s = V \frac{\partial V}{\partial s} + \frac{\partial V}{\partial t} \qquad [4.6]$$

For the increment of the normal component, Fig. 4.2(c) shows that

$$\frac{\partial V_n}{\partial s} ds = \left(V + \frac{\partial V}{\partial s} ds\right) \sin d\theta$$

and for small $d\theta$, $\sin d\theta = d\theta$, which from Fig. 4.2(b) is equal to ds/r. Thus

$$\frac{\partial V_n}{\partial s} ds = \left(V + \frac{\partial V}{\partial s} ds\right) \frac{ds}{r}$$

With the second-order differential neglected, this yields

$$\frac{\partial V_n}{\partial s} = \frac{V}{r} \qquad [4.7]$$

For the local component of a_n, we have simply $\partial V_n/\partial t$, because V at point P at t_0 by definition had no normal component. Finally then, after substitution in Eq. 4.3b,

$$a_n = \frac{V^2}{r} + \frac{\partial V_n}{\partial t} \qquad [4.8]$$

For steady flow, $a_n = V^2/r$, a result that we know from mechanics and that earlier was presented, with $V = \omega r$, as $a = \omega^2 r$, the acceleration toward the center in solid-body rotation.

4.2   *Momentum*

Newton's second law of motion applied to a fixed quantity of matter states that the product of the mass and the time rate of change of velocity is equal to the summation of the external forces acting on the matter; i.e.,

$$\Sigma \mathbf{F} = \frac{M}{g_c} \frac{D\mathbf{V}}{Dt} \qquad [4.9]$$

We can use this relation to analyze the motion of every particle of fluid in a given field, but it requires an exact knowledge of the forces everywhere and then a summation over the whole field for all particles. The analysis for a single particle leads to the *equations of motion*, which form the basis for an exact solution of any fluid-flow problem. Although it is always necessary to introduce simplifications that destroy the exactness in order to obtain a particular solution, in many cases the inexactness does not preclude valuable conclusions.

Another possibility is to find a broad relation for the whole flow field, for which it is not essential to know the details at every point—in other words, an integral solution. This requires application of the momentum relation to a whole system of particles in flow and leads to an equally important statement known as the *momentum theorem* of fluid dynamics.

We shall first deal with the force-acceleration relationship of a single particle, i.e., at a point. This particle, though single, is *any* particle, and so a general result can be obtained if conditions in the field are known.

4.3 *Equations of motion*

We shall consider the forces and rate of change of momentum of a cubic element for convenience in using Cartesian coordinates. Fig. 4.3 shows an element of fluid of sides Δx, Δy, and Δz and density ρ, thus having a mass $\Delta M = \rho \, \Delta x \, \Delta y \, \Delta z$. At the center of the element, the pressure is p.

The forces on the element may be divided into *surface* forces and *body* forces. The surface forces are those due to *pressure*, which must act normal to the surfaces, and those due to *shear*, which must act in the plane of the surfaces. Analysis of the combined stress due to pressure and shear is complex and will not be attempted here. (Later on, a nonrigorous analysis for two-dimensional, incompressible flow will be given, which leads to a correct formulation of utility for many flow problems.) Therefore, any relationship obtained will be valid only for nonviscous or *ideal* flow. This restriction may seem serious but actually is not, for, as noted in Chapter 3, many useful answers result from consideration of ideal flow.

Body forces depend on the mass of the element and are regarded as acting at the centroid of the element. Such forces are those due to gravity (i.e., weight) and electromagnetic effects, for instance.

In Fig. 4.3 the pressure forces on each face of the element are shown. The element is small enough that a linear pressure gradient is assumed, which becomes exact when the element is shrunk to infinitesimal proportions (see Sect. 2.2). The body forces are X', Y', and Z'. With the x direction as an example, the sum of the forces is

$$\Sigma F_x = \left(p - \frac{\partial p}{\partial x} \frac{\Delta x}{2} \right) \Delta y \, \Delta z - \left(p + \frac{\partial p}{\partial x} \frac{\Delta x}{2} \right) \Delta y \, \Delta z + X'$$

$$= -\frac{\partial p}{\partial x} \Delta x \, \Delta y \, \Delta z + X'$$

Similarly,

$$\Sigma F_y = -\frac{\partial p}{\partial y} \Delta x \, \Delta y \, \Delta z + Y'$$

and

$$\Sigma F_z = -\frac{\partial p}{\partial z} \Delta x \, \Delta y \, \Delta z + Z'$$

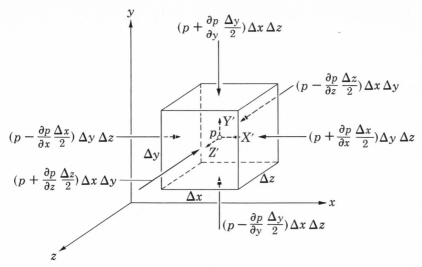

Figure 4.3

The acceleration, in general, is DV/Dt. Again with the x direction as an example, substituting Eq. 4.2a for the x-direction acceleration and formulating the force–rate of change of velocity relationship as Eq. 4.9, or

$$\Sigma F_x = \frac{M}{g_c}\frac{Du}{Dt}$$

we have

$$-\frac{\partial p}{\partial x}\Delta x\,\Delta y\,\Delta z + X' = \frac{\rho}{g_c}\Delta x\,\Delta y\,\Delta z\left(u\frac{\partial u}{\partial x}+v\frac{\partial u}{\partial y}+w\frac{\partial u}{\partial z}+\frac{\partial u}{\partial t}\right)$$

Shrinking the element to infinitesimal dimensions, so that the use of average pressure on each surface is exact, and dividing through by the mass, $\rho\,\Delta x\,\Delta y\,\Delta z$, give us

$$-\frac{1}{\rho}\frac{\partial p}{\partial x}+X=\frac{1}{g_c}\left(u\frac{\partial u}{\partial x}+v\frac{\partial u}{\partial y}+w\frac{\partial u}{\partial z}+\frac{\partial u}{\partial t}\right)$$

where $X = X'/\rho\,\Delta x\,\Delta y\,\Delta z$, the body force per unit mass.

Performing the same operations for the y and z directions, we obtain the *Euler* equations of motion in Cartesian coordinates.

$$-\frac{1}{\rho}\frac{\partial p}{\partial x}+X=\frac{1}{g_c}\left(u\frac{\partial u}{\partial x}+v\frac{\partial u}{\partial y}+w\frac{\partial u}{\partial z}+\frac{\partial u}{\partial t}\right) \qquad [4.10a]$$

$$-\frac{1}{\rho}\frac{\partial p}{\partial y}+Y=\frac{1}{g_c}\left(u\frac{\partial v}{\partial x}+v\frac{\partial v}{\partial y}+w\frac{\partial v}{\partial z}+\frac{\partial v}{\partial t}\right) \qquad [4.10b]$$

$$-\frac{1}{\rho}\frac{\partial p}{\partial z}+Z=\frac{1}{g_c}\left(u\frac{\partial w}{\partial x}+v\frac{\partial w}{\partial y}+w\frac{\partial w}{\partial z}+\frac{\partial w}{\partial t}\right) \qquad [4.10c]$$

These three equations can be expressed in vector notation as

$$- \frac{1}{\rho} \operatorname{grad} p + \mathbf{S} = \frac{1}{g_c} \frac{D\mathbf{V}}{Dt} \qquad\qquad [4.10d]$$

where $\mathbf{S} = \mathbf{i}X + \mathbf{j}Y + \mathbf{k}Z$. The Euler equations of motion are valid at any point in the field for the unsteady, three-dimensional, compressible flow of an ideal fluid. For reference, the corresponding equations for compressible viscous flow, the *Navier-Stokes* equations, are given in the appendix to this chapter for the case of constant viscosity.

Even in the absence of viscous forces, the equations of motion are somewhat intractable for integration over a finite region unless simplifying assumptions are made; it is necessary to prescribe the various components in terms of the coordinates everywhere in the field, which leads to mathematical difficulties in a general case. However, under certain conditions, the three partial-differential equations can be reduced to a single ordinary differential equation. This reduction allows simple integration to be carried out. The conditions under which reduction is possible are (1) for flow along a streamline and (2) for irrotational flow throughout a field.

4.4   *Flow along a streamline*

If we limit our discussion to flow along a streamline, we can introduce Eqs. 3.3, defining the streamline.

$$v\,dx = u\,dy \qquad w\,dx = u\,dz \qquad v\,dz = w\,dy$$

Each Eq. 4.10 contains u, v, and w, but by means of the streamline relations we can transform each into terms containing only either u or v or w. Substituting in Eq. 4.10a for $v = u\,dy/dx$ and $w = u\,dz/dx$, we obtain

$$- \frac{1}{\rho} \frac{\partial p}{\partial x} + X = \frac{1}{g_c}\left(u\frac{\partial u}{\partial x} + u\frac{\partial u}{\partial y}\frac{dy}{dx} + u\frac{\partial u}{\partial z}\frac{dz}{dx} + \frac{\partial u}{\partial t} \right)$$

Multiplying through by dx, we have

$$- \frac{1}{\rho} \frac{\partial p}{\partial x}\,dx + X\,dx = \frac{1}{g_c}\left(u\frac{\partial u}{\partial x}\,dx + u\frac{\partial u}{\partial y}\,dy + u\frac{\partial u}{\partial z}\,dz + \frac{\partial u}{\partial t}\,dx \right)$$

Since we can write

$$\frac{\partial u}{\partial t}\,dx = \frac{\partial u}{\partial t}\,dt\,\frac{dx}{dt} = u\frac{\partial u}{\partial t}\,dt$$

we can group the right-hand side to give

$$-\frac{1}{\rho}\frac{\partial p}{\partial x}\,dx + X\,dx = \frac{u}{g_c}\left(\frac{\partial u}{\partial x}\,dx + \frac{\partial u}{\partial y}\,dy + \frac{\partial u}{\partial z}\,dz + \frac{\partial u}{\partial t}\,dt\right)$$

The term in parentheses is a total differential, du, where $u = u(x, y, z, t)$ and therefore

$$-\frac{1}{\rho}\frac{\partial p}{\partial x}\,dx + X\,dx = \frac{u}{g_c}\,du = d\left(\frac{u^2}{2g_c}\right)$$

Applying the same procedure to the other Euler-equation components, i.e., putting Eq. 4.10b in terms of v and multiplying by dy, and putting Eq. 4.10c in terms of w and multiplying by dz, and regrouping, we obtain

$$-\frac{1}{\rho}\frac{\partial p}{\partial x}\,dx + X\,dx = \frac{u}{g_c}\,du = d\left(\frac{u^2}{2g_c}\right)$$

$$-\frac{1}{\rho}\frac{\partial p}{\partial y}\,dy + Y\,dy = \frac{v}{g_c}\,dv = d\left(\frac{v^2}{2g_c}\right)$$

$$-\frac{1}{\rho}\frac{\partial p}{\partial z}\,dz + Z\,dz = \frac{w}{g_c}\,dz = d\left(\frac{w^2}{2g_c}\right)$$

Adding these equations yields

$$-\frac{1}{\rho}\left(\frac{\partial p}{\partial x}\,dx + \frac{\partial p}{\partial y}\,dy + \frac{\partial p}{\partial z}\,dz\right) + X\,dx + Y\,dy + Z\,dz$$

$$= d\left(\frac{u^2}{2g_c} + \frac{v^2}{2g_c} + \frac{w^2}{2g_c}\right) = d\left(\frac{V^2}{2g_c}\right)$$

since
$$V^2 = u^2 + v^2 + w^2$$

Now $p = p(x, y, z, t)$, and so

$$dp = \frac{\partial p}{\partial x}\,dx + \frac{\partial p}{\partial y}\,dy + \frac{\partial p}{\partial z}\,dz + \frac{\partial p}{\partial t}\,dt$$

With $(\partial p/\partial t)\,dt$ added to the term in parentheses on the left-hand side and $-(\partial p/\partial t)\,dt/\rho$ added to the right-hand side for equality, the relation reduces to

$$-\frac{1}{\rho}\,dp + X\,dx + Y\,dy + Z\,dz = d\left(\frac{V^2}{2g_c}\right) - \frac{1}{\rho}\frac{\partial p}{\partial t}\,dt \qquad [\textbf{\textit{4.11}}]$$

We have succeeded in reducing the three Euler equations of motion to a single equation for flow *along a streamline*. We may integrate this if we have information on the pressure-density relationship for the fluid, on the nature of the body forces, and on the time dependence. Before examining particular cases, we shall look at irrotational flow.

4.5   *Irrotational flow*

We can simplify by using Eqs. 3.20, which relate the velocity components in
irrotational flow.

$$\frac{\partial v}{\partial x} - \frac{\partial u}{\partial y} = 0 \qquad \frac{\partial u}{\partial z} - \frac{\partial w}{\partial x} = 0 \qquad \frac{\partial w}{\partial y} - \frac{\partial v}{\partial z} = 0$$

By substituting, we can obtain each of Eqs. 4.10 in terms of components in a
single direction. Thus in Eq. 4.10a we substitute $\partial v/\partial x$ for $\partial u/\partial y$ and $\partial w/\partial x$
for $\partial u/\partial z$. Multiplying by dx yields

$$-\frac{1}{\rho}\frac{\partial p}{\partial x}\,dx + X\,dx = \frac{u}{g_c}\frac{\partial u}{\partial x}\,dx + \frac{v}{g_c}\frac{\partial v}{\partial x}\,dx + \frac{w}{g_c}\frac{\partial w}{\partial x}\,dx + \frac{1}{g_c}\frac{\partial u}{\partial t}\,dx$$

all derivatives being with respect to x or t. Performing similar operations
on Eqs. 4.10b and 4.10c and again making substitutions of the form
$(\partial u/\partial t)\,dx = u\,(\partial u/\partial t)\,dt$, etc., give us

$$-\frac{1}{\rho}\frac{\partial p}{\partial x}\,dx + X\,dx = \frac{1}{g_c}\left(u\frac{\partial u}{\partial x}\,dx + v\frac{\partial v}{\partial x}\,dx + w\frac{\partial w}{\partial x}\,dx + u\frac{\partial u}{\partial t}\,dt\right)$$

$$-\frac{1}{\rho}\frac{\partial p}{\partial y}\,dy + Y\,dy = \frac{1}{g_c}\left(u\frac{\partial u}{\partial y}\,dy + v\frac{\partial v}{\partial y}\,dy + w\frac{\partial w}{\partial y}\,dy + v\frac{\partial v}{\partial y}\,dt\right)$$

$$-\frac{1}{\rho}\frac{\partial p}{\partial z}\,dz + Z\,dx = \frac{1}{g_c}\left(u\frac{\partial u}{\partial z}\,dz + v\frac{\partial v}{\partial z}\,dz + w\frac{\partial w}{\partial z}\,dz + w\frac{\partial w}{\partial t}\,dt\right)$$

Adding these equations and substituting total differentials as before, we have

$$-\frac{1}{\rho}\left(\frac{\partial p}{\partial x}\,dx + \frac{\partial p}{\partial y}\,dy + \frac{\partial p}{\partial z}\,dx\right) + X\,dx + Y\,dy + Z\,dz$$
$$= \frac{1}{g_c}\,(u\,du + v\,dv + w\,dw)$$

Then we add $-\,(\partial p/\partial t)\,dt/\rho$ to each side and note that $V^2 = u^2 + v^2 + w^2$,
so that

$$-\frac{1}{\rho}\,dp + X\,dx + Y\,dy + Z\,dz = d\left(\frac{V^2}{2g_c}\right) - \frac{1}{\rho}\frac{\partial p}{\partial t}\,dt \qquad \textbf{[4.11a]}$$

which is the same as the equation for flow along a streamline. We have now
demonstrated that the Euler equations can be reduced to a single, integrable
expression that holds throughout a field for irrotational flow as well as along
a streamline for any flow.

4.6 *Body force—gravity*

The effect of gravitational attraction between a fluid and the earth is always present; i.e., the weight of the fluid is a body force.

$$\text{body force per unit mass} = \frac{\text{weight}}{\text{mass}} = \frac{\rho g \, \Delta x \, \Delta y \, \Delta z / g_c}{\rho \, \Delta x \, \Delta y \, \Delta z} = \frac{g}{g_c}$$

expressed as pounds force per pound mass in our system of units.

Gravitation acts only in the vertical direction, which is the z direction if we take the xy plane as horizontal. With the customary representation of the positive z direction as upward, the positive z direction is vertically upward from the earth's surface, and the gravitational force is downward. Therefore, in Eq. 4.11, $X = Y = 0$, and $Z = -g/g_c$, and we may write

$$-\frac{1}{\rho} \, dp - \frac{g}{g_c} \, dz = d\left(\frac{V^2}{2g_c}\right) - \frac{1}{\rho} \frac{\partial p}{\partial t} \, dt \qquad [\textbf{4.11b}]$$

For steady flow, where $\partial/\partial t = 0$, the last term disappears, and the equation may be rewritten as

$$\frac{dp}{\rho} + \frac{g}{g_c} \, dz + \frac{V \, dV}{g_c} = 0 \qquad [\textbf{4.12}]$$

We shall call Eq. 4.12 the *simple Euler equation*, valid for steady flow along a streamline or for irrotational flow, with gravitation as the only body force. We might note that Eq. 4.12 is the hydrostatic equation with a motion term added. Thus we can obtain the hydrostatic equation from the more general Euler equation by putting $V = 0$ (or $V = \text{constant}$).

4.7 *Integration for constant density—the Bernoulli equation*

For the steady state, the last term of Eq. 4.11b disappears. The only remaining term to be converted into direct form for integration is the first one, dp/ρ. The simplest relationship, valid for liquids in nearly all cases and for gases in some, is to take ρ as constant. Then Eq. 4.11b becomes

$$-\frac{1}{\rho} \int dp - \frac{g}{g_c} \int dz = \int d\left(\frac{V^2}{2g_c}\right) + C$$

and

$$\frac{p}{\rho} + \frac{g}{g_c} z + \frac{V^2}{2g_c} = C = E_0 \qquad [\textbf{4.13a}]$$

Eq. 4.13a is the *Bernoulli* equation for the steady, irrotational flow of a constant-density fluid (steady, incompressible, ideal flow). The units of each component are foot-pounds force per pound mass, or energy per unit mass. The first energy term is that due to pressure, the second that due to elevation (gravity), and the third that due to velocity (kinetic). The Bernoulli equation then states that the sum of these specific-energy terms is constant for incompressible ideal flow, and this constant may be called the *total specific energy* for the flow field, E_0. (Note that steady flow will be assumed from now on unless otherwise stated.)

It is important to realize that Eq. 4.13a is an *energy* equation, although it has been derived from a *force* equation. The energy equation arose mathematically when the Euler equations were multiplied by "lengths" dx, dy, and dz, respectively, to yield forces acting over distances. Because the starting point was force, the energy quantities represent mechanical energy, and so the Bernoulli equation expresses the *conservation of "mechanical" energy* along a streamline or in irrotational flow of an incompressible fluid. Thermal energy may be transferred to or from the fluid during its passage, but if it does not affect the forces involved, its presence is immaterial. If the density is not constant, a thermal effect can change the force effects, i.e., mechanical energy is not conserved, as we shall see later.

The form of the Bernoulli equation can be modified, to give alternative interpretations that are very useful. Thus, if we divide through by g/g_c, we obtain

$$\frac{p}{\rho g/g_c} + z + \frac{V^2}{2g} = C' = h_0 \qquad [4.13b]$$

Each term now has units of *feet*. The factor $\rho g/g_c$ is the specific weight, γ, and the Bernoulli equation is often written as $p/\gamma + z + V^2/2g$. This form is of considerable utility in hydraulics, where invariably water (or at any rate, a liquid) is being considered and the expression "feet of head" is convenient. Thus we say that water in a tank 10 ft above the floor has a head of 10 ft with respect to the floor, or that a pump delivers a head of 50 ft of water. The *total head*, constant in ideal flow, is the sum of pressure head, elevation head, and velocity head. It is symbolized by h_0.

A third form results when we multiply Eq. 4.13a through by ρ, obtaining

$$p + \rho \frac{g}{g_c} z + \frac{\rho V^2}{2g_c} = C'' = p_0 \qquad [4.13c]$$

Now the units are those of *pressure*, with p the *static* pressure, $\rho(g/g_c)z$ the pressure due to elevation, and $\rho V^2/2g_c$ the *dynamic* pressure, the sum being the total pressure, p_0.

E_0, h_0, or p_0 is sometimes known as the *Bernoulli constant*. It retains its constant value along a given streamline in any steady flow, although it may vary from streamline to streamline. In irrotational flow, it remains constant throughout the whole field.

4.8   *Use of the Bernoulli equation—general*

The Bernoulli relation as given by Eqs. 4.13 applies only to steady, incompressible, ideal flow. No actual flows are ideal, as there are always viscous effects, but there are many situations in which the viscous effects are so small that they can be neglected. Later we shall learn how to apply the Bernoulli equation to the flow of a real fluid, taking into account appreciable losses, but for the present we shall concentrate on ideal flow.

Fig. 4.4 illustrates the general principle of use. Water flows upward from a pipe into a converging section, through a *throat* or passage of minimum area, and through a diverging section into a pipe of the same size as the entry pipe. The water has varying velocity, elevation, and pressure, as

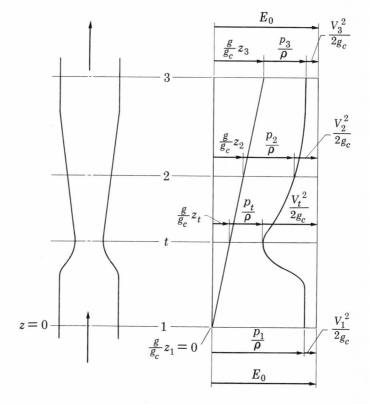

Figure 4.4

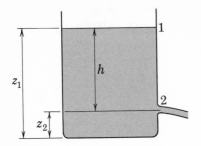

Figure 4.5

shown on the specific-energy diagram at the right. The total energy, E_0, is constant, but the three components making it up change at different stations along the duct. The datum level may be considered as station 1. Hence $z_1 = 0$, and thus at station 1

$$\frac{p_1}{\rho} + 0 + \frac{V_1{}^2}{2g_c} = E_0$$

At station t, the throat, the velocity has increased, because, from the continuity equation with constant density, $V_t = V_1 A_1/A_t$. Likewise, the elevation has increased to z_t, and so, with E_0 constant, the pressure must have decreased. Station 2 is an intermediate point in the diverging section, where velocity is decreasing but elevation is still increasing. In the final section, station 3, the velocity is the same as at entry, but the pressure has decreased owing to the increase in elevation.

Use of the Bernoulli equation together with the continuity equation provides solutions for many problems. A typical case is that in which the kinetic-energy quantities are known (from continuity and duct size) and the change in elevation is fixed, so that the change in pressure can be calculated. Torricelli's theorem, enunciated before Bernoulli's time, that the velocity of efflux from an orifice is proportional to the square root of the head is a consequence of the Bernoulli relationship. The exact conditions are as shown in Fig. 4.5.

The liquid is at atmospheric pressure at its free surface and at discharge, so that $p_1 = p_2$. At the free surface of elevation, z_1, the velocity is zero, and at the discharge elevation, z_2, the velocity is V_2. Therefore, with the Bernoulli equation,

$$\frac{p}{\rho g/g_c} + z + \frac{V^2}{2g} = \text{constant}$$

we have

$$\frac{p_1}{\rho g/g_c} + z_1 + \frac{V_1{}^2}{2g} = \frac{p_2}{\rho g/g_c} + z_2 + \frac{V_2{}^2}{2g}$$

Substituting the appropriate values for this case, noting that $p_1 = p_2$ and hence that these terms cancel, we obtain

$$z_1 + 0 = z_2 + \frac{V_2^2}{2g}$$

$$\frac{V_2^2}{2g} = z_1 - z_2 = h$$

or
$$V_2 = \sqrt{2gh} \qquad [4.14]$$

This is the velocity acquired by a free-falling body from a height, h. Eq. 4.14 can be argued from such dynamic principles.

The basic Bernoulli equation is simple, and its application leads to explanations of many common phenomena, such as the action of a siphon, the travel of a free jet, and so forth. Many of these are treated in problems for the student, and some will be discussed under real flow. One important application will be demonstrated here, however—that pertaining to flow around an immersed body.

It was seen earlier that a flow pattern in ideal flow could be established by the superposition of a number of simple flow elements. Because the flow is irrotational by definition, the Bernoulli equation can be used to find the pressure at any point. Flow around a circular cylinder will serve as an example.

4.9 *Pressure distribution around a circular cylinder*

Sect. 3.17 gave the solution for flow around a circular cylinder from the combination of uniform flow and a doublet. It is convenient in representing pressure distributions to use a *pressure coefficient*, C_p, defined as the difference between the local pressure, p, at any point and the pressure in the freestream (pressure at infinity), p_∞, divided by the dynamic pressure of the freestream; i.e.,

$$C_p = \frac{p - p_\infty}{\rho U_\infty^2 / 2g_c} \qquad [4.15]$$

This is a dimensionless coefficient, and so it applies for flows of any velocity and fluid density. According to the development of Sect. 3.17, the freestream velocity, U_∞, becomes U, and the local velocity anywhere in the flow is V, with the accompanying local pressure being p. With the change in elevation pressure regarded as negligible, the Bernoulli relation then becomes

$$p_\infty + \frac{\rho U^2}{2g_c} = p + \frac{\rho V^2}{2g_c}$$

Hence
$$p - p_\infty = \frac{\rho}{2g_c}\,(U^2 - V^2)$$

and

$$C_p = \frac{p - p_\infty}{U^2/2g_c} = 1 - \frac{V^2}{U^2} \qquad [4.16]$$

Eq. 4.16 for the pressure coefficient is valid everywhere in the flow field, and the velocity V can be calculated as shown in Sect. 3.17. To find the pressure distribution on the surface of the cylinder, we have $V = u_\theta$ and $r = a$, giving Eq. 3.44 of Sect. 3.17,

$$u_\theta = -2U \sin \theta$$

Therefore, $$C_p = 1 - \frac{4U^2 \sin^2 \theta}{U^2} = 1 - 4 \sin^2 \theta \qquad [4.17]$$

Substituting various values of θ, we obtain

θ	C_p	θ	C_p
0	1	$\pm 2\pi/3$	-2
$\pm \pi/6$	0	$\pm 3\pi/4$	-1
$\pm \pi/4$	-1	$\pm 5\pi/6$	0
$\pm \pi/3$	-2	π	1
$\pm \pi/2$	-3		

$\theta = 0$ and $\theta = \pi$ represent the stagnation points, where p is the total pressure. The flow accelerates on either side of the front stagnation stream-

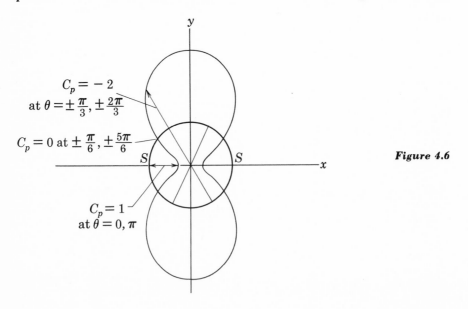

$C_p = -2$
at $\theta = \pm \dfrac{\pi}{3}, \pm \dfrac{2\pi}{3}$

$C_p = 0$ at $\pm \dfrac{\pi}{6}, \pm \dfrac{5\pi}{6}$

$C_p = 1$
at $\theta = 0, \pi$

Figure 4.6

line, the increased velocity resulting in a reduced pressure. The local pressure, p, is equal to the freestream pressure, p_∞, at $\theta = \pm \pi/6$ and $\theta = \pm 5\pi/6$ (30° on either side of the x axis). C_p then becomes negative; i.e., the pressure is reduced below the freestream pressure. The minimum pressure occurs at $\pm \pi/2$, i.e., along the y axis. This pressure distribution is plotted on a polar diagram in Fig. 4.6, with the cylinder itself as datum, i.e., $C_p = 0$. Positive values of C_p are then plotted along the radius of the circle *inward* from the circumference at the corresponding value of θ, with negative values plotted *outward* from the circumference. As the velocity distribution is symmetrical about either axis, the pressure distribution is also symmetrical, and there is no unbalanced pressure force on the cylinder in irrotational flow.

4.10   *Pressure distribution around a cylinder with circulation*

Sect. 3.18 demonstrates that the velocity at the surface of a cylinder with clockwise circulation is

$$V = u_\theta = -2U \sin \theta - \frac{\Gamma}{2\pi a}$$

The pressure coefficient is then

$$C_p = \frac{p - p_\infty}{\rho U^2/2g_c} = 1 - \frac{V^2}{U^2} = 1 - \frac{[-2U \sin \theta - (\Gamma/2\pi a)]^2}{U^2} \qquad [4.18]$$

The pressure distribution, like the velocity distribution, depends on the value of the circulation. Fig. 3.31 shows that the velocity pattern is symmetrical about the y axis and thus the pressure distribution, and hence the force distribution, is symmetrical. There is then no unbalanced force in the x direction. In the y direction, however, there is an unbalanced force, which can be calculated as follows.

The force due to pressure, $p\,dA$, at any point on a cylinder of radius a is $pa\,d\theta$ per unit length of cylinder (Fig. 4.7), and the component in the y direction is $pa \sin \theta\,d\theta$. The total force, F_y, is

$$F_y = -\int_0^{2\pi} pa \sin \theta\,d\theta$$

with the minus sign to allow for the condition that the force is in the negative y direction when θ is positive. Substituting for p from Eq. 4.18 and expanding the squared term gives

$$p = p_\infty + \frac{\rho U^2}{2g_c} - \frac{\rho}{2g_c}\left(4U^2 \sin^2 \theta + 4U \sin \theta \frac{\Gamma}{2\pi a} + \frac{\Gamma^2}{4\pi^2 a^2}\right)$$

Multiplying through by $a \sin \theta\,d\theta$ for the integral yields terms in $\sin \theta$,

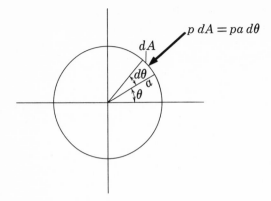

Figure 4.7

$\sin^2\theta$, and $\sin^3\theta$. The first and last of these are zero when integrated from 0 to 2π; hence there remains

$$F_y = \frac{\rho U\Gamma}{\pi g_c} \int_0^{2\pi} \sin^2\theta\, d\theta = \frac{\rho U\Gamma}{\pi g_c}\, [-\tfrac{1}{2}\cos\theta\sin\theta + \tfrac{1}{2}\theta]_0^{2\pi} = \frac{\rho U\Gamma}{g_c} \quad [\textbf{4.19}]$$

F_y is directed vertically upward (positive direction) for the flow pattern of U positive (left to right) and Γ clockwise. The force F_y is thus the *lift* per unit length of cylinder. Eq. 4.19 may be utilized for the calculation of the lift of an airfoil section. It will be noted that the lift of the circular cylinder is independent of the size of the cylinder. It can further be shown that the shape of the cylinder is unimportant in ideal flow and therefore that the lift of a right cylinder of any cross section is equal to $\rho U\Gamma/g_c$ per unit length (Sect. 8.15). The strength of the circulation is unspecified, and its value for any particular airfoil depends on an empirical observation and consideration of flow in a real fluid. The importance of the concepts of circulation and lift in ideal flow lies in the possibility of replacing an actual airfoil by some system of superposed ideal flows, which can be analyzed. The resulting picture, in conjunction with a knowledge of boundary-layer flow, can then be used for estimating the behavior of the actual airfoil. This subject will be discussed further after real-fluid flow has been studied.

4.11   *Measurement of head or pressure*

Of the three terms in the Bernoulli equation, Eq. 4.13, the middle one, that due to elevation, is obviously obtained by linear measurement of the change in elevation, $z_1 - z_2$. The sum of the static pressure and the dynamic pressure is readily measured in a forward-facing, open-ended tube connected to a manometer or pressure gage as shown in Fig. 4.8. The flow is brought to

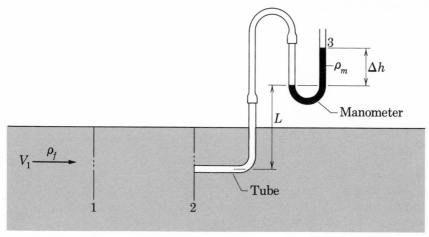

Figure 4.8

rest or stagnated at the mouth of the tube, and so application of the Bernoulli equation between 1 and 2, along a horizontal streamline, yields

$$p_1 + \frac{\rho_f V_1{}^2}{2g_c} = p_2 + 0$$

Using the hydrostatic equation between 2 and 3, with $p_3 = 0$, to determine gage pressure, we have

$$p_2 = \rho_f \frac{g}{g_c} L + \rho_m \frac{g}{g_c} \Delta h$$

where the subscripts f and m refer to the flowing fluid and the manometer fluid, respectively. Thus finally

$$p_1 + \frac{\rho_f V_1{}^2}{2g_c} = \frac{g}{g_c} (\rho_m \, \Delta h + \rho_f L) \qquad\qquad [4.20]$$

For a gas (where the elevation term is negligible) or for a liquid flowing horizontally, the sum of p and $\rho V^2/2g_c$ is often called the *total pressure* (or total head, if expressed in feet), although strictly this designation should be reserved for the sum of the three terms of the Bernoulli equation. The open-ended tube in Fig. 4.8 is known as a *Pitot* tube (after its inventor) or a *total-head* tube. It must be aligned along a streamtube, an arrangement implying uniform velocity across the flow area corresponding to the tube diameter and parallelism of the tube axis and the streamlines. In practice, this arrangement implies a small-diameter tube if there is any noticeable velocity gradient and also the absence of yaw or pitch. However, a few degrees of yaw or pitch can be tolerated, and in spite of the violent change of

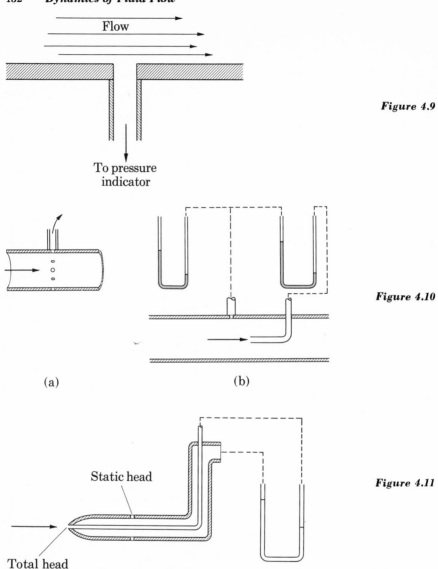

Figure 4.9

To pressure
indicator

(a)   (b)

Figure 4.10

Static head

Figure 4.11

Total head

flow pattern in the immediate neighborhood of the tube end, total-head readings can usually be made easily and accurately.

Static-pressure measurement alone, on the other hand, requires considerable care. Since no element of the dynamic pressure must be included, the piezometer opening must be parallel with the streamline, or, in other words, the axis of the pressure pickup must be perpendicular to the flow (Fig. 4.9). In a straight duct, a hole or ring of holes through the wall of the duct is the common arrangement, Fig. 4.10(a).

The dynamic pressure or velocity head can be determined by a combination of Pitot-tube and static-pressure measurement as shown in Fig. 4.10(b). The right-hand side of the manometer is subject to $p + \rho V^2/2g_c$, and the left-hand side is subject only to p. If the fluid is a gas, the static pressure can be measured by another manometer from the same pickup point for use in computation of the density. A combined instrument, known as a *Pitot-static* tube, is shown in Fig. 4.11. The side holes must be positioned exactly (various "standard" designs are available), since the flow at the nose and the flow around the stem cause opposite effects that must counteract one another if a true reading is to be obtained.

4.12   *The momentum theorem of fluid flow*

The Euler equations, derived from momentum principles applied to a particle of fixed mass and integrated over an irrotational flow field, can be used for the determination of the pressure forces on the boundaries of a finite system, but they are restricted to ideal flow. Another approach is necessary for information on the flow of a real fluid over a whole flow field. This is supplied by the momentum theorem. The approach is still general in that we are not seeking the detailed mechanism of real-fluid flow but are merely looking for a force–momentum relationship in terms of pressures and velocities, with the momentum restricted to linear momentum for the time being. Newton's second law of motion applies to a fixed quantity of matter or to a *system*, and we wish to apply it to a region in space through which fluid is flowing continuously, i.e., to a *control volume*, as in the treatment of mass flow in Chapter 3.

Consider a region or *control volume*, R, of arbitrary shape, bounded by an area or *control surface*, S, denoted by heavy lines (Fig. 4.12), through which fluid is flowing. The control volume may be moving in space, but for Newton's law to be applicable, the velocities and accelerations must be measured with respect to a space-fixed coordinate system, which in normal

Figure 4.12

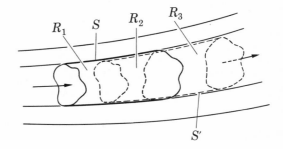

mechanics we approximate as the earth. We shall develop first the relationship for a *stationary* control volume, as this is straightforward, and then the relationship for a *moving* control volume with linear acceleration, which requires careful definitions.

At time $t = 0$, S encloses a given mass of fluid occupying region R. An instant of time, Δt, later, this same mass has moved to a new position in space bounded by surface S' and occupying region R', denoted by dashed lines. The primes indicate values at time $t = \Delta t$.

At time $t = 0$, the fluid is in region R, consisting of regions R_1 and R_2. The momentum of the fluid in R, $\mathbf{M}_R$, is the sum of the component momenta in R_1 and R_2; thus

$$\mathbf{M}_R = \mathbf{M}_{R_1} + \mathbf{M}_{R_2}$$

At time $t = \Delta t$, the fluid has moved to R', comprising regions R_2 and R_3. The momentum of this system of fixed mass at $t = \Delta t$ is $\mathbf{M}_{R'}$, the sum of the momentum in R_2, denoted by $\mathbf{M}_{R_2'}$ because conditions may have changed in time Δt, and the momentum in region R_3, $\mathbf{M}_{R_3'}$. Hence

$$\mathbf{M}_{R'} = \mathbf{M}_{R_2'} + \mathbf{M}_{R_3'}$$

The change in momentum, $\Delta\mathbf{M}_R$, of the mass originally contained in S is then

$$\Delta\mathbf{M}_R = \mathbf{M}_{R'} - \mathbf{M}_R = (\mathbf{M}_{R_2'} + \mathbf{M}_{R_3'}) - (\mathbf{M}_{R_1} + \mathbf{M}_{R_2})$$

which may be rearranged to give

$$\Delta\mathbf{M}_R = (\mathbf{M}_{R_2'} - \mathbf{M}_{R_2}) + (\mathbf{M}_{R_3'} - \mathbf{M}_{R_1})$$

The quantity $\mathbf{M}_{R_2'} - \mathbf{M}_{R_2}$ is the change in momentum of that part of the mass still in R, and the quantity $\mathbf{M}_{R_3'} - \mathbf{M}_{R_1}$ is the difference between the momentum that has passed out of S and the momentum that has passed into S in time Δt.

The rate of change of momentum in time Δt is then

$$\frac{\Delta\mathbf{M}_R}{\Delta t} = \frac{\mathbf{M}_{R_2'} - \mathbf{M}_{R_2}}{\Delta t} + \frac{\mathbf{M}_{R_3'} - \mathbf{M}_{R_1}}{\Delta t}$$

In the limit, as $\Delta t \to 0$, $S' \to S$, and the first term on the right-hand side becomes the *time rate of change of momentum of the fluid within R and bounded by S*. The momentum of an infinitesimal element is the product of its mass, $\rho\, dR$, and its velocity, $\mathbf{V}_R$, with the subscript R emphasizing that the properties are those of the fluid *within* the control region, R. The total momentum within R is then $\int_R \rho_R \mathbf{V}_R\, dR$, and in the limit,

$$\lim_{\Delta t \to 0} \frac{\mathbf{M}_{R_2'} - \mathbf{M}_{R_2}}{\Delta t} = \frac{d}{dt} \int_R \rho_R \mathbf{V}_R\, dR$$

The second term, $(\mathbf{M}_{R_3'} - \mathbf{M}_{R_1})/\Delta t$, becomes in the limit the *time rate of net efflux of momentum across the control surface*, S. This time rate is the summation of the products of mass flow rate, $d\dot{m}$, and velocity, $\mathbf{V}_S$, across each infinitesimal element of S; i.e., $\int_S \mathbf{V}_S \, d\dot{m}$. The mass flow rate is the product of density, velocity, and area, with the velocity normal to the area; i.e., $d\dot{m} = \rho \mathbf{V} \cdot d\mathbf{S}$. The quantity $d\dot{m}$ is a scalar referred to the control surface; in other words, the velocity, $\mathbf{V}_S$, for the flow rate is *relative* to S. In the case of a stationary control volume, this relative velocity is the absolute velocity, and no differentiation is necessary. However, when we come to a moving control volume, we must remember that the velocity in $\mathbf{V}_S \cdot d\mathbf{S}$ is relative to S and must so distinguish it. The net efflux rate is in the limit

$$\lim_{\Delta t \to 0} \frac{\mathbf{M}_{R_3'} - \mathbf{M}_{R_1}}{\Delta t} = \int_S (\rho_S \mathbf{V}_S) \mathbf{V}_S \cdot d\mathbf{S}$$

Subscript S emphasizes that the values of ρ and $\mathbf{V}$ are those of the fluid at the control surface, S.

By Newton's law, the time rate of change of momentum is equal to the sum of the forces on the mass of fluid within R and bounded by S, thus:

$$\Sigma \mathbf{F} = \frac{1}{g_c} \left(\frac{d}{dt} \int_R \rho_R \mathbf{V}_R \, dR + \int_S (\rho_S \mathbf{V}_S) \mathbf{V}_S \cdot d\mathbf{S} \right) \qquad [4.21]$$

This is the momentum equation for fluid flow applied to a control volume, R, with velocities and time rates of change taken with respect to the earth. The subscripts R and S on ρ and $\mathbf{V}$ are not really essential, as those on the integral signs indicate "over the region" and "over the surface," respectively, but it is helpful initially to retain them.

If the velocities and densities are uniform over the volume or surface for which the integration is made, the integrals are simple products. If there are only one entry station, 1, and one discharge station, 2, with uniform properties throughout, then

$$\int_S (\rho_S \mathbf{V}_S) \mathbf{V}_S \cdot d\mathbf{S} = \int_1^2 \mathbf{V}_S (\rho_S \mathbf{V}_S \cdot d\mathbf{S}) = \int_1^2 \mathbf{V}_S \, d\dot{m} = \dot{m}_2 \mathbf{V}_2 - \dot{m}_1 \mathbf{V}_1$$

and Eq. 4.21 becomes

$$\Sigma \mathbf{F} = \frac{1}{g_c} \left[\frac{d}{dt} (M \mathbf{V}_R) + \dot{m}_2 \mathbf{V}_2 - \dot{m}_1 \mathbf{V}_1 \right]$$

For steady flow, $(d/dt)(M\mathbf{V}_R) = 0$, and $\dot{m}_2 = \dot{m}_1 = \dot{m}$, so that the equation reduces to

$$\Sigma \mathbf{F} = \frac{\dot{m}}{g_c} (\mathbf{V}_2 - \mathbf{V}_1) \qquad [4.22]$$

where V_1 and V_2 are the absolute velocities of the fluid entering and leaving the control surface, respectively.

ΣF is the total of the forces acting on the control volume. For any actual situation we can prescribe the control surface and thereby simplify the problem considerably. In the first place, we can choose the limits of the control surface as the limits of the fluid only, i.e., excluding any solid boundaries, such as a duct, or any solid body immersed in the fluid, such as an aircraft wing or a turbine blade. The alternative is to take the control surface to include solid boundaries or a solid body immersed in the fluid.

The momentum equation is used in many ways, and we shall demonstrate these two major applications: first, to find the force on the enclosing duct or immersed body when information is available about the state and behavior of the fluid; second, to find the state and behavior of the fluid when all the forces can be specified. Looking at the former, consider the generalized case of Fig. 4.13(a), in which fluid is entering and leaving an enclosure. We need know nothing in detail about what happens *inside* the enclosure if we know the state of the fluid at entry and exit. The enclosure is simply a "black box," which may be only a length of straight pipe or may be as complex as a complete turbojet engine.

Let us choose the control surface as the fluid boundary. Then S is the inside surface of the duct and planes across the entry and exit sections, 1 and

Figure 4.13

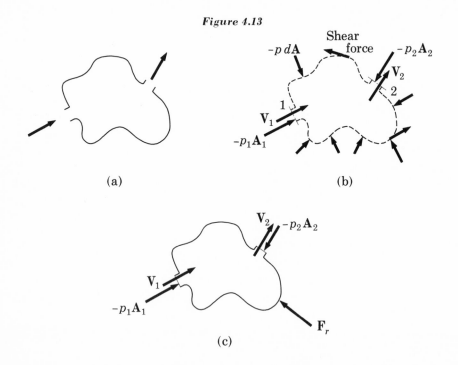

(a)

(b)

(c)

2, as shown in Fig. 4.13(b). For simplicity, suppose that the velocities and pressures at the entry and exit sections are uniform so that simple products rather than integrals can be used. The control surface at 1 and 2 can be made normal to velocities $\mathbf{V}_1$ and $\mathbf{V}_2$ so that no shear forces act on these sections of S. The surface forces on the fluid are then $-p_1\mathbf{A}_1$ and $-p_2\mathbf{A}_2$, at the entry and exit, respectively, plus the pressure and shear forces, $\int p\ dA_i$ and $\int \tau\ dA_i$, exerted by the duct on the fluid internally. In most instances it is these latter forces that we do not know, and so we can only denote them by a resultant force, $\mathbf{F}_i$. There may also be a body force acting on the fluid, $\mathbf{F}_b$.

The sum of the forces is then

$$\Sigma \mathbf{F} = -p_1\mathbf{A}_1 - p_2\mathbf{A}_2 + \mathbf{F}_b + \mathbf{F}_i \qquad [4.23]$$

This is equated to the two momentum terms of Eq. 4.21. For steady flow and uniform velocities, the momentum flux across the control surface becomes $\dot{m}(\mathbf{V}_2 - \mathbf{V}_1)$, and the rate of change of momentum in the control volume is zero. Hence we have

$$-p_1\mathbf{A}_1 - p_2\mathbf{A}_2 + \mathbf{F}_b + \mathbf{F}_i = \frac{\dot{m}}{g_c}(\mathbf{V}_2 - \mathbf{V}_1)$$

and

$$\mathbf{F}_i = \frac{\dot{m}}{g_c}(\mathbf{V}_2 - \mathbf{V}_1) + p_1\mathbf{A}_1 + p_2\mathbf{A}_2 - \mathbf{F}_b \qquad [4.24]$$

For the assumed conditions, all the quantities on the right-hand side are known, and the result is $\mathbf{F}_i$, the resultant force on the *fluid* inside the control volume. By Newton's third law this must be equal and opposite to the force on the *duct*, $\mathbf{F}_d$, due to the passage of the fluid through it; i.e., $\mathbf{F}_d = -\mathbf{F}_i$. Thus the force on the duct has been found, and nothing needs to be known about the processes inside it. The relationships have been formulated in vectors here. For an actual situation they would be expressed in scalar coordinates. With the usual conventions as to direction, the various terms would be given signs, $\mathbf{F}_i$, if unknown, being arbitrarily made positive. The resultant sign of the right-hand side of the equation determines the direction of $\mathbf{F}_i$.

Often it is desirable to include the solid boundaries in the control volume. For the case of Fig. 4.13, the control surface is then *outside* the duct and areas $\mathbf{A}_1$ and $\mathbf{A}_2$. Now the internal forces exerted on the fluid by the duct are balanced by the equal and opposite forces exerted by the fluid on the duct. There must, however, be an external force, $\mathbf{F}_e$, on the duct itself to hold it in place, and this is equal and opposite to the sum of the pressure, body, and momentum terms. So for equilibrium, $\mathbf{F}_e$ must be included as shown in Fig. 4.13(c). We can write an equation similar to Eq. 4.24, as

$$\mathbf{F}_e = \frac{\dot{m}}{g_c}(\mathbf{V}_2 - \mathbf{V}_1) + p_1\mathbf{A}_1 + p_2\mathbf{A}_2 - \mathbf{F}_b \qquad [4.25]$$

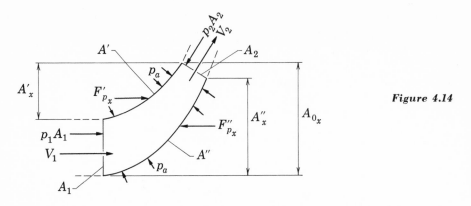

Figure 4.14

and obtain the resultant force directly. Once again the direction of $\mathbf{F}_e$ is determined by the resultant sign of the right-hand side of the equation. Note that $\mathbf{F}_e$ is the external force required to hold the solid boundary stationary and that it is accordingly in the opposite direction to the force on the solid boundary.

It should be noted that in each case the resultant force on the duct is due to the passage of the fluid through the control surface. The pressures p_1 and p_2 at A_1 and A_2 are then *absolute* pressures, and $\mathbf{F}$ is an absolute resultant force. The *net* force on the enclosure is due to $\mathbf{F}$ *and* any other known external forces. For a moving control volume, these forces would be due to pressure and shear, denoted by $\int p_e \, dA_e$ and $\int \tau_e \, dA_e$, respectively, and together usually called *drag*.

For a stationary control volume with a uniform atmospheric pressure, p_a, the shear force is zero, and the pressure force is $\int p_a \, dA_e$. This term reduces to a single expression, as can be seen from the following two-dimensional case.

In Fig. 4.14, atmospheric pressure, p_a, acts uniformly on the exterior of the duct. With the x direction as an example, this pressure force on A' is $p_a A'_x$ and on A'' is $-p_a A''_x$, giving a resultant, F_{p_x},

$$F_{p_x} = p_a(A'_x - A''_x)$$

From the geometry of the figure,

$$A'_x = A_0 - A_1$$
and
$$A''_x = A_0 - A_2 \sin \theta$$

Therefore, $A'_x - A''_x = (A_0 - A_1) - (A_0 - A_2 \sin \theta) = A_2 \sin \theta - A_1$

Hence $$F_{p_x} = p_a(A_2 \sin \theta - A_1)$$

From Eq. 4.25 the resultant absolute force, F_{e_x}, due to the fluid traversing the duct (omitting any body force) is

$$F_{e_x} = \frac{\dot{m}}{g_c} (V_2 \cos\theta - V_1) - p_1 A_1 - (-p_2 A_2 \sin\theta)$$

$$= \frac{\dot{m}}{g_c} (V_2 \cos\theta - V_1) - p_1 A_1 + p_2 A_2 \sin\theta \qquad [4.26]$$

with p_1 and p_2 as absolute pressure. The net force, F_{n_x}, due to the fluid inside and the atmospheric pressure outside is then

$$F_{n_x} = F_{e_x} - F_{p_x}$$

$$= \frac{\dot{m}}{g_c} (V_2 \cos\theta - V_1) - p_1 A_1 + p_2 A_2 \sin\theta - p_a(A_2 \sin\theta - A_1)$$

$$= \frac{\dot{m}}{g_c} (V_2 \cos\theta - V_1) - (p_1 - p_a)A_1 + (p_2 - p_a)A_2 \sin\theta \qquad [4.27]$$

Comparing Eqs. 4.26 and 4.27 for F_{e_x} and F_{n_x}, the absolute and net resultant forces, we see that the net force can be obtained directly if *gage* pressures are used for p_1 and p_2. Thus for surroundings at atmospheric pressure, the pressures on the entry and exit areas are taken as gage pressures. For a fluid entering or discharging at atmospheric pressure, p_1 or p_2 as a gage pressure is zero. The use of gage pressures is a considerable simplification for most problems, and it is not often that the external pressure is non-uniform. When it is, it is usually handled separately as a problem of drag.

Although this discussion of the choice of the control surface, the resultant forces on the fluid and on the body, and the formulation of the pressure forces has been somewhat lengthy, the procedure it introduces will seem straightforward after a few problems have been worked. An understanding of the details of the analysis is essential.

For a *moving* control volume, the control region must include the whole moving system, because if the structure and internal apparatus are in motion, force is necessary for a rate of change of their momentum just as much as for a rate of change of the fluid momentum. The analysis remains the same, with the momenta $\mathbf{M}_{R_2}$ and $\mathbf{M}_{R_2'}$ referring not only to the fluid but to all mass in the control region. The velocity $\mathbf{V}_R$ in the first integral relationship is again an absolute velocity, but $\mathbf{V}_S$ must be examined carefully. One $\mathbf{V}_S$ is the velocity in the general momentum expression $M\mathbf{V}$. However, the other $\mathbf{V}_S$ is the velocity associated with the mass flow rate, $\dot{m}$, and, as mentioned previously, $\dot{m}$ refers to the flow at the control surface. Hence this $\mathbf{V}_S$ will be denoted by $\mathbf{V}_{rs}$, meaning velocity relative to S. Eq. 4.21 thus becomes

$$\Sigma\mathbf{F} = \frac{1}{g_c} \left(\frac{d}{dt} \int_R \rho_R \mathbf{V}_R \, dR + \int_S (\rho_S \mathbf{V}_S) \mathbf{V}_{rs} \cdot d\mathbf{S} \right) \qquad [4.28a]$$

which is valid for a control volume having a linear motion with respect to the origin of the fixed coordinate system (the earth)

The equation can be evaluated more readily and put into a more convenient form if the vector relationship of the absolute and relative velocities is utilized. If A is moving with an absolute velocity $\mathbf{U}$ and the velocity of B relative to A is $\mathbf{V}_r$, then the absolute velocity, $\mathbf{V}$, is the vector sum of $\mathbf{U}$ and $\mathbf{V}_r$ (see Sect. 3.3),

$$\mathbf{V} = \mathbf{U} + \mathbf{V}_r$$

For Eq. 4.28a, $\mathbf{V}_R = \mathbf{U} + \mathbf{V}_{r_R}$, and $\mathbf{V}_S = \mathbf{U} + \mathbf{V}_{rs}$. Making these substitutions, we obtain

$$\Sigma \mathbf{F} = \frac{1}{g_c}\left(\frac{d}{dt}\int_R \rho_R(\mathbf{U} + \mathbf{V}_{r_R})\,dR + \int_S \rho_S(\mathbf{U} + \mathbf{V}_{rs})\mathbf{V}_{rs}\cdot d\mathbf{S}\right)$$

with the subscripts R and S on the relative velocities for emphasis. Expanding the terms under the integral signs gives us

$$\Sigma \mathbf{F} = \frac{1}{g_c}\left(\frac{d}{dt}\int_R \rho_R\mathbf{U}\,dR + \frac{d}{dt}\int_R \rho_R\mathbf{V}_{r_R}\,dR + \int_S (\rho_S\mathbf{U})\mathbf{V}_{rs}\cdot d\mathbf{S}\right.$$
$$\underset{1}{} \qquad\qquad \underset{2}{} \qquad\qquad \underset{3}{}$$
$$\left. + \int_S (\rho_S\mathbf{V}_{rs})\mathbf{V}_{rs}\cdot d\mathbf{S}\right) \qquad [4.28b]$$
$$\underset{4}{}$$

Each term has been given a number for ease of presentation, and each will now be analyzed.

Term 1. Since the control-volume velocity, $\mathbf{U}$, is independent of the extent of the region R, this term may be expanded again, thus:

$$\frac{d}{dt}\int_R \rho_R\mathbf{U}\,dR = \frac{d\mathbf{U}}{dt}\int_R \rho_R\,dR + \mathbf{U}\int_R \frac{\partial}{\partial t}\rho_R\,dR$$

The first term on the right-hand side is the product of the acceleration, $d\mathbf{U}/dt$, of the control volume and the instantaneous mass of the material in the control volume, $\int \rho_R\,dR$, which we shall designate as M_R. The second term on the right-hand side may have the order of integration and differentiation reversed because the region R is independent of time. Therefore,

$$\mathbf{U}\int_R \frac{\partial}{\partial t}\rho_R\,dR = \mathbf{U}\frac{d}{dt}\int_R \rho_R\,dR$$

which is interpreted as the product of control-volume velocity, $\mathbf{U}$, and the time rate of increase of mass in the control volume.

Term 2. Writing this term in the form

$$\frac{d}{dt}\int_R \rho_R\mathbf{V}_{r_R}\,dR = \frac{d}{dt}\int_R \mathbf{V}_{r_R}(\rho_R\,dR)$$

we see that it is the time rate of change of the momentum within the control volume with respect to the control volume. Thus fluid may be accelerating in the region with respect to the control surface.

Term 3. Again the velocity $\mathbf{U}$ is independent of the surface, and so the term may be written as

$$\int_S (\rho_S \mathbf{U}) \mathbf{V}_{rs} \cdot d\mathbf{S} = \mathbf{U} \int_S \rho_S \mathbf{V}_{rs} \cdot d\mathbf{S}$$

The expression under the integral sign is the net rate of efflux of mass across the control surface, and the whole term is the product of this and the control-volume velocity.

Term 4. This term is the net rate of efflux of momentum at the control surface relative to the control surface.

The sum of terms 1, 2, 3, and 4 in the expanded and revised versions just discussed is

$$M_R \frac{d\mathbf{U}}{dt} + \mathbf{U} \frac{d}{dt} \int_R \rho_R \, dR + \frac{d}{dt} \int_R \mathbf{V}_{r_R} \rho_R \, dR + \mathbf{U} \int_S \rho_S \mathbf{V}_{rs} \cdot d\mathbf{S}$$
$$+ \int_S (\rho_S \mathbf{V}_{rs}) \mathbf{V}_{rs} \cdot d\mathbf{S}$$

The sum of the second and fourth terms is

$$\mathbf{U} \left(\frac{d}{dt} \int_R \rho_R \, dR + \int_S \rho_S \mathbf{V}_{rs} \cdot d\mathbf{S} \right)$$

The terms in parentheses are the time rate of increase of mass in the control volume and the net rate of efflux of mass across the control surface. By the continuity principle, their sum is zero (Eq. 3.5). With these terms eliminated, Eq. 4.28 can be formulated as

$$\Sigma \mathbf{F} = \frac{1}{g_c} \left(M_R \frac{d\mathbf{U}}{dt} + \frac{d}{dt} \int_R \rho_R \mathbf{V}_{r_R} \, dR + \int_S (\rho_S \mathbf{V}_{rs}) \mathbf{V}_{rs} \cdot d\mathbf{S} \right) \quad [\textbf{4.29}]$$

This is Newton's second law applied to a moving control volume with a linear velocity, $\mathbf{U}$, with respect to the earth. The first term in parentheses is the product of the mass of the whole control volume (solid and fluid) and the acceleration of this mass. The other two terms are similar to those obtained for the stationary control volume, but with the velocities *relative* to the volume and the surface, respectively. It will be noted that applying Eq. 4.29 to a stationary control volume, so that $\mathbf{U} = 0$, $\mathbf{V}_{r_R} = \mathbf{V}_R$, and $\mathbf{V}_{rs} = \mathbf{V}_S$, results in Eq. 4.21, as it should. A control volume moving with *constant* velocity, $d\mathbf{U}/dt = 0$, yields a relationship similar to Eq. 4.21 but in terms of *relative* velocity. The advantage of Eq. 4.29 over Eq. 4.21 is that the velocities can be evaluated more immediately and that, if the forces $\Sigma \mathbf{F}$ are known and the state of the fluid entering and leaving the control surface is known (e.g., for a propulsion engine with steady flow), the acceleration, $d\mathbf{U}/dt$, of a complete vehicle may be calculated. From this can be found the velocity after a finite time interval and, finally, the distance traveled. Some typical and important applications will now be demonstrated.

4.13   *The momentum equation applied to duct flow*

Fig. 4.15 shows a stationary duct through which fluid is flowing at a steady rate. The shape of the duct is quite irregular to emphasize the general nature of the analysis, although body force is omitted. The problem is to find the force on the duct required to keep it in place. Results from practical examples of this system would include the forces on piping systems, nozzles, and complete turbojet engines on the ground.

The control surface is taken as the outside walls of the duct and areas A_1 and A_2 perpendicular to the entry and exit velocities, $\mathbf{V}_1$ and $\mathbf{V}_2$. These velocities are one-dimensional in that they are uniform across A_1 and A_2. The fluid pressures p_1 and p_2 are taken with respect to the outside, or ambient, pressure; i.e., they are gage pressures for uniform atmospheric pressure. They are likewise taken as uniform across A_1 and A_2, as are the corresponding densities, ρ_1 and ρ_2.

Since the duct is stationary, $d\mathbf{U}/dt = 0$, and the flow is steady; thus $d/dt \int \rho \mathbf{V}_R \, dR = 0$. We can therefore, use Eq. 4.21 in the form

$$\Sigma \mathbf{F} = \frac{1}{g_c} \int_S (\rho \mathbf{V}_S) \mathbf{V}_S \cdot d\mathbf{S} \qquad [4.30]$$

The system is two-dimensional, or with no unbalanced properties in the z direction, so that components are taken in the x and y directions.

The forces acting on the control surface are the fluid pressures p_1 and p_2 on A_1 and A_2 and an external force, $\mathbf{F}_e$, needed to keep the duct stationary under the action of these pressures and the rate of change of momentum.

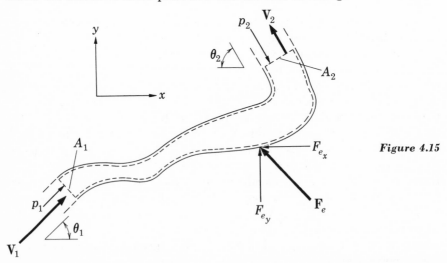

Figure 4.15

The figure shows this external force together with its components, F_{e_x} and F_{e_y}. Although it is helpful to be able to predict the direction of F_{e_x} or F_{e_y}, it is not essential. If the direction is assumed to be positive and the numerical answer is negative, then the direction is known to be negative, and vice versa. With the customary sign convention, then, the forces in the x and y directions are

$$F_x = p_1 A_1 \cos \theta_1 + p_2 A_2 \cos \theta_2 - F_{e_x}$$
$$F_y = p_1 A_1 \sin \theta_1 - p_2 A_2 \sin \theta_2 + F_{e_y}$$

The momentum fluxes, with uniform values of ρ and V and with V normal to A_1 and A_2, are

for the x direction, $\quad \rho_2 V_2 A_2(- V_2 \cos \theta_2) - \rho_1 V_1 A_1(V_1 \cos \theta_1)$
for the y direction, $\quad \rho_2 V_2 A_2(V_2 \sin \theta_2) - \rho_1 V_1 A_1(V_1 \sin \theta_1)$

Equating ΣF with a momentum flux according to Eq. 4.21 gives us

$$p_1 A_1 \cos \theta_1 + p_2 A_2 \cos \theta_2 - F_{e_x} = \frac{- \rho_2 V_2{}^2 A_2 \cos \theta_2 - \rho_1 V_1{}^2 A_1 \cos \theta_1}{g_c}$$

Therefore,

$$F_{e_x} = p_1 A_1 \cos \theta_1 + p_2 A_2 \cos \theta_2 + \frac{\rho_2}{g_c} V_2{}^2 A_2 \cos \theta_2 + \frac{\rho_1}{g_c} V_1{}^2 A_1 \cos \theta_1$$

Similarly,

$$p_1 A_1 \sin \theta_1 - p_2 A_2 \sin \theta_2 + F_{e_y} = \frac{\rho_2 V_2{}^2 A_2 \sin \theta_2 - \rho_1 V_1{}^2 A_1 \sin \theta_1}{g_c}$$

Therefore,

$$F_{e_y} = - p_1 A_1 \sin \theta_1 + p_2 A_2 \sin \theta_2 + \frac{\rho_2}{g_c} V_2{}^2 A_2 \sin \theta_2 - \frac{\rho_1}{g_c} V_1{}^2 A_1 \sin \theta_1$$

F_{e_x} and F_{e_y} are then the external forces required to keep the duct in place, with their directions, assumed negative for F_{e_x} and positive for F_{e_y}, determined by the resultant signs of the right-hand sides of their equations. Since the flow is steady, we could write the momentum terms as $\rho_1 V_1 A_1 = \dot{m}_1 = \dot{m}_2 = \dot{m} = \rho_2 V_2 A_2$. Then the results could be expressed as

$$F_{e_x} = p_1 A_1 \cos \theta_1 + p_2 A_2 \cos \theta_2 + \frac{\dot{m}}{g_c} (V_2 \cos \theta_2 - V_1 \cos \theta_1)$$

and $\quad F_{e_y} = - p_1 A_1 \sin \theta_1 + p_2 A_2 \sin \theta_1 + \frac{\dot{m}}{g_c} (V_2 \sin \theta_2 - V_1 \sin \theta_1)$

Now let us look at a moving control volume exemplified by a rocket in vertical flight (Fig. 4.16). A rocket contains all its propellants internally in solid or liquid form. Since it requires no air, there is no intake duct. The

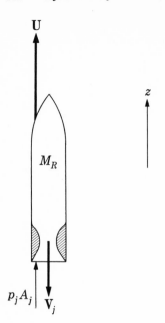

Figure 4.16

control surface is taken as the outside of the rocket vehicle itself and the area of the nozzle exit. The direction of flight is vertically upward, and the exit gases are directed vertically downward, both along the axis of the rocket. For this moving control volume we use Eq. 4.29,

$$\Sigma \mathbf{F} = \frac{1}{g_c} \left(\underset{1}{M_R \frac{d\mathbf{U}}{dt}} + \underset{2}{\frac{d}{dt} \int_R \rho_R \mathbf{V}_{r_R} \, dR} + \underset{3}{\int_S (\rho_S \mathbf{V}_{r_S}) \mathbf{V}_{r_S} \cdot d\mathbf{S}} \right) \qquad [\mathbf{4.29}]$$

We shall examine the terms separately, noting the direction by signs.

Term 1. We are concerned only with the z direction, assuming axial symmetry. There is undoubtedly a body force due to gravity in this case if the rocket is anywhere near the earth's surface. For a vertical trajectory, this is the weight, and so $F_b = -M_R g/g_c$. Usually the exhaust gas is "under-expanded" (Chapter 7), which means roughly that the nozzle is not large enough to reduce the pressure developed in the combustion chamber to atmospheric pressure. Calling the pressure at the nozzle outlet p_j, where j indicates jet discharge, and making it absolute pressure, we obtain for the pressure force, F_p,

$$F_p = (p_j - p_a) A_j$$

where p_a is atmospheric pressure and A_j is nozzle-outlet area. This force is left in terms of $p_j - p_a$ here, because in vertical ascent the gage pressure changes as the atmospheric pressure, p_a, varies with altitude. There is also a force on the exterior of the rocket due to drag, or air resistance, but at this stage we can only designate it by a symbol, $-F_D$. The sum of the forces is then

$$\Sigma F = - M_R \frac{g}{g_c} + (p_j - p_a) A_j - F_D$$

Term 2. This term is the system acceleration. M_R is the mass of all the material in the control volume, and as it includes the propellants that are continually being used up, it is the instantaneous mass.

Term 3. This term is the rate of change of momentum in the control volume. $\int \rho_R \, dR$ is the instantaneous mass within the control volume, consisting on the one hand of solid or liquid material, such as vehicle structure, stored propellants, and payload, and on the other hand of gases in the combustion chamber and nozzle. The velocity V_{r_R} is that relative to the control volume. For the solid or liquid material it is zero. For gases it has a finite value, but if the flow is steady, its time rate of change with respect to R is zero. Even for an unsteady flow, the mass of gas at any instant is usually very small compared to the mass of solid and liquid material and can be ignored. Thus

$$\frac{d}{dt} \int_R \rho_R V_{r_R} \, dR = 0$$

Term 4. This term is the momentum flux. With no inlet area and a uniform flow of gas at the exit,

$$\int_S (\rho_S V_{rs}) V_{rs} \cdot dS = - \rho_j V_j{}^2 A_j = - \dot{m}_p V_j$$

where $\dot{m}_p$ is the mass rate of flow of the propellants, $\rho_j V_j A_j$. The minus sign is inserted because the mass rate of flow is a scalar and V_j, jet velocity, is in the negative direction.

Substitution of these terms in Eq. 4.29 yields

$$- M_R \frac{g}{g_c} + (p_j - p_a) A_j - F_D = \frac{M_R}{g_c} \frac{dU}{dt} - \frac{\dot{m}_p V_j}{g_c} \qquad [\textbf{4.31a}]$$

If the propulsion characteristics are known, i.e., $\dot{m}_p$, V_j, p_j, and A_j, together with an estimate of F_D, then the acceleration, dU/dt, can be found at a given time for an instantaneous mass, M_R.

Eq. 4.31a can be rearranged to give

$$\left[\frac{\dot{m}_p V_j}{g_c} + (p_j - p_a) A_j \right] - \left(M_R \frac{g}{g_c} + F_d \right) = \frac{M_R}{g_c} \frac{dU}{dt} \qquad [\textbf{4.31b}]$$

The first term in parentheses is called the *thrust* of the rocket. The second term represents the resistance to motion due to drag and gravity. The difference is equal to the product of the mass and acceleration of the vehicle. Further examination of this "rocket equation" will be made in Chapter 9.

4.14   *The momentum equation applied to freestream flow*

We have just studied the application of the momentum theorem to duct flow, in which a given amount of fluid is enclosed by walls. Now let us consider the case of a body immersed in an infinite stream of fluid, the body being an airfoil or a projectile as shown in Fig. 4.17(a). The flow is assumed to be steady.

We want to measure the drag or resistance of the projectile. With a real fluid, the flow pattern is very disordered at the rear end, resulting in a wake of turbulent, eddying flow. The larger eddies quickly die down through the action of viscous shear, leaving a region of lower velocity, as shown in Fig. 4.17(b). Theoretically the flow pattern induced by the body extends to infinity, but practically the streamlines ahead and to the side are disturbed for only a few diameters around the body. Thus we may choose an outer

Figure 4.17

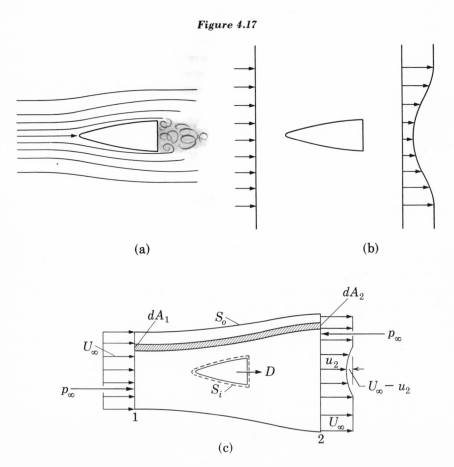

(a)

(b)

(c)

control surface, S_o, bounded laterally by streamlines and with the ends normal to streamlines, and an inner control surface, S_i, around the body, as in Fig. 4.17(c). The upstream surface of S_o, A_1, is at freestream pressure, p_∞, and the velocity normal to it is the freestream velocity, U_∞. The downstream surface, A_2, is located near enough to the body that the velocity deficiency of the wake is included but far enough downstream that the pressure has returned to the freestream value. The lateral surfaces of S_o are sufficiently far removed from the body that again the pressure on the boundary is the freestream value. Therefore, the pressure, and hence the density, is the same over the whole of control surface S_o. No momentum crosses the lateral boundaries of S_o, since they are streamlines, and none crosses S_i, since it is a solid body. With no resultant pressure or shear stresses on S_o, the only remaining force is that due to pressure and shear stresses on S_i, i.e., the drag, D. The direction of the drag is clearly downstream, and so for the momentum equation, $\Sigma F =$ the force on the fluid or the force required to hold the body in place $= -D$. For this case of a stationary control volume with steady flow, Eq. 4.21 becomes

$$\Sigma \mathbf{F} = \frac{1}{g_c} \int_S (\rho \mathbf{V}_S) \mathbf{V}_S \cdot d\mathbf{S}$$

or
$$-D = \frac{1}{g_c}\left[\int_{A_2} u_2(\rho u_2 \, dA_2) - \int_{A_1} U_\infty(\rho U_\infty \, dA_1) \right]$$

For continuity, $\int \rho u_2 \, dA_2 = \int \rho U_\infty \, dA_1$, and if we make the further assumption that the flow in the control region is divided into streamtubes then

$$-D = \frac{\rho}{g_c} \int_{A_2} u_2(u_2 - U_\infty) \, dA_2$$

and
$$D = \frac{\rho}{g_c} \int_{A_2} u_2(U_\infty - u_2) \, dA_2 \qquad [4.32]$$

Thus a velocity traverse across the wake extending laterally out to a region where the velocity defect has disappeared is sufficient to obtain the drag on the body.

4.15   *The thrust function*

For uniform, steady flow across a given area, the momentum equation gives rise to a pressure force, pA, and a momentum flux, $\rho V^2 A / g_c$. The combination occurs so frequently that the sum is sometimes called the *thrust* or *impulse function*, F_T. Accordingly, we may write

$$F_T = pA + \frac{\rho V^2}{g_c} A \qquad [4.33]$$

For flow in a straight duct in the positive x direction, the net force on the fluid or required to hold the duct in place is equal to the difference between the thrust function at discharge and that at entry, thus:

$$F_i = F_e = \left(p_2 A_2 + \frac{\rho_2 V_2{}^2 A_2}{g_c} \right) - \left(p_1 A_1 + \frac{\rho_1 V_1{}^2 A_1}{g_c} \right) \qquad [4.34a]$$

or

$$F_e = F_{T_2} - F_{T_1}$$

For the special situation of frictionless flow in a constant-area duct, there can be no resultant force, and so $F_e = 0$, and $F_{T_1} = F_{T_2}$; i.e., the thrust function is constant. Hence

$$p_2 A_2 + \frac{\rho_2 V_2{}^2 A_2}{g_c} = p_1 A_1 + \frac{\rho_1 V_1{}^2 A_1}{g_c} \qquad [4.34b]$$

The state of the fluid in a constant-area duct can be changed, for example, by heat transfer or, as we shall see later, by a sudden, discontinuous effect known as *shock*. With no net force, constancy of the thrust function is a useful condition in the analysis of flow before and after the state change.

4.16   *Angular momentum*

The discussion so far has been limited to *linear* momentum, i.e., purely translational motion. For rotating systems, we must consider *angular* momentum or *moment* of momentum. The basic law of mechanics states that the sum of the moments of the external forces acting on a system is equal to the rate of change of moment of momentum of the system when both are taken about the same point.

For the control-volume approach, we can use exactly the same type of analysis that we used for linear momentum, substituting moment of force for force and moment of momentum for (linear) momentum. The moment of force about a point is given by $\mathbf{F} \times \mathbf{r}$, the cross product of force $\mathbf{F}$ and position vector $\mathbf{r}$, where $\mathbf{r}$ is given by the line between the point and the line of action of $\mathbf{F}$. The moment of momentum is similarly given by $\mathbf{M} \times \mathbf{r}$, and so the terms are the same as in the momentum equation, Eq. 4.21, except that this time they are expressed as cross products with $\mathbf{r}$; i.e.,

$$\Sigma \mathbf{F} \times \mathbf{r} = \frac{1}{g_c} \left[\frac{d}{dt} \int_R \rho \mathbf{V} \times \mathbf{r} \, dR + \int_S \rho (\mathbf{V} \times \mathbf{r}) \mathbf{V} \cdot d\mathbf{S} \right] \qquad [4.35]$$

This is the angular-momentum equation for a stationary control volume, to which the analysis is confined. In practice we are concerned with solid boundaries rotating at constant velocity, and the velocity $\mathbf{V}$ in the equation $\rho\mathbf{V}\cdot d\mathbf{S} = d\dot{m}$ is the fluid velocity relative to the rotor. This is analogous to $\mathbf{V}_{rs}$ in the situation for linear momentum. Hereafter we shall consider only steady flow, so that the first momentum term in Eq. 4.35 disappears.

The major application of this relationship is to turbomachinery, i.e., pumps, compressors, and turbines, in which case the vector equation may be reduced to a single scalar equation with all velocities in the plane of rotation. We then have rotation about an axis rather than about a point. The scalar moment of force is Fr_n, with r_n the shortest distance between the axis of rotation and the line of action of the force. Fr_n is called the *torque*, T. The flux of angular momentum is $\int \rho r_n V\mathbf{V}\cdot d\mathbf{S}$; hence

$$\Sigma T = \frac{1}{g_c}\int_S \rho r_n V\mathbf{V}\cdot d\mathbf{S}$$

With uniform properties across the control surface and with r_n having a single mean value for all the fluid entering and another for discharge, as is commonly assumed, then

$$\Sigma T = \frac{\dot{m}}{g_c}\,(r_{n_2}V_2 - r_{n_1}V_1) \qquad\qquad [\textbf{\textit{4.36}}]$$

The term $r_n V$ is the product of *absolute* velocity, V, and r_n, the shortest distance between the axis of rotation and the line giving the direction of the velocity. Thus in Fig. 4.18, representing discharge from a duct rotating counterclockwise with constant angular velocity, ω, the flux of angular momentum is $\dot{m}r_n V$. The fluid discharges at velocity V_r *relative* to the duct or rotor, which itself has a tangential velocity $U = \omega r$. The absolute velocity, V, is the vector sum of U and V_r (Sect. 3.3). V may be resolved into a *tangential* component, V_u, and a *radial* component, V_m, as shown in

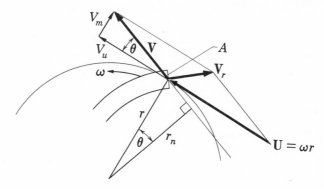

Figure 4.18

the velocity triangle in the figure. From the geometry, we have

$$r_n V = r \cos \theta \frac{V_u}{\cos \theta} = r V_u$$

where r is the radius of rotation at the point of discharge. This is a more convenient formulation than $r_n V$, for it is easier to use the radius r than the distance r_n. Furthermore, V_u is the "useful" component of absolute velocity contributing to the torque; V_m, whose direction is through the origin, has no effect on torque.

Eq. 4.36 may therefore be written as

$$\Sigma T = \frac{\dot{m}}{g_c} (r_2 V_{u_2} - r_1 V_{u_1}) \qquad [4.37]$$

where $\dot{m} = \rho V_r A$.

The control surface is chosen to enclose the rotor and to cut the shaft, so that the mechanical torque is transmitted via the shaft. In general, there are moments due to pressure and shear stress on the fluid where it enters and leaves the control surface, but ordinarily they are either zero or negligibly small. In most turbomachines, the pressure acts equally all around the circumference of the rotor, so that there is no net torque, and the shear stress is usually neglected. The exceptions to this rule are few, and their analysis will be withheld until Chapter 10, which takes up turbomachines in detail. The torque, T, then, becomes the shaft torque, wholly due to the rate of change of angular momentum.

Let us look at two illustrations, one of a pump or compressor and one of a turbine. Fig. 4.19 shows simple radial-flow machines, consisting of continuous rings of vanes or blades of uniform width and of inner radius r_i and outer radius r_o. For the pump or compressor in Fig. 4.19(a), the rotation is clockwise, and the fluid enters at r_i and leaves at r_o. For the turbine in Fig. 4.19(b), the rotation is counterclockwise, and the fluid enters at r_o and leaves at r_i. The velocity diagrams give, for the inlet and the outlet, the absolute velocity of the fluid, V, the relative velocity of the fluid, V_r, and the (absolute) linear velocity of the rotor, $U = \omega r$. Velocity V is shown resolved into its tangential component, V_u, and its radial component, V_m. The direction of rotation is called positive. The control surface encloses the rotor and cuts the shaft, the rotor and shaft being solidly connected. The sides of the blades are enclosed by end plates, so that fluid enters and leaves only around the circumferences of the circles described by r_i and r_o.

For the pump, Eq. 4.37 yields

$$T = \frac{\dot{m}}{g_c} (r_o V_{u_o} - r_i V_{u_i}) \qquad [4.38]$$

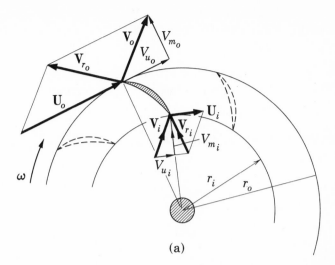

(a)

Figure 4.19

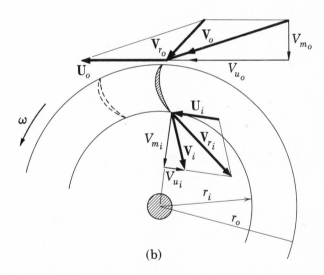

(b)

as V_{u_o} and V_{u_i} are both positive. Since the control surface encloses the rotor, T is the external torque applied to the rotor. This would be the torque necessary from a prime mover to increase the angular momentum of the fluid. The increase appears in the fluid as increased pressure and kinetic energy.

For the turbine, Eq. 4.37 yields

$$T = \frac{\dot{m}}{g_c}[r_i(-V_{u_i}) - r_o V_{u_o}] = -\frac{\dot{m}}{g_c}(r_o V_{u_o} + r_i V_{u_i}) \qquad [\textit{4.39}]$$

V_{u_i} is negative in this case, because it is directed oppositely to the rotation (generally, it can be directed in either direction). According to Eq. 4.39, the external torque is negative and thus clockwise, and it is supplied by the load, which might be an electrical generator.

Although torque is the basic quantity, we are interested practically in the *energy* transfer, either as the specific energy transferred or as the rate of energy transfer, i.e., power. Torque is transmitted via the shaft at a rate of ω rad/sec, and so, if we multiply Eq. 4.37 through by the angular velocity of the rotor, we obtain the total rate of energy transfer.

Hence
$$\omega T = E = \frac{\dot{m}}{g_c} (\omega r_2 V_{u_2} - \omega r_1 V_{u_1})$$

and with $\omega r = U$, the linear speed of the rotor,

$$E = \frac{\dot{m}}{g_c} (U_2 V_{u_2} - U_1 V_{u_1}) \qquad [4.40]$$

Eq. 4.40 is the form of the torque–angular momentum relationship that is most useful. Its consequences for various types of turbomachines will be discussed in Chapter 10.

4.17   *Conservation of energy*

The fundamental law of conservation of energy states that energy can be neither created nor destroyed (once again, we are excluding nuclear reactions). The principle applies to a given quantity of matter, and it is necessary here to apply it to a flow of matter in terms of field properties.

From the law of conservation of energy comes the first law of thermodynamics, which differentiates between energy in transition, as heat and work, and stored energy. For a system of fixed mass, this is stated as

$$Q = \Delta E + W \qquad [4.41]$$

where Q is the quantity of heat transferred to the system, ΔE is the increase of stored energy in the system, and W is the work done by the system. Thus in this context the term energy is exclusive of heat and work. Heat is energy transferred solely by virtue of temperature difference, and work is energy whose sole external effect could be the rise of a weight. Work may include electrical energy. The energy quantity E is the total stored energy contained in the system; it may include mechanical energy such as potential and kinetic energy, electrical and magnetic energy, chemical energy (e.g., as fuel), and molecular energy due to the random motion (translational, rotational, vibrational) of the individual molecules. The last-named is customarily called the *internal* energy* and given the symbol U.

4.18   *The general energy equation*

Now let us apply Eq. 4.41 for the conservation of energy to a control volume, as we did the momentum theorem. We shall consider only a stationary control volume. Fig. 4.20 is similar to Fig. 4.12, but here we are concerned with energy and not momentum. Note that we are dealing with a constant mass of material occupying region R at time $t = 0$ and region R' at time $t = \Delta t$, where $R = R_1 + R_2$, $R' = R_2 + R_3$, and the corresponding surfaces are S and S'. With the symbol E_R for energy, and a prime to indicate the state at time $t = \Delta t$, then, for the same mass of material,

at $t = 0$, $\qquad\qquad E_R = E_{R_1} + E_{R_2}$

at $t = \Delta t$, $\qquad\qquad E_{R'} = E_{R_2'} + E_{R_3'}$

Thus the change in energy, ΔE, during the time interval Δt is

$$\Delta E = E_{R'} - E_R = (E_{R_2'} + E_{R_3'}) - (E_{R_1} + E_{R_2})$$

or, on rearrangement of the right-hand side,

$$\Delta E = (E_{R_2'} - E_{R_2}) + (E_{R_3'} - E_{R_1})$$

In this last form, we see that the change of energy of the moving mass can be expressed as the sum of the change inside the control region, $E_{R_2'} - E_{R_2}$, and the net flow of energy across the control surface, $E_{R_3'} - E_{R_1}$. $E_{R_3'}$ is the

Figure 4.20

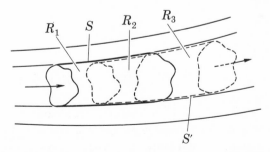

---

* Thermodynamic literature generally agrees upon the use of "internal" energy for the energy of molecular motion, although sometimes it so names the complete energy content, to distinguish it from energy passing in or out of the system. The remaining energy quantities are variously called "extrinsic," "stored," and so forth.

energy flowing out across the control surface, and E_{R_1} is the energy flowing in, both during time Δt.

The time rate of change of energy of the system is obtained on division through by Δt.

$$\frac{\Delta E_R}{\Delta t} = \frac{E_{R_2'} - E_{R_2}}{\Delta t} + \frac{E_{R_3'} - E_{R_1}}{\Delta t} \qquad [4.42]$$

In the limit as $\Delta t \to 0$, $S' \to S$, and the first term on the right-hand side becomes the rate of change of energy in the region R, bounded by S; hence

$$\lim_{\Delta t \to 0} \frac{E_{R_2'} - E_{R_2}}{\Delta t} = \frac{dE_R}{dt}$$

For E_R we can substitute $\int_R e_R \rho_R \, dR$, where e is the specific energy (energy per unit mass), and so

$$\frac{dE_R}{dt} = \frac{d}{dt} \int_R e_R \rho_R \, dR \qquad [4.43]$$

The second term on the right-hand side of Eq. 4.42 becomes in the limit the energy flux out across S. Thus we may write, using the same symbols as before, and with $\mathbf{V}_S$ the velocity of the fluid at the control surface,

$$\lim_{\Delta t \to 0} \frac{E_{R_3'} - E_{R_1}}{\Delta t} = \int_S e_S \rho_S \mathbf{V}_S \cdot d\mathbf{S} \qquad [4.44]$$

The first law, Eq. 4.41, formulated as a time-rate equation is

$$\frac{dQ}{dt} = \frac{dE}{dt} + \frac{dW}{dt} \qquad [4.45]$$

From Eqs. 4.43 and 4.44,

$$\frac{dE}{dt} = \frac{d}{dt} \int_R e_R \rho_R \, dR + \int_S e_S \rho_S \mathbf{V}_S \cdot d\mathbf{S}$$

Writing $dQ/dt = \dot{Q} = \int_S \dot{q} \, dS$ and $dW/dt = \dot{W} = \int_S \dot{w} \, dS$, where $\dot{q}$ and $\dot{w}$ are specific rates, we obtain

$$\dot{Q} = \frac{d}{dt} \int_R e_R \rho_R \, dR + \int_S e_S \rho_S \mathbf{V}_S \cdot d\mathbf{S} + \dot{W} \qquad [4.46]$$

In Eq. 4.46, the left-hand term and the last term on the right-hand side are the rates at which heat, Q, transmitted by conduction and radiation, and work, W, are transferred across the boundaries of the control volume. Work may include that due to pressure and shear stress on the boundaries and that done by the shaft, e.g., a propeller or turbine. The first term on the right-hand side is the time rate of increase of stored energy within the control volume, and the second term is the stored-energy flux across the control surface. The heat-energy term, $\dot{Q}$, is apparent, but the stored-energy term and the work term need more explanation.

4.19   *Energy terms*

The forms of the energy quantity, e, are many and varied, and it is convenient to classify them as potential, kinetic, internal (molecular), chemical, electrical, and magnetic energy. From the statement of the first law, only changes of energy are required, and any arbitrary datum may be used for each kind of energy quantity, provided that it is used consistently. The symbol e denotes specific energy, and the following terms will be expressed per unit mass.

Potential energy in the usual sense is due to gravitation. It is expressed as gz/g_c, where z is the distance in the direction of the gravitational field from any arbitrary datum.

Kinetic energy is associated with the directed bulk motion of the fluid and is expressed as $V^2/2g_c$.

Internal, or *intrinsic* energy, denoted by u, is associated with the random motion of the molecules and atoms. For fluids under normal conditions, u is a function of temperature only, and we write $du = c_v\, dT$, where c_v is the constant-volume specific heat and T is the absolute temperature. For liquids, with a constant c_v, this relation is nearly always sufficiently accurate. For gases, c_v is a function of temperature, and for the ideal gas, $u = \int_0^T c_v\, dT$, with $c_v = f(T)$. This variation must be taken into account for exact calculations. For most gases, tables of internal energy through a range of temperature are available.* However, over temperature ranges commonly occurring in many processes, a constant value of c_v may be used, with $\Delta u = c_v\, \Delta T$. This makes for considerable simplification in analysis and in practice. If the temperature range is wide, a more accurate answer can be obtained with a mean value of c_v between T_1 and T_2.

Chemical energy, which produces a chemical reaction, is ordinarily included as a form of internal energy of reactants and products. Techniques of accounting for chemical reaction by means of heating values or heats of reaction are usually part of the study of thermodynamics and are assumed to be already known.

Electrical energy and *magnetic* energy, until recent years often regarded as negligible, are no longer ignored. Their effects appear in gas flow at high temperature, and the development of rocket-propulsion devices, for which

---

* See, e.g., J. H. Keenan and J. Kaye, *Gas Tables*, Wiley, New York, 1948.

high temperature is concomitant with high speed in the atmosphere, has necessitated a very intensive investigation of them. Because of the possibility of utilizing high-speed, high-temperature gas flow to produce useful effects, viz., electric power or thrust, we must study electrical and magnetic energy as part of the energy equation. However, we shall not do so for a time, since it is preferable to carry further the relatively simple but very important analysis of flow with only mechanical- and internal-energy terms.

4.20 Work terms

The forms of work in the first-law statement applied to fluid flow are the work arising from pressure and shear stress on the control surface and the work transferred through the control surface "mechanically" by a shaft (or by an electric current convertible to the rise or fall of a weight).

The rate of work performed on the control surface by a pressure p is the product of the force due to pressure on the surface and the velocity of the fluid; i.e.,

$$\dot{W}_p = \int p \mathbf{V}_S \cdot d\mathbf{S}$$

where $\dot{W}_p$ is the rate of the so-called *flow* work, W_p. It is convenient to multiply and divide by the density, ρ, in this relation, so that

$$\dot{W}_p = \int \frac{p}{\rho} \rho \mathbf{V}_S \cdot d\mathbf{S} \qquad [4.47]$$

Writing $p/\rho = pv$, where v is specific volume, we may read Eq. 4.47 as mass flow rate times pv product, familiar from thermodynamics.

The work performed by a shear stress is difficult to evaluate exactly in the general case, unless we can restrict it to purely viscous effects and write $\tau = \mu \, du/dy$ (see Sect. 1.4). The difficulty is usually obviated if the control surface is chosen so that either it is normal to the velocity or the velocity is zero at the boundary. Thus in duct flow the entry and exit areas are arranged normally to the flow direction, and, with the no-slip condition, the velocity is zero at the walls, and no work crosses them, even though stress exists.

Work crossing the control surface by mechanical means such as a piston or turbine shaft is called *shaft* work. It is denoted by W_s, and its rate by $\dot{W}_s$.

4.21 The simple, steady-flow energy equation

Collecting these statements relating to energy, e, and work, W, we have for e

$$e = \frac{g}{g_c} z + \frac{V^2}{2g_c} + u \qquad [4.48a]$$

or in differential form

$$de = \frac{g}{g_c}\,dz + \frac{V\,dV}{g_c} + du \qquad [\textbf{4.48b}]$$

and for an ideal gas

$$de = \frac{g}{g_c}\,dz + \frac{V\,dV}{g_c} + c_v\,dT \qquad [\textbf{4.48c}]$$

For W, we have

$$\dot{W} = \int_S \frac{p}{\rho}\,\rho\mathbf{V}_S \cdot d\mathbf{S} + \dot{W}_s \qquad [\textbf{4.49}]$$

These can be substituted in Eq. 4.46 to give a general statement, but as we are restricting ourselves to *steady flow* and a fixed control volume, the term $d/dt \int e\rho\,dR$ will disappear. Since we now have to deal only with the flux term, we shall drop the subscript S from $\mathbf{V}$. The subscript s (for shaft) in $\dot{W}_s$ remains. Thus

$$\dot{Q} = \int_S e\rho\mathbf{V} \cdot d\mathbf{S} + \dot{W}$$

Substituting Eq. 4.48a for e and Eq. 4.49 for $\dot{W}$ yields

$$\dot{Q} = \int_S \left(\frac{g}{g_c}z + \frac{V^2}{2g_c} + u\right)\rho\mathbf{V} \cdot d\mathbf{S} + \int_S \frac{p}{\rho}\,\rho\mathbf{V} \cdot d\mathbf{S} + \dot{W}_s$$

Collecting terms under the integral sign, we obtain

$$\dot{Q} = \int_S \left(\frac{p}{\rho} + \frac{g}{g_c}z + \frac{V^2}{2g_c} + u\right)\rho\mathbf{V} \cdot d\mathbf{S} + \dot{W}_s \qquad [\textbf{4.50a}]$$

This is called the *simple, steady-flow energy equation.* It covers a very large number of everyday engineering flow problems, the restrictions being steady flow, no electrical and magnetic effects as energy terms, and no work due to shear stress on the boundaries. It may be put into other useful forms. If the fluid flow is uniform and each element of fluid at the evaluating station has the same energy, then we may write $\int_S \rho\mathbf{V} \cdot d\mathbf{S} = \dot{m}$, the mass flow rate, and divide through by $\dot{m}$, to get

$$q = \left(\frac{p_2}{\rho_2} - \frac{p_1}{\rho_1}\right) + \frac{g}{g_c}(z_2 - z_1) + \frac{V_2{}^2 - V_1{}^2}{2g_c} + u_2 - u_1 + w_s \qquad [\textbf{4.50b}]$$

This is a specific-energy equation, energy per unit mass, i.e., foot-pounds force or Btu per pound mass of fluid. In differential form, Eq. 4.50b becomes

$$dq = d\left(\frac{p}{\rho}\right) + \frac{g}{g_c}\,dz + \frac{V\,dV}{g_c} + du + dw_s \qquad [\textbf{4.50c}]$$

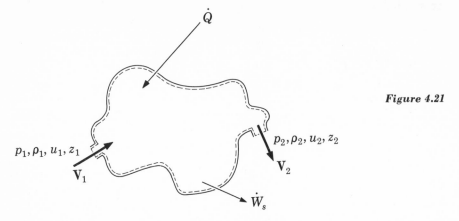

Figure 4.21

Furthermore, because p/ρ and u occur together, we can bring in enthalpy, h, by definition equal to $u + p/\rho$. Hence

$$dq = dh + \frac{g}{g_c}\,dz + \frac{V\,dV}{g_c} + dw_s \qquad [\textbf{4.50d}]$$

Fig. 4.21 shows a generalized example of the use of the steady-flow energy equation having many different practical applications. Fluid at a rate $\dot{m}$ is flowing into a duct, which may be as simple as a pipe or as complex as a steam turbine, with uniform velocity V_1 and uniform values of the properties p_1, ρ_1, and u_1. V_2, p_2, ρ_2, and u_2 are the corresponding quantities at discharge. The control surface indicated by a dashed line is at the boundary of the fluid and the walls of the duct and is normal to the velocities at entry and exit. Heat may be transferred across the walls of the duct at a rate $\dot{Q}$, and shaft work may be taken out of the duct through the walls at a rate $\dot{W}_s$. In the usual convention for our statement of the steady-flow equation, $\dot{Q}$ is positive when heat is transferred *into* the control volume, $\dot{W}_s$ is positive when work is transferred *out* of the system, and the energy integral term is flux out minus flux in. If $\dot{Q}$ is a cooling process and $\dot{W}_s$ refers to shaft work supplied, these are given negative signs. Then, by Eq. 4.50a,

$$\dot{Q} = \rho_2 V_2 S_2 \left(\frac{p_2}{\rho_2} + \frac{g}{g_c} z_2 + \frac{V_2{}^2}{2g_c} + u_2 \right)$$
$$- \rho_1 V_1 S_1 \left(\frac{p_1}{\rho_1} + \frac{g}{g_c} z_1 + \frac{V_1{}^2}{2g_c} + u_1 \right) + \dot{W}_s$$

or with $\rho_1 V_1 S_1 = \rho_2 V_2 S_2 = \dot{m}$,

$$\dot{Q} = \dot{m} \left[\frac{p_2}{\rho_2} - \frac{p_1}{\rho_1} + \frac{g}{g_c}(z_2 - z_1) + \frac{V_2{}^2 - V_1{}^2}{2g_c} + u_2 - u_1 \right] + \dot{W}_s \qquad [\textbf{4.51}]$$

As a specific-energy equation,

$$q = \frac{p_2}{\rho_2} - \frac{p_1}{\rho_1} + \frac{g}{g_c}(z_2 - z_1) + \frac{V_2{}^2 - V_1{}^2}{2g_c} + u_2 - u_1 + w_s \quad [4.52]$$

These equations can be used, for instance, to find the work required to compress air from state 1 to state 2 or to find the work output of a turbine when the initial and final states of the fluid are known. We shall apply them in simplified form to the flow of a gas in a duct with no heat transfer and no shaft work. Note that we are not concerned with what is happening inside the duct, which, as far as it affects the energy equation, is a "black box," but only with values at the boundaries. Thus the flow inside can be reversible or irreversible.

4.22 *Relationship of Euler, Bernoulli, and steady-flow energy equations*

It has been demonstrated that a force-momentum relationship applied to a fluid element led to the Euler equation of motion, Eq. 4.10, which, when applied along a streamline or for irrotational flow, led to an energy equation, Eq. 4.11. For constant-density, steady flow, the Bernoulli equation, Eq. 4.13, resulted. Owing to their derivation from the force-momentum relationship, the energy terms represented "mechanical" energy. These same terms appear in the steady-flow energy equation, together with other terms representing "thermal" energy. Let us see how the Euler equation and the steady-flow energy equation are related for a flow system to which both types of relationship are applicable under given conditions. This might be flow in a duct with no shaft work but possible heat transfer.

Starting with the simple, steady-flow energy equation in differential form, Eq. 4.50c, with no shaft work, we have

$$dq = d\left(\frac{p}{\rho}\right) + \frac{g}{g_c}\,dz + \frac{V\,dV}{g_c} + du$$

Expanding $d(p/\rho)$ to $dp/\rho + p\,d(1/\rho)$ gives us

$$dq = p\,d\left(\frac{1}{\rho}\right) + \frac{dp}{\rho} + \frac{g}{g_c}\,dz + \frac{V\,dV}{g_c} + du \quad [4.53]$$

Now from thermodynamics we have the relationship involving entropy, Eq. 1.21, valid as a statement of property relations regardless of any particular process,

$$T\,ds = du + p\,dv$$

which with $v = 1/\rho$ and $dv = d(1/\rho)$ can be written

$$du = T \, ds - p \, d\left(\frac{1}{\rho}\right)$$

Substituting for du in Eq. 4.53 yields

$$dq = p \, d\left(\frac{1}{\rho}\right) + \frac{dp}{\rho} + \frac{g}{g_c} \, dz + \frac{V \, dV}{g_c} + T \, ds - p \, d\left(\frac{1}{\rho}\right)$$

which reduces to

$$\frac{dp}{\rho} + \frac{g}{g_c} \, dz + \frac{V \, dV}{g_c} = - \, T \, ds + dq \qquad [4.54]$$

The Euler equation says that the left-hand side is zero for *ideal*, or *reversible*, flow; hence for this case $dq = T \, ds$, which agrees with the laws of thermodynamics for ideal flow. If the flow is reversible and *adiabatic*, then, with $dq = 0$, $ds = 0$. For *irreversible*, adiabatic flow, $dq = 0$, and therefore, from Eq. 4.54,

$$\frac{dp}{\rho} + \frac{g}{g_c} \, dz + \frac{V \, dV}{g_c} + T \, ds = 0 \qquad [4.55]$$

With no energy transfer to the fluid, the second law of thermodynamics tells us that ds must be positive for an irreversible process. Thus $T \, ds$ represents a *dissipation* or *loss* of useful mechanical energy. Eq. 4.55 is the Euler equation with a generalized term, $T \, ds$, indicating irreversibility. In the simple duct flow used for illustration, the loss can be due only to frictional or viscous effects.

For incompressible flow, Eq. 4.55 can be integrated between any two stations 1 and 2 to give

$$\frac{p_1}{\rho} + \frac{g}{g_c} \, z_1 + \frac{V_1^2}{2g_c} = \frac{p_2}{\rho} + \frac{g}{g_c} \, z_2 + \frac{V_2^2}{2g_c} + \int_1^2 T \, ds \qquad [4.56]$$

Here $\int T \, ds$ represents a dissipation or loss of useful mechanical energy. Eq. 4.56, then, is an energy equation for incompressible flow with $\int T \, ds$ indicating irreversibility. If $ds = 0$, the flow is ideal or reversible, and the relationship is the Bernoulli equation. Eq. 4.56 is sometimes called the "Bernoulli equation with losses," with $\int T \, ds$ written as a general loss term, E_L. For the Bernoulli relationship in other forms, as a head equation (Eq. 4.13b) or as a pressure equation (Eq. 4.13c), the loss term may be written as h_L or p_L, respectively. E_L, h_L, or p_L may be obtained from measurement of p, ρ, z, and V at any two stations; or the loss can be estimated from a detailed knowledge of the flow mechanics. Then one of the downstream energy terms can be calculated. Potential energy as height above a datum depends only on the initial and final elevations (i.e., it is a point function), and so change of gz/g_c is independent of friction or any other effects. For incompressible flow, velocity change is controlled only by area, from the continuity relationship $A_1 V_1 = A_2 V_2$. Accordingly, the difference between the total energy at station 1 and that at station 2, the loss E_L, can only be a loss of pressure. We therefore conclude that irreversibility due to frictional effects in steady, incompressible flow without shaft work is manifested as a decrease in pressure.

From the steady-flow energy equation for the same situation, Eq. 4.50b, with $q = w_s = 0$ and $\rho_1 = \rho_2 = \rho$, we have

$$\frac{p_1}{\rho} + \frac{g}{g_c} z_1 + \frac{V_1{}^2}{2g_c} = \frac{p_2}{\rho} + \frac{g}{g_c} z_2 + \frac{V_2{}^2}{2g_c} + u_2 - u_1 \qquad [\mathbf{4.57}]$$

On comparison of Eqs. 4.56 and 4.57,

$$\int_1^2 T \, ds \equiv E_L \equiv u_2 - u_1$$

i.e., the decrease in pressure due to loss E_L appears as an increase in internal energy, a temperature rise. For compressible flow we can make no such statement; with variable density there is a more complex situation with respect to velocity via the continuity equation and the equation of state of the gas, since $p = f(\rho)$.

This discussion has shown some important consequences of the momentum and energy equations and emphasized certain relationships. We shall summarize some of these, as follows:

1. Several terms are used in the literature for describing ideal flow, among them "reversible," "nonviscous," "inviscid," "frictionless," "potential," and "absence of shear stress."

2. The simple Euler equation (and hence the Bernoulli equation) can be derived from the steady-flow energy equation, with the restrictions that the flow is reversible and that there is no shaft work.

3. The Euler equation is valid only for reversible flow, which may be diabatic, whereas the energy equation is valid at all times.

4. The Bernoulli equation was initially derived from a force-momentum relationship; therefore, although it is expressed as an energy equation, its terms represent "mechanical" energy. Heat transfer may occur but does not affect the energy relationship, and so the mechanical energy is said to be conserved. The general Euler equation, which is valid for compressible flow as well as for incompressible flow, admits no such interpretation, and with variable density there is internal interchange between mechanical energy and thermal energy.

5. The Bernoulli equation may be used with a loss term for irreversible flow. This loss appears as a reduction in pressure, and the energy appears as internal energy.

4.23   *Integration of the Euler equation for compressible flow*

Because compressible flow is usually confined to gases, we may apply to it the simple Euler equation, Eq. 4.12, omitting the gz/g_c term, as gravitational effect is normally negligible. Thus the *simple Euler equation for a gas* is

$$\frac{dp}{\rho} + \frac{V\,dV}{g_c} = 0 \qquad [4.58]$$

Before integration is possible, a relationship must be established between two of the three variables. This must obviously involve the two state properties, p and ρ. Any relationship valid for a reversible process may be used. The polytropic function p/ρ^n represents perfect-gas behavior in many processes. By far the most important of these is the adiabatic process, for which $n = k$, the ratio of the specific heats, c_p/c_v, and we shall deal here only with the reversible, adiabatic (or isentropic) process for a perfect gas (one obeying the equation of state, $pv = RT$). We have, then,

$$\frac{p}{\rho^k} = \frac{p_1}{\rho_1{}^k} = \frac{p_2}{\rho_2{}^k} = C$$

and hence

$$\frac{1}{\rho} = \frac{p_1{}^{1/k}}{\rho_1}\frac{1}{p^{1/k}} = \frac{C^{1/k}}{p^{1/k}}$$

Substituting this in Eq. 4.58, and integrating between stations 1 and 2, we obtain

$$C^{1/k}\int_1^2 \frac{dp}{p^{1/k}} + \frac{1}{g_c}\int_1^2 V\,dV = 0$$

Integration yields

$$\frac{k}{k-1}\,C^{1/k}[p_2{}^{(k-1)/k} - p_1{}^{(k-1)/k}] + \frac{V_2{}^2 - V_1{}^2}{2g_c} = 0$$

or, with $p_1{}^{(k-1)/k}$ outside,

$$\frac{k}{k-1}\,C^{1/k}p_1{}^{(k-1)/k}\left[\left(\frac{p_2}{p_1}\right)^{(k-1)/k} - 1\right] + \frac{V_2{}^2 - V_1{}^2}{2g_c} = 0$$

Substituting $p_1{}^{1/k}/\rho_1$ for $C^{1/k}$ gives us

$$\frac{k}{k-1}\frac{p_1}{\rho_1}\left[\left(\frac{p_2}{p_1}\right)^{(k-1)/k} - 1\right] + \frac{V_2{}^2 - V_1{}^2}{2g_c} = 0 \qquad [4.59a]$$

For the ideal gas, $p_1/\rho_1 = RT_1$, and $kR/(k-1) = c_p$; hence

$$c_p T_1 \left[\left(\frac{p_2}{p_1} \right)^{(k-1)/k} - 1 \right] + \frac{V_2{}^2 - V_1{}^2}{2g_c} = 0 \qquad [\textbf{4.59b}]$$

Eqs. 4.59 can be used for the reversible, adiabatic, compressible flow of an ideal gas with no shaft work. They correspond to the Bernoulli equation for incompressible flow and are sometimes called the "Bernoulli equation for compressible flow." The additional restriction for compressible flow is that the flow be *adiabatic*.

4.24   *The energy equation for simple, adiabatic flow*

Because so many of the problems of compressible flow are for adiabatic processes, we shall consider in detail the energy equation for adiabatic flow. Furthermore, as we shall be dealing mostly with gases or vapors, we shall omit the gravitational-energy term as negligible in comparison with other quantities. With $q = 0$ and $\Delta z = 0$, Eq. 4.50b becomes

$$0 = \left(\frac{p_2}{\rho_2} - \frac{p_1}{\rho_1} \right) + 0 + \frac{V_2{}^2 - V_1{}^2}{2g_c} + u_2 - u_1 + w_s$$

and from the useful definition of $u + p/\rho$ as h, then

$$h_2 - h_1 + \frac{V_2{}^2 - V_1{}^2}{2g_c} = -w_s \qquad [\textbf{4.60}]$$

This tells us that in adiabatic flow the sum of the *increases* in enthalpy and kinetic energy of a fluid is equal to the shaft work done *on* the fluid (w_s by definition is positive for shaft work transferred from the region). This relationship is the basic equation for many problems having to do with the transfer of energy between a fluid and a rotor, e.g., in pumps, turbines, and turbomachines of all kinds. The topic is discussed in detail in Chapter 10, and for the remainder of this chapter we shall deal with flow with no shaft work, i.e., the simple flow of a fluid through a duct.

With $w_s = 0$, Eq. 4.60 becomes

$$h_2 - h_1 + \frac{V_2{}^2 - V_1{}^2}{2g_c} = 0 \qquad [\textbf{4.61a}]$$

or, in differential form,

$$dh + \frac{V \, dV}{g_c} = 0 \qquad [\textbf{4.61b}]$$

Eq. 4.61 is valid for *adiabatic flow with no shaft work* and negligible gravitational energy, and since it is derived directly from the energy equation, the flow need not be reversible. It is a simple expression, but it has very important consequences. First, however, let us compare it with the simple Euler equation for a gas, Eq. 4.58,

$$\frac{dp}{\rho} + \frac{V \, dV}{g_c} = 0 \qquad\qquad [4.58]$$

This is valid for *reversible flow with no shaft work*, but the flow need not be adiabatic.

For adiabatic flow, then, Eq. 4.61b is always true, whereas Eq. 4.58 holds only when the flow is, in addition, reversible. Thus $dh = dp/\rho$ *only* for reversible flow. (This concept is familiar from thermodynamics, where $1/\rho = v$ and hence $dh = v \, dp$ only for reversible, adiabatic flow.) The enthalpy relation, Eq. 4.61, is therefore more general, and we shall use it frequently. However, we shall also use the momentum relation, Eq. 4.58, when the flow is reversible.

Integration of Eq. 4.58 yielded

$$c_p T_1 \left[\left(\frac{p_2}{p_1} \right)^{(k-1)/k} - 1 \right] + \frac{V_2{}^2 - V_1{}^2}{2g_c} = 0 \qquad\qquad [4.59b]$$

Now for a perfect gas $dh = c_p \, dT$, and so substitution in Eq. 4.61b and integration give us

$$\int_1^2 c_p \, dT + \int_1^2 \frac{V \, dV}{g_c} = 0$$

which with constant specific heat becomes

$$c_p(T_2 - T_1) + \frac{V_2{}^2 - V_1{}^2}{2g_c} = 0 \qquad\qquad [4.62]$$

If the flow is also reversible, then with $T_2 - T_1 = T_1(T_2/T_1 - 1)$ and $T_2/T_1 = (p_2/p_1)^{(k-1)/k}$, Eqs. 4.59b and 4.62 are identical, as they should be for reversible, adiabatic flow.

4.25   *Stagnation or total values*

In the energy equation, there are usually an enthalpy term, h, and a kinetic-energy term, $V^2/2g_c$. Just as it is convenient to express h as the sum of u and p/ρ because they occur so often together, it is convenient to express the sum of enthalpy and kinetic energy as *stagnation* or *total enthalpy*, with the symbol h_0. Thus

$$h_0 = h + \frac{V^2}{2g_c} \qquad\qquad [4.63]$$

We use h_0 quite generally, even when heat is being transferred, for in the absence of gravitational energy, it represents the total stored energy. The

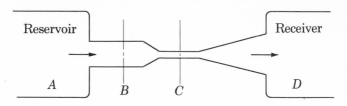

Figure 4.22

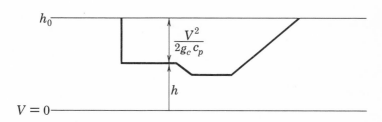

steady-flow energy equation, Eq. 4.52, then reduces to

$$q = \Delta h_0 + w_s$$

Stagnation enthalpy is particularly meaningful in adiabatic flow with no shaft work, i.e., simple flow in a duct, because then $\Delta h_0 = 0$ or $h_{0_1} = h_{0_2}$; in other words, the stagnation enthalpy is *constant*. The term "stagnation" arises from the fact that when a gas flowing with velocity V is brought to rest (e.g., at a stagnation point), h changes to h_0. Although it is probably more widely used than its synonym, "total," the reader must not get the idea that a fluid has to be "stagnated" in order to have a value for h_0.

As an illustration, Fig. 4.22 depicts flow from a reservoir through a duct into another reservoir or receiver. Both reservoir A and receiver D are so large that the velocity may be considered negligible, and the whole system is insulated, so that the flow is adiabatic. Hence Eq. 4.63 holds, and we have

$$h_0 = h_A + 0 = h_B + \frac{V_B{}^2}{2g_c} = h_C + \frac{V_C{}^2}{2g_c} = h_D + 0 = h_0$$

At A the fluid is at rest, and its stagnation enthalpy is $h_0 = h_A$. At B the fluid has acquired significant velocity, and at C it has a further velocity increment. At D the fluid has been virtually brought to rest, and its stagnation enthalpy is $h_0 = h_D$. At B and C and everywhere along the duct, the fluid has kinetic energy, with varying enthalpy, but h_0 is everywhere the same. Under the given conditions, it is constant for the fluid and may be used in calculation at any station.

For a perfect gas, $dh = c_p\, dT$, and so we have

$$\int_1^2 c_p\, dT + \int_1^2 \frac{V\, dV}{g_c} = 0$$

If state 1 is where the velocity is V and the temperature T, and state 2 is where $V = 0$ and $T = T_0$ (the stagnation state), then, with c_p constant,

$$c_p(T_0 - T) + \frac{V^2}{2g_c} = 0 \qquad [4.64a]$$

or

$$T_0 = T + \frac{V^2}{2g_c c_p} \qquad [4.64b]$$

T is the temperature as ordinarily conceived, but we may now call it the *static* temperature, to differentiate it from the *stagnation* temperature, T_0. For homogeneous dimensions, the term $V^2/2g_c c_p$ must be a temperature, and it is sometimes called the *dynamic* or *kinetic* temperature or the temperature equivalent of velocity or kinetic energy. Note that once again the stagnation value is the value attained when a gas is brought to rest. Like stagnation enthalpy, stagnation temperature is constant in the simple, adiabatic flow of a perfect gas, reversible or irreversible.

This analysis shows that the measurement of temperature in a flowing gas presents some problems, because, apart from the possibility of errors arising from radiation or conduction, any instrument is exposed partially or wholly to the dynamic temperature. Thus it may record a temperature anywhere between the static value, T, and the stagnation value, T_0. It is usually necessary to calibrate the instrument for velocity effect or to employ a design with a known dynamic-temperature effect.

The static temperature, T, is that experienced by an observer moving with the stream of fluid. It must be carefully noted that T is the value relevant to other properties of the gas, such as density or viscosity, because it is a measure of the true molecular state. $V^2/2g_c c_p$ represents a bulk kinetic energy of ordered motion, which, although it may be associated with the static temperature, is nevertheless an arbitrary variable.

It is helpful to keep in mind the order of magnitude of dynamic temperature. Using a c_p value of 0.24 Btu/lb-°R, valid for air at ordinary temperatures, and inserting $J = 778$ ft-lb/Btu for consistent units, we have

$$\frac{V^2}{2g_c c_p J} = \frac{V^2}{64.4 \times 0.24 \times 778} \approx \left(\frac{V}{110}\right)^2 \qquad [4.65]$$

with V in feet per second. Thus at a velocity of 110 fps the dynamic temperature is 1°F; at 550 fps it is 25°F; and at the high speeds of supersonic aircraft, it is very considerable.

When a flowing gas is slowed down and the temperature rises, there is a concomitant rise in pressure if the process is adiabatic or anywhere near it. Most gas processes in which the velocity changes are adiabatic. If a process is also reversible, the pressure change can be calculated from the temperature change by the thermodynamic relationship for a reversible, adiabatic process. *Stagnation* or *total pressure* is *defined* as the pressure attained by a flowing gas when brought to rest reversibly and adiabatically. If at velocity V the gas has a temperature T and a pressure p, the stagnation pressure, p_0, is evaluated from the expression

$$\frac{p_0}{p} = \left(\frac{T_0}{T}\right)^{k/(k-1)}$$

[*4.66*]

The stagnation pressure is the highest pressure that the gas can attain if brought to rest in an adiabatic process. It is therefore a measure of the availability of energy and can be determined at any given station. In this sense, it does not matter whether the process actually taking place between two stations, 1 and 2, is reversible and adiabatic or indeed of any particular nature whatsoever. The stagnation pressures at 1 and 2, p_{0_1} and p_{0_2}, are functions only of the actual states of those stations. Stagnation pressure is then a property of a flowing fluid calculable if we know the state of the fluid in terms of p and T and its velocity, V.

If we examine a change of stagnation pressure between stations 1 and 2, we can learn something about the flow process. Fig. 4.23 shows stagnation on a T-s diagram. Suppose that at point A the gas has velocity V, pressure p, and temperature T. Its stagnation state is at B, where the velocity is zero and the pressure and temperature are p_0 and T_0, respectively, p_0 being the defined stagnation pressure and T_0 being the actual stagnation temperature. Now, still regarding the whole flow as *adiabatic*, let us consider some other station downstream in the flow at which the state has changed owing to a reduction in velocity. If the process has been *reversible*, it is represented by AC. Since T_0 is constant for the adiabatic process, the stagnation process is CB, and thus the stagnation pressure remains p_0. If the process has been

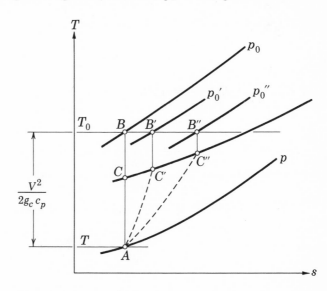

Figure 4.23

irreversible, there is an increase of entropy, and the process might be represented by AC'. With T_0 still constant, the stagnation process is $C'B'$, and it can be seen from the constant-pressure line through B' that the stagnation pressure has been reduced to p_0'. Similarly, a process involving greater irreversibility is represented by AC'', with a further decrease of stagnation pressure to p_0''. In a *reversible*, adiabatic process, then, the stagnation pressure remains constant, and in an *irreversible*, adiabatic process, it decreases—hence the statement that the stagnation pressure is a measure of the availability of energy, even though the total energy is constant. The change of stagnation pressure may be expressed analytically in the following manner.

For an adiabatic process between states 1 and 2, we have

$$\frac{p_{0_1}}{p_1} = \left(\frac{T_{0_1}}{T_1}\right)^{k/(k-1)} \quad \text{and} \quad \frac{p_{0_2}}{p_2} = \left(\frac{T_{0_2}}{T_2}\right)^{k/(k-1)}$$

which simply give the stagnation pressure at each station in terms of the state at that station. Dividing one by the other yields

$$\frac{p_{0_1}}{p_{0_2}}\frac{p_2}{p_1} = \left(\frac{T_{0_1}}{T_{0_2}}\frac{T_2}{T_1}\right)^{k/(k-1)}$$

and since $T_{0_1} = T_{0_2} = $ constant,

$$\frac{p_{0_1}}{p_{0_2}} = \frac{(T_2/T_1)^{k/(k-1)}}{p_2/p_1} \qquad [4.67]$$

From thermodynamics, we have a general relationship for change of entropy,

$$ds = c_p \frac{dT}{T} - R \frac{dp}{p}$$

Therefore,

$$\frac{1}{R}\int_1^2 ds = \frac{c_p}{R}\int_1^2 \frac{dT}{T} - \int_1^2 \frac{dp}{p}$$

Substituting $k/(k-1) = c_p/R$ and integrating, we obtain

$$\frac{\Delta s_{1-2}}{R} = \frac{k}{k-1}\ln\frac{T_2}{T_1} - \ln\frac{p_2}{p_1} = \ln\frac{(T_2/T_1)^{k/(k-1)}}{p_2/p_1}$$

and finally

$$\frac{(T_2/T_1)^{k/(k-1)}}{p_2/p_1} = e^{\Delta s_{1-2}/R}$$

Substituting for the right-hand side of Eq. 4.67 gives us

$$\frac{p_{0_1}}{p_{0_2}} = e^{\Delta s_{1-2}/R} \qquad [4.68]$$

Thus for reversible, adiabatic flow with $\Delta s = 0$, $p_{0_1} = p_{0_2}$, as previously shown diagrammatically. For irreversible flow, $\Delta s > 0$, and hence $p_{0_2} < p_{0_1}$, indicating a decrease in stagnation pressure.

When the Bernoulli equation for incompressible flow was developed, the total pressure, p_0, was expressed as

$$p_0 = p + \frac{g}{g_c} z + \frac{\rho V^2}{2g_c}$$

For a gas the gravitational factor is omitted, and the equation becomes

$$p_0 = p + \frac{\rho V^2}{2g_c}$$

with p the static pressure and $\rho V^2/2g_c$ the dynamic pressure. Thus p_0 here is the stagnation pressure for incompressible flow. For a compressible fluid, the stagnation pressure is the sum of static pressure p and some "dynamic" pressure, which we can call simply p_d but which is not equal to $\rho V^2/2g_c$ since the density is not constant in compressible flow. Nevertheless, for a given condition, $\rho V^2/2g_c$ may be calculated for compressible flow and is often referred to as dynamic pressure. This situation is unfortunate, for it would be better to reserve the name for the difference between stagnation pressure and static pressure in both incompressible and compressible flow. It arises from the fact that coefficients of various sorts, sucn as the pressure coefficient defined in the discussion of flow around a cylinder, are formulated in terms of $\rho V^2/2g_c$, established with ρ and V evaluated at some datum state, very often the initial or approach condition. This is true for both incompressible and compressible flow. Because $\rho V^2/2g_c$ is an often used factor, it is often denoted by a symbol, q. In summary, it is stressed that we shall use $q = \rho V^2/2g_c$ for dynamic pressure, with V evaluated at some arbitrary reference station. For incompressible flow, $q = \rho V^2/2g_c = p_0 - p$, the difference between stagnation and static pressures. For compressible flow, $q = \rho V^2/2g_c$ may be evaluated, but it is *not* equal to $p_0 - p$.

Stagnation or total pressure can be measured in compressible fluid flow by means of the Pitot or total-head tube described earlier. The true dynamic pressure, p_d, can then be obtained as the difference between the Pitot reading and the static pressure measured at the same point; again note that this is not equal to $\rho V^2/2g_c = q$ and therefore cannot be used directly in the calculation of velocity. It is remarkable and very fortunate that stagnation pressure can be determined so easily, inasmuch as it requires a reversible, adiabatic, i.e., ideal, process, a difficult achievement in fluid-flow practice in general. The stagnation process in a freestream is the closest to such a process in fluid flow.

4.26   *Use of the momentum and energy equations*

We now have general and particular forms of the three basic conservation laws for fluid flow, those of continuity, momentum, and energy. We shall use them repeatedly in subsequent developments. It is sometimes not immediately apparent why in one instance we start with, say, momentum and continuity, in another instance choose energy and continuity, and on occasion utilize all three. The following discussion may be helpful.

In analyzing a problem, the first thing to do is to select a control volume and a control surface. It is helpful, and necessary in many circumstances, to draw the control surface on the diagram illustrating the problem, but in simple cases we can imply it by referring to stations in a flow system with the boundary of the control surface obvious. A problem can very often be simplified by judicious choice of the control surface. Two examples have already been given, one for the momentum equation and one for the energy equation. The former (Sect. 4.14) showed how, in the expression for the drag of a body in freestream flow, the choice of the lateral control surface along distant streamlines resulted in simple pressure and momentum-flux terms. The latter (Sect. 4.21) showed how, in duct flow, the choice of the duct surface as the control surface eliminated the need for specifying viscous forces, as no viscous work could cross the surface. Sometimes it is wise to make analyses for more than one control surface, as they may illuminate other aspects of the problem.

The next step is to decide what relationship to use. This involves essentially an examination of the problem to see what can be stated in simple fashion. For flow in the absence of external shear stresses, the forces can usually be readily formulated in terms of pressure and body forces, and so a momentum equation is indicated, either a form of the Euler equations or the integral-momentum equation for fluid flow. When the external shear stresses for simple uniform flow can be expressed by means of the viscous-stress relationship (see Sect. 1.4), more detailed knowledge is obtained if this is put into the momentum equation. In some situations there are *internal* shear stresses (such as those incurred in the mixing of fluid streams) that preclude the use of ideal-flow relationships but that do not entail external forces.

With respect to the energy equation, although the total energy is always conserved, the "mechanical" energy is conserved only in ideal, incompressible flow; i.e., in irreversible flow, mechanical energy is *dissipated* (Sect. 4.22). However, for compressible flow that is also adiabatic but not necessarily reversible, the energy equation as conservation of stagnation enthalpy or temperature provides a useful relationship between temperature and velocity.

Having set down the relationships known to be valid for the problem to be investigated, we can see whether enough equations are available to determine the unknown quantity, remembering that state relations (e.g., the equation of state for ideal gases and thermodynamic relationships from the first and second laws) are often valuable, particularly in compressible flow.

In many of the demonstrations that follow, or that may be encountered elsewhere, a desired result will be obtained with the greatest economy for the sake of brevity, and it will not always be immediately apparent how, apart from basic relationships, the answer was achieved directly from the particular relationships chosen. These demonstrations are, of course, products of experience, and the student is advised to examine the analyses to learn not only why certain relationships are used but also, if possible, why others are not. In tackling new problems, one is bound to travel up some blind alleys, but if the basic relationships are correct and a sufficient number of equations are available, a solution must be possible. Some of the problems in connection with this chapter provide practice in the choice of initial relationships, and the most important precaution is to think carefully before rushing into detailed algebraic manipulation.

4.27 *Velocity of wave propagation in a fluid*

It has been seen that the velocity of a fluid has a basic significance, not only intrinsically but in compressible flow for its effect on the other properties. This velocity is a bulk velocity, but there is also a fundamental velocity in a fluid, that of the speed of propagation of a disturbance. For instance, in ordinary low-speed flow, the presence of an obstacle is felt in all directions around it; i.e., a streamline pattern is produced, as described extensively for the kinematics of flow. Alternatively, a body set in motion in an otherwise static body of fluid creates disturbances that reach all parts of the fluid system in various, but finite, time intervals. The problem is to investigate the nature of the propagation of such disturbances.

We may distinguish two kinds of propagation, one throughout the body of a fluid, e.g., an aircraft flying through the atmosphere, and the other over the surface of a liquid, e.g., a boat traveling on the sea. They will be treated in turn, and it should be noted that they illustrate the application of the basic conservation laws just discussed.

For propagation throughout the body of a fluid, a one-dimensional model is used for simplicity, and it is valid for propagation in all directions. This is a physical model to demonstrate a single finite disturbance, and later it will be generalized. Fig. 4.24 shows a duct fitted with a movable piston of

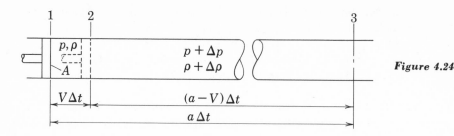

Figure 4.24

area A. Both fluid and piston are initially at rest, and then the piston is moved a short distance from plane 1 to plane 2 in time Δt, the piston velocity being V. The fluid next to the piston is set in motion, and, if the fluid were incompressible, the whole body of fluid to the right of the piston would also be set in motion. For a compressible fluid, however, there is an increment of pressure, Δp, and hence of density, $\Delta \rho$, and this incremental disturbance is propagated along the duct at a velocity a and reaches plane 3 in time Δt. It is assumed that the propagation velocity, a, is very much greater than the piston velocity, V.

Now we can apply the laws of continuity and momentum to this situation. For continuity, the mass of fluid displaced by the piston during its movement from 1 to 2 must be equal to the increase of mass of fluid between 2 and 3 evidenced by the increase of density, $\Delta \rho$, due to the propagation of the disturbance through the fluid. Thus

$$\rho A V \,\Delta t = \Delta \rho \, A (a - V) \,\Delta t$$

Because $V \ll a$, then $a - V \approx a$, and the relationship reduces to

$$\rho V = a \,\Delta \rho$$

For momentum, we can assume no shear stress, and therefore the force acting on the fluid owing to the motion of the piston during time Δt is $A \,\Delta p$. This must equal the rate of change of momentum of the fluid. A mass of fluid $M = \rho A (a \,\Delta t)$ is accelerated from rest to velocity V in time Δt, and thus the rate of change of momentum is

$$\frac{MV}{\Delta t} = \frac{\rho A (a \,\Delta t) V}{\Delta t} = \rho A a V$$

Equating this to the force gives us

$$A \,\Delta p = \frac{\rho A a V}{g_c}$$

and

$$\rho V = \frac{\Delta p \, g_c}{a}$$

Equating the values of V from continuity and momentum yields

$$a\,\Delta\rho = \frac{\Delta p\,g_c}{a}$$

and

$$a^2 = \frac{\Delta p}{\Delta\rho/g_c}$$

In the limit, as all increments become infinitesimal,

$$a = \sqrt{g_c\frac{dp}{d\rho}} \qquad\qquad [\textbf{4.69}]$$

This model pictures the production and propagation of a finite disturbance, but now let us look at an analysis assuming that a disturbance has been created and that we want to find its velocity.

Fig. 4.25(a) shows a disturbance or pulse traveling from left to right in a duct into undisturbed fluid of pressure p and density ρ. The fluid through which the pulse has passed has been given increments of velocity ΔV, of pressure Δp, and of density $\Delta\rho$. This represents an unsteady state, but we can simplify it to steady motion by imposing a velocity $-a$ on the whole fluid, as pointed out in Sect. 3.3. We then have the situation shown in Fig. 4.25(b), with the fluid of pressure p and density ρ flowing with velocity a from right to left through a stationary front that raises the pressure by Δp and the density by $\Delta\rho$, the velocity after the front being $a - \Delta V$. Taking a small control surface enclosing the pulse and again assuming no shear at the walls, we may write for continuity,

$$\rho A a = (\rho + \Delta\rho)A(a - \Delta V) = A(\rho a + a\,\Delta\rho - \rho\,\Delta V - \Delta\rho\,\Delta V)$$

which becomes, on omission of the second-order term $\Delta\rho\,\Delta V$,

$$\rho\,\Delta V = a\,\Delta\rho$$

Figure 4.25

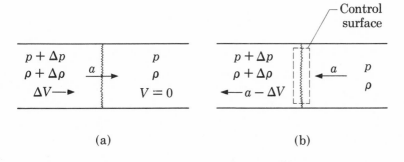

(a)   (b)

and for momentum, with the usual sign convention of positive to the right,

$$A[(p + \Delta p) - p] = \frac{\dot{m}}{g_c}[-(a - \Delta V) - (-a)] = \frac{\dot{m}}{g_c}\Delta V = \frac{\rho a A}{g_c}\Delta V$$

and

$$\rho\, \Delta V = g_c\frac{\Delta p}{a}$$

Equating the values of $\rho\, \Delta V$ from momentum and continuity, we have

$$a\, \Delta\rho = g_c\frac{\Delta p}{a}$$

and

$$a^2 = \frac{\Delta p}{\Delta\rho/g_c}$$

and in the limit,

$$a = \sqrt{g_c\frac{dp}{d\rho}} \qquad\qquad [4.69]$$

which is the same result as before. This analysis demonstrates the use of the momentum equation and the device of superposing a velocity to obtain steady flow.

Eq. 4.69, then, is an expression for the rate of propagation of a disturbance in a fluid derived under the restrictions of (1) infinitesimal increments and (2) absence of damping forces. Thus it is not valid for very large changes of state as, for instance, in an explosion. However, it is immediately applicable to the propagation of sound, which is exactly the creation of very small pressure disturbances in a gas. Accordingly, a is called the *acoustic, sound,* or *sonic velocity.* Since it depends on the rate of change of pressure with density, a knowledge of the p-ρ relationship is required. For gases, the propagation of sound occurs under conditions such that the process is adiabatic, and with the restriction of no damping implicit in the derivation, the process is also reversible. For a perfect gas, we can use the relationship $p/\rho^k = $ constant; hence

$$\frac{dp}{d\rho} = k\frac{p}{\rho}$$

On substitution into Eq. 4.69,

$$a = \sqrt{g_c k\frac{p}{\rho}} \qquad\qquad [4.70]$$

From the equation of state of a perfect gas, we can replace p/ρ by RT, thus:

$$a = \sqrt{g_c k R T} \qquad\qquad [4.71]$$

This is a most important result, stating that the acoustic velocity in a gas is proportional to the square root of the absolute temperature. For air at near ground-level temperature,

$$a = \sqrt{32.2 \times 1.4 \times 53.3T} \approx 49\sqrt{T} \qquad\qquad [4.72]$$

At 60°F, $a = 1117$ ft/sec, and at $-70°$F (stratosphere), $a = 968$ ft/sec.

For fluids other than perfect gases, the basic relationship, Eq. 4.69, must be used. From this we see that for an incompressible fluid the propagation velocity is infinite. For liquids, with very low compressibility, it is very high, of the order of 5000 ft/sec for water, as an example.

It is necessary to emphasize one obvious fact, namely, that although a is called *acoustic* velocity, its relevance in fluid mechanics is as a velocity of *wave propagation*. In spite of the colloquial parlance of the "sound barrier" and the terms "subsonic" and "supersonic," we should still be concerned with a even if we had no sense of hearing.

4.28   *Relationship of flow velocity and propagation velocity— Mach number*

Because there is a finite and, for many fluid phenomena, relatively low value of wave propagation, it is apparent that the ratio of the bulk fluid velocity, i.e., the flow velocity, V, to the propagation velocity, a, is of great consequence. The common, everyday manifestations of fluid flow occur with V very much less than a, a fact that has been implicit in all our development so far. We have assumed that the flow lines around a body acquire their particular pattern well upstream from the body itself, implying that the disturbance caused by the body is communicated at a speed much higher than that of the fluid itself. In the reverse situation, with flow velocity greater than propagation velocity, the flow regime must be quite different. This we shall examine in detail later on. Even when the flow velocity is low compared with the propagation velocity, there is often some local region where the local flow velocity is high or even exceeds the propagation velocity. Thus, for the flow around a cylinder, the maximum flow velocity occurs at $\theta = 90°$, being then double the approach velocity (Sect. 3.17). It is therefore possible to have a mixed-flow pattern, with the main part of the flow subsonic and local areas supersonic.

Since the propagation velocity varies with temperature, the flow velocity by itself is not sufficient for assessing the flow regime. It is the *ratio* of flow velocity to propagation velocity that is important. This dimensionless ratio, V/a, is called the *Mach number* and denoted by M. Hence, for a gas,

$$\text{M} = \frac{V}{a} = \frac{V}{\sqrt{g_c k R T}} \qquad [\textbf{4.73}]$$

If Mach number rather than velocity is the valid criterion, it seems logical to replace V with M in many of the expressions developed for compressible flow. It leads to simplification in many cases because of the dependence on temperature, T. Transformations of some of the expressions follow.

For the incompressible dynamic pressure, $q = \rho V^2/2g_c$, we obtain

$$q = \frac{\rho V^2}{2g_c} = \frac{\rho M^2 a^2}{2g_c} = \frac{p}{RT} \frac{M^2 g_c k RT}{2g_c} = \frac{k}{2} p M^2 \qquad [4.74]$$

The relationship for stagnation temperature, Eq. 4.64b, is

$$T_0 = T + \frac{V^2}{2g_c c_p} = T + \frac{M^2 g_c k RT}{2g_c c_p} = T + \frac{M^2 T}{2} \frac{kR}{c_p} = T + \frac{M^2 T}{2}(k-1)$$

$$[4.64b]$$

or
$$\frac{T_0}{T} = 1 + \frac{k-1}{2} M^2 \qquad [4.75]$$

For stagnation pressure, from Eq. 4.66,

$$\frac{p_0}{p} = \left(\frac{T_0}{T}\right)^{k/(k-1)} = \left(1 + \frac{k-1}{2} M^2\right)^{k/(k-1)} \qquad [4.76]$$

Much of the future analysis of compressible flow will be made in terms of Mach number rather than of velocity. It should be observed that, like velocity, the Mach number nearly always occurs as M^2 rather than as M, which implies a kinetic-energy interpretation rather than one of velocity per se, although M itself is used as the criterion of a flow regime.

For a given value of k, ratios of stagnation states to static states are a function only of Mach number, and thus they can be computed and tabulated. Values of p/p_0, ρ/ρ_0, and T/T_0 for various values of k are given as functions of the independent variable M in gas tables.*

4.29   *Limits of use of incompressible-flow relations*

To illustrate the utility of the Mach number, as well as to provide a useful expression, we shall now demonstrate the relationship of the compressible-flow dynamic pressure, $p_d = p_0 - p$, to the incompressible-flow dynamic pressure, $q = \rho V^2/2g_c$, with M in place of V. This relationship might well have been developed in Sect. 4.25 but was carefully avoided until the concept of the Mach number had been introduced. A helpful exercise is to try to perform the following analysis in terms of V rather than M. It emphasizes the desirability of Mach number rather than velocity as a parameter.

The comparison sought is between p_d and q, thus:

$$\frac{p_d}{q} = \frac{p_0 - p}{\rho V^2/2g_c}$$

From Eq. 4.74,
$$\frac{p_d}{q} = \frac{p[(p_0/p) - 1]}{(k/2)p M^2} = \frac{2}{kM^2}\left(\frac{p_0}{p} - 1\right)$$

* See, e.g., footnote on p. 155.

Substituting from Eq. 4.76, we obtain

$$\frac{p_d}{q} = \frac{2}{k M^2} \left[\left(1 + \frac{k-1}{2} M^2 \right)^{k/(k-1)} - 1 \right]$$

The term in parentheses may be expanded by means of the series expansion

$$(1 + x)^n = 1 + nx + \frac{n(n-1)x^2}{2!} + \frac{n(n-1)(n-2)x^3}{3!} + \cdots$$

Hence

$$\frac{p_d}{q} = \frac{2}{k M^2} \left[1 + \frac{k}{k-1} \frac{k-1}{2} M^2 + \frac{1}{2} \frac{k}{k-1} \left(\frac{k}{k-1} - 1 \right) \left(\frac{k-1}{2} M^2 \right)^2 \right.$$

$$\left. + \cdots - 1 \right] = \frac{2}{k M^2} \left[\frac{k M^2}{2} + \frac{k M^4}{8} + \frac{(2-k)k M^6}{48} + \cdots \right]$$

$$= 1 + \frac{M^2}{4} + \frac{(2-k)M^4}{24} + \cdots \qquad [\textbf{4.77}]$$

With $k = 1.4$ (air at normal temperatures), this reduces to

$$\frac{p_d}{q} = 1 + \frac{M^2}{4} + \frac{M^4}{40} + \cdots \qquad [\textbf{4.78}]$$

This series converges rapidly for low Mach number, and only a few terms are necessary for quantitative accuracy. However, it converges only for $x^2 < 1$, which here means $M < 2.24$. For $M = 0$ (incompressible flow), $p_d/q = 1$, as it should; for $M = 0.1$ ($V \approx 112$ ft/sec), $p_d/q = 1.0025$; for $M = 0.2$, $p_d/q = 1.012$; for $M = 0.5$, $p_d/q = 1.064$; for $M = 1$, $p_d/q = 1.276$. Thus we conclude that we may use $p_d = \rho V^2/2g_c$ (i.e., consider the flow incompressible for a suitable purpose) up to $M = 0.2$ for 1% accuracy. For $M = 0.2$ at atmospheric temperature, $V \approx 220$ ft/sec, a value applicable to many gas-flow problems. In many instances, treating a gas as incompressible is a considerable simplification, and Eq. 4.77 gives an indication of its limits with respect to accuracy. It is *not* recommended that Eqs. 4.77 and 4.78 be used to calculate p_0, as $p + p_d(1 + M^2/4 + \cdots)$. The procedure is cumbersome, and it is better to use Eq. 4.76, even if this necessitates calculating T or T_0 from the velocity.

4.30 *Velocity of propagation of surface waves*

The previous analysis developed the idea of wave propagation in an infinite medium and was valid for all compressible fluids. For a liquid with a free surface, however, there is possibility of a disturbance causing a displacement of fluid in a direction normal to the free surface and propagation of this

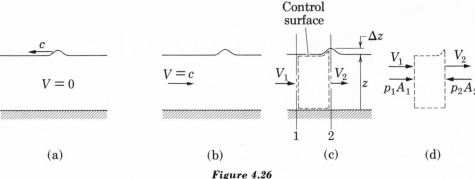

Figure 4.26

disturbance as a surface wave. The liquid is regarded as incompressible, and the adjacent medium is assumed to have such a low density compared with that of the liquid that any motion or displacement in it has no effect on the behavior of the liquid.

We take as our model a surface disturbance of small amplitude that travels with a propagation velocity c as shown in Fig. 4.26(a). This is an unsteady condition, and in order to simplify the analysis to the steady state, we again employ the device discussed in Sect. 3.3, whereby a velocity V is imposed on the system, equal in magnitude to c but opposite in direction. Thus the picture becomes as shown in Fig. 4.26(b). Now consider stations 1 and 2 in Fig. 4.26. We can again apply the laws of continuity and momentum, making the simplifying assumption that the only force acting is that due to gravity, i.e., pressure variation due to liquid height. From continuity between 1 and 2, we have, for unit breadth,

$$V_1 z_1 = V_2 z_2$$

The flow is steady, and we assume that the shear stress is negligible. The fluid is unconfined; hence there can be no force other than pressure, and so the general momentum relationship, Eq. 4.21, becomes, for the control surface shown in Fig. 4.25(d),

$$p_1 A_1 - p_2 A_2 = \frac{(\rho V_2 A_2) V_2}{g_c} - \frac{(\rho V_1 A_1) V_1}{g_c}$$

With unit width of flow, $A_1 = z_1$, and $A_2 = z_2$. The average pressure for depth of fluid z is $\frac{1}{2} \rho g z / g_c$. Making these substitutions, we obtain

$$\frac{1}{2} \rho \frac{g}{g_c} z_1 z_1 - \frac{1}{2} \rho \frac{g}{g_c} z_2 z_2 = \frac{\rho z_2 V_2^2}{g_c} - \frac{\rho z_1 V_1^2}{g_c}$$

or
$$\frac{g}{2} (z_1^2 - z_2^2) = z_2 V_2^2 - z_1 V_1^2$$

Substituting for V from the continuity relationship, $V_2 = V_1 A_1 / A_2 = V_1 z_1 / z_2$, gives us

$$\frac{g}{2}\left(z_1{}^2 - z_2{}^2\right) = \frac{V_1{}^2 z_1{}^2}{z_2} - z_1 V_1{}^2 = V_1{}^2 z_1 \left(\frac{z_1 - z_2}{z_2}\right)$$

Dividing through by $z_1 - z_2$ yields

$$\frac{g}{2}\left(z_1 + z_2\right) = V_1{}^2 \frac{z_1}{z_2}$$

and

$$V_1{}^2 = \frac{g z_2 (z_1 + z_2)}{2 z_1}$$

Now V_1 was made equal to c, and $z_2 = z + \Delta z$; therefore,

$$c^2 = \frac{g(z + \Delta z)(2z + \Delta z)}{2z} = \frac{g(2z^2 + 3z\,\Delta z + \Delta z^2)}{2z} = gz\left(1 + \frac{3}{2}\frac{\Delta z}{z} + \frac{\Delta z^2}{z^2}\right)$$

We may certainly neglect $\Delta z^2 / z^2$ in comparison with unity, and if $\Delta z \ll z$, then

$$c \approx \sqrt{gz} \qquad\qquad [4.79]$$

This is a simple relationship* for the velocity of a surface wave, or *celerity* as it is often called, that distinguishes it from the wave-propagation velocity, a, in a compressible fluid. Eq. 4.79 is approximate and subject to several restrictions, namely, to waves of small amplitude in shallow liquid, with the only dynamic elements being due to inertia and gravity. Since a more exact expression is rather complicated, Eq. 4.79 is widely used for many purposes.

Similarly to Mach number, the ratio of flow velocity, V, to celerity, c, is a dimensionless parameter. As $V/c = V/\sqrt{gz}$, it is a special form of what is called the *Froude number*. The Froude number, as we shall see later, is the dimensionless parameter $V/\sqrt{gL}$, where in general L is a characteristic dimension of the system under consideration. In this case of wave propagation in a shallow depth of liquid, $L = z$.

4.31 *Momentum and energy equations with electromagnetic body force*

The Euler relations (Eqs. 4.10) were developed for general body forces X, Y, and Z and then integrated for a single special body force, gravitation. Sect. 4.19 discussed the nature of possible stored-energy terms in the energy equations and excluded electromagnetic effects for the time being. Having

---

* This relationship may be derived by means of the Bernoulli equation instead of Eq. 4.21, i.e., if the loss of mechanical energy is assumed negligible. Compare the results of Problem 4.23 on hydraulic jump with this analysis, and rationalize the conclusions.

obtained some widely applicable results for ordinary, simple flow, now we shall look at the question of combined electric and magnetic forces and energies. These are known as magnetofluiddynamic, magnetoaerodynamic, or *magnetohydrodynamic* effects. We shall use the last term here because it seems to be most common, even though the first term might appear to be more logical and all-embracing. Fortunately, the sesquipedalian word "magnetohydrodynamic" has been shortened to simply "MHD."

It is necessary only to broaden the momentum and energy equations, and not to alter their development, to include force and energy due to MHD effects. To do this, though, we must recollect some of the laws relating to the motion of conductors in the presence of magnetic fields.

4.32   *Flow with MHD effects*

The basic MHD effect is illustrated by the flow of an electrically conducting fluid in the presence of a magnetic field perpendicular to the flow. Fig. 4.27 shows a duct through which fluid flows in the positive x direction with velocity $\mathbf{U}$. The top and bottom walls of the duct are of conductive material and thus can act as electrodes, while the side walls are electrically insulated but permeable to the transverse magnetic field of strength $\mathbf{B}$ webers/m^2. The fluid must be a *plasma*, i.e., lightly ionized with some free ions and electrons but neutral overall. A flow of plasma in the magnetic field induces an electric field of intensity $\mathbf{U} \times \mathbf{B}$ volts/m, if $\mathbf{U}$ is in meters per second (mks units). This electric field is analogous to that produced by a solid conductor moving in a transverse magnetic field, and the corresponding "right-hand" rule applies, so that $\mathbf{U} \times \mathbf{B}$ is directed upward, in the positive y direction.

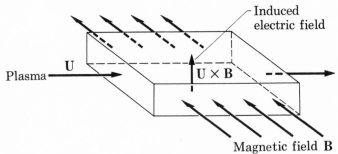

Figure 4.27

If now the top and bottom walls, acting as electrodes, are connected to an external circuit, as shown in Fig. 4.28, a current of density $\mathbf{j}$ amp/m^2

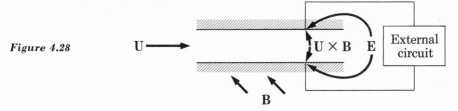

Figure 4.28

will flow. The external circuit, with its current flow, **j**, results in an electric field, **E**, which is considered as applied to the electrodes.

With simplifying assumptions about the nature of the plasma in a magnetic field, acceptable for demonstrating MHD principles, it may be said to have a scalar conductivity of σ mhos/m (the reciprocal of resistance R). Since the net electric field causing current to flow through the plasma is the vector sum of the induced **U ✕ B** and the applied **E** fields, the current **j** through the plasma, and hence through the external circuit, is given by Ohm's law, so that

$$\mathbf{j} = \sigma(\mathbf{U} \times \mathbf{B} + \mathbf{E}) \qquad [4.80]$$

Because the plasma has a finite, and small, conductivity, σ, its resistance, $1/\sigma$, produces *ohmic* or *Joule* heating corresponding to the usual relationship I^2R, or, as $R = 1/\sigma$, j^2/σ, in units of energy per unit volume.

Again analogously to the behavior of solid conductors, a Lorentz or body force **F** given by **j ✕ B** new/m³ acts on the plasma. The direction of this body force depends on the direction of the current with respect to the magnetic field, and this in turn depends on the nature of the circuit.

We may distinguish two major cases. In the first case, if the external circuit is a simple electrical load, e.g., a resistance, the applied field, **E**, although opposite to the induced field, is less than **j ✕ B**. Then the current flow, **j**, is in the positive y direction or upward as in Fig. 4.29(a), and the body force, **F**, is in the negative x direction. In scalar terms, the current is

Figure 4.29

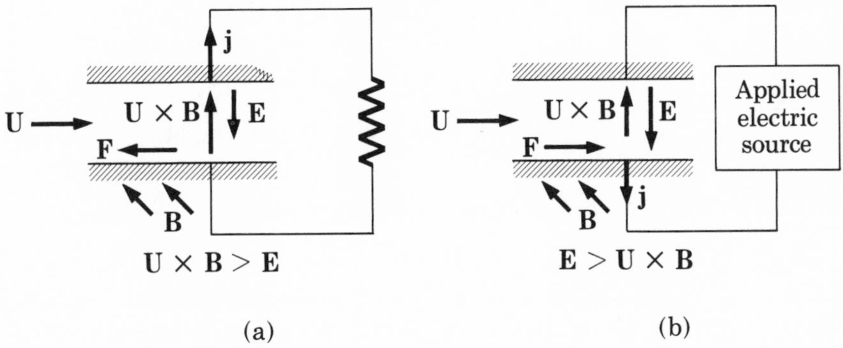

U ✕ B > E

(a)

E > U ✕ B

(b)

given by

$$j = \sigma(UB - E) \qquad [4.81]$$

and the MHD body force is given by

$$X = -jB \qquad [4.82]$$

This arrangement yields an MHD *power generator*, with useful power output jE. The opposing force produces a pressure drop in the plasma, and external mechanical work is required to overcome this loss and other fluid losses in the duct system.

In the second case, if the external circuit contains an electrical source such that the applied field, **E**, is greater than **U** $\times$ **B**, then the current, **j**, is in the negative y direction or downward, and the body force, **F**, is in the positive x direction, as in Fig. 4.29(b). In scalar terms

$$j = \sigma(E - UB) \qquad [4.83]$$

and $$X = jB \qquad [4.84]$$

This arrangement has an accelerating effect on the plasma and may be used for propulsive purposes. The plasma may be any conducting fluid, such as mercury or an ionized gas, the latter being utilized for large-scale power generation. The great difficulty in making engineering use of MHD effects is that a gas has to be at a very high temperature before it becomes sufficiently conductive. This problem can be alleviated somewhat by "seeding" with compounds containing such elements as potassium, sodium, and cesium, which are readily ionized. However, temperatures still must be of the order of 5000°F for worthwhile results, and thus practical application is largely limited by materials.

Other possible uses of MHD are to control a fluid ionized by natural effects so as to yield a beneficial result. As an example, when a body such as a rocket or space vehicle reenters the earth's atmosphere, the friction at hypervelocities heats the air near the surface of the body to extremely high temperatures, so that it is ionized naturally. If a magnetic field is provided, it is possible to produce a retarding force, causing the body to slow down. Suitably applied electromagnetic fields may also help in controlling the flow pattern near the surface of the body, so that the intense heating due to friction is reduced.

The momentum equation for steady flow is, from Eq. 4.11,

$$-\frac{1}{\rho} dp + X\, dx + Y\, dy + Z\, dz = d\left(\frac{U^2}{2g_c}\right)$$

The Lorentz force is a body force in the x direction, and with the MHD generator as an example, is given by $-jB/\rho$ in units of specific energy. The z-direction body force is, in general, the gravitational effect, $-g\, dz/g_c$, and there is no y component. Therefore, Eq. 4.11 becomes

$$-\frac{1}{\rho} dp - \frac{jB}{\rho} dx - \frac{g}{g_c} dz = d\left(\frac{U^2}{2g_c}\right)$$

or
$$\frac{1}{\rho} dp + \frac{jB}{\rho} dx + \frac{g}{g_c} dz + \frac{U\,dU}{g_c} = 0 \qquad [4.85]$$

Eq. 4.85 is a form of the Euler equation for one-dimensional steady flow with MHD effects.

For energy, we have the steady-flow energy equation for one-dimensional flow, expressed in differential form by Eq. 4.50c,

$$dq = d\left(\frac{p}{\rho}\right) + \frac{g}{g_c} dz + \frac{U\,dU}{g_c} + du + dw_s \qquad [4.50d]$$

Again with the MHD generator as an example, the useful net work out is simply electrical work, analogous to the EI product for conventional circuits, or, in our terms, jE. This is in units of power per unit volume, which must be divided by $\rho U/dx$ to become units of specific energy, since

$$\frac{\text{energy}}{\text{mass}} = \frac{\text{energy}}{\text{volume} \times \text{time}} \times \frac{\text{volume}}{\text{mass}} \times \text{time}$$

and
$$\text{time} = \frac{\text{distance}}{\text{velocity}}$$

Thus the work term is $jE\,dx/\rho U$. Noting that the flow is adiabatic, assuming a perfect gas with negligible gravitational effect, and using $u + p/\rho = h = c_p T$, we obtain for the energy equation

$$c_p\,dT + \frac{U\,dU}{g_c} = -\frac{jE}{\rho U} dx \qquad [4.86]$$

which is Eq. 4.64 with an additional term for MHD effects. Hence for work out of the system (positive work), there must be a decrease of stagnation enthalpy.

We can look at the energy equation in another way. The change of stagnation enthalpy of the plasma is manifested in two effects. Firstly, the plasma experiences the retarding Lorentz force, jB, and does work to overcome it in the amount $-jB\,dx/\rho$, units of energy per unit mass. However, because of the Joule heating effect, j^2/σ, energy is returned to the fluid in the amount $j^2\,dx/\sigma\rho U$, units of energy per unit mass. Thus

$$c_p\,dT + \frac{U\,dU}{g_c} = -\frac{jB}{\rho} dx + \frac{j^2}{\sigma\rho U} dx = -\frac{jE}{\rho U} dx \qquad [4.87]$$

In other words, the plasma does work, $jB\,dx/\rho$, of which a portion, $j^2\,dx/\sigma\rho U$, returns to "reheat" it, so that only the remaining portion, $jE\,dx/\rho U$, is delivered to the environment.

An electrical efficiency, η, of the MHD generator may be stated as the ratio of useful power out divided by the sum of the power out and the Joule heating loss. In terms of energy rate per unit volume,

$$\eta = \frac{jE}{jE + j^2/\sigma} \qquad [4.88a]$$

and with $j = \sigma(UB - E)$, this becomes

$$\eta = \frac{E}{UB} \qquad [4.88b]$$

which is the ratio of applied voltage to induced voltage.

We shall not go further into the analysis of MHD. There are so many assumptions and qualifications to be made in application that numerical answers might be misleading at this stage. The object has been to show how the basic conservation equations can be used when electromagnetic effects are present, these relations being fundamental to the study of a very new field having considerable possibilities.

4.33 Summary

This chapter has been concerned with the laws of conservation of momentum and energy as related to fluid flow and is basic to all that follows. It is most important that the conditions applying to the various simplified forms be thoroughly understood, particularly with respect to reversible or irreversible flow. It is too cumbersome to reiterate all the conditions under which a relationship is valid each and every time it is used, and so we must be prepared to recognize the restrictions of a particular form when it appears.

Newton's law of motion applied to a fluid particle results in the *Euler equations of motion*, Eqs. 4.10, valid for the three-dimensional, time-variant, compressible flow of an ideal fluid. These differential equations are intractable for solution except for special cases. Two such general cases are noted, flow along a streamline and irrotational flow. Both result in the same form, Eq. 4.11a,

$$-\frac{1}{\rho} \, dp + X \, dx + Y \, dy + Z \, dz = d\left(\frac{V^2}{2g_c}\right) - \frac{1}{\rho} \frac{\partial p}{\partial t} \, dt \qquad [4.11a]$$

For incompressible, steady flow, with the only body force that of gravity, the integral of Eq. 4.11 is the *Bernoulli equation*, Eq. 4.13a,

$$\frac{p}{\rho} + \frac{g}{g_c} \, z + \frac{V^2}{2g_c} = E_0 \qquad [4.13a]$$

The Bernoulli equation expresses the *conservation of "mechanical" energy* in *incompressible* flow and may be given also in terms of head (Eq. 4.13b) or pressure (Eq. 4.13c).

Integration of the Euler equations calls for a knowledge of the flow in all parts of the field, and a general statement of Newton's second law of motion results in the *momentum equation of fluid flow*, Eq. 4.21. For steady flow, with uniform velocities at both inlet and outlet, the general equation reduces to Eq. 4.22,

$$\Sigma \mathbf{F} = \frac{\dot{m}}{g_c} (\mathbf{V}_2 - \mathbf{V}_1) \qquad [4.22]$$

By means of a suitably chosen control volume, the total force or, if some of the forces can be particularized, the unknown forces can be found from the rate of change of momentum. If the forces are wholly known, then Eq. 4.22 becomes a precise statement of the force–rate of change of momentum balance of the system.

Application of the law of conservation of energy to a fluid system requires the use of the first law of thermodynamics, with careful definition of the terms heat, work, and energy. This yields the general energy equation, Eq. 4.46, which, on elaboration of the general energy term, *e*, into potential, kinetic, and internal energy, becomes Eq. 4.50a,

$$\dot{Q} = \int_S \left(\frac{p}{\rho} + \frac{g}{g_c} z + \frac{V^2}{2g_c} + u \right) \rho \mathbf{V} \cdot d\mathbf{S} + \dot{W}_s \qquad [4.50a]$$

Eq. 4.50a is valid for steady flow in a region where shear stress may be present but produces no work terms and where there are no capillary, chemical, electrical, or magnetic effects. It is in terms of total *rate* of energy flow. For uniform flow at entry and exit stations, in terms of energy per *unit mass*, Eq. 4.50b is applicable,

$$q = \frac{p_2}{\rho_2} - \frac{p_1}{\rho_1} + \frac{g}{g_c} (z_2 - z_1) + \frac{V_2^2 - V_1^2}{2g_c} + u_2 - u_1 + w_s \qquad [4.50b]$$

Eqs. 4.50 are forms of the *simple, steady-flow energy equation*.

Comparison of the Bernoulli equation, Eq. 4.13, with the simple, steady-flow energy equation without shaft work, Eq. 4.50c, shows that the losses appear as internal energy and heat transferred. Comparison of the simple Euler equation, Eq. 4.58, with the simple, adiabatic, steady-flow energy equation without shaft work, Eq. 4.61b, shows that the former is a statement of the latter for reversible flow.

For compressible flow in the absence of gravity, the Euler equation becomes Eq. 4.58,

$$\frac{dp}{\rho} + \frac{V \, dV}{g_c} = 0 \qquad [4.58]$$

which may be integrated if the pressure-density relation is known. For reversible, adiabatic flow, Eqs. 4.59 result.

For adiabatic flow, reversible or irreversible, the simple energy equation becomes

$$h_0 = h + \frac{V^2}{2g_c} = \text{constant} \qquad [4.63]$$

This leads to the concepts of *stagnation enthalpy* and, for a gas, *stagnation temperature*, both constant in adiabatic flow with no shaft work. *Stagnation pressure* is defined in terms of a *reversible adiabatic process* in which it remains constant; it decreases in *irreversible* adiabatic flow. In the *incompressible* flow of a gas, stagnation pressure is static pressure plus dynamic pressure, $p_0 = p + \rho V^2/2g_c$, but in *compressible* flow, $p_0 - p \neq \rho V^2/2g_c$ but some multiple of it, as demonstrated by Eq. 4.78.

The introduction of the propagation velocity, a, of a disturbance in a compressible fluid gives rise to the concept of Mach number, $M = V/a$, and the use of Mach number rather than velocity in various forms of the momentum and energy equations. Finite values of wave-propagation velocity within a compressible fluid and on the surface of a liquid lead to a realization that flow regimes in which the flow velocities are greater than the propagation velocities require different treatment from those in which the flow velocities are less than the propagation velocities.

Finally the Euler and energy equations can be extended to include simple magnetohydrodynamic effects, being transformed to Eqs. 4.85 and 4.87.

The Euler equations of motion are valid only for ideal flow. If viscous forces are introduced, the situation becomes very complex, as there are three viscous stresses in each plane. H. Schlichting presents, in his *Boundary Layer Theory,*[*] a complete development for real flow. The results, the *Navier-Stokes* equations, are of great importance, for they are the basic relationships for the flow of a real fluid. These equations in Cartesian coordinates for compressible flow of a fluid of constant viscosity are as follows:

for the x direction,

$$-\frac{1}{\rho}\frac{\partial p}{\partial x} + X + \frac{1}{3g_c}\frac{\mu}{\rho}\frac{\partial}{\partial x}\left(\frac{\partial u}{\partial x} + \frac{\partial v}{\partial y} + \frac{\partial w}{\partial z}\right) + \frac{\mu}{\rho g_c}\left(\frac{\partial^2 u}{\partial x^2} + \frac{\partial^2 u}{\partial y^2} + \frac{\partial^2 u}{\partial z^2}\right)$$
$$= \frac{1}{g_c}\left(u\frac{\partial u}{\partial x} + v\frac{\partial u}{\partial y} + w\frac{\partial u}{\partial z} + \frac{\partial u}{\partial t}\right) \qquad [4.89a]$$

for the y direction,

$$-\frac{1}{\rho}\frac{\partial p}{\partial y} + Y + \frac{1}{3g_c}\frac{\mu}{\rho}\frac{\partial}{\partial y}\left(\frac{\partial u}{\partial x} + \frac{\partial v}{\partial y} + \frac{\partial w}{\partial z}\right) + \frac{\mu}{\rho g_c}\left(\frac{\partial^2 v}{\partial x^2} + \frac{\partial^2 v}{\partial y^2} + \frac{\partial^2 v}{\partial z^2}\right)$$
$$= \frac{1}{g_c}\left(u\frac{\partial v}{\partial x} + v\frac{\partial v}{\partial y} + w\frac{\partial v}{\partial z} + \frac{\partial v}{\partial t}\right) \qquad [4.89b]$$

[*] 4th ed., McGraw-Hill, New York, 1960.

for the z direction,

$$-\frac{1}{\rho}\frac{\partial p}{\partial z} + Z + \frac{1}{3g_c}\frac{\mu}{\rho}\frac{\partial}{\partial z}\left(\frac{\partial u}{\partial x} + \frac{\partial v}{\partial y} + \frac{\partial w}{\partial z}\right) + \frac{\mu}{\rho g_c}\left(\frac{\partial^2 w}{\partial x^2} + \frac{\partial^2 w}{\partial y^2} + \frac{\partial^2 w}{\partial z^2}\right)$$
$$= \frac{1}{g_c}\left(u\frac{\partial w}{\partial x} + v\frac{\partial w}{\partial y} + w\frac{\partial w}{\partial z} + \frac{\partial w}{\partial t}\right) \quad [\textbf{4.89c}]$$

or

$$-\frac{1}{\rho}\operatorname{grad} p + \mathbf{S} + \frac{1}{3g_c}\frac{\mu}{\rho}\operatorname{grad}\operatorname{div}\mathbf{V} + \frac{\mu}{\rho g_c}\nabla^2\mathbf{V} = \frac{1}{g_c}\frac{D\mathbf{V}}{Dt} \quad [\textbf{4.89d}]$$

where $\mathbf{S} = \mathbf{i}X + \mathbf{j}Y + \mathbf{k}Z$.

A comparison of Eqs. 4.89 with the Euler equations, Eqs. 4.10, shows that the first two terms on the left-hand side and the term on the right-hand side are similar. The remaining two terms on the left-hand side are those entering through viscous action. The Navier-Stokes equations, in conjunction with varying boundary conditions, describe all real-flow problems, with considerable simplifications being made for mathematical solution. Thus it will be observed that the first viscous term disappears for incompressible flow, since div $\mathbf{V} = 0$. Eqs. 4.89 can be expressed in vector form as

$$-\frac{1}{\rho}\nabla p + \mathbf{S} + \frac{\mu}{\rho g_c}\nabla^2\mathbf{V} = \frac{1}{g_c}\frac{D\mathbf{V}}{Dt} \quad [\textbf{4.90}]$$

Problems

4.1. Find the magnitude and direction of the resultant acceleration of a fluid particle as it moves through the point 1, 2 in the steady, two-dimensional field given by $\psi = xy + y^2$.

4.2. Show that, in source flow, the acceleration in steady flow is

$$\frac{Du_r}{Dt} = u_r\frac{\partial u_r}{\partial r}$$

4.3. For a three-dimensional point source of strength 8π ft³/sec, show that the total acceleration at a point 2 ft from the center is 0.25 ft/sec² and is a *deceleration*.

4.4. Write the Euler equations of motion for a two-dimensional flow with the following special conditions: the body force is in the x direction only; the pressure force in the y direction is constant; velocity in the y direction varies in the y direction but not in the x direction.

4.5. An insurance-underwriter Class A pump for fire-truck duty should deliver a maximum flow of 1500 gal/min at 150 psig, total pressure at the pump. Assuming that no losses occur between the pump and the delivery nozzle at the end of the hose, find the height to which the pump can deliver water and the diameter of the nozzle for the maximum flow.

4.6. In (a) sea-level air is being drawn through a duct past an airfoil into a vacuum tank. In (b) the airfoil is moving through sea-level air at a speed of 200 ft/sec. In

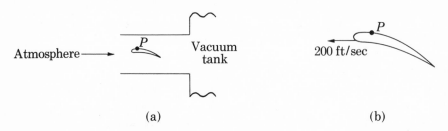

(a)   (b)

both cases, the relative velocity between airfoil and air at point p is 400 ft/sec. Find the static pressure at p in each case, assuming air at a constant density of 0.0765 lb/ft³.

4.7. Assuming ideal flow throughout,
  a. Find the depth of water, h, necessary in the head tank in order to provide a flow rate of 3 gal/min.
  b. Find the manometer reading, Δh, in in. Hg for this condition.

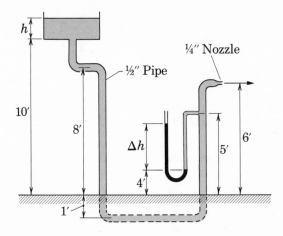

4.8. You wish to pump a stream of water from a nozzle through the air to a pond whose nearest edge is 100 ft away. The diameter of the nozzle is 3 in. The pond is at the same elevation as the nozzle, but the water supply is 25 ft below the nozzle. Neglecting friction, determine the minimum power required.

4.9. Air is fed from a large reservoir, A, through a 3 in. diameter duct and diffusing section to the atmosphere at B. Assume ideal, incompressible, isothermal flow with a

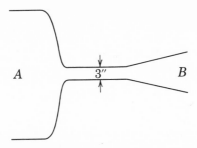

barometer reading of 29.35 in. Hg and air temperature of 75°F throughout. If a flow rate of 1.73 lb/sec and a velocity of 210 ft/sec at B are necessary,

    a. Find the required area at B.

    b. Find the reservoir pressure, p_A, in in. H_2O.

    c. Find the pressure in in. H_2O in the 3 in. diameter duct.

4.10. Oil of sp gr 0.9 flows steadily from the constant-head reservoir through the constant-area pipe to the atmosphere. Assuming ideal flow, find the manometer reading, Δh, in in. Hg. The oil is separated from the mercury by a column of water.

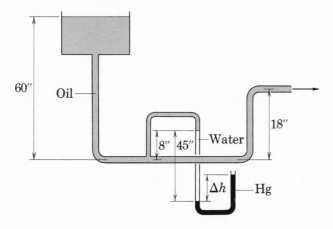

4.11. A free jet of fluid with a flow rate of $\dot{m}$ lb/sec strikes the plates as shown in (a), (b), (c), and (d). For each case, write an expression for the horizontal force

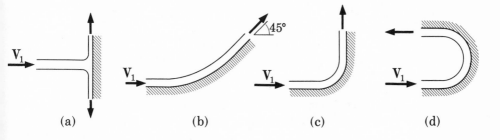

    (a)   (b)   (c)   (d)

on the plate in terms of the entering velocity, V_1. Assume no losses and no effects due to elevation.

4.12. A circular cylinder of 2 in. diameter is placed in a stream of air flowing from left to right, which has freestream values of 14.31 psia pressure, 70°F temperature, and 200 ft/sec velocity. Assuming ideal flow, with the cylinder center at the origin of the coordinates,

a. Find the pressure at the surface of the cylinder along the x axis on the downstream side.

b. Find the pressure at the surface of the cylinder on the y axis.

c. Find the pressure at point 1.5, 1.5 (coordinate values in in.).

4.13. Water at 60 psi enters the nozzle (station 1) with a flow rate of 300 gal/min and a velocity of 10 ft/sec. It leaves the nozzle (station 2) with a velocity of 90 ft/sec, flowing to atmosphere. Find the force required to hold the nozzle in position.

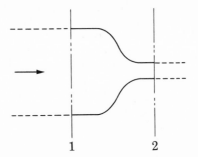

1   2

4.14. For a simple turbojet engine with atmospheric intake and discharge, show that

$$F = \frac{\dot{m}}{g_c} (V_j - U)$$

where F is thrust, $\dot{m}$ is mass flow rate, V_j is jet velocity, and U is forward speed. For a stationary turbojet, $F = mV_j/g_c$ from the preceding equation; i.e., intake momentum flux is zero. Yet, for a turbojet on the ground with the engine running, there is a significant air velocity at the inlet, and it is quite a problem to prevent the ingress of solid matter. Explain this apparent paradox.

4.15. A 90° reducing elbow in a horizontal plane has water flowing through it as shown. At inlet, the velocity is 8 ft/sec, the pressure is 10 psi, and the pipe diameter

Outlet

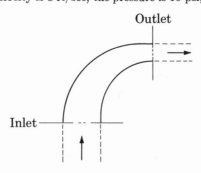

Inlet

is 6 in. At outlet, the pipe diameter is 3 in. Assuming ideal flow, find the force necessary to hold the elbow in place. The elbow is part of a continuous piping system.

4.16. A lawn sprinkler has two arms, each containing a nozzle of $\frac{1}{16}$ in. diameter at 6 in. radius, the nozzles being tangentially opposed and discharging horizontally. Water enters at the axis of rotation with no tangential velocity, and the total flow rate is 0.75 gal/min.

    a. Find the net torque on the rotor when held stationary.

    b. Find the horsepower used in overcoming air resistance and bearing friction if the sprinkler rotates at 150 rpm.

4.17. An inward radial-flow turbine has a nozzle angle, α, of 30° and an inlet rotor-tip speed of 30 ft/sec, with a ratio of inlet to outlet rotor diameter, $d_1/d_2 = 2$.

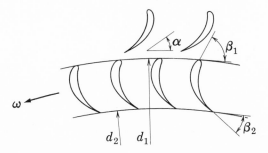

The radial-flow velocity is constant at 20 ft/sec across the rotor, and there is no angular momentum at the outlet. Find the correct blade angles at inlet (β_1) and outlet (β_2) and the theoretical specific rate of energy transfer for ideal flow under these conditions.

4.18. A fluid flows steadily in a duct. No shaft work crosses the boundaries of the duct. Given the following data for stations 1 and 2,

	1	2
Pressure, psia	40	30
Temperature, °F	250	280
Density, lb/ft³	0.157	0.143
Elevation, ft	143	254
Internal energy, Btu/lb	112	127
Velocity, ft/sec	220	340
Area of duct, ft²	0.25	

    a. Find the change in total energy between stations. In what form must this energy be?

    b. Find the change in the sum of mechanical energy and work due to pressure between stations.

    c. Find the force on the duct, assuming that the flows at inlet and outlet are parallel and in the same direction.

4.19. Water flows from reservoir *A* through a constant-diameter pipe at 16 ft/sec to reservoir *B*. The water spills over the edge of reservoir *B* and flows down the rough surface at a constant average velocity of 16 ft/sec to reservoir *C*. Assume that losses

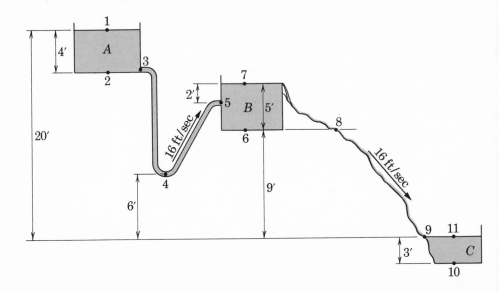

for processes 2–3 and 5–6 are negligible and that any loss between 3 and 5 is divided equally between 3–4 and 4–5. Present, in tabular form, the velocity, pressure, elevation, and total head for each numbered point (take *g* = 32 ft/sec² for simple numerical results). Indicate whether each process, 1–2, 2–3, etc., is reversible or irreversible.

4.20. A water siphon having a uniform pipe of 3 in. diameter is arranged as shown. Assuming ideal flow,

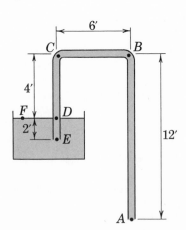

a. Find the rate of discharge, Q, in ft³/sec and the pressure head at B.
b. Plot the kinetic, potential, flow, and total energy versus position along the centerline from E to A.
c. Find the maximum rate of discharge possible with AB made longer, the length required to produce this flow rate, and the pressure at B under these conditions.
d. Find the pressure head at B if the friction loss between E and B is 3 ft and that between B and A is 4 ft.

4.21. Two streams of an incompressible fluid are flowing concentrically as shown, each occupying a flow area A but the central stream having twice the velocity of the surrounding stream. When they are mixed at constant area, the final velocity is

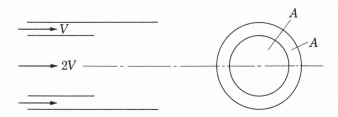

uniform. Assume no loss due to wall shear stress. Show that the *rate* of mechanical-energy dissipation is $\frac{3}{8}\rho A V^3/g_c$ in ft-lb$_f$/sec.

4.22. Show for a sudden enlargement in a pipe with incompressible flow that the loss of head, h_L, is

$$h_L = \frac{V_1^2}{2g} \left(1 - \frac{A_1}{A_2}\right)^2$$

Assume that no wall shear stress exists and that the pressure over the whole area at the enlargement is uniform and equal to that at plane 1.

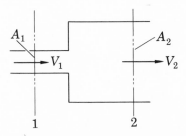

4.23. Water flowing freely in an open channel sometimes undergoes a discontinuity known as a *hydraulic jump*, shown qualitatively at (a). Idealizing this change as instantaneous as shown at (b) and assuming no shear stress at either channel bed or air interface, show that

$$\frac{y_2}{y_1} = -\frac{1}{2} + \sqrt{\frac{1}{4} + \frac{2V_1^2}{gy_1}}$$

(a)   (b)

Is there any loss of total energy in the hydraulic jump? Any loss of mechanical energy? If so, find expressions for them in terms of y_1 and y_2.

4.24. Air is flowing steadily in a pipe at a rate of 10 lb/sec. At station 1, the pressure is 50 psia, the temperature is 200°F, and the internal diameter of the pipe is 6 in. At station 2, the temperature is 100°F. At station 3, the temperature is 75°F, and the area of the pipe is 15 in. If the flow is adiabatic throughout, with no shaft work, but reversible between 1 and 2 and irreversible between 2 and 3, find for each station the stagnation temperature, the stagnation pressure, the static pressure, $q = \rho V^2/2g_c$, the difference between the stagnation and static pressures, and the area of the duct.

4.25. An airplane is flying at 20,000 ft, where the atmospheric pressure is 6.753 psia and the temperature is −12.3°F. A Pitot-static tube mounted on the plane in the freestream gives a differential manometer reading equivalent to 8.5 in. H_2O. Estimate the speed of the plane, assuming incompressible flow.

4.26. Repeat Problem 4.24, finding the Mach number at each station and using the Mach-number relationships as far as possible to obtain the values required.

4.27. Given the compressibility of water, K, as a constant value of 300,000 psi, with $K = \rho(dp/d\rho)$, calculate the pressure to which water must be compressed in order to leave a nozzle at atmospheric pressure with a jet velocity equal to its sonic velocity.

4.28. In a small, return-flow, supersonic wind tunnel, air flows from a large reservoir through a converging section to the test section in which models are placed. A model is to be tested at a Mach number of 3.0 under a pressure of 6.0 psia and a temperature of −60°F. The cross-sectional area of the model may be considered negligible with respect to the test-section area.

    a. If the test section has an area of 16 in.^{2}, find the mass flow rate in lb/sec.

    b. Find the stagnation and dynamic values of pressure and temperature in the test section.

    c. Assuming steady, adiabatic, reversible flow, find the required reservoir pressure and temperature.

4.29. Air flows along a duct under adiabatic conditions. At station 1, where the area of the duct is 12 in.^{2}, the air has a pressure of 35 psig, a temperature of 200°F, and a velocity of 550 ft/sec. If the velocity at station 2, farther along the duct, must be 880 ft/sec, find the area required at station 2 (a) for reversible flow along the duct, and (b) if there is a loss of stagnation pressure of 3 psi between stations 1 and 2.

4.30. Show for the ideal, isothermal flow of a perfect gas that for two stations, 1 and 2,

$$\frac{p_2}{p_1} = e^{(k/2)(M_1{}^2 - M_2{}^2)}$$

4.31. Air flows into a pipe from a large reservoir kept at constant pressure p_1. If the flow is isothermal, show that for reversible flow the dynamic temperature of the air at any station 2 along the pipe is equal to $[(k-1)/k]T \ln p_1/p_2$, where $k = c_p/c_v$.

Dimensional Analysis and Similitude

5.1 *Introduction*

Confronted with a new problem in fluid mechanics, or in any other engineering discipline, we have in general two methods of approach, one of direct experiment and one of analysis. Usually we combine the two, because only in the very simplest cases can analysis give the complete answer. Experiment, however, can be costly, and often the results are difficult to assimilate when there are a number of variables, since we are limited to representation in three dimensions at most. Suppose, for instance, that we want to determine the variation of pressure loss with flow rate of a fluid flowing in a pipe. For a particular fluid in a pipe of given size, the relationship could be obtained quite readily and would be as shown in Fig. 5.1(a). If the fluid were a liquid with constant density, we could plot the results at other temperatures as in Fig. 5.1(b). If it were compressible, however, we would find that both pressure and temperature affected the loss and that we required another set of curves showing the effect of pressure while the temperature was constant. To secure any general results, we would want to alter the length and diameter of the pipe and to use different fluids. We would end up with a multiplicity of curves. We could combine some of them after analyzing the results to see if a fixed relationship existed for any of the variables, but it would be time-consuming and in some cases extremely difficult, if not impossible, to hit upon the correct grouping. Moreover, analysis might not lead us to a solution even if we were able to set up differential equations expressing the physical relationship.

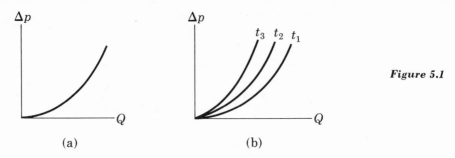

Figure 5.1

(a)   (b)

A third type of approach is possible that can give us considerable insight into a problem and that in particular can show us how to group the variables to assist the experimental procedure. It consists in selecting the variables known to enter into the problem and combining them in a rational manner by means of an algebraic theory of *dimensions*. Its roots lie in a principle already familiar and dating back to Fourier in the early nineteenth century, namely, that the physical relationship must be dimensionally correct, i.e., have *dimensional homogeneity*. The fact that physical entities or variables have dimensions leads to the fact that they can be combined in only a limited number of ways in a given situation. *Dimensional analysis* is a method of seeking such relationships in the most direct and certain manner, from a knowledge *only* of the dimensions of the variables involved and not of any physical analysis (or, at the most, the very minimum).

Dimensional analysis can be used in any problem based on physical laws and is widely used in mechanics, of both solids and fluids, and in heat transfer. It is commonly first encountered in fluid mechanics, where it is extremely important, hence our attention to it. The method is valid for all technologies and has been applied in the field of cosmology to the behavior of stars, with which we have little hope of direct experiment.

5.2 *Dimensions*

A dimension is a quality of a physical entity, such as length, mass, or time. It can be measured in terms of a selected unit amount of the entity, and its quantity is an abstract number equal to the number of times the unit can be contained in it. Typical *units* of measurement are the foot, the pound, and the second. Thus when we say that a piece of wood is 10 ft long, we are expressing the dimension of length in units of feet. Here dimensions will be written in brackets, as $[L]$, $[T]$, etc., and the identity symbol ($\equiv$) rather than the equal symbol ($=$) will be used for equivalence.

Not all variables have separate dimensions; e.g., area and volume do not have their own units but are measured as products of length units $[L^2]$ and $[L^3]$. In this way the number of primary dimensions is kept small, and other units are derived from them.

As soon as a variable is given a dimension as well as a quantity, certain rules must be observed. We know already, for instance, we cannot add pounds and feet. A physical relationship must be expressed in the correct dimensions to have meaning; i.e., it must have dimensional homogeneity.

The problem then arises of choosing the primary dimensions that are of greatest utility. Note that the criterion is utility and is not absolute; i.e., we can conceive readily and measure relatively easily such entities as length, mass, force, and time and find that other mechanical quantities can be expressed in terms of these. If viscosity and work were readily measured, it would be possible to express length, time, etc., in terms of them as derived dimensions.

In mechanics, length $[L]$ and time $[T]$ are used and universally agreed upon. There is then a choice between force $[F]$ and mass $[M]$, which are not independent, since Newton's law relates them if we write it in dimensional form as $[F] \equiv [M][L/T^2]$. We may use both $[F]$ and $[M]$ if Newton's Law is written as $F = Ma/g_c$, with g_c being a dimensional constant having dimensions $[M/F][L/T^2]$. There is some advantage in using both $[F]$ and $[M]$ and always including g_c, for the practice automatically ensures that g_c enters the final results in the correct place to distinguish units on the basis outlined in Chapter 1. It does, however, lengthen the required algebraic procedure by adding a variable. We shall assume that the problem of units is understood (i.e., the difference between pound mass and pound force) and choose between $[F]$ and $[M]$. Either is satisfactory, but we shall settle on $[M]$ as being fundamental and thus express all dimensions in terms of $[M]$, $[L]$, and $[T]$, using $[F] \equiv [M][L/T^2]$ to convert variables that are customarily in force units.

We shall not attempt to list all common variables in terms of their dimensions but shall give only a few examples. Pressure is force per unit area $\equiv [F/L^2] \equiv [ML/T^2L^2] \equiv [M/LT^2]$. Power is force times distance per unit time $\equiv [FL/T] = [(ML/T^2)L/T] \equiv [ML^2/T^3]$. Viscosity is stress per unit rate of strain $\equiv [(F/A)/(V/T)] \equiv [M/T^2L]/[L/TL] \equiv [M/LT]$. Angular velocity is radians per unit time $\equiv (\text{arc/radius})/\text{time} \equiv [L/L]/[T] \equiv [1/T]$.

In a problem involving thermal entities, it is sometimes convenient to introduce temperature, θ, and heat, H, as additional primary dimensions. If the problem involves only heat transfer, the extra dimensions are desirable and useful, but a thermodynamic problem needs further consideration because there is mutual conversion of heat and work. Heat is a form of energy, and there is a fixed relationship between thermal energy and mechanical energy represented by the proportionality factor J in $Q = JW$ ($J = 778.28$ ft-lb$_f$/Btu). If thermal energy and mechanical energy are being interchanged, the situation can be indicated by the use of J as a dimensional constant in the total of entities in the physical relationship. Likewise, temperature is a form of specific energy of the molecules, and for a gas it is related to the mechanical entities through an equation of state, e.g., $pv = RT$ for an ideal gas. Thus the gas constant, R, must enter as another dimensional constant. In the analysis of compression or expansion of gases, work is one of the major variables, and, in general, there may be transfer of heat. Consequently, we would include W, Q, J, and R as entities, with dimensions $[ML^2/T^2]$, $[H]$, $[ML^2/T^2H]$, and $[L^2/T^2\theta]$,* respectively. If the process were adiabatic, we could omit Q and J but would retain R, because work and internal energy are being interchanged.

5.3   *Dimensional analysis*

The first step in dimensional analysis is to list the variables that are considered to enter into the problem. Usually we think of one important dependent variable, α_1, as a function of several independent variables, α_2, α_3, . . . , α_n. In algebraic form

$$\alpha_1 = f_1(\alpha_2, \alpha_3, \ . \ . \ . \ , \alpha_n)$$
or
$$f_2(\alpha_1, \alpha_2, \alpha_3, \ . \ . \ . \ , \alpha_n) = 0$$

Let us introduce dimensional analysis with a simple example that can be solved by inspection. Taking the case of equilibrium in fluid statics, we assume that the pressure, p, at any point is dependent on the fluid density, ρ, the gravitational attraction that we identify by g, and the position of the point, which we characterize by distance from a datum, z. Thus

$$p = f(\rho, g, z)$$

In dimensional form this becomes

$$\left[\frac{M}{LT^2}\right] \equiv f\left\{\left[\frac{M}{L^3}\right], \left[\frac{L}{T^2}\right], [L]\right\}$$

A little study shows that for dimensional homogeneity the function on the right-hand side must be the simple product of the variables; i.e.,

$$p \propto \rho g z$$
or
$$p = C\rho g z$$

where C is a dimensionless constant.

This demonstration raises some important points. The first concerns

* $R = pv/T \equiv \left[\dfrac{M}{LT^2} \dfrac{L^3}{M} \dfrac{1}{\theta}\right] \equiv [L^2/T^2\theta]$

the choice of independent variables upon which we assumed the pressure to depend. Here we cheated with an exact answer from previous analysis, and so we chose those variables that we knew to be correct and chose them in a particular manner to get an answer in a form that was familiar. In any real problem for which dimensional analysis is used from the beginning because of a lack of other knowledge, considerable thought must be given to the choice of variables. In the first place, no important variable entering into the physical relationship can be omitted, and the inclusion of a superfluous one may complicate matters. If dimensional homogeneity cannot be obtained, we can be sure that some variable has been omitted, i.e., that the relationship as stated is not a true physical relationship. On the other hand, an extraneous variable will sometimes not appear in our final answer. Obviously some degree of engineering experience and judgment is required, albeit of much less precise nature than for an exact analysis.

The second point concerns the particular manner in which the effect of the variable is introduced; e.g., we introduced body force as weight by using density and gravitational acceleration. We can alter our end result for convenience if we do not upset dimensional homogeneity. In our example we might have taken specific weight, γ, and obtained $p \propto \gamma z$, a perfectly correct answer and, in some circumstances, possibly a better one. This is a warning that although a dimensional analysis may be correct, it may not always be in the best form.

The third point is that although the answer is specific in the statement that pressure is linearly dependent on the product $\rho g z$, the constant in the final equation can only be found by experiment. In general, all we can determine by dimensional analysis is that a number of variables must be combined in a certain manner to give a particular grouping; the relationship among various groups is unknown.

The fourth point is that the answer might be stated as

$$\frac{p}{\rho g z} = \text{constant}$$

with the left-hand side forming a *dimensionless group*. With more variables in the problem, we would obtain not one dimensionless group but several, and it is the function of dimensional analysis to show what these groups may be. Dimensionless groups are usually called π-terms or π-groups, and our answer can be stated as

$$\pi = \frac{\rho}{\rho g z}$$

as a result of dimensional analysis.

It is apparent that for more complex problems simple inspection is not adequate, and furthermore, as the variables can seldom be grouped into only one π-term, we must know how many such terms are necessary and sufficient.

The formal procedure of dimensional analysis can be quite complicated and can lead to much philosophic argument as to the real nature of dimensions. Here we shall regard it as a technique that yields very useful results and justify it only to the extent of rendering it plausible.*

The heart of dimensional analysis lies in the π-theorem, first enunciated by Buckingham, which may be summarized as follows. If a physical relationship can be expressed as

$$\alpha_1 = f_1(\alpha_2, \alpha_3, \ldots, \alpha_n) \qquad [5.1a]$$

and hence as $\qquad f_2(\alpha_1, \alpha_2, \alpha_3, \ldots, \alpha_n) = 0 \qquad [5.1b]$

then it can also be expressed as

$$\phi_1(\pi_1, \pi_2, \pi_3, \ldots, \pi_i) = 0 \qquad [5.2a]$$

or $\qquad \pi_1 = \phi(\pi_2, \pi_3, \ldots, \pi_i) \qquad [5.2b]$

in which each π-term is formed of two or more variables and in which the number of π-terms, i, is *generally* equal to $n - m$, where m is the number of primary dimensions used for describing n variables. For the immediately following exposition, it will be assumed that $i = n - m$, and a modification of this rule will be deferred until Sect. 5.6.

To find the π-terms in Eq. 5.2, we shall assume that Eq. 5.1 can be expressed as the sum of a number of power series of all the variables α, i.e.,

$$A(\alpha_1{}^{a_1} \alpha_2{}^{a_2} \ldots \alpha_n{}^{a_n}) + B(\alpha_1{}^{b_1} \alpha_2{}^{b_2} \ldots \alpha_n{}^{b_n}) + \cdots = 0$$

where A, B, etc., are numerical coefficients and a_1, a_2, b_1, b_2, etc., are exponents. Dividing through by the first term yields

$$1 + \frac{B}{A}(\alpha_1{}^{b_1-a_1} \alpha_2{}^{b_2-a_2} \ldots \alpha_n{}^{b_n-a_n}) + \cdots = 0$$

For dimensional homogeneity all the terms must be dimensionless because the first term (unity) is dimensionless. Thus for dimensional analysis we need take only one term of the series to represent the dimensional grouping. Writing the exponents in generalized form (i.e., $b_1 - a_1 = a$, $b_2 - a_2 = b$, etc.) we can then indicate the dimensionless character of the function by

$$[\alpha_1{}^a \alpha_2{}^b \alpha_3{}^c \ldots \alpha_n{}^x] \equiv [M^0 L^0 T^0 \ldots] \qquad [5.3]$$

i.e., by equating each variable α expressed in its dimensions to the product of the primary dimensions with zero exponents. According to the usual algebraic laws, the sum of the exponents of each primary dimension on the left-hand side is equal to zero.

* For full insight, these references may be consulted: H. E. Huntley, *Dimensional Analysis*, Rinehart, New York, 1955; H. L. Langhaar, *Dimensional Analysis and Theory of Models*, Wiley, New York, 1951; E. R. Van Driest, "On Dimensional Analysis and the Presentation of Data in Fluid Flow Problems," *J. Appl. Mech.*, **13**, A-34 (1946).

Let us see how this procedure works for the problem solved earlier by inspection. Stated in the form of Eq. 5.3, it is

$$\left[\left(\frac{M}{LT^2} \right)^a \left(\frac{M}{L^3} \right)^b \left(\frac{L}{T^2} \right)^c (L)^d \right] \equiv [M^0 L^0 T^0]$$

There are four unknown exponents, a, b, c, and d, although only three equations corresponding to M, L, and T can be found. However, we can take the dth root without changing the dimensionless character of either side and thus consider d as unity in the previous equation, obtaining (noting that the exponents a, b, and c are new)

$$\left[\left(\frac{M}{LT^2} \right)^a \left(\frac{M}{L^3} \right)^b \left(\frac{L}{T^2} \right)^c (L) \right] \equiv [M^0 L^0 T^0] \qquad [5.4]$$

Forming equations for the exponents of M, L, and T in turn, we have

for M, $\qquad\qquad\qquad\qquad a + b = 0$ $\qquad\qquad\qquad\qquad$ [1]

for L, $\qquad\qquad\qquad -a - 3b + c + 1 = 0$ $\qquad\qquad\qquad$ [2]

for T, $\qquad\qquad\qquad\qquad -2a - 2c = 0$ $\qquad\qquad\qquad\qquad$ [3]

From 1, $b = -a$, and from 3, $c = -a$. Substituting these in 2 yields

$$-a + 3a - a + 1 = 0$$
$$a = -1$$

Hence $b = 1$, and $c = 1$. Resubstituting the original variables in Eq. 5.4, which is the π-term, yields

$$\pi = p^{-1} \rho g z$$

or $\qquad\qquad\qquad\qquad\qquad \pi = \dfrac{p}{\rho g z}$

since the π-term can be raised to any power (in this case -1) because it is dimensionless. Use of the simple rule for the number of necessary π-terms gives, with $n = 4$ and $m = 3$, $i = n - m = 1$. Thus only one π-term is required. The grouping of the variables in the π-term means that a change of either ρ, g, or z is reflected directly as a corresponding change in p, or, as usually stated, that p is directly proportional to ρ, g, and z.

Now consider a problem in which there is more than one π-term. Suppose that the pressure loss, Δp, along a pipe depends on the length, s, diameter, d, fluid density, ρ, fluid velocity, V, and fluid viscosity, μ. Thus

$$\Delta p = f_1(s, d, \rho, V, \mu) = 0$$

Following the procedure as before, we obtain

$$f_2(\Delta p, s, d, \rho, V, \mu) = 0$$

and

$$\left[\left(\frac{M}{LT^2} \right)^a (L)^b (L)^c \left(\frac{M}{L^3} \right)^d \left(\frac{L}{T} \right)^e \left(\frac{M}{LT} \right) \right] \equiv [M^0 L^0 T^0]$$

The π-theorem states that with $n = 6$ and $m = 3$ three π-terms are necessary. Forming equations from the exponents, we have

for M, $\qquad\qquad\qquad a + d + 1 = 0$ $\qquad\qquad\qquad$ [1]

for L, $\qquad\qquad -a + b + c - 3d + e - 1 = 0$ $\qquad$ [2]

for T, $\qquad\qquad\qquad -2a - e - 1 = 0$ $\qquad\qquad\qquad$ [3]

This time there are five unknowns and three equations, and therefore we must solve in terms of two of the unknowns. In terms of a and b,

from 1, $\qquad\qquad\qquad d = -a - 1$

from 3, $\qquad\qquad\qquad e = -2a - 1$

from 2, $\quad c = a - b + 3d - e + 1 = a - b + 3(-a - 1) - (-2a - 1)$
$$\qquad\qquad\qquad\qquad\qquad\qquad\qquad + 1 = -b - 1$$

Hence

$$\Delta p^a s^b d^{-b-1} \rho^{-a-1} V^{-2a-1} \mu \equiv [M^0 L^0 T^0]$$

Grouping the terms of like exponents together gives

$$\left[\left(\frac{\Delta p}{\rho V^2} \right)^a \left(\frac{s}{d} \right)^b \left(\frac{\mu}{\rho V d} \right) \right] \equiv [M^0 L^0 T^0] \qquad\qquad [5.5]$$

Each term in Eq. 5.5 is dimensionless and thus is a π-term. Since we took only one power series of the total number representing the function, the exponents a and b have no particular significance, and we must return to the functional equation (Eq. 5.2),

$$\phi_1 \left(\frac{\Delta p}{\rho V^2}, \frac{s}{d}, \frac{\mu}{\rho V d} \right) = 0$$

or $\qquad\qquad\qquad\qquad \dfrac{\Delta p}{\rho V^2} = \phi \left(\dfrac{s}{d}, \dfrac{\mu}{\rho V d} \right) \qquad\qquad\qquad$ [5.6a]

which may be written as

$$\Delta p = \rho V^2 \phi \left(\frac{s}{d}, \frac{\mu}{\rho V d} \right) \qquad\qquad [5.6b]$$

It will be seen that the original relationship for Δp as a function of five variables, s, d, ρ, V, μ, has been transformed into one containing $n - m = i = 3$ dimensionless groups or π-terms, in accordance with the π-theorem. We have $\pi_1 = \Delta p / \rho V^2$, $\pi_2 = s/d$, and $\pi_3 = \mu / \rho V d$.

The function ϕ is unknown, but dimensional analysis in this manner cannot supply a more definite answer, for which we would have to resort to experiment. However, six variables have been reduced to three groups, and all results can be plotted on one graph with, say, $\Delta p/\rho V^2$ as ordinate, $\mu/\rho V d$ as abscissa, and s/d as parameter. Dimensional analysis, then, does tell us something about the relationship among variables, i.e., the rational way in which they may be combined. It should be noted, however, that although the π-theorem states the minimum number of π-terms required for completely describing the physical relationship (which is also the maximum number of *independent* groups), the particular terms just obtained are the result of chance in the algebraic procedure (the selection of a and b as unknown exponents). Other π-terms are possible and could be entirely adequate in describing the physical relationship, but they would not necessarily be the most useful.

The number, N, of π-terms possible from n variables with m primary dimensions is given by

$$N = \frac{n!}{(m + 1)!(n - m - 1)!} \qquad [5.7]$$

Thus, with $n = 6$ and $m = 3$, $N = 15$, of which three have been found. We can find others by altering the algebraic procedure for solving the simultaneous equations formed from the exponents, but it is usually simpler to take combinations of π-terms already found. Since a π-term is dimensionless, it can be raised to any power and combined with one or more other π-terms to yield a new dimensionless group. In the pipe-flow problem we could find a new group as π_4; e.g.,

$$\pi_4 = \frac{\pi_1}{\pi_3^2} = \frac{\Delta p}{\rho V^2}\left(\frac{\rho V d}{\mu}\right)^2 = \frac{\rho d^2 \, \Delta p}{\mu^2}$$

As only three independent π-terms are necessary, we could then select π_1, π_2, and π_4 to represent the relationship. Note that we must not choose π_1, π_3, and π_4 because they are not independent.

5.4   *Alternative method of dimensional analysis*

The previous section described the method (due to Rayleigh) of finding π-terms that is most commonly used and that demonstrates most easily the logic of dimensional analysis. There is, however, another method (that of Buckingham) that offers some advantages and that is recommended here. The steps are as follows:

    1. Determine the dimensions of all n variables α and hence the value of m.

2. Find the necessary number of π-terms, $i = n - m$.

3. Select m variables α that do not of themselves form a dimensionless product in any combination.

4. Set up the equations for the i π-terms by taking the product of these m α's, each with unknown exponent, and each of the remaining $(n - m)$ α's in turn and applying the condition that each group must be dimensionless, thus:

for π_1, $\qquad\qquad [\alpha_1{}^{a_1}\alpha_2{}^{a_2} \, . \, . \, . \, \alpha_m{}^{a_m}\alpha_{m+1}] \equiv [M^0L^0T^0 \, . \, . \, .]$

for π_2, $\qquad\qquad [\alpha_1{}^{b_1}\alpha_2{}^{b_2} \, . \, . \, . \, \alpha_m{}^{b_m}\alpha_{m+2}] \equiv [M^0L^0T^0 \, . \, . \, .]$

for π_i, $\qquad\qquad [\alpha_1{}^{x_1}\alpha_2{}^{x_2} \, . \, . \, . \, \alpha_m{}^{x_m}\alpha_n] \equiv [M^0L^0T^0 \, . \, . \, .]$

5. Solve the simultaneous equations for the exponents of each group, and form the i π-terms.

6. Then $\pi_1 = \phi(\pi_2, \pi_3, \, . \, . \, . \, , \pi_i)$.

With the pipe-flow problem as an example, the steps are as follows:

1. $n = 6; m = 3$.

2. $i = 6 - 3 = 3$.

3. Select V with dimensions $[L/T]$, ρ with dimensions $[M/L^3]$, and d with dimension $[L]$, as m variables that will not form a dimensionless product.

4. For π_1, combine these with variable Δp of dimensions $[M/LT^2]$.

$$\left[\left(\frac{L}{T}\right)^a \left(\frac{M}{L^3}\right)^b (L)^c \left(\frac{M}{LT^2}\right)\right] \equiv [M^0L^0T^0]$$

for M, $\qquad\qquad b + 1 = 0 \qquad\qquad\qquad b = -1 \qquad\qquad$ [1]

for L, $\qquad\qquad a - 3b + c - 1 = 0 \qquad c = 0 \qquad\qquad$ [3]

for T, $\qquad\qquad - a - 2 = 0 \qquad\qquad\quad a = -2 \qquad\qquad$ [2]

Therefore $\qquad\qquad\qquad \pi_1 = V^{-2}\rho^{-1} \Delta p = \dfrac{\Delta p}{\rho V^2}$

For π_2, combine the three original variables with variable s of dimension $[L]$.

$$\left[\left(\frac{L}{T}\right)^a \left(\frac{M}{L^3}\right)^b (L)^c(L)\right] = [M^0L^0T^0]$$

for M, $\qquad\qquad b = 0 \qquad\qquad\qquad\qquad\; b = 0 \qquad\qquad$ [1]

for L, $\qquad\qquad a - 3b + c + 1 = 0 \qquad c = -1 \qquad\quad$ [3]

for T, $\qquad\qquad - a = 0 \qquad\qquad\qquad\quad\; a = 0 \qquad\qquad$ [2]

Therefore, $\qquad\qquad\qquad\qquad \pi_2 = \dfrac{s}{d}$

For π_3, combine the three original variables with variable μ of dimensions $[M/LT]$.

$$\left[\left(\frac{L}{T}\right)^a \left(\frac{M}{L^3}\right)^b (L)^c \left(\frac{M}{LT}\right) \right] = [M^0 L^0 T^0]$$

for M,	$b + 1 = 0$	$b = -1$	[1]
for L,	$a - 3b + c - 1 = 0$	$c = -1$	[3]
for T,	$-a - 1 = 0$	$a = -1$	[2]

Therefore
$$\pi_3 = V^{-1}\rho^{-1}d^{-1}\mu = \frac{\mu}{\rho V d}$$

Thus the same three π-terms as before have been found. The rationale of this method lies in the fact that the correct number of equations has been set up to produce the required number of π-terms and that each variable has been included at least once; hence the physical relationship must be described by the resulting dimensionless groups in accordance with the statement of the π-theorem.

This alternative method is slightly longer than the direct method because i sets of simultaneous equations must be solved. They are, however, simpler sets of equations than in the direct method. The advantages of the alternative method are these:

1. As each π-term is formed separately, it can be immediately checked for nondimensionality, and any algebraic mistake can be rectified. In the direct method such a mistake may cause considerably more trouble.

2. The forms of the π-terms can largely be decided in advance. If, for instance, the dependent variable is avoided in the choice of the m variables not forming a dimensionless product, it can appear only once in the π-terms, and thus an explicit relationship can be established for it. Similarly, if any "special" variables are similarly avoided, they too can appear only once. By "special" variables we mean fluid properties other than density, ρ; it is desirable for such variables as viscosity, surface tension, etc., to appear in one π-term only.

Two notes on the alternative method may be helpful: (1) the selection of m variables that in original combination do not produce a dimensionless group by themselves is usually quite easy if one of the primary dimensions occurs only once. In the example, both $[M]$ and $[T]$ occur only once, although the single appearance of just one of them would satisfy the condition. (2) If one of the equations set up for solution of the exponents contains two variables of *like* dimensions, then the resulting π-term will inevitably be their ratio—hence the algebraic procedure can be omitted ($\pi_2 = s/d$ could have been stated without further work in the example).

5.5 *Number of π-terms and primary dimensions*

It was noted earlier that the number of π-terms necessary to describe the physical relationship is *generally* equal to $n - m$, where m is the number of primary dimensions used. Although this is true in the majority of instances, there are sufficient exceptions to warrant a warning. If the rule is stated as $i = n - k$, then k can be established with rigor and certainty through the formation of a dimensional matrix and the use of determinants to find the rank of the matrix, the rank being the number k. However, this procedure, attributed to Langhaar (see footnote on p. 202), is somewhat lengthy, and the method of Van Driest (see footnote on p. 202) is recommended instead. It states that k is equal to the greatest number of variables that do not by themselves give a dimensionless product. Since k can never exceed m, the number of primary dimensions, if m variables do not make a dimensionless product, then the next lowest number must be tried.

Another note of warning is in order: the primary dimensions used must be truly independent. It is quite possible that although, say, $[M]$, $[L]$, and $[T]$ are all required to characterize the variables, two of them may always have the same relationship. For instance, mass and time may appear only together as mass per unit time, i.e., $[M/T]$, and thus not be independent. If this happens, the combination should be considered as only one variable, say, $[M']$ in the example. This circumstance is most likely when a large number of primary dimensions are used, and the constant combination of two of them may go unnoticed.

In general, it is helpful to use many primary dimensions if possible, since, as $i = n - m$ in most cases, the number of π-terms is thereby reduced. This idea can be carried a stage further by the method of "directional" or "vector" dimensional analysis, in which, instead of one dimension's $[L]$ being used for all space characteristics, notice is taken of the direction of the space variable in three-coordinate geometry. Thus in the pipe-flow example the direction of length would be given dimension $[L_1]$, and the direction of pipe diameter dimension $[L_2]$. The pressure term, force per unit area, has force in the L_1 direction and area in the L_2 direction; hence $\Delta p \equiv [ML_1/T^2]/[L_2{}^2] = [ML_1/T^2L_2{}^2]$. The viscosity, stress per unit rate of strain, requires a mental picture of its physical effect. According to Sect. 1.4, the viscous stress is a force in the L_1 direction divided by the surface area in which it acts, which is characterized by L_1L_2. Therefore, the stress has dimensions $[ML_1/T^2]/[L_1L_2] = [M/L_2T^2]$. The rate of strain is the gradient of velocity across the direction of flow; i.e., $[L_1/T]/[L_2] = [L_1/TL_2]$. Hence $\mu \equiv [M/L_2T^2]/[L_1/TL_2] = [M/L_1T]$. Thus, with density as $[M/L_1L_2{}^2]$, we have

$$\left[\frac{ML_1}{TL_2{}^2}\right] = f\left[L_1, L_2, \frac{M}{L_1L_2{}^2}, \frac{L_1}{T}, \frac{M}{L_1T}\right]$$

There are six variables as before, but now there are four primary dimensions, M, L_1, L_2, and T, and so two π-terms are required. Solving for these, we find

$$\frac{\Delta p}{\rho V^2} = \phi\left(\frac{\mu s}{\rho V d^2}\right) = \phi\left[\left(\frac{\mu}{\rho V d}\right)\left(\frac{s}{d}\right)\right]$$

The addition of the extra primary dimension shows that, although we still do not know the exact form of the function ϕ, the terms $\mu/\rho V d$ and s/d are similarly affected and, as demonstrated, may be combined. In exchange for this information, we must interpret more precisely the action of the variables. The analysis of viscosity in particular limits the result to laminar flow (Sect. 1.11). We shall not dwell longer on vector dimensional analysis, even though it does have considerable application. Further discussion for those interested is found in Huntley (see footnote on p. 202).

5.6   *Dimensional analysis of the general flow problem*

Consider the problem of flow in general. The variables can be many, as they must include all the fluid properties thought to have effects—such as density, viscosity, compressibility, surface tension, and gravitational effect. The first two have already been treated. Compressibility is most conveniently dealt with as its inverse, elasticity, $E = -dp/(dv/v) \equiv [M/LT^2]$. Surface tension, σ, was defined in Chapter 1 as force per unit length $\equiv [M/T^2]$. Gravitational effect may be characterized by specific weight, γ, or by gravitational acceleration, g, and here we shall choose the latter.

The geometry can be specified in three coordinates by three linear dimensions; but it has been stated that variables of like dimensions appear as their ratio, and since ordinary dimensional analysis cannot discriminate among particular linear dimensions, the simplest procedure is to use only one linear dimension as typical of all. However, we shall use two in order to demonstrate a certain point later. These will be designated by s and d, which might represent length and diameter in pipe flow or chord (width) and thickness in free flow around an airfoil. Some characteristic representing flow rate is required. This might be mass flow rate, $\dot{m}$, volume flow rate, Q, or fluid velocity, V. The last-named is simplest, and as density and linear dimension are variables, $\dot{m}$ and Q are also easily obtained.

The most important consideration we have left to the last—namely, what main performance variable should be used as dependent variable? In pipe flow, it would be the change of pressure, as this is the parameter that is usually of major importance and that can be readily measured. In free-stream flow, it would be a force of some sort, e.g., the drag or resistance or the lift force around an airfoil. Here we shall arbitrarily select change of pressure, $\Delta p \equiv [M/LT^2]$, which dimensionally can be interpreted as force per unit area, so that force itself can be obtained on multiplication of Δp by area or, dimensionally, by $[L^2]$.

The problem is functionally thus:

$$\Delta p = f(V, s, d, \rho, \mu, E, \sigma, g)$$

There are nine variables, and six π-terms are required, as $k = m$, and so $i = 9 - 3 = 6$. Following the preferred method of analysis allows the π-terms, out of the 136 possible, to appear in the most convenient manner. The three variables chosen for combining with each of the others in turn are V, ρ, and d, for Δp, μ, E, σ, or g should not appear more than once. The choice of s or d is immaterial, as dimensionally they are equivalent. The analysis then yields

$$\pi_1 = \frac{s}{d} \qquad \pi_2 = \frac{\Delta p}{\rho V^2} \qquad \pi_3 = \frac{\rho V d}{\mu}$$

$$\pi_4 = \frac{\rho V^2}{E} \qquad \pi_5 = \frac{\rho V^2 d}{\sigma} \qquad \pi_6 = \frac{V^2}{gd}$$

This problem was formulated quite generally, and its results have validity in all flow situations. The first three π-terms have been encountered previously, and the last three enter by virtue of the inclusion of other fluid properties. These six π-terms will be analyzed individually, for they are more than mere groups of variables that happen to be dimensionless because of an algebraic procedure. They have profound *physical* significance, which might have been suspected from the fact that they characterize a true physical relationship.

5.7   *Physical significance of π-terms*

π_1, s/d, expresses a geometrical relationship and implies that the shape, as a ratio of linear dimensions, is a controlling factor, rather than the actual magnitude of each individual dimension. If a third linear dimension had been included, say, w, then another ratio, w/d, would have appeared, and a three-dimensional geometry would have been characterized completely.

The remaining terms all contain ρV or ρV^2 and thus seem to share some element of similar meaning. The term $\rho V^2 = \rho V(V)$ suggests an inertia force per unit area. With this specific inertia force designated as F_i/d^2, then $F_i/d^2 \propto \rho V^2$.

In π_2, $\Delta p/\rho V^2$, Δp is the pressure force per unit area, and so

$$\frac{\Delta p}{\rho V^2} \propto \frac{\text{pressure force per unit area}}{\text{inertia force per unit area}} \qquad [5.9]$$

π_2 then expresses the ratio of the force due to change of pressure in the fluid to the force due to motion (inertia) of the fluid. Most of the dimensionless groups appearing frequently in dimensional analysis have distinctive names, sometimes after their originators and sometimes after outstanding workers in the field. The group $\Delta p/\rho V^2$ is known as the *pressure coefficient* or *Euler* number. It is the basic performance parameter in a flow field and depends on other groups that produce modifying influences in various circumstances.

π_3, $\rho V d/\mu$, can be rearranged as $\rho V^2/(\mu V/d)$ so that the specific inertia term is in the numerator. The denominator, $\mu V/d$, can then be recognized as a measure of shear stress due to viscous action (Sect. 1.4), and thus π_3 can be interpreted as

$$\frac{\rho V d}{\mu} = \frac{\rho V^2}{\mu V/d} \propto \frac{\text{inertia force per unit area}}{\text{viscous force per unit area}} \qquad [5.10]$$

This is known as the *Reynolds* number and given the symbol Re. Since every real fluid has viscosity, the Reynolds number is always a factor in a flow regime; in fact, it is usually the most important correlating factor. There are occasions, however, as we shall see later, when its effect may be regarded as secondary to those of other parameters.

In π_4, $\rho V^2/E$, E is the elasticity or pressure change per unit change of volume; hence the parameter expresses the ratio of inertia force to elastic force. It is simpler but more meaningful when rearranged as $V^2/(E/\rho)$, with E/ρ interpreted. Since $E = -dp/(dv/v)$ may be written, with $v = 1/\rho$, as $E = dp/(d\rho/\rho)$, $E/\rho = dp/d\rho$. It has been noted (Eq. 4.59) that $dp/d\rho = a^2$, where a is the velocity of wave propagation or acoustic velocity in the fluid. Thus

$$\frac{\rho V^2}{E} \equiv \frac{V^2}{E/\rho} \equiv \frac{V^2}{dp/d\rho} \equiv \frac{V^2}{a^2} \equiv \mathrm{M}^2 \qquad [5.11]$$

where M is the *Mach* number. Furthermore, from Eq. 4.61, $a^2 = g_c k R T$, and from the kinetic theory of gases, the temperature, T, is a measure of the specific kinetic energy of the molecules, $\overline{c^2}$, where $\overline{c^2}$ is the average squared velocity. Therefore, $V^2/a^2 = \mathrm{M}^2$ can be visualized as expressing the ratio of specific bulk, or directed kinetic energy, V^2, to specific molecular energy, $\overline{c^2}$. The Mach number has already been introduced as a flow parameter, and we see that it evolves inevitably as a result of inertia and elastic (or compressible) effects. It normally becomes important only for gas flow, and its value is a measure of compressibility.

π_5, $\rho V^2 d/\sigma$, can be rearranged as $\rho V^2/(\sigma/d)$, and with σ as surface tension force per unit length, σ/d is surface tension force per unit area. Hence

$$\frac{\rho V^2 d}{\sigma} = \frac{\rho V^2}{\sigma/d} \propto \frac{\text{inertia force per unit area}}{\text{surface tension force per unit area}} \qquad [5.12]$$

π_5 is known as the *Weber* number, denoted by We. We learned in Chapter 1 that surface tension forces are large only when the radius of curvature is small. The Weber number, as the ratio of inertia force to surface tension force, gives us a quantitative value as a criterion. One manifestation of surface tension in fluid flow occurs in free flow over a sharp edge, when the liquid fails to spring clear of the lip.

π_6, V^2/gd, can be rewritten as $\rho V^2/\rho gd$, with ρgd signifying the gravitational force per unit area. Thus

$$\frac{V^2}{gd} = \frac{\rho V^2}{\rho gd} \propto \frac{\text{inertia force per unit area}}{\text{gravitational force per unit area}} \qquad [5.13]$$

π_6 is called the *Froude* number, Fr. It has significance when both gravity and inertia act on a free surface in motion. It plays a vital part in characterizing the effect of, e.g., wave action or flow over a weir. The analysis of the speed of propagation, or celerity, of a surface wave resulted in a Froude number; Eq. 4.79 gave $c \approx \sqrt{gz}$ as the celerity of a shallow wave, or $Fr = c^2/gz = 1$. In this case the characteristic dimension, d, is the depth of liquid, z. In other cases, d may be some other dimension subject to wave action.

The π-terms discussed here are all ratios of like quantities, either *geometric*, as s/d, or *dynamic*, as any of the other groups. In other analyses for fluid flow, the ratio of two velocities may appear as a π-term, expressing a *kinematic* condition. The original problem of nine variables,

$$\Delta p = f(V, s, d, \rho, \mu, E, \sigma, g)$$

can now be written

$$\frac{\Delta p}{\rho V^2} = \phi\left(\frac{s}{d}, \text{Re}, \text{M}, \text{We}, \text{Fr}\right) \qquad [5.14]$$

In most problems two of the parameters Re, M, We, and Fr are important, but sometimes only one (e.g., Re in the pipe-flow analysis) is significant.

The interpretation of dimensionless groups as ratios of like physical quantities is not essential to the operation of dimensional analysis, which stands by itself as a mathematical technique. However, it does show us the physical relationships underlying the algebraic procedure and helps us to estimate the importance of variables in particular circumstances. It also helps us to understand similarity of flows and to appreciate the use of models in obtaining test data. Accordingly, any π-term resulting from dimensional analysis should be analyzed for its physical significance as a means of interpreting the behavior of the system.

5.8   *Similitude and model testing*

The concept of dimensionless groups as ratios of geometric quantities such as linear dimensions, kinematic quantities such as velocities, and dynamic quantities such as forces due to inertia, pressure, and fluid properties leads to the idea of similitude or similarity. Similitude will be discussed more exactly shortly, but it is apparent that if two physical conditions are such that all the π-terms have the same value, regardless of the individual values of the separate variables, then the conditions are identical. Complete physical similitude implies (1) *geometric* similitude, which means that the linear-dimension ratios are everywhere the same, i.e., the shapes are similar regardless of size; (2) *kinematic* similitude, which means that the velocity ratios are everywhere the same, i.e., the velocity triangles representing flow conditions are similar; and (3) *dynamic* similitude, which means that the ratios of the different forces are everywhere the same. For fluid flow, the streamlines are everywhere similar.

It is doubtful whether complete physical similitude is ever attained, despite the effort applied, but for most practical purposes it can be approached sufficiently closely to be of great utility. Its most obvious use is in models of small linear scale, with which relatively inexpensive experiments can be performed, giving results applicable to the originals or prototypes. For instance, models of pumps and turbines can be tested, the prototypes of which may be many feet in diameter and may require many thousands of horsepower to operate. A change of linear scale implies that other variables must be changed so that the π-terms remain similar. In the simple pipe-flow example, a large water supply and considerable power would be necessary for the determination of the pressure-loss characteristics of a 12 in. pipe, as well as a long length of pipe for accurate measurements. The principle of similitude, however, allows the use of a pipe of, say, 1 in. diameter and $\frac{1}{12}$ the length of the prototype. The fluid velocity, pressure, and temperature can be varied to keep Re and $\Delta p/\rho V^2$ comparable to the prototype's operating conditions, or, as is sometimes done, a different fluid can be used. Models are extensively utilized for aircraft, ships, and turbomachinery. As an example of the last application, detailed tests were carried out on models for the Grand Coulee Dam project—the prototypes were to be gigantic machines of 20 ft diameter requiring 60,000 hp, so that even seemingly costly experimentation with models was a relatively cheap way of ensuring successful operation. Contracts for very large installations often demand attested experimental results from models of the proposed equipment.

When several π-terms are significant, it is often impossible to preserve complete similitude, for a change of linear scale requires exact relations among the other variables that cannot always be satisfied. Thus for ships both the Reynolds and Froude numbers are important, and, because in this instance any model fluid other than water is not feasible, $\rho V d/\mu$ and V^2/gd cannot both be kept the same by a change of linear scale. In spite of this disadvantage, marine architects make great use of models in towing tanks, estimating viscous effects by analyzing tests mainly controlled by wave effects and vice versa.

5.9   *Similitude from the differential equations*

A method of dimensional analysis more sophisticated than those already outlined is based on the differential equations governing a problem. Although it can provide a more rigorous statement of similitude, it also requires considerably more knowledge of behavior.

We have seen that similarity of two flows implies the same ratios of geometric, kinematic, and dynamic quantities in both. We convey the same idea if we explain the similarity of two flows by saying the flows are identical if a scale factor is applied to each variable. This scale factor may be different for each variable but is constant throughout the flow field. With this "differential similitude" method we find the relationship among the scale factors necessary to produce similarity. We shall again use the problem of pressure drop in pipe flow with viscous shear as an example, but here we must first make an exact analysis to obtain the differential equation.

Fig. 5.2 shows a small cylindrical element of fluid in the pipe, together with the forces due to pressure and to viscous shear stress. A force balance yields

$$p\pi r^2 - (p + dp)\pi r^2 - \tau 2\pi r\, dx = 0$$

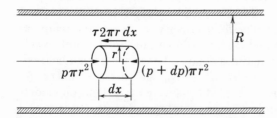

Figure 5.2

which may be reduced to

$$\frac{dp}{dx} = -\frac{2\tau}{r} \qquad [5.15]$$

Assuming that the flow is laminar and that the shear stress is wholly due to the fluid viscosity, then $\tau = -\mu\, du/dr$, where u is the local velocity at radius r and the minus sign enters because r is measured from the axis and not from the wall (see Sect. 1.4). With this value of τ substituted,

$$\frac{dp}{dx} = \frac{2\mu}{r}\frac{du}{dr} \qquad [5.16]$$

The boundary condition is that $u = 0$ at $r = R$. The pressure, p, is not a function of r, only of x, and x is independent of r. Therefore, the variables u and r could be separated, and Eq. 5.16 integrated. However, here the equation is being used to illustrate similitude, and as much information as possible will be obtained from the differential form, since the method is most useful when the differential equation cannot be readily solved.

Suppose that we have two such cases of viscous flow in a pipe, a and b. They are characterized by pipe radii R_a and R_b, pipe lengths L_a and L_b, viscosities μ_a and μ_b, average velocities V_a and V_b, and pressure levels p_a and p_b, respectively. If these parameters are the same for both cases, obviously the flows are identical. If the parameters are not the same, the flows are said to be similar if each variable of one flow, when multiplied by a constant scale factor, becomes identical with its counterpart of the other flow. The differential equation leads to a governing condition that states what the relationship among the scale factors must be for the flows to be similar. The characterizing parameters furnish the scale factors, S, thus:

linear-scale factor in the x direction, $\qquad S_x = \dfrac{L_b}{L_a} = \dfrac{x_b}{x_a}$

linear-scale factor in the r direction, $\qquad S_r = \dfrac{R_b}{R_a} = \dfrac{r_b}{r_a}$

velocity-scale factor, $\qquad S_u = \dfrac{V_b}{V_a} = \dfrac{u_b}{u_a}$

viscosity-scale factor, $\qquad S_\mu = \dfrac{\mu_b}{\mu_a}$

The pressure-scale factor is not so easily expressed. There is no characteristic static pressure in pipe flow; pressure is constant across a pipe and, with an incompressible fluid, its absolute level is immaterial. But we are interested in pressure difference, which we may reasonably assume to be in some way dependent on the dynamic pressure, $\rho V^2/2_c g$, and which we may therefore take as ρV^2. Hence

pressure-scale factor, $\qquad S_p = \dfrac{\rho_b V_b{}^2}{\rho_a V_a{}^2} = \dfrac{p_b}{p_a}$

The differential equations for the two flows are

$$\frac{dp_a}{dx_a} = \frac{2\mu_a}{r_a}\frac{du_a}{dr_a} \qquad [5.17]$$

$$\frac{dp_b}{dx_b} = \frac{2\mu_b}{r_b}\frac{du_b}{dr_b} \qquad [5.18]$$

The second equation is put into the form of the first by means of the scale-factor relationships, i.e., $dx_b = S_x\,dx_a$, etc., yielding

$$\frac{S_p\,dp_a}{S_x\,dx_a} = \frac{2S_\mu\mu_a}{S_r r_a}\frac{S_u\,du_a}{S_r\,dr_a}$$

or

$$\frac{dp_a}{dx_a} = \frac{2\mu_a}{r_a}\frac{du_a}{dr_a}\frac{S_\mu S_u S_x}{S_r{}^2 S_p} \qquad [5.19]$$

Eq. 5.19 for the second flow is identical to Eq. 5.17 for the first flow except for the coefficient on the right-hand side. For the flows to be similar, then,

$$\frac{S_\mu S_u S_x}{S_r{}^2 S_p} = 1 \qquad [5.20]$$

Of the five scale factors, four may have any values, but the value of the fifth is determined from Eq. 5.20, which is the governing condition for similitude. The scale factors can be converted back to the terms in which they were defined, so that

$$\left(\frac{\mu_b}{\mu_a}\frac{V_b}{V_a}\frac{L_b}{L_a}\right)\left(\frac{R_a{}^2}{R_b{}^2}\frac{\rho_a V_a{}^2}{\rho_b V_b{}^2}\right) = 1$$

or, on reduction and rearrangement,

$$\left(\frac{\mu_b}{\rho_b V_b R_b}\right)\left(\frac{L_b}{R_b}\right) = \left(\frac{\mu_a}{\rho_a V_a R_a}\right)\left(\frac{L_a}{R_a}\right) \qquad [5.21]$$

which is recognized as equality of the products of the reciprocal of Re and the length-diameter ratio of the pipe (radius = diameter/2). These were the two dimensionless parameters obtained by dimensional analysis previously. We conclude that the two flows are similar if the Reynolds numbers and length-diameter ratios of the pipe are the same.

One of the most frequent uses of the differential method is in conjunction with known sets of differential equations having various boundary conditions. With the Navier-Stokes equations, terms may be omitted to suit many problems. By means of the Navier-Stokes equations together with the energy and continuity equations, many problems can be stated, but often they are unsolvable in closed forms. Dimensional analysis of the type just demonstrated can provide useful information. An advantage of the differential-similitude method is that the dimensionless groups obtained are in the logical form for use and no choice has to be made among them.

The method shows clearly the application and meaning of scale factors. We can arrive at the result more directly than we have if we make the defining differential equations dimensionless by using the characterizing parameters. With superscript primes denoting dimensionless variables,

$$x' = \frac{x}{L}$$

$$r' = \frac{r}{R}$$

$$u' = \frac{u}{V}$$

$$p' = \frac{p}{\rho V^2}$$

It will be noted that ρV^2 again represents the characterizing parameter for p (in the light of the preceding analysis) and that μ has not been made dimensionless. Here we are not obtaining scale ratios between two different flows but expressing local values of variables as fractions of characteristic values. The viscosity is constant in a given flow and therefore does not require a nondimensional treatment.

Substituting for dp, dx, du, dr, and r in Eq. 5.16 gives us

$$\frac{\rho V^2}{L} \frac{dp'}{dx'} = \frac{2\mu}{Rr'} \frac{V}{R} \frac{du'}{dr'}$$

or

$$\frac{dp'}{dx'} = \frac{\mu L}{\rho V R^2} \frac{2\,du'}{r'\,dr'} = \left(\frac{\mu}{\rho V R}\right)\left(\frac{L}{R}\right)\frac{2\,du'}{r'\,dr'}$$ [5.22]

This equation is dimensionless, with each variable a ratio of actual local value to characteristic value. It then has a solution depending only on the value of the coefficient $\mu L/\rho V R^2$; in other words, the same solution is obtained for different flows if the dimensionless parameter $\mu L/\rho V R^2$ is the same.

5.10 *Summary of dimensional methods*

The ordinary method of dimensional analysis using the π-theorem is the most general, as only the variables entering into the relationship need be known. However, the information obtained is also the most general, in that the answer is in the form of an unknown function of $(n - k)$ π-terms. The variation of the general method using directed linear dimensions reduces the number of π-terms and gives certain additional information. The method using the differential equation is even more positive, for it gives directly the necessary π-terms and sometimes conveys a little more information, but it requires considerably more knowledge and analysis of the nature of the problem.

We apply dimensional analysis for two major purposes: first, to establish logical experimental procedures providing the most information in the least testing time and to correlate the results in the most convenient manner; and second, through model testing, to acquire information otherwise unobtainable on the probable behavior of prototypes. Dimensional analysis is of inestimable value in fluid dynamics and heat transfer, which rely heavily on the concept of correlation with appropriate dimensionless groups.

Problems

5.1. The thrust, T, of a propeller is assumed to depend on the tip diameter, d, the fluid density, ρ, the fluid viscosity, μ, the rpm, N, and the forward speed, V, relative to the distant fluid. By means of dimensional analysis, find a group of parameters that correlates the behavior of the propeller. Assess the physical significance of the parameters that you obtain.

5.2. If it is assumed that the velocity of a jet of water issuing from an orifice in the side of a tank is dependent only upon the height of the water above the center of the orifice, the specific weight of the water, and the density of the water, what is the functional equation for the velocity, and how does it compare with the actual equation for ideal flow, $V = \sqrt{2gh}$?

5.3. Examine Problem 1.6 from the point of view of dimensional analysis.

5.4. For the accelerometer of Problem 2.11, assume that the height, h, depends on the acceleration, a, the length, L, the fluid density, ρ, and the gravitational acceleration, g, and compare the answer obtained by dimensional analysis with the analytical result.

5.5. (a) The height, h, to which a liquid rises in a small-bore tube owing to surface-tension forces (the capillarity rise) is a function of the specific weight of the liquid, γ, the radius of the tube, r, and the surface tension of the liquid, σ. By dimensional analysis, find an expression for h involving nondimensional variables only.

    (b) If the capillary rise for liquid A is 1 in. in a tube of radius 0.010 in., what will be the rise for liquid B, which has the same surface tension but four times the density of A, in a tube of radius 0.005 in.?

5.6. Assuming that the behavior of a pump can be assessed in terms of the volume flow rate, Q, the delivered head of liquid, H, the power, P, the speed in rpm, N, a characteristic linear dimension of the pump, d, and the liquid density, ρ, find a set of dimensionless parameters that expresses the performance. (Be careful with your choice of dimensions for head, H.)

5.7. An aircraft with a representative dimension of 10 ft (the width of the wing section) is to have a design speed of 450 mph at 30,000 ft. The laboratory wind tunnel has a working section in which the air is at 60 psia and 40°F. Find the correct size of the model in order for similar flow conditions to hold in the wind tunnel and at the operational altitude.

5.8. Using the method of dimensional analysis, find an expression for the force, D, on a body of a size characterized by its width, d, moving with speed V through a fluid of density ρ and viscosity μ. The compressibility of the fluid may be neglected. If $D = 1000$ lb when $V = 100$ ft/sec as the body moves through air at ground level, what prediction can be made about D at 20,000 ft?

ALTITUDE, FT	ρ, LB/FT^3	$10^7\mu$, LB/SEC-FT
0	0.0765	120
20,000	0.0408	109

5.9. A fluid coupling consists of a pump rotor and turbine rotor through which fluid flows continuously. The pump side is driven by the prime mover, and the turbine side is connected to the load. Power is transmitted only through the fluid, as the pump and turbine are mechanically separate. Taking the power output as a function of the size of the unit, the speed of the pump, the speed of the turbine, and the fluid density and viscosity, obtain by means of dimensional analysis a set of parameters that allows the power to be expressed in terms of the other variables.

5.10. A "viscous-drag" pump delivers high-pressure fluid by utilizing the viscosity of the fluid to draw it through small-clearance passages. Assuming that the pressure rise, Δp, depends on the fluid density, ρ, the fluid viscosity, μ, the rotor diameter, d, the clearance space, b, and the shaft-rotational speed, N, find a suitable set of dimensionless parameters that might be used for correlating test data. What is the most specific statement that can be made regarding the relationship among these parameters?

6

Characteristics of Real-Fluid Flow

6.1 *Introduction*

Let us take stock of our analysis of moving fluids to date. In Chapter 3 the motion of an ideal fluid was described in purely kinematic terms, and we learned how to find the streamlines and thus velocities at any point in a simple flow field. In Chapter 4 the dynamics of flow was examined; exact equations for ideal flow (the Euler equations) resulted, as well as the momentum and energy equations for fluid flow in which losses due to shear stress could be included generally although the nature of the losses and the details of the actual flow causing them remained unknown. Chapter 5, on dimensional analysis, showed that the variables entering into a particular real fluid-flow configuration had a certain relationship and that groups of variables in dimensionless form were characteristic of flow. With these concepts behind us, we can now discuss the behavior of real fluids, taking into account the special property of viscosity that is responsible in large part for the observed phenomena. Once again, we shall approach the problem in stages, studying first incompressible flow and then extending the analysis to compressible flow. Although the latter introduces some new features, the viscous effects are the same as in incompressible flow, and thus the realm of gas dynamics represents an extension of the basic concepts and not a new departure.

Flow in general can be divided into (1) *flow in ducts*, i.e., flow bounded by solid surfaces, and (2) *flow around bodies* immersed in an otherwise unbounded fluid. This division is only for convenience, as the basic phenomena of fluid behavior apply in both situations. The next two chapters will be concerned with developing our knowledge of these two types of flow, but first we shall consider the behavior of real fluids common to both.

Our comprehension of real-fluid behavior requires a distinction between a *boundary layer* in which the major shear-stress effects are concentrated and an area in which the ideal-flow postulate is satisfactory. Another requisite is the idea of two regimes of flow, that of *laminar* flow and that of *turbulent* flow. Our first question in analyzing flow will be, is it laminar, or is it turbulent? Or more often perhaps, what parts are laminar, and what parts are turbulent? Then we shall investigate the nature and extent of the boundary layer and its effect on the flow. Sometimes the whole area is a boundary layer, as in pipe flow some distance from the entrance, as we shall see shortly.

6.2   *Boundary-layer concept*

If the flow around a slender, streamlined, two-dimensional body such as that shown in Fig. 6.1 is examined by means of pressure taps and Pitot tubes, it is found that in general the streamlines are very similar to those calculated by the methods of potential flow studied in Chapter 3. The exception would be in the region very close to the surface and in the region immediately behind the body (stippled in the diagram). In ideal flow the surface of the body is a streamline, with the fluid therefore having a velocity right at the surface. A real fluid, however, has the property of viscosity, which, from observation, implies zero velocity of the fluid at the surface, i.e., the no-slip condition. The stippled region then constitutes one of retarded flow, with velocity zero at the surface and increasing outward until at some distance from the surface it becomes that of the main or ideal flow, having reached the freestream value. In the low-velocity region, which is comparatively thin, the *velocity gradient* is large, producing large shear stresses in accordance with the Newtonian relationship $\tau = \mu \, du/dy$. Out in the freestream the fluid still has viscosity, but as the velocity gradient is very small or nonexistent, the shear stress is small enough to be neglected in comparison with that close to the surface. A characteristic of the boundary

Figure 6.1

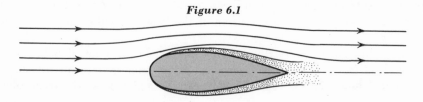

layer is that it builds up from zero thickness at the first point of contact of fluid and surface, the *leading edge*, becoming increasingly thicker along the surface in the direction of flow. It varies with the type of fluid, body shape, and conditions of flow but is usually quite thin except over long distances or in special circumstances. In Fig. 6.1 it is exaggerated for clarity of presentation, as it will be in other figures, and some quantitative evaluation will be obtained later.

At the rear of the body, the *trailing edge*, the retarded fluid in the boundary layer flows from the surface and forms a *wake*, gradually mixing with the freestream until it disappears some distance downstream. Within the boundary layer, the flow lines are generally ordered, and the pressure on the surface is very nearly what it would be for ideal flow over the body. It is this viscous action, with accompanying tangential stress, that causes the loss of momentum of the fluid and produces a force on the body. This drag force is due to the boundary layer, and in it lies the key to real-fluid behavior.

If the flow around an unstreamlined or *bluff* body is examined, it is found that there may be a larger area of disordered flow to the rear than with a streamlined body, in fact, an area in which the flow has an eddying pattern, possibly unsteady even if the main flow is steady. Such a pattern is shown for a cylinder in Fig. 6.2. Here the boundary layer over the rear portion of the surface is not distinct as an ordered region of retarded flow but has broken up into a confused region. The flow is said to have *separated* from the surface, and the pressure distribution on the surface beyond the point of separation is no longer in any way similar to that predicted for ideal flow. An additional force is present owing to the unbalanced pressure distribution. It should be understood that, although this additional force is a normal one, the separation is initially caused by a viscous force, which is tangential. Thus it is the action of viscosity in building up a boundary layer, a small effect in itself, that leads to separation and a different pressure distribution.

Figure 6.2

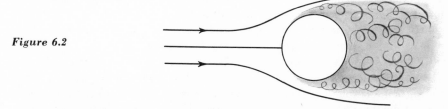

Fig. 6.3 shows a much-magnified boundary layer on a section of surface. The effective edge of the boundary layer is indicated by a dashed line, and at each station, *A*, *B*, *C*, and *D*, the magnitude of the velocity is plotted from a reference line drawn normal to the surface. At the surface the velocity is zero, and it increases outward through the boundary layer until

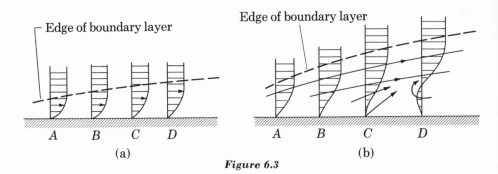

Figure 6.3

it is essentially at the freestream value at the edge of the layer. A representation such as this of the velocity variation over a certain distance is called a *velocity distribution* or *velocity profile*.

In Fig. 6.3(a) the pressure in the freestream is constant in the flow direction ($dp/dx = 0$), as it might be in flow along a flat plate. The boundary layer is increasing in thickness, with the velocity distribution retaining essentially the same form from station to station. In Fig. 6.3(b), however, the pressure is increasing in the direction of flow ($dp/dx > 0$, this pressure distribution being brought about independently by some particular configuration of the main flow, i.e., not being directly caused by the boundary layer). With such an *adverse* pressure gradient, the slow-moving fluid in the boundary is further retarded, as shown at *B*, and may eventually come to rest near the surface, as shown at *C*, after which it reverses its direction at points downstream, as shown at *D*. Here *C* is the *separation point*, where ordered flow stops, and downstream from it the flow is composed of eddies. In bodies of finite size, such as in Fig. 6.2, this situation results in a large wake and a resulting loss of momentum. Although the study of the separation region is largely empirical because of its disorganized character, a knowledge of the velocity distribution in the freestream in ideal flow gives preliminary information on conditions leading to separation and hence suggests the best design for minimum drag.

In duct flow the same type of boundary layer builds up from the leading edge as in flow around a body, but as the fluid is confined by solid surfaces, the growth of the layer may be at a different rate from that over a body in a freestream. If the duct is sufficiently long, two opposite layers may meet and yield a complete cross section of flow that is subject to shear stresses. Fig. 6.4 demonstrates this process in a pipe, with velocity distribution across a diameter shown at various stations along the pipe.

At entrance station *A* (assuming parallel flow into the entry), the velocity distribution is uniform. At *B* the boundary layer has developed inward from the pipe walls, but leaving an area in the center where the velocity is still uniform, albeit accelerated by virtue of the continuity

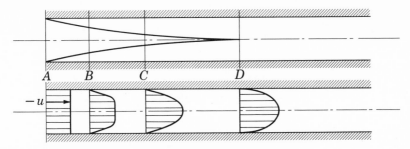

Figure 6.4

principle. At C the boundary layer continues to grow, until at D it has coalesced at the axis, and the velocity distribution is in the form of a continuous curve across a diameter. Beyond D the velocity distribution remains the same, since a uniform situation has been produced; the flow is then said to be *fully developed*. Fully developed flow will be assumed in most of the following discussion of duct flow. Such an assumption is necessary for any generalized statements about flow in ducts because the incompletely developed region is one of nonuniform flow, different for every particular case. Some analysis of it can be made, but only in the case of laminar flow is a reasonably exact solution possible. The effect of the *entrance length*, i.e., the distance from the entry to the point of fully developed flow, is usually handled empirically by means of a coefficient modifying an expression for some feature of behavior in fully developed flow. This point has been stressed because in practice we encounter many cases of ducts of relatively small length-diameter ratio and we are liable to use data for fully established flow without due consideration of the entrance-length effect.

It is essential to emphasize the complete contrast between flow over an immersed body and fully developed flow in a straight pipe. For the former, a potential-flow solution yields an almost-correct velocity distribution and hence pressure distribution imposed on the boundary layer, whose effect can then be worked out. For straight-pipe flow, the velocity distribution is entirely due to real-fluid effects, and no potential-flow solution exists. For flow in a curved duct or in a duct of varying cross section, a potential-flow solution can again offer help in predicting a pressure distribution within which the viscous effects must operate.

6.3   *Laminar and turbulent flow*

A simple conception of laminar flow as opposed to turbulent flow was given in Chapter 1 as a guide to the very general use of the terminology. Let us now turn to the classic experiment of Osborne Reynolds, which he

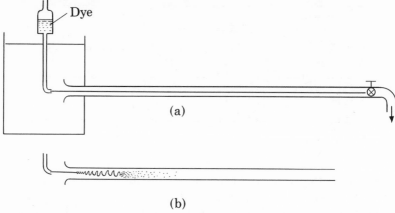

(a)

(b)

Figure 6.5

presented to the Royal Society in London in 1883,* for a more detailed discussion. Here the actual results will be paraphrased, and the apparatus schematized for economy of presentation.

As the basis of Reynolds' experiments, flow in a transparent tube is made visible by means of injected dye (Fig. 6.5). Water from a reservoir is allowed to move along the tube through a rounded entrance section, the flow rate being controlled by a discharge valve. A filament of dye can be continuously injected into the tube from apparatus at the mouth of the entrance section.

The system is filled with water and allowed to settle at least long enough for gross eddies to be damped out. Then the discharge valve is opened slightly to allow a low flow rate, and dye is injected slowly in the mouth. Under these conditions the dye remains as a smooth, distinct filament along the tube axis until it reaches the control valve, the only mixing being of a molecular nature (Fig. 6.5(a)). As the valve is opened to allow a continually increasing flow rate, the filament becomes unstable downstream from its entrance point and eventually breaks up altogether into eddies so that the dye diffuses rapidly throughout the tube (Fig. 6.5(b)); close examination reveals that the eddies contain large numbers of particles. The first regime, characterized by molecular diffusion, is known as laminar, streamline, or viscous flow. The second regime, characterized by eddy diffusion, is known as turbulent flow, although called sinuous by Reynolds.

* The original paper is recommended as a fascinating account of a simple experiment having extremely significant results. Its style is a welcome change from the terse scientific expositions of today. Even the title is distinctive, "An Experimental Investigation of the Circumstances which Determine whether the Motion of Water will be Direct or Sinuous, and of the Law of Resistance in Parallel Channels." See *Phil. Trans. Roy. Soc. London*, **174**, 935 (1883).

The velocity at which the flow becomes turbulent is called the *critical velocity*, and it had been noted for many years before Reynolds' report. Reynolds' achievement was to show conclusively that velocity alone was not the criterion for turbulence, but that a certain value combining fluid density, fluid velocity, tube size, and fluid viscosity as $\rho V d/\mu$ was the controlling parameter. This is recognized as the Reynolds number resulting earlier from dimensional analysis, and it was so-named in honor of Reynolds' work. It is valid not only for water but also for all other fluids, both liquids and gases.

The critical Reynolds number based on pipe diameter at the point where laminar flow becomes turbulent flow is not constant and depends very much on the pipe entrance and on the history of the entering fluid. A smooth, rounded entrance and a quiescent fluid promote laminar flow and hence a high critical Reynolds number, whereas a sharp-edged entrance and a fluid subject to irregular motion immediately before entry lead to a low critical Reynolds number. A number of about 2000 is taken here as the value below which irregular motions are damped out and the flow is laminar regardless of entry conditions or fluid history. No exact upper limit is known to exist, and laminar flow with a Reynolds number up to 40,000 has been observed in exceptional circumstances. In most engineering situations where laminar flow is likely, an upper limit of 2300 is reasonable. If possible, however, it is desirable to design away from region of the critical Reynolds number because of its uncertainty and because of the likelihood of instability, with the flow fluctuating between the two regimes.

Laminar and turbulent flow regimes also occur in the boundary layer over an immersed body. If the freestream flow is turbulent in the sense of immediate diffusion of dye filaments, the boundary-layer flow downstream from the leading edge of a surface is still laminar for some distance before becoming turbulent, the turbulence therein being much more marked than in the freestream. Again the critical region is characterized by a Reynolds number, but this time the linear dimension of pipe diameter is replaced by that of distance along the surface from the leading edge. The critical Reynolds number is again dependent on the form of the leading edge and the condition of the approach fluid, but it has a quite different order of magnitude from that for duct flow, being about 1×10^5 to 5×10^5 for most bodies.

In following chapters we shall examine many situations, both for laminar flow and for turbulent flow. It should be apparent that laminar flow, for which we have the simple relationship $\tau = \mu\, du/dy$, is likely to be much simpler than turbulent flow. The remainder of this chapter is given mostly to a discussion of turbulence and its properties, but before proceeding with this, we shall derive a very useful and fairly general relationship for viscous flow that we can apply in a number of instances and then adapt to yield information on turbulent flow.

6.4   *Simplified two-dimensional viscous flow*

As was pointed out in Chapter 4, the introduction of viscous forces into the equations of motion is a complex procedure; the results are given by the Navier-Stokes equations (appendix to Chapter 4). However, much of the analysis of viscous flow is made in circumstances that permit considerable simplification, and so we shall now derive a relationship applicable in more than one circumstance and thus having some generality.

The case to be considered is that of an incompressible flow which is predominantly in one direction but which may have small velocity components in the directions normal to flow. Pressure and viscous forces are assumed to act in the flow direction only, and there are no body forces. The flow may be two-dimensional kinematically, but force and momentum are also assumed to be effective in the flow direction only. These conditions may seem restrictive, but in fact they cover two-dimensional boundary layers (and three-dimensional boundary layers are only now beginning to be the objects of intensive study) and much of the viscous flow in ducts.

Fig. 6.6 depicts the situation. A small element of fluid of sides Δx and Δy, with unit length in the z direction, is in a flow with a varying velocity, u, where $u = u(x, y, t)$. The sides Δy are acted upon by pressure forces, and there may be a pressure gradient in the x direction. The sides Δx are acted upon by shear forces which differ in magnitude and *direction* by virtue of the velocity gradient across Δy. The top side is "pulled" along because the velocity outside it is greater than that on its surface. The bottom side is retarded by the lower velocity outside it. From Newton's law, $F_x = Ma_x/g_c = (M/g_c)\,(Du/Dt)$, then,

$$p\,\Delta y - \left(p + \frac{\partial p}{\partial x}\,\Delta x\right)\Delta y - \tau\,\Delta x + \left(\tau + \frac{\partial \tau}{\partial y}\,\Delta y\right)\Delta x = \frac{\rho}{g_c}\,\Delta x\,\Delta y\,\frac{Du}{Dt}$$

Expanding and dividing through by $\Delta x\,\Delta y$ gives us

$$-\frac{\partial p}{\partial x} + \frac{\partial \tau}{\partial y} = \frac{\rho}{g_c}\left(u\,\frac{\partial u}{\partial x} + v\,\frac{\partial u}{\partial y} + \frac{\partial u}{\partial t}\right)$$

Figure 6.6

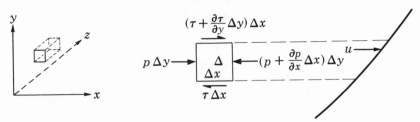

Substituting for the shear stress, $\tau = (\mu/g_c)\,\partial u/\partial y$, so that

$$\frac{\partial \tau}{\partial y} = \frac{\partial}{\partial y}\left(\frac{\mu}{g_c}\frac{\partial u}{\partial y}\right) = \frac{\mu}{g_c}\frac{\partial^2 u}{\partial y^2}$$

we can write

$$-\frac{1}{\rho}\frac{\partial p}{\partial x} + \frac{\mu}{\rho g_c}\frac{\partial^2 u}{\partial y^2} = \frac{1}{g_c}\left(u\frac{\partial u}{\partial x} + v\frac{\partial u}{\partial y} + \frac{\partial u}{\partial t}\right) = \frac{1}{g_c}\frac{Du}{Dt} \qquad [6.1]$$

This can be compared to Eq. 4.89a, the Navier-Stokes equation for the x direction. Since the flow is two-dimensional, no z- or w-terms appear, and with no body force, X disappears. The third term of Eq. 4.89a likewise disappears, since the flow in this case is incompressible, and so div $\mathbf{V} = 0$, or $(\partial u/\partial x + \partial v/\partial y) = 0$. The fourth term of Eq. 4.89a, which represents the viscous effect, is simplified to $\partial^2 u/\partial y^2$, since shear stress is regarded as effective only owing to the variation of u with y, the variation of u with x being negligible by comparison. The derivation here may contribute to the acceptance of the Navier-Stokes equations, which were not derived. The assumptions stated qualitatively at the beginning of this derivation make it tantamount to a more rigorous "order of magnitude" analysis based on the Navier-Stokes equations.*

6.5 *Turbulence*

Turbulence is the random irregular motion of fluid particles in time and space. "Irregular" implies that the motion cannot be specified completely, and "random" implies that, despite the irregularity, statistical values of various quantities may be obtained. Variations in both time and space are necessary because otherwise some regularity might be observed. Generally turbulence is of small scale relative to the over-all conditions in engineering flow systems; i.e., the irregular velocities are small with respect to the bulk velocity, and the linear dimensions of the fluctuations are small with respect to the geometry, of a fluid system. Actual values of turbulent quantities in nature may be large to an observer, e.g., gusts of wind in a storm.

Turbulence is generated by viscous forces at surfaces and by movements of adjacent layers of fluid at different velocities. Thus in flow over an airfoil the surface of the airfoil produces a boundary layer that is usually turbulent beyond an initial laminar length. In the wake following the trailing edge, turbulence is generated by fluid layers of different velocities. A turbulent

---

* See, e.g., H. Schlichting, *Boundary Layer Theory*, 4th ed., McGraw-Hill, New York, 1960.

motion tends to decay if no external source of energy is present. For instance, if a wire grid of large mesh is placed across a wind tunnel, large-scale eddies develop behind the wires. These interact with each other, dissipating into a succession of smaller eddies, until the dissipation is carried out by purely viscous effects, i.e., on a molecular scale.

Turbulence therefore implies the motion of groups of particles of fluid. Sometimes it is useful for analysis to visualize a turbulent process as one in which each such group of particles preserves its identity for a certain time interval, but this cannot be a true physical picture. At any time, a group of particles is changing its character.

It is convenient to start the analysis of a turbulent flow by separating a velocity vector into gross or bulk velocity components, upon each of which is superimposed a secondary velocity component corresponding to the irregular, random motion in that direction. Thus if u_i, v_i, and w_i are the instantaneous components in the x, y, and z directions of a steady flow velocity, $\mathbf{V}$, then

$$u_i = u + u'$$
$$v_i = v + v'$$
$$w_i = w + w' \qquad [6.2]$$

where u, v, and w are the averages of bulk velocities and u', v', and w' are the superimposed fluctuating components. It may be noted that in what has been called one-dimensional turbulent flow, say, in the x direction, there may be components v' and w' even though v and w are zero. Similarly, such fluid properties as pressure and density have instantaneous values p_i and ρ_i, with fluctuating values p' and ρ'.

Because the fluctuating components are usually small, and because at any fixed point in space the velocity components vary rapidly in magnitude, special means of measurement must be adopted. The instrument used for this purpose is the *hot-wire anemometer*, one common form of which consists of very short lengths of extremely thin wire (diameter of 1×10^{-4} to 5×10^{-4} in). The wires are heated by a steady electric current, and their resistance is measured by a suitable amplifier and bridge circuit. Electrical resistivity is proportional to wire temperature, and wire temperature depends on the velocity of the fluid flowing over the wire. Because of their extremely low thermal capacity, the wires are almost immediately responsive to the minute fluctuations of velocity that represent turbulence. The output signal can be led to an oscilloscope, and a chart of the turbulence obtained, as shown in Fig. 6.7. This figure indicates that at any particular instant of time, t_x, $u_i = u + u'$. The average velocity is defined by

$$u = \frac{1}{\Delta t} \int_0^{\Delta t} u_i \, dt \qquad [6.3]$$

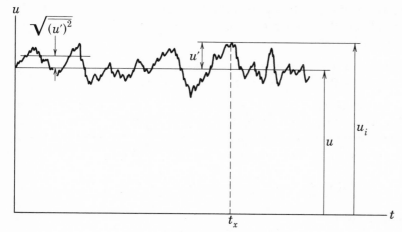

Figure 6.7

where Δt is sufficiently large that a true average results but not so large that any periodicity of the whole flow is contained in it. For the fluctuating velocity u', the average value, $\overline{u'}$, is

$$\overline{u'} = \frac{1}{\Delta t} \int_0^{\Delta t} u' \, dt = 0 \qquad [6.4]$$

Although the average value of u' (and of v' and w') is zero, there is a finite root-mean-square value, $\sqrt{\overline{u'^2}}$, with

$$\overline{u'^2} = \frac{1}{\Delta t} \int_0^{\Delta t} u'^2 \, dt \qquad [6.5]$$

This root-mean-square value is called the *intensity* of turbulence. Most often it is expressed as the relative intensity, thus:

$$\frac{\sqrt{\overline{u'^2}}}{u} \quad \text{and} \quad \frac{\sqrt{\overline{v'^2}}}{v} \quad \text{and} \quad \frac{\sqrt{\overline{w'^2}}}{w} \qquad [6.6]$$

and quoted as a percentage. In one- or two-dimensional flow, three-dimensional turbulence may be present, and then the denominator for the intensity is the total velocity, V.

The momentum equation, Eq. 6.1, is valid if the values of pressure and velocity are the instantaneous values, p_i, u_i, and v_i, but no solution is possible because these are irregular and random. Much useful information is furnished, however, if the instantaneous values are replaced by the sums of the average and fluctuating values and the averages taken. With instantaneous values, Eq. 6.1 becomes

$$-\frac{1}{\rho}\frac{\partial p_i}{\partial x} + \frac{\mu}{\rho g_c}\frac{\partial^2 u_i}{\partial y^2} = \frac{1}{g_c}\left(u_i\frac{\partial u_i}{\partial x} + v_i\frac{\partial u_i}{\partial y} + \frac{\partial u_i}{\partial t}\right)$$ [6.7]

Rather than substituting at once, we add the term $u_i(\partial u_i/\partial x + \partial v_i/\partial y)/g_c$ to the right-hand side. Since the part in parentheses is the continuity relationship for incompressible flow and therefore equal to zero, Eq. 6.7 is actually unchanged, although its right-hand side is written

$$\frac{1}{g_c}\left(u_i\frac{\partial u_i}{\partial x} + u_i\frac{\partial u_i}{\partial x} + v_i\frac{\partial u_i}{\partial y} + u_i\frac{\partial v_i}{\partial y} + \frac{\partial u_i}{\partial t}\right)$$

This is equivalent to

$$\frac{1}{g_c}\left(\frac{\partial u_i^2}{\partial x} + \frac{\partial u_i v_i}{\partial y} + \frac{\partial u_i}{\partial t}\right)$$

Hence Eq. 6.7 becomes

$$-\frac{1}{\rho}\frac{\partial p_i}{\partial x} + \frac{\mu}{\rho g_c}\frac{\partial^2 u_i}{\partial y^2} = \frac{1}{g_c}\left(\frac{\partial u_i^2}{\partial x} + \frac{\partial u_i v_i}{\partial y} + \frac{\partial u_i}{\partial t}\right)$$

which is again rearranged to give

$$-\frac{1}{\rho}\frac{\partial p_i}{\partial x} + \frac{1}{g_c}\frac{\partial}{\partial y}\left(\frac{\mu}{\rho}\frac{\partial u_i}{\partial y} - u_i v_i\right) = \frac{1}{g_c}\left(\frac{\partial u_i^2}{\partial x} + \frac{\partial u_i}{\partial t}\right)$$ [6.8]

We now replace each instantaneous value by the sum of the average and fluctuating values, differentiate, and replace the values in the derivatives by their averages, some of which may be zero (Eq. 6.4). We shall deal with each term of Eq. 6.8 in turn.

For the first term,

$$\frac{1}{\rho}\frac{\partial p_i}{\partial x} = \frac{1}{\rho}\frac{\partial}{\partial x}(p + p') = \frac{1}{\rho}\left(\frac{\partial p}{\partial x} + \frac{\partial p'}{\partial x}\right)$$

The average value of p is p, but according to the definition in Eq. 6.4, the average value of p' is zero. Thus

$$\frac{1}{\rho}\frac{\partial p}{\partial x} = \frac{1}{\rho}\frac{\partial p}{\partial x}$$ [6.9]

For the second term, taking first the expressions inside the partial differential sign, we have

$$\frac{\mu}{\rho}\frac{\partial u_i}{\partial y} - u_i v_i = \frac{\mu}{\rho}\frac{\partial}{\partial y}(u + u') - (u + u')(v + v') = \frac{\mu}{\rho}\left(\frac{\partial u}{\partial y} + \frac{\partial u'}{\partial y}\right)$$
$$- (uv + u'v + uv' + u'v')$$

The average value of uv is simply uv because both u and v are steady, positive values; $u'v$ and uv' disappear because both are products of a steady value and a fluctuating value whose average is zero; the average value of $u'v'$ is $\overline{u'v'}$ because the products of $+u'$ and $+v'$ and of $-u'$ and $-v'$ are both positive. Therefore,

$$\frac{\mu}{\rho}\frac{\partial u_i}{\partial y} - u_i v_i = \frac{\mu}{\rho}\frac{\partial u}{\partial y} - uv - \overline{u'v'}$$

Taking the partial derivative with respect to y gives us

$$\frac{\partial}{\partial y}\left(\frac{\mu}{\rho}\frac{\partial u}{\partial y} - uv - \overline{u'v'}\right) = \frac{\mu}{\rho}\frac{\partial^2 u}{\partial y^2} - u\frac{\partial v}{\partial y} - v\frac{\partial u}{\partial y} - \frac{\partial \overline{u'v'}}{\partial y} \qquad [6.10]$$

The third term, the first on the right-hand side, is handled similarly.

$$\frac{\partial u_i^2}{\partial x} = \frac{\partial}{\partial x}(u + u')^2 = \frac{\partial}{\partial x}(u^2 + 2uu' + u'^2) = \frac{\partial}{\partial x}(u^2 + \overline{u'^2})$$

$$= 2u\frac{\partial u}{\partial x} + \frac{\partial \overline{u'^2}}{\partial x} \qquad [6.11]$$

For the last term,

$$\frac{\partial u_i}{\partial t} = \frac{\partial}{\partial t}(u + u') = \frac{\partial u}{\partial t} + \frac{\partial u'}{\partial t} = \frac{\partial u}{\partial t} \qquad [6.12]$$

Substituting Eqs. 6.9 through 6.12 back into Eq. 6.8, we obtain

$$-\frac{1}{\rho}\frac{\partial p}{\partial x} + \frac{\mu}{\rho}\frac{\partial^2 u}{\partial y^2} - \frac{u}{g_c}\frac{\partial v}{\partial y} - \frac{v}{g_c}\frac{\partial u}{\partial y} - \frac{1}{g_c}\frac{\partial \overline{u'v'}}{\partial y}$$

$$= \frac{1}{g_c}\left(2u\frac{\partial u}{\partial x} + \frac{\partial \overline{u'^2}}{\partial x} + \frac{\partial u}{\partial t}\right) \qquad [6.13]$$

Since $\partial u/\partial x + \partial v/\partial y = 0$ and $u\,\partial u/\partial x + v\,\partial u/\partial y + \partial u/\partial t = Du/Dt$, Eq. 6.13 becomes

$$-\frac{1}{\rho}\frac{\partial p}{\partial x} + \frac{\mu}{\rho g_c}\frac{\partial^2 u}{\partial y^2} - \frac{1}{g_c}\left(\frac{\partial \overline{u'^2}}{\partial x} + \frac{\partial \overline{u'v'}}{\partial y}\right) = \frac{1}{g_c}\frac{Du}{Dt} \qquad [6.14]$$

It should be remarked that this two-dimensional flow not only has $w = 0$ but also has assumed $w' = 0$. A more complex relationship results if $w' \neq 0$.

Comparing Eq. 6.14 with Eq. 6.1, we see that the difference lies in the last term in parentheses on the left-hand side, which contains two quantities expressing the effects of the fluctuating velocity components. After multiplication through by ρ, which is constant and can go inside the differential, the terms $-\rho\overline{u'^2}/g_c$ and $-\rho\overline{u'v'}/g_c$ represent respectively a normal stress and a shear stress, both due to fluctuating components. These are called the *Reynolds* stresses, and there are similar terms for three-dimensional flow, $-\rho\overline{v'^2}$, $-\rho\overline{w'^2}$, $-\rho\overline{v'w'}$, and $-\rho\overline{u'w'}$, making six in all. It will be realized that the normal stress affects a pressure reading, and corrections are necessary if

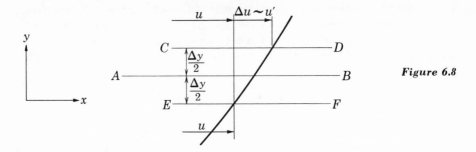

Figure 6.8

this stress is sufficiently great to make the relative intensity high. This is not a straightforward matter, particularly for static pressure, and estimates of probable correction factors have to be accepted.

The shear stress, $-\rho\overline{u'v'}$, is of great interest because it is the turbulent or eddy stress. We can write

$$\tau_{\text{total}} = \tau_{\text{viscous}} + \tau_{\text{turbulent}} = \frac{\mu}{g_c}\frac{\partial u}{\partial y} - \frac{\rho}{g_c}\overline{u'v'} \qquad [6.15]$$

In turbulent flow generally, the turbulent stress is much greater than the viscous stress, and so the latter can often be ignored in comparison. However, although the turbulent shear stress has been isolated, we still cannot determine its value for any flow in general or for every part of a particular flow. Nevertheless, by knowing its nature, we can replace it by terms dependent on it and develop working analyses.

The shear-stress term $-\rho\overline{u'v'}$ has a negative sign; in order for it to yield positive stress, which it must, the value of $\overline{u'v'}$ must then, on the *average*, be negative. The term itself, and its negative value, can be evolved by another method that introduces a physical picture of turbulent shear stress.

Let us consider flow in the x direction with a velocity gradient, as shown in Fig. 6.8, fixing our attention on plane AB. Fluid flowing along planes CD and EF, a very small distance, $\Delta y/2$, above and below AB, exchanges momentum across AB by virtue of the transverse fluctuations of velocity, v'. Across a unit area of AB there is an instantaneous mass flow rate, $\rho v'$. Fluid moving up from EF has an average longitudinal (x direction) velocity of u, which is less than the average velocity in CD by the amount Δu. The fluid from EF originally has longitudinal velocity fluctuations equally positive and negative, but on its arrival in CD, where the velocity is $u + \Delta u$, the velocity fluctuations on the average are negative. Similarly, fluid moving down across AB to EF, with a negative v', has an x-direction velocity excess of u'. Δy is chosen so that the average value of u' along CD is equal to Δu, and thus we may say $\Delta u \approx u'$. It is this deficit of momentum relative to the fluid in CD and the excess relative to the fluid in EF that gives rise to the turbulent shear stress. It is apparent that $+v'$ is usually associated with $-u'$, and $-v'$ with $+u'$, so that the product $u'v'$ is usually negative. Owing to the random nature of turbulence, this is true most of the time but not always. With $\overline{u'v'}$ negative, the shear stress $-\rho\overline{u'v'}/g_c$ is positive.

The association of u' and v' in this analysis is an instance of a *correlation* between the fluctuating components of velocity. Correlation depends on magnitude and direction. If $+v'$ were always associated with $-u'$ and of equal magnitude, then the *correlation coefficient* would be unity. If the two were *never* associated, the coefficient would be zero. Ordinarily it is somewhere between these two values. A correlation coefficient, R, for this case is expressed as

$$R = \frac{-\overline{u'v'}}{\sqrt{\overline{u'^2}}\,\sqrt{\overline{v'^2}}} \qquad [6.16]$$

If $u' = -v'$, $R = 1$. Correlation coefficients may be found for combinations of fluctuating velocity components in all planes, both in time and space. Eq. 6.16 represents a correlation in time of u' and v' at one point in space. Two x-direction fluctuations, u_1' and u_2', a short distance apart can be measured at the same time. In this way, a statistical picture of turbulent behavior in a given flow can be built up.

To relate all the details of turbulent flow is an extremely complex process. Accordingly, simplified schemes have been adopted to explain some of the consequences of turbulence. One assumption is that *isotropy* exists, i.e., that the intensity components at a point are equal in all directions— $\sqrt{\overline{u'^2}} = \sqrt{\overline{v'^2}} = \sqrt{\overline{w'^2}}$ —or, stated more generally, that the turbulence is invariant under rotation of the coordinate system. No actual flow can be truly isotropic, although isotropy can be approached in certain circumstances. The value of the assumption is that an analysis of isotropic turbulence can form a basis for theoretical treatment and thus can give indications of actual behavior. The theory can be checked in many instances by the artificial production of approximate isotropic turbulence, e.g., a short distance downstream from a wire mesh. Another assumption is that homogeneity exists, i.e., that the fluctuating components are independent of position in the flow field.

Although these assumptions lead to a statistical theory that provides some information on turbulence, the phenomenological approach has to date been more valuable in yielding relationships for quantitative use with turbulent flows. An example is the concept of mixing length, originally developed by Prandtl in 1925.

Prandtl postulated that an element of fluid moves a certain distance before losing its identity, this distance being the mixing length, ℓ, analogous to the mean free path in molecular motion. The mixing length also provides a measure of the *scale* of turbulence. Prandtl's hypothesis was simple but

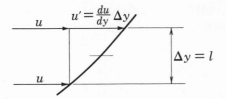

Figure 6.9

very effective. With a figure similar to Fig. 6.8 and the analysis of momentum transport across a transverse distance, Δy, then from Fig. 6.9 we see that $u' = (du/dy) \Delta y$. Prandtl defined the mixing length $\ell = \Delta y$ by the relation

$$u' = \frac{du}{dy} \ell$$

In other words, the fluctuating velocity component in the x direction, u', is of the order of the differences of two velocities in the x direction separated by a transverse distance, ℓ. It might appear that we have only replaced unknown fluctuating velocities with an unknown, and quite fictitious, length. However, the introduction of the velocity gradient du/dy is an advantage, for it is analogous to that in the expression for purely viscous flow, $\tau = \mu(du/dy)$. Furthermore, it is much easier to make assumptions about the dependence of ℓ on other factors than about the dependence of u' and v' on these factors. Since Prandtl also considered v' dependent on ℓ and du/dy, we may write

$$- \rho \overline{u'v'} = \rho \ell^2 \left(\frac{du}{dy} \right)^2 \qquad [6.17]$$

Eq. 6.15 then becomes

$$\tau_{\text{total}} = \tau_{\text{viscous}} + \tau_{\text{turbulent}} = \mu \frac{du}{dy} - \rho \overline{u'v'} = \mu \frac{du}{dy} + \rho \ell^2 \left(\frac{du}{dy} \right)^2$$

The mixing length will be used in the analysis for turbulent flow in ducts in the next chapter.

Most fluid flows of engineering importance are turbulent flows. Since we have less knowledge of them than of laminar flows, we have to rely to an unsatisfactory degree on empirical data. ("Exact" solutions for laminar-flow problems are limited only by the difficulty of mathematical technique and not by insufficient knowledge of the physical situation.) In addition to turbulence in ordinary duct flow and in flow over bodies, turbulence is manifest on a very large scale in the earth's atmosphere, a gigantic flow field that is just beginning to be mapped by means of photographs from orbiting satellites. Thus meteorologists are interested in the phenomena of turbulence. On an even more tremendous scale, turbulence in the solar system, which contains clouds of particles from the sun and elsewhere, and in the outer reaches of space, where there are clouds of "dust," is of concern to astronomers and cosmologists. Although the conditions are different in all these cases, turbulence, as the random, irregular motion of particles in space and time, is evidently one of the natural modes of matter outside the solid state.

Problems

6.1. Show that Eq. 6.1 reduces to the simple Euler equation, Eq. 4.58, for the ideal, one-dimensional, steady flow of gas.

6.2. Show that the equation of continuity is satisfied if the instantaneous velocities are replaced by the average and fluctuating velocities.

6.3. Show that the pressure indicated by a Pitot (total-head) tube due to turbulent fluctuations in velocity is

$$p_0 = p + \frac{\rho u^2}{2g_c}\left(\frac{1 + \overline{u'^2} + \overline{v'^2} + \overline{w'^2}}{u^2}\right)$$

where u is the mean velocity along the axis of the tube that is parallel to the mean flow direction.

6.4. For water at 60°F and for air at standard conditions flowing in a 2 in. diameter pipe, find the velocities for which the Reynolds number is (a) 2000, (b) 10,000, and (c) 100,000. Find the flow rates in each case in gal/min and ft³/min, respectively.

6.5. Find the Reynolds number for gasoline of sp gr 0.70 at 50°F flowing at the rate of 4 gal/min through a pipe of 1⅛ in. i.d.

7

Flow in Ducts

7.1 *Introduction*

Analysis of the behavior of the flow of fluids in ducts is of major importance in fluid dynamics, whether its purpose is to estimate the loss of useful energy in the conveyance of fluid from a source to a point of use or to determine the particular qualities necessary to produce a desired effect, as in turbine or rocket nozzles. The "useful" energy depends on the application. In incompressible flow, it is invariably the pressure, as has been seen from the discussion of a loss term in the Bernoulli relationship, Sect. 4.22. In adiabatic flow, there is no loss of total energy, but the dissipation of pressure to internal energy is regarded as a loss, as the increase of temperature cannot be utilized. As an example, the loss of pressure between the reservoir and the rotor of a hydraulic turbine lowers the shaft output of the turbine, even though the energy remains as internal energy. In compressible flow, although the loss as increase of entropy must decrease the availability of the energy, some portion of it may be recovered. Here we shall divide our study, dealing first with incompressible flow in straight ducts of constant area, as (1) laminar flow and (2) turbulent flow, and then with incompressible flow in ducts of varying area and in bends. Much of this material is valid for compressible flow as well, which presents special problems of its own. Because heat transfer affects the density of compressible fluids, it will also be considered.

The analysis will be carried out in terms of a duct of circular cross section, as this is the preeminent shape for engineering use by reason of stress and manufacture. This is fortunate from the point of view of detailed analysis, since flow in a circular duct, or *pipe flow*, is generally treated with satisfactory accuracy as symmetrical about the axis, or axisymmetric. Any other shape introduces asymmetries leading to secondary flow patterns superimposed on the main flow and often obscuring the basic performance factors. Correlation of performance factors such as friction coefficient with a cross section that is not circular is therefore based on flow in an equivalent circular duct (see Sect. 7.3). Unless it is stated to the contrary, we shall always be dealing with *fully developed* flow (Sect. 6.2); i.e., the flow pattern is unvarying in the direction of flow.

7.2   *Shear stress in pipe flow—general*

Consider a small cylindrical element of fluid along the axis of fluid flowing in a pipe (Fig. 7.1). The velocity is constant along the length of the pipe but is not uniform across the diameter, although it is assumed symmetrical about the axis. No unbalanced body forces are present, and so equilibrium is established through the action of forces due to pressure and shear stress. The pressure forces act normally on the surface of the cylinder, those on the longitudinal walls canceling out owing to symmetry. The pressure is independent of radius from the axis; i.e., it is uniform across a plane normal to the flow direction. The shear stress acts tangentially on the walls of the cylinder of length dx. It is called the *effective* shear stress, τ_{eff}, because in this general case it may be due either to purely viscous effects (laminar flow) or to the transport of particle momentum (turbulent flow) or to both. Referring to the figure, a force balance yields

$$p\pi r^2 = (p + dp)\pi r^2 + \tau_{\text{eff}} 2\pi r\, dx$$

from which

$$\tau_{\text{eff}} = -\frac{dp}{dx}\frac{r}{2} \qquad [7.1]$$

Since the flow is fully developed, so that the velocity gradient across the pipe is not a function of distance along the pipe, τ_{eff} is independent of x; and since p is independent of r, the variables may be separated and an integration made between station 1, where $x = L_1$, and station 2, where $x = L_2$, the

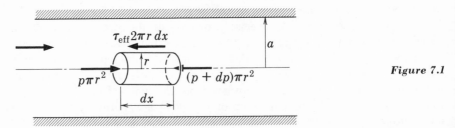

Figure 7.1

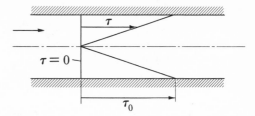

Figure 7.2

pipe length being $L_2 - L_1 = L$. Thus

$$\tau_{\text{eff}} \int_{L_1}^{L_2} dx = -\frac{r}{2} \int_1^2 dp$$

and
$$\tau_{\text{eff}} = \frac{r}{2L} (p_1 - p_2) \qquad [7.2]$$

Hence τ_{eff} is a linear function of radius, with a value of zero at the pipe axis $(r = 0)$ and a value of τ_0 at the wall, where $r = a$, the pipe radius. τ_0 is called the *wall shear stress*. This is shown in Fig. 7.2.

Rearranging Eq. 7.2 for $r = a$ at $\tau_{\text{eff}} = \tau_0$ gives us

$$\tau_0 = \frac{a}{2L} (p_1 - p_2)$$

or, for $a = d/2$, where d is the pipe diameter,

$$p_1 - p_2 = \Delta p = 4\frac{L}{d}\tau_0 \qquad [7.3]$$

(Note that we define Δp here as initial pressure minus final pressure in order to obtain a positive value.) A knowledge of τ_0 allows a calculation of the pressure drop due to friction along a pipe of length L. We shall examine this result for laminar and turbulent flow, but first it is useful to express the pressure drop in another form.

In Chapter 5 this case of pipe flow was analyzed by several methods. The result in terms of dimensionless parameters is

$$\Delta p = \rho V^2 \phi_1 \left(\frac{L}{d}, \frac{\rho V d}{\mu}\right) \qquad [5.6b]$$

where $\mu/\rho V d$ has been inverted and L replaces s, as no confusion need now arise between symbols for variables and symbols for dimensions. Eq. 7.3 shows that Δp is directly proportional to L/d, and therefore, in Eq. 5.6b, $\phi_1(L/d, \rho V d/\mu)$ may be written as $(L/d)\phi_2(\rho V d/\mu)$. The remainder of the expression, $\rho V^2 \phi_2(\rho V d/\mu)$, where $\rho V d/\mu$ is the Reynolds number, must then be equal to four times the wall shear stress, τ_0. This function of Reynolds number, $\phi_2(\rho V d/\mu)$, is called the *friction coefficient* or factor, f. Dividing ρV^2 by the constant $2g_c$ in order to have the dynamic pressure in our system of units, we obtain

$$\tau_0 = \frac{\rho V^2}{2g_c} \frac{f}{4} \qquad\qquad [7.4a]$$

or, alternatively,

$$f = \frac{4\tau_0}{\rho V^2/2g_c} \qquad\qquad [7.4b]$$

Thus an experimental value of τ_0 or f permits the other to be evaluated. We shall need Eqs. 7.4 later.

Eq. 7.4a can be substituted into Eq. 7.3, yielding

$$\Delta p = f \frac{L}{d} \frac{\rho V^2}{2g_c} \qquad\qquad [7.5]$$

or, as a head rather than a pressure relationship,

$$\Delta h = \frac{\Delta p}{\rho g/g_c} = f \frac{L}{d} \frac{V^2}{2g} \qquad\qquad [7.6]$$

where f is the friction coefficient. Eqs. 7.5 and 7.6 are sometimes known by the names of Darcy, Weisbach, and Fanning, who arrived at this general form for pressure- and head-drop relationships. Before the recognition of the Reynolds number and the fact that f could be expressed as $\phi(\text{Re})$, there were innumerable expressions for the pressure drop in a pipe of the general form $\Delta p = k(L/d)V^n$, where each value of the coefficient k and the exponent n was valid only for a given fluid in a certain restricted range of values of velocity, pipe length, and pipe diameter. It was this state of affairs that led von Karman to call hydraulics "the science of the variable constant."

7.3 Hydraulic radius and equivalent diameter

For ducts of cross section other than circular, the basic pressure–shear stress relationships result (Fig. 7.3) in

$$pA = (p + dp)A + \tau_0 s\, dx$$

where s is the perimeter, yielding

$$\tau_0 = \frac{A}{s} \frac{\Delta p}{L}$$

Following the same arguments as used for the circular duct, substituting for shear stress in terms of friction factor, we find that the pressure-loss equation, Eq. 7.5, reads

$$\Delta p = f \frac{sL}{4A_c} \frac{\rho V^2}{2g_c}$$

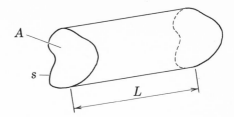

Figure 7.3

The term $4A/s$ replaces the diameter, d, and is called the *equivalent diameter*, d_e. A/s is the ratio of cross-sectional *area of flow* to the *wetted* perimeter and is called the *hydraulic radius*, r_h. Hence $d_e = 4r_h$. For irregular-shaped ducts, the equivalent diameter, d_e, is used in place of the diameter, d, including the Reynolds number as well.

For a rectangular duct of sides a and b, $d_e = 4ab/2(a + b) = 2ab/(a + b)$. For such a duct with one side very small compared to the other, i.e., with $b \ll a$, then b can be neglected in the denominator, so that $d_e \approx 2ab/a = 2b$ or twice the minimum dimension. For an annulus of inner and outer diameters d_1 and d_2, $d_e = \pi(d_2{}^2 - d_1{}^2)/\pi(d_2 + d_1) = d_2 - d_1$, i.e., twice the annular width.

The italicized words in the definition should be carefully noted, as sometimes a duct carrying a liquid is not completely filled or is said not to run full. A is the *flow* area, not the duct area, and s is the perimeter of the duct in contact with or *wetted* by the liquid, i.e., not including the free surface.

The value d_e has been useful in correlating performances of ducts that are not circular. There are some discrepancies, particularly with ducts having sharp corners, which may give rise to significant secondary flow patterns causing additional loss, but these occur most often with turbulent flow, and the correlation for laminar flow is satisfactory.

7.4   *Laminar flow in a pipe*

For laminar flow, the shear stress is wholly due to the viscosity. Therefore,

$$\tau_{\text{eff}} = \tau = \frac{\mu}{g_c} \frac{du}{dy} \qquad [1.3]$$

Eq. 1.3 was defined so that du/dy was positive; i.e., velocity u increased as distance y from the wall increased, and so the shear stress was positive, which must always be the case. For a circular pipe, the linear dimension r is measured from the axis toward the wall in the direction of decreasing velocity (since the velocity must be zero at the wall). Thus, substituting r for y and inserting the minus sign for the reason just stated, we have

$$\tau = -\frac{\mu}{g_c}\frac{du}{dr}$$

Substituting this value for τ_{eff} in Eq. 7.2 gives us

$$-\frac{\mu}{g_c}\frac{du}{dr} = \frac{r}{2L}(p_1 - p_2)$$

With the variables separated, this can be integrated between any radius, r, where the velocity is u and the pipe wall, where $r = a$ and $u = 0$. Hence, again with $p_1 - p_2 = \Delta p$,

$$-\int_u^0 du = \frac{g_c}{2}\frac{\Delta p}{\mu L}\int_r^a r\,dr$$

and

$$u = \frac{g_c\,\Delta p}{4\mu L}(a^2 - r^2) = \frac{g_c\,\Delta p\,a^2}{4\mu L}\left(1 - \frac{r^2}{a^2}\right) \qquad [7.7]$$

Thus u is a parabolic function of r that is zero at the walls and a maximum at the pipe axis. The maximum value is

$$u_{\max} = \frac{g_c\,\Delta p\,a^2}{4\mu L} \qquad [7.8]$$

The velocity distribution is shown in Fig. 7.4.

It is helpful to find an expression for the pressure loss, Δp, in terms of the average velocity, V, and thence in terms of the flow rate, $Q = VA$. The group $g_c\,\Delta p/4\mu L$ is constant for integration across the pipe and accordingly can be denoted by C for conciseness. Then Eq. 7.7 becomes

$$u = C(a^2 - r^2)$$

Defining the average velocity, V, as

$$V = \frac{\int u\,dA}{A}$$

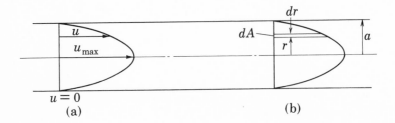

Figure 7.4

and with $dA = 2\pi r\,dr$ and $A = \pi a^2$ (Fig. 7.4b), we have

$$V = \frac{2\pi C}{\pi a^2}\int_0^a (a^2 - r^2)r\,dr = \frac{2C}{a^2}\left[\frac{a^2 r^2}{2} - \frac{r^4}{4}\right]_0^a = \frac{Ca^2}{2}$$

The maximum velocity from Eq. 7.8 is Ca^2, so that the average velocity is one-half of the maximum velocity.

Resubstituting for C yields

$$V = \frac{g_c\,\Delta p\,a^2}{8\mu L} \qquad\qquad [7.9]$$

or

$$\Delta p = \frac{8\mu L V}{g_c a^2} = \frac{32\mu L V}{g_c d^2} \qquad\qquad [7.10]$$

where pipe diameter $d = 2a$. We might note here a comparison of this exact result with the expression obtained by dimensional analysis in Chapter 5. For the most general method we obtained

$$\Delta p = \rho V^2 \phi\left(\frac{\mu}{\rho V d}, \frac{L}{d}\right)$$

From Eq. 7.10, we see for the particular case of laminar flow that the function ϕ is simply the product of the two terms to the first power, but with an unknown constant; i.e.,

$$\Delta p = k\rho V^2\,\frac{\mu}{\rho V d}\frac{s}{d} = k\,\frac{\mu s V}{d^2}$$

This is Eq. 7.10 with $k = 32/g_c$ and s replacing L.

Returning to Eq. 7.10 and introducing $Q = VA = V\pi d^2/4$, we have

$$\Delta p = \frac{128\mu L Q}{\pi d^4 g_c} \qquad\qquad [7.11]$$

Eqs. 7.10 and 7.11 are forms of the *Hagen-Poiseuille equation* giving the relationship between flow rate and pressure loss over a given length of pipe for *laminar* flow. It is seen that pressure drop is proportional to the first power of velocity (or flow rate). The equation was developed independently about 1840 by Hagen and Poiseuille, hence its name.

We can put Eq. 7.10 into the general form with a friction factor, f, Eq. 7.5, by multiplying and dividing the right-hand side by ρV^2 and rearranging, thus:

$$\Delta p = \frac{32\mu L V}{g_c d^2 \rho V^2}\rho V^2 = 64\,\frac{\mu}{\rho V d}\frac{L}{d}\frac{\rho V^2}{2g_c} = \frac{64}{\mathrm{Re}}\frac{L}{d}\frac{\rho V^2}{2g_c} = f\frac{L}{d}\frac{\rho V^2}{2g_c} \qquad [7.12]$$

where $f = 64/\mathrm{Re}$ for this laminar-flow case. Eqs. 7.10 and 7.12 are similar. The former brings out the fact that the pressure drop is directly proportional to velocity and independent of density. The latter, with certain simple values of f for particular cases, is in general more desirable, and for turbulent flow it is the only way that Δp is normally expressed, although then f usually does not have a simple value.

The friction factor is not influenced by the surface roughness in laminar flow, because with purely viscous shear stress the basic mechanism of resistance is homogeneous everywhere in the fluid.

7.5   Laminar flow between parallel plates

Another laminar-flow case of importance is flow between parallel plates of infinite width, which, in practice, means of sufficient width that the end effects are negligible. This can be made more general if one plate is regarded as capable of moving in the flow direction with constant velocity U. The situation is then as shown in Fig. 7.5.

This flow can be analyzed ab initio if a force balance on a small element is considered, as was done for the flow through a circular duct. However, this flow configuration is covered by the general two-dimensional case treated in Chapter 6, which itself was an application of the Navier-Stokes equations with certain restrictions. The equation developed was

$$\mu \frac{\partial^2 u}{\partial y^2} - \frac{\partial p}{\partial x} = \frac{\rho}{g_c}\left(u \frac{\partial u}{\partial x} + v \frac{\partial u}{\partial y} + \frac{\partial u}{\partial t}\right) \qquad [6.1]$$

For the case here, this can be simplified yet further. Only steady flow is under consideration; hence, $\partial u/\partial t = 0$. For laminar flow bounded by parallel walls, there is no v component of velocity. For fully developed flow, u is a function of y only; hence, $\partial u/\partial x = 0$. Eq. 6.1 thus reduces to

$$\mu \frac{d^2 u}{dy^2} - \frac{dp}{dx} = 0 \qquad [7.13a]$$

with ordinary derivatives replacing partial derivatives, as u is a function only of y and p is a function only of x.

The boundary conditions are $u = 0$ at $y = 0$ and $u = U$ at $y = h$, the

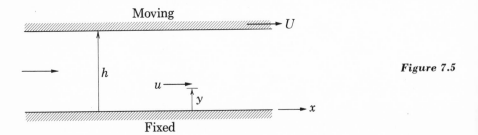

Figure 7.5

latter condition resulting from the no-slip requirement at a solid surface. Rearranging Eq. 7.13a as

$$\frac{d}{dy}\left(\frac{du}{dy}\right) = \frac{1}{\mu}\frac{dp}{dx}$$

and then, since dp/dx is constant with respect to y, integrating once, we obtain

$$\frac{du}{dy} = \frac{1}{\mu}\frac{dp}{dx}\,y + A$$

A second integration gives

$$u = \frac{1}{2\mu}\frac{dp}{dx}\,y^2 + Ay + B \qquad\qquad [\textit{7.13b}]$$

There are two boundary conditions for the two constants of integration. With $u = 0$ at $y = 0$, $B = 0$. With $u = U$ at $y = h$,

$$A = \frac{U}{h} - \frac{1}{2\mu}\frac{dp}{dx}\,h$$

Inserting this value of A in Eq. 7.14 and rearranging yield

$$u = U\frac{y}{h} - \frac{1}{2\mu}\frac{dp}{dx}\,y(h - y) \qquad\qquad [\textit{7.13c}]$$

The type of flow represented by Eq. 7.13c is known as *Couette* flow, and two special cases can be examined. First, for both plates stationary ($U = 0$),

$$u = -\frac{1}{2\mu}\frac{dp}{dx}\,y(h - y) \qquad\qquad [\textit{7.14}]$$

which is a parabolic velocity distribution with $u_{\max}$ at $y = h/2$. This is called *Poiseuille* flow. Note that dp/dx is negative, so that the value of the right-hand side is positive. It can be shown by the methods of the previous section that for this case of two-dimensional flow the average velocity is two-thirds of the maximum velocity.

Second, for zero pressure gradient, i.e., with the whole fluid flow caused by the motion of the top plate,

$$u = U\frac{y}{h} \qquad\qquad [\textit{7.15}]$$

This is a linear velocity distribution, and the flow is known as *simple Couette* flow.

A combination of the two flows, as given by the complete Eq. 7.13, is a superposition of a parabolic velocity distribution on a linear one, with the exact form depending on the relative values of U and dp/dx. The three situations are shown in Fig. 7.6, with the combined-flow example a typical dis-

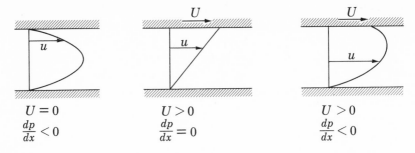

Figure 7.6

tribution when u is everywhere in the same direction as U. Couette flow is important as a starting point for the hydrodynamic theory of lubrication.

7.6   *Turbulent flow in smooth pipes—experimental*

From the discussion of turbulence in Chapter 6, it will be appreciated that the problem of turbulent flow in pipes is likely to be complex. Actual values of friction factor used in engineering work are largely empirical, but analysis provides a satisfactory explanation of the observed trends. Furthermore, very good agreement between actual and theoretical behavior has been obtained by simple methods involving the mixing-length hypothesis. Here behavior will be treated first in relation to experimental data for smooth pipes. A theoretical analysis will follow. Then the problem of rough pipes will be taken up. By the term "smooth pipes," we mean pipes with such surfaces as glass, plastic, or polished metal. Seamless drawn copper or brass comes close to being smooth. Rough pipes include anything from commercial standard steel or iron pipes up to concrete pipes.

Among the first correlations of friction factor in turbulent flow was that of Blasius, who in 1911 made a critical survey of data and formulated the empirical equation

$$f = \frac{0.316}{\mathrm{Re}^{1/4}} \qquad\qquad [7.16]$$

valid for smooth pipes at Reynolds numbers up to about 10^5. It may be noted immediately that the friction factor varies much more slowly with Reynolds number for turbulent flow than it does for laminar flow. Furthermore, if it is assumed that an Re of 2300 is one with which it is possible to have either laminar or turbulent flow, for the former, as $64/\mathrm{Re}$, $f \approx 0.0278$, whereas for the latter, from Eq. 7.16, $f \approx 0.0447$. In fact, in turbulent flow

Re would have to be nearly 17,000 before f would be reduced to its value for laminar flow at Re = 2300. Thus turbulent flow leads to higher losses than laminar flow for equivalent Reynolds numbers, as we might expect.

For Reynolds numbers greater than 10^5, the Blasius relationship is inaccurate, giving friction factors that are too low. At Re $\approx 10^6$, the experimental value for f is about 20% higher than the Blasius value. Empirical results from a number of different workers show that the relationship is not a linear plot on logarithmic paper; i.e., a simple power law is not sufficient.

In addition to friction factor, the distribution of velocity across a pipe is of considerable interest. It is found that the velocity distribution in turbulent flow is much flatter than that in laminar flow, but with a much steeper gradient near the walls. A typical distribution is shown in Fig. 7.7, compared with the parabolic distribution of laminar flow. Both are pictured for the same mean velocity, and, because of the steep gradient, it is impossible on this scale to indicate the turbulent distribution near the walls.

Nikuradse, who was responsible for a great deal of the work on turbulent pipe flow that we now regard as classic, made a study of velocity distributions and demonstrated that they become flatter as the Reynolds number increases. An empirical relationship based on his data states that, except very close to the wall, the ratio of velocity u at distance y from the wall to the maximum velocity, u_{max}, at the pipe axis is

$$\frac{u}{u_{max}} = \left(\frac{y}{a}\right)^{1/n} \qquad [7.17]$$

where n is dependent on the Reynolds number. Thus $n = 6$ at Re = 4×10^3, $n = 7$ at Re = 1.1×10^5, and $n = 10$ at Re = 3.2×10^6. The degree to which the distribution is peaked can be assessed by the ratio of average velocity V to maximum velocity u_{max}. For $n = 6$, 7, and 10, the ratios V/u_{max} are, respectively, 0.791, 0.817, and 0.865 (cf. $V/u_{max} = 0.5$, laminar flow). When a simple and general expression for turbulent velocity distribution is required, it is common to take $n = 7$. The result is known as the *seventh-root law*. It can be shown that the Blasius relation (Eq. 7.16) with $f \propto 1/\text{Re}^{1/4}$ is consistent with an assumption of the seventh-root law for velocity.

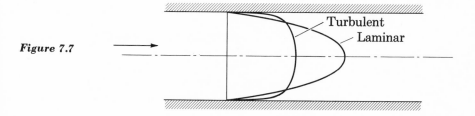

Figure 7.7

7.7   *Turbulent flow in smooth pipes—analytical*

A satisfactory analytical expression for smooth pipes should account primarily for the velocity distribution and then for the empirical friction factor.

It was Prandtl who in 1933 proposed the first simple analytical relationship for pipe flow, based on his mixing-length concept discussed in Chapter 6. If the viscous shear is neglected, i.e., if large values of the Reynolds number are assumed, then Eq. 6.15 can be written as

$$\tau = -\frac{\rho \overline{u'v'}}{g_c} = \frac{\rho \ell^2}{g_c}\left(\frac{du}{dy}\right)^2 \qquad [7.18]$$

The mixing length, ℓ, must be zero at the wall surface and increase outward. The assumption was made that ℓ is directly proportional to distance y from the wall; i.e., $\ell = ky$, and thus $\ell^2 = k^2 y^2$. The assumption was also made that the shear stress remains constant; i.e., $\tau = \tau_0$. This is a reasonable assumption for a thin layer near the wall, where a change of shear stress may be small compared to the absolute level, but a very far-reaching assumption for the region outside this layer. Remember that in Sect. 7.2 it was found that the shear stress increased linearly with radius from the axis to the walls. Making these substitutions in Eq. 7.18, then, we obtain

$$\tau_0 = \frac{k^2 \rho y^2}{g_c}\left(\frac{du}{dy}\right)^2$$

or
$$du = \frac{1}{k}\sqrt{\frac{g_c \tau_0}{\rho}}\frac{dy}{y} \qquad [7.19]$$

With k and dy/y dimensionless, $\sqrt{g_c \tau_0/\rho}$ must have the dimensions of velocity. It is called the *friction* or *shear* velocity and given the symbol u^* (u "star"), so that

$$u^* = \sqrt{\frac{g_c \tau_0}{\rho}}$$

Rearranged to give τ_0 directly, this is

$$\tau_0 = \frac{\rho u^{*2}}{g_c}$$

which, apart from a factor of $\frac{1}{2}$, expresses shear stress at the wall as a dynamic pressure based on shear velocity. Substituting u^* for $\sqrt{g_c \tau_0/\rho}$ in Eq. 7.19 yields

$$du = \frac{1}{k}u^*\frac{dy}{y} \qquad [7.20]$$

For a given pipe flow, u^* is constant, and integration of Eq. 7.20 gives

$$u = \frac{1}{k} u^* \ln y + C \qquad [7.21]$$

Although we have assumed various conditions near the wall, these equations cannot hold right at the wall, because, from the defining equation (Eq. 7.2) for shear stress, with $y = 0$, $\tau = 0$, and so the constant, C, cannot be determined. Prandtl made the assumption that $\ell \propto y$ and $\tau = \tau_0$ across the pipe and evaluated C by substituting the boundary condition, $u = u_{max}$ at $y = a$. Hence

$$u_{max} = \frac{1}{k} u^* \ln a + C$$

and

$$C = u_{max} - \frac{1}{k} u^* \ln a$$

Inserting this value of C in Eq. 7.21, we obtain

$$u = u_{max} + \frac{u^*}{k} \ln \frac{y}{a}$$

or

$$\frac{u_{max} - u}{u^*} = - \frac{1}{k} \ln \frac{y}{a} \qquad [7.22]$$

This is Prandtl's velocity-distribution equation. The term $u_{max} - u$ is called the velocity *defect* or *deficiency*. Eq. 7.22 corresponds very well with actual velocity distributions found by Nikuradse and others, if a value of $k = 0.4$ is taken. Therefore, for the purpose of velocity distribution, Prandtl's assumptions are justified, in spite of their apparently sweeping nature. Another way of looking at the relationship is to refer back to Nikuradse's results, which express velocity distribution in terms of the fractional exponent $1/n$, with n increasing very slowly with Reynolds number and approaching a limit. This situation suggests a logarithmic expression of the distribution, as thereby a limit can be approached asymptotically and results extrapolated to very high Reynolds numbers.

Although Eq. 7.22 was developed on the basis of flow near the wall and then extended with a high degree of empirical success throughout the main body of flow, it cannot hold at the wall, where turbulence disappears, nor can it be exact at the pipe axis, where, for axisymmetric flow with a continuous velocity gradient, du/dy should be zero. Eq. 7.20 gives $du/dy \neq 0$. However, the Eq. 7.22 can be transformed into *a universal velocity-distribution* relationship with some further development.

Because of the absence of turbulence right at the wall, it is reasonable to assume that viscous effects predominate and that there is a very thin laminar-flow region next to the wall, called the *laminar sublayer*. It is very difficult to obtain measurements in this zone, as any measuring instrument is of the same order of magnitude as the thickness of the layer itself and

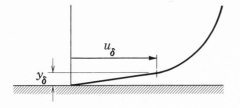

Figure 7.8

therefore disturbs the flow. However, such observations as are available, including some by the ultramicroscope, tend to confirm the presence of a laminar sublayer, not completely stable although without any manifestations characterizing turbulence.

The basis of the analysis is to suppose that the laminar sublayer extends out to a distance y_δ, where the velocity is u_δ, where it joins with the turbulent main flow (Fig. 7.8). In the laminar sublayer,

$$\tau_0 = \frac{\mu}{g_c} \frac{du}{dy}$$

and, for the very small thickness,

$$\frac{du}{dy} = \frac{u_\delta}{y_\delta}$$

so that

$$\tau_0 = \frac{\mu}{g_c} \frac{u_\delta}{y_\delta}$$

We can make this relationship dimensionless by dividing both sides by ρ and substituting $g_c \tau_0 / \rho = u^{*2}$; hence

$$\frac{g_c \tau_0}{\rho} = u^{*2} = \frac{\mu}{\rho} \frac{u_\delta}{y_\delta}$$

which we can rearrange to

$$\frac{u_\delta}{u^*} = \frac{\rho u^* y_\delta}{\mu} \qquad [7.23]$$

The left-hand side of Eq. 7.23 is the ratio of the velocity at the edge of the laminar sublayer to the friction velocity, and the right-hand side is a form of the Reynolds number depending on the thickness of the sublayer and the velocity at its edge. This dimensionless relationship is held to be the same for all flows and is thus a constant. Accordingly,

$$\frac{u_\delta}{u^*} = \frac{\rho u^* y_\delta}{\mu} = A \qquad [7.24]$$

Now the procedure is to utilize Eq. 7.24 to evaluate the constant in the turbulent relationship, Eq. 7.21, with $k = 0.4$.

$$u = 2.5u^* \ln y + C \qquad [7.25]$$

Thus, at $u = u_\delta$ and $y = y_\delta$,

$$u_\delta = 2.5u^* \ln y_\delta + C$$
$$C = u_\delta - 2.5u^* \ln y_\delta$$

Substituting this value of C in Eq. 7.25, we have

$$u = 2.5u^* \ln y + u_\delta - 2.5u^* \ln y_\delta = 2.5u^* \ln \frac{y}{y_\delta} + u_\delta$$

Dividing through by u^* and, from Eq. 7.24, substituting $A\mu/\rho u^*$ for y_δ and A for u_δ/u^*, we obtain,

$$\frac{u}{u^*} = 2.5 \ln \frac{\rho u^* y}{A\mu} + A$$

which, on rearrangement, is

$$\frac{u}{u^*} = 2.5 \ln \frac{\rho u^* y}{\mu} - 2.5 \ln A + A$$

The term $A - 2.5 \ln A$ can be replaced by a single constant, B, so that

$$\frac{u}{u^*} = B + 2.5 \ln \frac{\rho u^* y}{\mu} \qquad [7.26]$$

The constant B, which is a form of A for the dimensionless Eq. 7.24, must be calculated from experimental data. Eq. 7.26 is therefore a dimensionless velocity-distribution relationship of wider utility than the velocity-defect relationship, Eq. 7.22.

Fig. 7.9 shows that experimental results (curve 3) fit Eq. 7.26 very well. The equation gives a straight line (curve 1) with u/u^* plotted against $\ln (\rho u^* y/\mu)$. The fit is excellent from the highest values of $\rho u^* y/\mu$ down to about 30. The constant B has a value of 5.5. Correlation is not expected in the laminar sublayer, for which an exact relation similar to Eq. 7.26 can be formulated. Thus

$$\tau_0 = \frac{\mu}{g_c} \frac{du}{dy}$$

and, on integration,

$$\tau_0 = \frac{\mu}{g_c} \frac{u}{y} + k$$

where k is a constant. As $u = 0$ at $y = 0$, then $k = 0$. Making $u^{*2} = g_c \tau_0/\rho$ as before, by dividing through by ρ, yields

$$\frac{g_c \tau_0}{\rho} = u^{*2} = \frac{\mu u}{\rho y}$$

and

$$\frac{u}{u^*} = \frac{\rho u^* y}{\mu} \qquad [7.27]$$

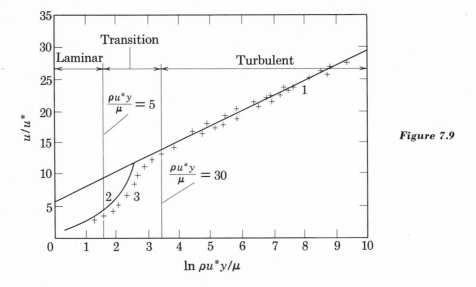

Figure 7.9

This is plotted as curve 2 in Fig. 7.9 (although the relationship is linear, it is not linear on the semilog graph of the figure).

Curves 1 and 2 intersect at a u/u^* value of about 11.6, which would indicate the edge of the laminar sublayer if there were an abrupt change from laminar to turbulent flow. As the curves, 1 and 2, for the two types of flow are not tangent to one another and as it is physically unreasonable to expect a sudden change, it is customary to recognize a laminar-turbulent region, called the *transition*, or *buffer, layer*. This region is apparent in Fig. 7.9, in which the data points fall below the turbulent curve at a $(\rho u^* y/\mu)$ value of somewhere below 70 and do not form a good fit with the laminar curve until a value of about 5. Although there is agreement that the laminar sublayer extends to a $\rho u^* y/\mu$ value of 5, there is less agreement on the extent of the transition layer, this being dependent on the degree of correlation required between the experimental data and curve 1 for turbulent flow. One analysis uses a $\rho u^* y/\mu$ value of 70, whereas another uses a value of 30. We shall use the latter here to summarize the results, together with a relation of von Karman to correlate the data. The over-all result of this universal velocity distribution is as follows:

laminar sublayer, $0 < \dfrac{\rho u^* y}{\mu} \leq 5$ $\dfrac{u}{u^*} = \dfrac{\rho u^* y}{\mu}$ [7.28a]

transition layer, $5 < \dfrac{\rho u^* y}{\mu} \leq 30$ $\dfrac{u}{u^*} = -3.05 + 5 \ln \dfrac{\rho u^* y}{\mu}$ [7.28b]

turbulent region, $\dfrac{\rho u^* y}{\mu} > 30$ $\dfrac{u}{u^*} = 5.5 + 2.5 \ln \dfrac{\rho u^* y}{\mu}$ [7.28c]

These numerical values are important not only for the purpose of analyzing the fluid-flow pattern per se but also because the thickness of the various layers determines the heat-transfer characteristics in forced convection. There is a very close analogy between *momentum* transfer as evidenced by friction characteristics, *energy* transfer as evidenced by heat-transfer characteristics, and *mass* transfer as evidenced by diffusion characteristics.

The relationships developed from the mixing-length theory can be used to provide expressions for the average velocity, V, and for the friction factor, f. For the average velocity, we have

$$V = \frac{Q}{A} = \frac{\int_0^a u \, dA}{\pi a^2}$$

From Eq. 7.22,

$$u = u_{\max} + 2.5u^* \ln \frac{y}{a}$$

Replacing y with $a - r$ and putting $dA = 2\pi r \, dr$, we obtain

$$V = \frac{\int_0^a \{u_{\max} + 2.5u^* \ln [(a - r)/a]\} \, r \, dr}{\pi a^2}$$

The resulting integral is

$$V = u_{\max} - 3.75u^* \qquad [7.29]$$

With $u^* = g_c \tau_0 / \rho$ and $g_c \tau_0 / \rho = fV^2/8$ (Eq. 7.4a), then

$$V = u_{\max} - 1.326V \sqrt{f}$$

and, with an adjustment of the constant 3.75 to 4.07 to fit more closely the experimental data,

$$\frac{V}{u_{\max}} = \frac{1}{1 + 1.44 \sqrt{f}} \qquad [7.30]$$

Eq. 7.30 is valuable in obtaining a measure of flow rate from a single Pitot-static reading at the pipe axis for $u_{\max}$, with the friction factor estimated from a chart of f vs. Re (this requires an iteration procedure, as Re depends on V). Note that although the starting equation is good only for the turbulent part of the flow and does not hold for the laminar sublayer or right at the pipe axis, these regions are such a small fraction of the whole area that the result is essentially correct.

Another development can be made to yield a predicted value of f from the Reynolds number. From the Nikuradse equation for the turbulent core,

$$\frac{u}{u^*} = 2.5 \ln \frac{u^* \rho y}{\mu} + 5.5$$

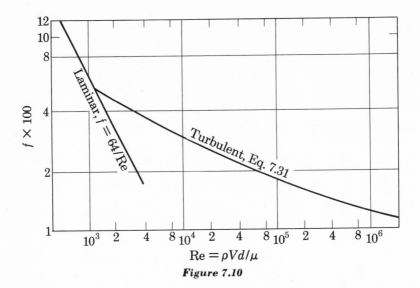

Figure 7.10

which, on substitution of $u = u_{max}$ at $y = a$, becomes

$$\frac{u_{max}}{u^*} = 2.5 \ln \frac{\rho u^* a}{\mu} + 5.5$$

But we also have $u_{max} = V(1 + 1.44 \sqrt{f})$, $u^* = \sqrt{g_c \tau_0/\rho}$, and $g_c \tau_0/\rho = fV^2/8$. With these substitutions, there results an equation in f and $\rho Va/\mu$, thus:

$$\frac{1 + 1.44 \sqrt{f}}{\sqrt{f/8}} = 2.5 \ln \left(\frac{\rho Va}{\mu} \sqrt{f/8}\right) + 5.5$$

With $a = d/2$ and with minor adjustments of constants for experimental data, this is

$$\frac{1}{\sqrt{f}} = 0.87 \ln (\text{Re} \sqrt{f}) - 0.8 \qquad [7.31]$$

where $\text{Re} = \rho Vd/\mu$, the Reynolds number for flow at an average velocity V in a pipe diameter d.

Eq. 7.31 is not immediately convenient, for the value of f is implicit. However, it is very simple, considering the complex nature of turbulent flow, and agrees very well with experimental results. It can be extrapolated safely to Reynolds numbers greater than any for which empirical data are available. A plot of this relationship, together with that for laminar flow, is shown in Fig. 7.10. (This is for demonstration only, as a working chart of friction factor for both smooth and rough pipes is given at the end of the chapter.)

7.8 *Turbulent flow in rough pipes*

The previous discussion is valid only for smooth pipes. In practice, many pipes are "rough" in the hydraulic sense. An attempt to correlate friction factor with Reynolds number for all classes of pipe surface would be frustrating except in the laminar-flow region. In the turbulent-flow region, no representative line would emerge, and the scatter of points might lead to the rejection of dimensional analysis as a method of correlation. However, the meaning would be not that the method of dimensional analysis is incorrect but that some significant variable has been omitted in the analysis. This can only be the condition of the pipe surface, or *roughness*, which can be included in the analysis by specification of a linear dimension, ϵ, characteristic of the height of the projections of the rough surface. A dimensionless group, ϵ/d, the relative roughness, would obviously be obtained, and the relationship would be

$$\Delta p = \rho V^2 \phi \left(\frac{\rho V d}{\mu}, \frac{L}{d}, \frac{\epsilon}{d} \right)$$

The behavior of rough pipes was placed on a firm basis in 1933 by Nikuradse, who coated the insides of pipes with grains of sand of fairly uniform size, established by sieving. His general results are shown in Fig. 7.11, which is a plot of Fig. 7.10 for smooth pipes with the data for rough pipes added. Three features should be noted, as follows:

1. For all values of relative roughness, there is a value of Re below which the friction factor is the same as for a smooth pipe.

Figure 7.11

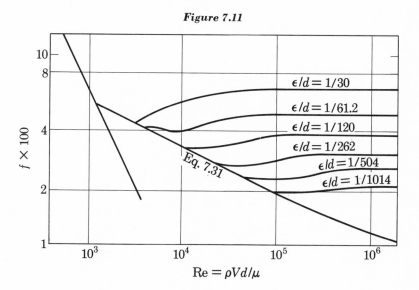

2. When the line for a given relative roughness departs from the smooth-pipe curve, the friction factor increases for a certain range of Re.

3. For all values of relative roughness, there is a value of Re above which the friction factor is constant.

These phenomena can be explained in simple fashion by means of the concept of zones of flow presented earlier. Thus, for 1, the laminar sublayer is sufficiently thick up to a critical value of Reynolds number that the projections or roughness elements are all contained within it, and it has previously been noted that roughness has no effect on laminar flow.

At the value of Reynolds number where the laminar sublayer is sufficiently thin that the roughness starts to project into the turbulent region, additional resistance occurs owing to pressure drag or very small-scale separation, as outlined in Sect. 6.2. As the Reynolds number increases, the laminar layer continues to get thinner until finally the purely viscous effect is negligible. The friction factor becomes constant, and the pressure drop becomes directly proportional to V^2. The pipe is then said to be "completely rough," and the flow "completely turbulent." (Do not confuse "completely turbulent" flow with "fully developed" flow. We are assuming the latter for all discussion but not necessarily the former.)

The velocity distribution in rough pipes is very much the same as in smooth pipes, except that the gradient is less steep near the walls, as might be expected from the physical action just postulated. We can obtain an expression for this distribution by using the general relationship Eq. 7.21 and assuming that, with fully rough pipes, the edge of the turbulent region is a distance y_t from the wall, with y_t being proportional to the roughness, ϵ, i.e., $y_t = k_1\epsilon$. At y_t, the velocity is u_t; hence, from Eq. 7.21,

$$u_t = 2.5u^* \ln k_1\epsilon + C$$

Therefore,

$$C = u_t - 2.5u^* \ln k_1\epsilon$$

Substituting this value of C into Eq. 7.21 yields

$$u = 2.5u^* \ln y + u_t - 2.5u^* \ln k_1\epsilon$$

which is rearranged to give

$$\frac{u}{u^*} = 2.5 \ln \frac{y}{\epsilon} + \frac{u_t - 2.5 \ln k_1}{u^*} = 2.5 \ln \frac{y}{\epsilon} + B$$

The constant B is evaluated from data such as Nikuradse's and is found to be 8.5. Thus the velocity distribution in the completely rough regime is

$$\frac{u}{u^*} = 8.5 + 2.5 \ln \frac{y}{\epsilon} \qquad [7.32]$$

A value of friction factor in the completely rough regime can be obtained by means of Eq. 7.29,

$$V = u_{max} - 3.75u^*$$ [*7.29*]

Substituting $y = a$ and $u = u_{max}$ into Eq. 7.32 and utilizing the shear-stress relationship (Eq. 7.4a), $g_c\tau_0/\rho V^2 = f/8 = (u^*/V)^2$, result in

$$f = \frac{1}{[0.87 \ln (a/\epsilon) + 1.68]^2}$$ [*7.33*]

Expressions for velocity distribution and friction factor in completely rough pipes, then, arise from the same concepts as those in smooth pipes. The transition regime can be analyzed in a similar manner, but, despite its importance from the viewpoint of correlation of the whole regime, it is not dealt with here as it is beyond the intended scope of this discussion. Pipes in engineering use do not display the inflection in the curve of friction factor vs. Reynolds number that the specially constructed pipes of uniform sand-grain roughness do, although the hydraulically smooth and completely rough portions of the curve are well correlated with the previous relationships.

7.9   *The friction factor for commercial pipes*

Pipes in engineering use generally have some degree of roughness, but not the uniform roughness of the pipes prepared by Nikuradse. The roughness is not geometrically similar to sand grains, and the distribution has a wide range. Thus no single parameter, ϵ/d, is sufficient to describe it. Furthermore, it is not practical to measure roughness on each occasion or to prescribe a certain value for it. However, an *equivalent* relative roughness, ϵ/d, has been established for each of the most frequently used types of pipe, corresponding to the Nikuradse sand roughness. In the completely turbulent zone, the friction factor of a particular type of pipe, say, galvanized iron, as measured experimentally is the same as that of a sand-roughened pipe of known roughness. Therefore, galvanized-iron pipes are characterized by a certain value of ϵ, and curves of f vs. Re with ϵ/d as parameter can be used for calculation.

Because commercial roughness is not uniform, a pipe characterized by a certain sand roughness, ϵ, behaves differently from a sand-roughened pipe in the transition region between smooth-pipe flow and turbulent flow. First of all, since the roughness factor is a representative value resembling a mean, there are some projections much larger than it indicates. Consequently, the

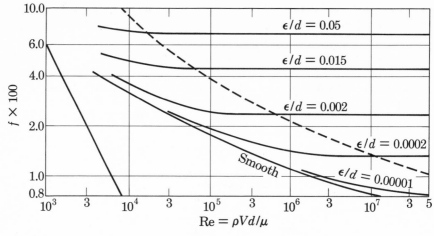

Figure 7.12

friction factor departs from the smooth-pipe zone at a lower Reynolds number than for the equivalent sand roughness. However, because most of the roughness is still in the laminar sublayer, the friction factor *decreases* with increase of Reynolds number until the completely rough zone is reached. The results are shown in Fig. 7.12 in what is known as a *Moody diagram*, after L. F. Moody,* who correlated extensive experimental data on equivalent roughness.

A large-scale working chart based on the Moody diagram is given at the end of the chapter. It shows friction factors from a Reynolds number of 600 in the laminar-flow region up to a Reynolds number of over 10^7 and equivalent relative-roughness factors from 5×10^{-6} to 5×10^{-2}. The dashed line crosses the point on each curve at which the flow becomes completely turbulent or rough. Some values of equivalent roughness for commercial pipes follow:

MATERIAL	ϵ, IN.	ϵ, FT
Glass, brass, copper, lead	Smooth	Smooth
Commercial steel, iron	0.0018	0.00015
Asphalted cast iron	0.0048	0.0004
Galvanized iron	0.006	0.0005
Cast iron	0.0102	0.00085
Concrete	0.012–0.12	0.001–0.01
Riveted steel	0.036–0.36	0.003–0.03

*L. F. Moody, "Friction Factors for Pipe Flow," *Trans. ASME*, **66,** 671 (1944).

7.10 *Effect of nonuniform velocity distribution*

For both laminar and turbulent flow, it is seen that the velocity distribution varies across a duct, and relationships between average velocity and maximum velocity have accordingly been determined. The rate of momentum transport, or momentum flux, and likewise that of kinetic-energy flux, for a given average velocity or flow rate vary with the velocity distribution.

Consider an incompressible fluid flowing in a pipe, having an average velocity $V = Q/A$ but having a radial-velocity distribution of the types previously discussed. In terms of V, the rate of transport of momentum is $\dot{m}V$, whereas in terms of the varying velocity, u, across the radius, it is

$$\int_A u \, d\dot{m} = \int_A u\rho u \, dA = \int_A \rho u^2 \, dA$$

Now $\dot{m}V = \rho A V V = \rho A V^2$, and so the ratio, k_m, of the true momentum to that based on average velocity is

$$k_m = \frac{\int_A \rho u^2 \, dA}{\rho A V^2} = \frac{(1/A) \int_A u^2 \, dA}{V^2}$$

or
$$\int \rho u^2 \, dA = k_m \rho A V \qquad [7.34]$$

The numerator of the equation for k_m is the average of squares while the denominator is the square of averages, and the former is always greater. Thus $k_m > 1$.

Similarly, for kinetic energy, the average rate of transport based on average velocity is $\dot{m}V^2/2 = \rho A V^3/2$, and the true rate is $\frac{1}{2}\int u^2 \, d\dot{m} = (\rho/2) \int_A u^3 \, dA$. The coefficient for kinetic energy is then

$$k_e = \frac{(1/A) \int_A u^3 \, dA}{V^3}$$

or
$$\int \rho u^3 \, dA = k_e \rho A V^3 \qquad [7.35]$$

Hence k_e is also greater than unity.

For nonuniform flow, the momentum coefficient should be used in the Bernoulli equation, thus

$$p + \rho \frac{g}{g_c} z + k_m \rho \frac{V^2}{2g_c} = \text{constant}$$

For laminar flow, $k_m = \frac{4}{3}$, but for turbulent flow, which has a much flatter velocity distribution, $k_m \approx 1.03\text{--}1.05$. Most engineering problems relating to flow in ducts are in the turbulent region, and, although k_m should be used for accuracy, it is often neglected, being so close to unity. For laminar flow, it is a necessary correction, and k_e is even more so, as $k_e = 2$ in this case. The coefficients k_m and k_e can be significant for certain geometries in turbulent flow in which a succession of obstacles in the flow path can produce a velocity distribution of a peaked nature, e.g., flow across rows and banks of tubes in a heat exchanger.

It should be remembered that a density variation produces the same general effect as a velocity variation; i.e., for variable density as well as for varying velocity,

$$k_m = \frac{\int_A \rho u^2 \, dA}{\bar{\rho} A V^2}$$

where ρ is the local density and $\bar{\rho}$ is the average density.

7.11   *Flow with change of area and direction*

Flow in straight pipes is the most important type of duct flow, but losses occur with change of flow area. In piping systems, losses due to change of pipe size, elbows, and miscellaneous fittings are often called "minor losses of head," which they may be in large-scale systems of water, oil, and gas distribution, where the straight-pipe lengths may be of the order of several hundred feet or even miles. In such cases, losses such as those listed constitute only a small fraction of the total loss of pressure. In other systems, however, such as wind tunnels, heat exchangers, and gas-turbine plants, losses due to change of area or direction are critical; velocities are high, and the system efficiency is very sensitive to these "parasitic" losses. Although the flow pattern and the nature of the loss mechanism are qualitatively understood in these instances, the values of the parameters involved are mostly empirical. This situation is largely due to the complex character of turbulent flow and to the phenomenon of *separation*, but it is also due to the almost limitless number of geometrical factors concerned. Some of the generalized analysis will be discussed here, valid for turbulent flow only. Above the critical value, there is little information on the effect of Reynolds number, which is apparently small.

7.12   *Flow with decreasing area—nozzles*

A decrease of area in incompressible flow, by the principle of continuity, must result in an increase of velocity (the compressible-flow case will be treated later). For a circular duct, $V \propto 1/d^2$. Thus for constant density and

(a)   (b)

Figure 7.13

viscosity the Reynolds number, Re = $\rho V d/\mu$, is proportional to $1/d$, and, by the Bernoulli·law, the pressure decreases. Both these factors are favorable to stable flow conditions, but particularly the latter, as the negative pressure gradient acts in the direction of flow of the slow-moving fluid near the walls so that there is no tendency for flow separation. A smooth and gradual decrease of area then leads to very low losses. If possible, there should be no sudden change of area; e.g., the transition in Fig. 7.13(b) is better than that in Fig. 7.13(a), although the latter may occasion only a small loss.

If the angle θ in Fig. 7.13(a) is too great, the flow may separate locally but reattach farther downstream, forming a *vena contracta*, or section of minimum flow area (Fig. 7.14). In the limit when $\theta = 90°$, there is a *sudden contraction*. The flow from station 1 to station c is smooth, and very little loss occurs, but from c to 2 it is accompanied by eddies and large-scale turbulence. The energy loss from 1 to 2 may be analyzed, and the analysis is a good example of the use of the basic equations of continuity, momentum, and energy.

We wish to obtain the loss in terms of the ratio A_2/A_1, which requires a knowledge of the *coefficient of contraction*, $C_c = A_c/A_2$. Three assumptions are made: (1) that all the loss occurs between c and 2 as mentioned; (2) that the pressure at c is the same across the whole cross section (i.e., vena con-

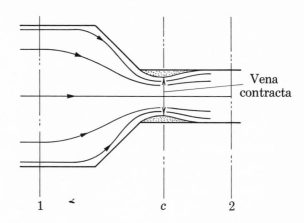

Vena
contracta

Figure 7.14

1   c 2

tracta and eddying region); and (3) that there is no significant wall shear stress between c and 2.

From assumption 1, using the Bernoulli equation with losses, we have

$$\Delta p_L = p_c - p_2 + \frac{\rho}{2g_c} (V_c{}^2 - V_2{}^2) \qquad [7.36]$$

From assumptions 2 and 3, the momentum equation yields

$$p_c A_2 + \frac{\dot{m} V_c}{g_c} = p_2 A_2 + \frac{\dot{m} V_2}{g_c}$$

and

$$p_c - p_2 = \frac{\dot{m}}{g_c A_2} (V_2 - V_c)$$

Introducing the continuity equation, $\dot{m} = \rho A_c V_c = \rho A_2 V_2$, we obtain

$$p_c - p_2 = \frac{\rho}{g_c} \left(V_2{}^2 - \frac{A_c}{A_2} V_c{}^2 \right) \qquad [7.37]$$

Eliminating $p_c - p_2$ by substituting Eq. 7.37 into Eq. 7.36 gives us

$$\Delta p_L = \frac{\rho}{g_c} \left(V_2{}^2 - \frac{A_c}{A_2} V_c{}^2 \right) + \frac{\rho}{2g_c} (V_c{}^2 - V_2{}^2)$$

Again using continuity to eliminate V_c, by $A_c V_c = A_2 V_2$, we have

$$\Delta p_L = \frac{\rho}{2g_c} \left[V_2{}^2 - 2\frac{A_2}{A_c} V_2{}^2 + \left(\frac{A_2}{A_c} \right)^2 V_2{}^2 \right]$$

$$= \frac{\rho V_2{}^2}{2g_c} \left[1 - 2\frac{A_2}{A_c} + \left(\frac{A_2}{A_c} \right)^2 \right] = \frac{\rho V_2{}^2}{2g_c} \left(1 - \frac{A_2}{A_c} \right)^2$$

and

$$\Delta p_L = \frac{\rho V_2{}^2}{2g_c} \left(1 - \frac{1}{C_c} \right)^2 = K_{sc} \frac{\rho V_2{}^2}{2g_c} \qquad [7.38]$$

From measurements by Weisbach,* A_2/A_1 and C_c are related as follows, with $K_{sc} = (1 - 1/C_c)^2$ given as well.

A_2/A_1	0.1	0.2	0.3	0.4	0.5	0.6	0.7	0.8	0.9
C_c	0.62	0.63	0.64	0.66	0.68	0.71	0.76	0.81	0.89
K_{sc}	0.37	0.35	0.32	0.27	0.22	0.17	0.10	0.06	0.02

These values of C_c, published in 1855, are still the customary ones in use. The development here has been presented in detail, not for its intrinsic importance, since the loss is not large, but because it incorporates the basic relationships, combined with simple but reasonable assumptions, and is therefore illustrative of the approach to many problems in fluid mechanics.

For contractions used as nozzles, i.e., smooth transitions to convert

* J. Weisbach, *Die Experimental-Hydraulik*, Engelhardt, Freiburg, 1855, p. 133.

pressure to kinetic energy, the performance for incompressible flow is usually expressed in terms of a nozzle coefficient, C_v, where

$$C_v = \frac{\text{ideal pressure drop}}{\text{actual pressure drop}} = \frac{\Delta p_i}{\Delta p_a}$$

From the Bernoulli equation and continuity,

$$\Delta p_i = p_1 - p_2 = \frac{\rho V_2^2}{2g_c} - \frac{\rho V_1^2}{2g_c} = \frac{V_1^2}{2g_c}\left[\left(\frac{A_1}{A_2}\right)^2 - 1\right]$$

Hence, with Δp_a the actual measured pressure drop for the same area ratio,

$$C_v = \frac{\Delta p_i}{\Delta p_a} = \frac{\rho V_1^2}{2g_c\,\Delta p_a}\left[\left(\frac{A_1}{A_2}\right)^2 - 1\right] \tag{7.39}$$

or, in terms of discharge velocity, V_2,

$$C_v = \frac{\rho V_2^2}{2g_c\,\Delta p_a}\left[1 - \left(\frac{A_2}{A_1}\right)^2\right] \tag{7.40}$$

Values of C_v are generally high, of the order of 0.98, for well-rounded nozzles.

Sudden contractions are inevitable in "headers" for furnaces, boilers, and heat exchangers in general, where numerous tubes are set in the wall of a reservoir containing fluid. For widely spaced tubes, $A_2/A_1 \to 0$, and thus the loss is of the order of 0.4 of the dynamic pressure or head in one of the tubes.

7.13   Flow with increasing area—diffusers

For flow with increasing area, or diffusion, the flow picture is quite different. In this case, the velocity decreases, and the pressure increases, setting up a positive pressure gradient. This *adverse* pressure gradient acts to thicken the layer of slow-moving fluid near the walls and, at some point, to cause it to stagnate and to separate (Fig. 7.15).

The creation of large-scale eddies means loss of directed energy and therefore a pressure loss, which can be high for large areas of separation. Obviously, the greater the angle of divergence, θ, the worse the pressure gradient and hence the loss due to separation. Both the total length of the

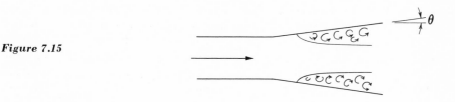

Figure 7.15

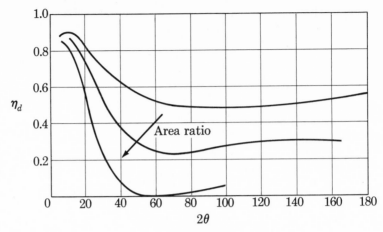

Figure 7.16

region of diffusion and the rate of divergence are important, as separation does not take place immediately except with extreme angles. Defining a *diffuser efficiency*, η_d, for incompressible flow as the ratio of actual pressure rise to the corresponding rise for ideal flow, by Bernoulli's equation we have

$$\eta_d = \frac{\Delta p_a}{\Delta p_i} = \frac{\Delta p_a}{(V_1{}^2/2g_c)[1 - (A_1/A_2)^2]} \qquad [7.41]$$

A general picture of the performance is given in Fig. 7.16. This shows η_d plotted against the included angle of divergence, 2θ, with the area ratio as parameter. The best efficiency is about 90%, occurring at a 2θ value of 5 to 8°, with efficiency decreasing rapidly for $2\theta > 10°$. The decrease of η_d for values of $2\theta < 5°$ is due to excessive wall friction, as a diffuser becomes essentially a straight pipe with a considerable L/d ratio for anything but a very small area ratio.

The figure demonstrates the great difficulty in providing efficient diffusion in a reasonable length. A conical diffuser from a 1 ft diameter pipe to a 2 ft diameter pipe needs a length of nearly 10 ft for an included angle 2θ of 6°. Such a length is seldom possible, and a compromise with efficiency is usually necessary.

In addition to divergence angle and area ratio, other effective variables are the shape (conical, rectangular, having two- or three-dimensional diffusion, etc.), the degree of entry turbulence, the entry-velocity distribution, etc., so that Fig. 7.16 is only qualitative. Recently Kline et al. at Stanford have made a fundamental investigation* of diffusion and have distinguished these four regimes of flow: (1) smooth, well-behaved flow; (2) transitory stall, unsteady in space and time; (3) fully developed stall, with the main

* See, e.g., S. J. Kline, D. E. Abbott, and R. W. Fox, "Optimum Design of Straight-Walled Diffusers," *J. Basic Eng.*, **81**, 321 (1959).

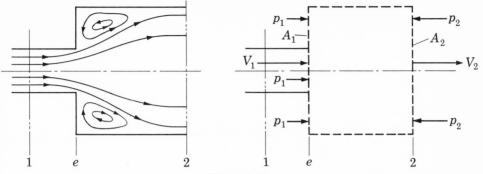

Figure 7.17

flow along one wall only; and (4) jetflow, with separation from both walls. Along with the requirement of good over-all pressure recovery, it is necessary in critical design to pay attention to the nature of the discharge flow, as it may have a major effect on subsequent processes. The addition of splitter plates to reduce the divergence angle can be helpful, but Kline has shown that the location and extent of these must be carefully determined.

Quite naturally, most diffuser data have been taken with uniform flow at entry to provide consistent conditions. In practice, the entry flow is often disordered, and so estimates of efficiency must be conservative. In the past, much disappointment has resulted from neglect of the velocity distribution, particularly with respect to splitter plates, which can do more harm than good if notice is not taken of the actual flow conditions.

The limiting case of diffusion, analogous to that with a nozzle, is a *sudden expansion* (Fig. 7.17). At station e, the point of sudden enlargement, the velocity and the pressure are taken as those in the entry pipe at 1; p_1 is considered to act over the whole enlargement area $A_1 = A_2$. By means of the continuity, momentum, and energy equations again, an expression for the loss can be obtained. Thus we have, for energy,

$$p_1 + \frac{\rho V_1{}^2}{2g_c} = p_2 + \frac{\rho V_2{}^2}{2g_c} + \Delta p_L$$

for momentum, $$p_1 A_2 - p_2 A_2 = \frac{\dot{m}}{g_c}(V_2 - V_1)$$

and for continuity, $$A_1 V_1 = A_2 V_2$$

Combining these to eliminate $p_1 - p_2$ yields

$$\Delta p_L = \frac{\rho V_1{}^2}{2g_c}\left(1 - \frac{A_1}{A_2}\right)^2 \qquad\qquad [7.42a]$$

or $$\Delta p_L = \frac{\rho}{2g_c}(V_1 - V_2)^2 \qquad\qquad [7.42b]$$

Discharge into a large reservoir or *from* a header, as noted for contractions, implies that $A_1/A_2 \to 0$. Hence one velocity head, $V_1^2/2g$, or one dynamic pressure, $\rho V_1^2/2g_c$, is lost.

7.14   *Flow around bends*

It has been seen previously (Sects. 2.6 and 4.1) that motion along a curved streamline introduces an acceleration toward the center of curvature and a corresponding radial pressure gradient. Flow around a bend is similar to ideal vortex flow (Sect. 3.11) in that the velocity decreases with increase of radius from the center of curvature (Fig. 7.18(a)). Thus, from the bend entry to the midpoint, the fluid is decelerated at the outer radii and accelerated at the inner radii, while the reverse occurs from the midpoint to the exit of the bend. The result is an increasing pressure in deceleration and a decreasing pressure in acceleration, so that separation is likely to take place before the midpoint at the outside of the bend and after the midpoint at the inside of the bend (Fig. 7.18(b)).

In real flow the fluid near the walls moves more slowly than that in the center, owing to wall friction, and is subject to the radial pressure gradient set up by the main flow. The fluid on the outside is therefore caused to flow around the walls to the inner radius, setting up a double eddy as a *secondary flow*, as shown in Fig. 7.19. The over-all result is a loss of energy due to the secondary flow and possibly a much greater loss if separation occurs. In any case, the flow at the bend discharge is no longer uniform and requires a length of several pipe diameters to settle down.

The loss depends on the total angle of bend, the radius ratio (mean radius of curvature/duct diameter), the aspect ratio for rectangular sections (width/height), and, to some extent, the Reynolds number. It is not possible here to provide any concise summary of loss coefficients, except to state that the order of loss is between 0.1 and 1.0 velocity heads, $V^2/2g$, or dynamic

Figure 7.18

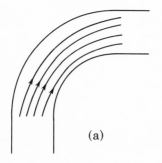

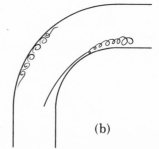

(a)   (b)

Figure 7.19

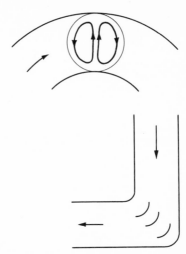

Figure 7.20

pressures, $\rho V^2/2g_c$. When such losses or poor velocity distributions are critical, as in wind tunnels, it is helpful to place curved vanes in sharp corners, as shown in Fig. 7.20.

7.15   *Loss in pipe fittings*

For regular commercial and industrial piping, it is not economically desirable to design changes of section and bends for minimum loss, the criterion being cheapness of manufacture. Thus contractions and expansions are usually abrupt, and bends become "elbows." A representative table* of loss coefficients, K, follows, with the loss expressed as $\Delta h = KV^2/2g$ or $\Delta p = K\rho V^2/2g_c$.

FITTING	K
45° standard elbow	0.42
Long-radius elbow	0.6
90° standard elbow	0.9
Standard tee	1.8
Return bend, 180°	2.2
Globe valve, wide open	10.0
Gate valve, wide open	0.19
¾ open	1.15
½ open	5.6
¼ open	24.0

* From Crane Co., Chicago, "Flow of Fluids," *Tech. Paper No.* 410, 1957.

7.16   Compressible flow in ducts

The preceding material in this chapter is applicable in general to compressible flow, provided that the flow is subsonic ($M < 1$). The friction coefficient as presented in the Moody diagram is valid for a very wide range of flow velocities, including the low supersonic region. However, many of the relationships derived are for constant density, and so a reexamination is essential when the change of density is considerable. Furthermore, we might expect some difference of behavior when the flow velocity is greater than the wave-propagation velocity, i.e., for $M > 1$.

Because the flow of gases in ducts of varying area is so important, for instance, in turbine nozzles, compressor casings, and propulsion systems such as turbojets, ramjets, and rockets, we shall first study it as ideal flow. For incompressible ideal flow, we would use the Bernoulli equation, but here density and temperature changes must be considered. In many of the most significant cases, no appreciable heat transfer occurs, and thus the flow is reversible and adiabatic (or isentropic). After introducing some new concepts for compressible flow, we shall discuss real flow with *friction*. Because heating or cooling a gas affects its density and hence its velocity (this effect is negligible for liquids), we must also analyze *diabatic* flow. A special instance of this is heating combined with friction to give *isothermal* flow. Finally we shall treat some aspects of incompressible flow in open channels in order to show certain analogies with compressible flow.

7.17   Reversible adiabatic flow with area change

The problem is to find some relationship among fluid properties that allows quantitative results to be obtained in as convenient a manner as possible and to provide a framework that furnishes some general picture of the way in which state changes occur or can be made to occur to achieve a given end.

Three basic relationships are available, those of conservation of energy, momentum, and continuity; and, if the fluid is a perfect gas, the equation of state and the laws governing properties in an isentropic process can be used. The Mach number is valuable as a parameter since it is dimensionless and permits wide generality.

1. Energy. The steady-flow energy equation, in this instance of adiabatic flow with no shaft work and negligible potential energy, is

$$c_p T_0 = c_p T + \frac{V^2}{2 g_c J} = \text{constant}$$

or, in differential form,

$$c_p \, dT_0 = c_p \, dT + \frac{V \, dV}{g_c J} = 0$$

2. Momentum. Because the flow is steady, reversible, and considered as one-dimensional, the Euler equation may be applied as

$$\frac{dp}{\rho} + \frac{V \, dV}{g_c} = 0 \qquad\qquad [4.58]$$

3. Continuity. For steady one-dimensional flow, we have

$$\dot{m} = A\rho V$$

which in differential form is

$$\frac{dA}{A} + \frac{d\rho}{\rho} + \frac{dV}{V} = 0 \qquad\qquad [7.43]$$

4. Equation of state. For a perfect gas,

$$pv = RT \qquad \text{or} \qquad p = \rho RT$$

In differential form, then,

$$\frac{dp}{p} = \frac{d\rho}{\rho} + \frac{dT}{T} \qquad\qquad [7.44]$$

5. Isentropic relationships. Basically, we have

$$pv^k = \frac{p}{\rho^k} = \text{constant}$$

In differential form this is

$$\frac{dp}{p} = k \frac{d\rho}{\rho} \qquad\qquad [7.45]$$

6. Mach number. By definition

$$\mathrm{M} = \frac{V}{a}$$

where $a = \sqrt{g_c k R T}$. Then

$$V = \mathrm{M} \sqrt{g_c k R T} \qquad\qquad [4.73]$$

For the first step, a relationship among velocity, Mach number, and pressure is established. Eq. 4.58 is divided through by V^2, yielding

$$\frac{dp}{\rho V^2} + \frac{dV}{g_c V} = 0$$

Substituting for V^2 from Eq. 4.73, $V^2 = M^2 g_c k RT$, and for ρ from the equation of state $\rho = p/RT$, gives us

$$\frac{dp}{g_c k M^2 p} + \frac{dV}{g_c V} = 0$$

and
$$\frac{dV}{V} = -\frac{1}{kM^2} \frac{dp}{p} \qquad [7.46]$$

i.e., for all values of M, whether subsonic (<1) or supersonic (>1), the velocity increases as the pressure decreases (for dV/V positive, dp/p must be negative). This is in accordance with the Bernoulli equation (for incompressible flow) but requires proof because, as will shortly be seen, with compressible flow the apparently straightforward or "intuitional" answer (usually based on our more ready knowledge of incompressible flow) is often the opposite of the true answer.

The next step is to introduce area as a variable in order to examine the effect of area change on velocity. This is accomplished by means of the continuity relationship. From Eq. 7.43,

$$\frac{dV}{V} = -\frac{dA}{A} - \frac{d\rho}{\rho}$$

and, on substitution of $\frac{1}{k}\frac{dp}{p} = \frac{d\rho}{\rho}$ from Eq. 7.45, we have

$$\frac{dV}{V} = -\frac{dA}{A} - \frac{1}{k}\frac{dp}{p} \qquad [7.47]$$

Equating the values of dV/V from Eqs. 7.46 and 7.47 yields

$$-\frac{1}{kM^2}\frac{dp}{p} = -\frac{dA}{A} - \frac{1}{k}\frac{dp}{p}$$

which may be changed to read

$$\frac{dA}{A} = \frac{1}{k}\frac{dp}{p}\left(\frac{1}{M^2} - 1\right) = \frac{dp}{p}\frac{(1 - M^2)}{kM^2} \qquad [7.48]$$

The same equations establish a relationship among V, A, and M, for simultaneous use with Eq. 7.48. From Eq. 7.43,

$$\frac{dA}{A} = -\frac{d\rho}{\rho} - \frac{dV}{V} \qquad [7.43]$$

which, with dp/kp substituted for $d\rho/\rho$ (from Eq. 7.45) and $-kM^2 dV/V$ substituted for dp/p (from Eq. 7.46), becomes

$$\frac{dA}{A} = -\frac{dp}{kp} - \frac{dV}{V} = \frac{M^2 dV}{V} - \frac{dV}{V}$$

Thus
$$\frac{dA}{A} = \frac{dV}{V}(M^2 - 1) \qquad [7.49]$$

Now, in Eqs. 7.48 and 7.49 the Mach-number parameters, in parentheses, can be either positive or negative, according to whether M is greater or less than unity; i.e., the expression changes sign when the flow goes from subsonic to supersonic or vice versa. There are five cases to be investigated: two for subsonic flow (M < 1), with increasing and decreasing pressure; two for supersonic flow (M > 1), with increasing and decreasing pressure; and, finally, one for M = 1.

1a. *Subsonic* flow, *increasing* pressure (dp/p positive). With M < 1, $1 - M^2$ is positive, and $M^2 - 1$ is negative. Therefore, from Eq. 7.48, dA/A must be positive; i.e., the pressure increases with increasing area, or, stated as a design condition, the area must increase if an increased pressure is desired. From Eq. 7.49, with $M^2 - 1$ negative an increase of area requires a decrease of velocity. This set of conditions yields a *subsonic diffuser*, i.e., an increase of area to reduce the velocity, giving an increase of pressure. (The remaining cases will be analyzed more briefly; they are modeled on this detailed discussion.)

1b. *Subsonic* flow, *decreasing* pressure (dp/p negative). From Eq. 7.48, dA/A must be negative, and from Eq. 7.49, dV/V must be positive. These conditions yield a *subsonic nozzle*, i.e., a decrease of area to increase the velocity, giving a decrease of pressure.

2a. *Supersonic* flow, *increasing pressure* (dp/p positive). M > 1, $1 - M^2$ is negative, and $M^2 - 1$ is positive. Therefore, from Eq. 7.48, dA/A must be negative, and from Eq. 7.49, dV/V must be negative. These conditions yield a *supersonic diffuser*, i.e., a decrease of area to decrease the velocity, giving an increase of pressure.

2b. *Supersonic* flow, *decreasing* pressure (dp/p negative). From Eq. 7.48, dA/A must be positive, and from Eq. 7.49, dV/V must be positive. These conditions yield a *supersonic nozzle*, i.e., an increase of area to increase the velocity, giving a decrease of pressure. Note the opposition in requirements for M < 1 and M > 1; i.e., increasing area is necessary for a subsonic diffuser and a supersonic nozzle, and decreasing area for a subsonic nozzle and a supersonic diffuser.

3. *Sonic* flow, M = 1. With M = 1, Eq. 7.48 shows that $dA/A = 0$; i.e., the passage section has *constant* area.

A synthesis of these results may now be made. Thus fluid in a reservoir, i.e., with negligible velocity, in order to attain the highest possible velocity, must flow to a region of lower pressure, since velocity increases only with decreasing pressure. At first, the duct must decrease in area, as the flow is initially subsonic (case 1b). So far, only qualitative effects have been discussed, and it is supposed that a sufficiently large pressure is available to produce the effects desired. If the fluid attains a Mach number of unity, it can do so only where the area change is zero (case 3), following which the area must increase (case 2b) for flow to become supersonic. The duct must

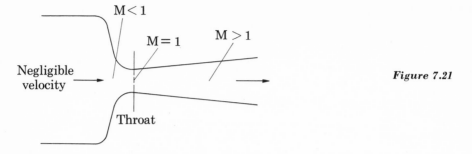

Figure 7.21

then take the shape shown in Fig. 7.21, which is known as a *convergent-divergent*, or *DeLaval, nozzle*. The section of minimum area where $dA/A = 0$ is called the *throat* of the nozzle.

In similar manner a shape can be deduced for a flow that is initially supersonic and that must be reduced to a very low velocity. This shape resembles a DeLaval nozzle in reverse; i.e., it entails a decrease of area to reduce a flow of $M > 1$ to a throat where $M = 1$, followed by an increase of area to reduce M to a low value.

Supersonic nozzles are used in steam turbines to provide a high-velocity jet of steam that acts on blades to produce power, in rockets and ramjets to provide a high-velocity jet to give thrust, and in wind tunnels to provide a supersonic stream of fluid for testing flight characteristics of models of aircraft and missiles. Supersonic diffusers are used in aircraft, missiles, and wind tunnels, although not exactly in the idealized way pictured here, as other, nonreversible effects usually occur to complicate the process. Subsonic nozzles and diffusers, in either convergent or divergent form, are common in almost every type of gas-flow process.

7.18 *Quantitative relationships*

The previous expressions reveal certain essential relationships in simple but qualitative fashion. For actual design it is necessary to introduce quantitative relationships. The problem may be to find the areas required to pass a given mass flow for a given pressure ratio through a nozzle or to calculate the mass flow that will pass through a given nozzle for a given pressure ratio. In any case, the starting point is the equation of continuity, $\dot{m} = A\rho V$. The state of the gas at one point has to be known, this usually being the initial condition, i.e., p_1, T_1, V_1, from which ρ_1 and the stagnation conditions can be obtained. Because the flow is isentropic, the relationships $p/\rho^k = $ constant, $T_2/T_1 = (p_2/p_1)^{(k-1)/k}$, etc., can be used to find the density, etc., at any other point where the pressure is known or assumed. For the velocity at any

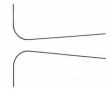

Figure 7.22

point, the Bernoulli equation for compressible flow (Eq. 4.59) can be used, after conversion into a direct form for velocity, with station 1 represented by stagnation conditions $(V_1 = 0, \ p_1 = p_0, \ T_1 = T_0)$ and $V_2 = V$ at any station where $p_2 = p$.

$$V = \left\{ \frac{2k}{k-1} g_c R T_0 \left[1 - \left(\frac{p}{p_0} \right)^{(k-1)/k} \right] \right\}^{\frac{1}{2}}$$

Alternatively, the velocity can be found from the temperature relationships, i.e., $V^2/2g_c c_p J = T_0 - T$, since T_0 is constant in adiabatic flow.

As only the initial and final states are given or known, any intermediate point along the length of the nozzle must be in terms of an assumed pressure ratio; i.e., a certain temperature will result and a certain area will be required when the pressure at the point has a certain value. The thermodynamic relationships say nothing about the desirable variation of area with length, and for the determination of this relationship, the empirical aerodynamic data relating to incompressible flow, previously treated, have to be used. For the subsonic part of a nozzle, the rate of change of area can be rapid, provided that the change is continuous, i.e., that abrupt contractions are avoided. For the supersonic part of a nozzle, the rate of area increase must be gradual, approximating that of a subsonic diffuser. The reasons for this are complex, and for the time being it will suffice to say that supersonic flow in a duct is essentially unstable in that too rapid changes of state lead to conditions where the flow no longer approaches reversible flow and discontinuities with large increases of entropy occur. Thus the general shape of a convergent-divergent nozzle is as shown in Fig. 7.22.

7.19   *Throat conditions*

The area of minimum section, or throat, can be a controlling factor for flow in a nozzle. For subsonic flow throughout, throat conditions are variable, but when the flow downstream is supersonic, the Mach number at the throat can only be unity (case 3). This unique condition is called a *choked* throat and results in some very important phenomena.

The stagnation temperature is constant in adiabatic flow, and so at the throat (subscript t) we have, from Eq. 4.75,

$$\frac{T_0}{T_t} = 1 + \frac{k-1}{2} M_t^2$$

which for $M_t = 1$ becomes

$$\frac{T_0}{T_t} = 1 + \frac{k-1}{2} = \frac{k+1}{2} \qquad [7.50]$$

Similarly, as the stagnation pressure is constant in reversible, adiabatic flow,

$$\frac{p_0}{p_t} = \left(\frac{T_0}{T_t}\right)^{k/(k-1)} = \left(\frac{k+1}{2}\right)^{k/(k-1)} \qquad [7.51]$$

Thus the *choked-throat condition* of pressure and temperature *is fixed for given initial upstream conditions* and does not depend on the downstream conditions (provided that over all the conditions are such as to allow supersonic flow downstream of the throat). The inverted values T_t/T_0 and p_t/p_0 are called the *critical* temperature and pressure ratios and depend only on the particular gas and its temperature, which affect $k = c_p/c_v$. For air at atmospheric temperature, $T_t/T_0 = 0.833$, and $p_t/p_0 = 0.528$.

For a given stagnation temperature and pressure, then, T_t, p_t, and hence ρ_t are fixed. As $M_t = 1$, V_t is fixed by T_t, and thus for a given nozzle (A_t fixed) the *mass flow is fixed*. Because downstream conditions do not affect the throat conditions, provided that $M_t = 1$, even if the discharge pressure is lowered, the mass flow remains at its maximum value. Therefore, the nozzle is said to be *choked*, and the flow is said to be a *choking* flow.

A physical reason for the choking flow is that the flow beyond the throat is supersonic; i.e., the flow velocity is greater than the wave-propagation velocity. Consequently, if the discharge pressure is altered, the "message" cannot be transmitted upstream until the whole flow has become subsonic.

Two points must be emphasized in connection with the foregoing discussion.

1. For given initial conditions, discharge pressure, and mass flow, there is only one solution for isentropic flow; i.e., there are unique values for the throat area and for the discharge area. Thus, if the discharge pressure is changed for a given nozzle, flow continues but cannot be isentropic everywhere along the flow path. This situation will require further study, as so far only relations for reversible adiabatic flow have been used.

2. A convergent-divergent nozzle need not *necessarily* have supersonic flow and a choked throat. If the over-all pressure ratio is sufficiently small, the whole flow is subsonic, with acceleration into the throat and diffusion thereafter. The criterion for choked flow is not only the over-all pressure

ratio but also the area ratio between throat and discharge. Ideally, it is possible for the conditions to be such that M = 1 is just attained at the throat, followed by subsonic diffusion to a higher pressure.

The performance of a convergent-divergent nozzle for reversible adiabatic flow can be summarized by means of Fig. 7.23. The ratio p/p_0, local pressure over initial pressure (with initial pressure being the stagnation pressure where V is negligible), as ordinate is plotted against distance along the nozzle as abscissa. Lines A and B represent two cases of subsonic flow throughout, with p_B being a lower receiver or exhaust pressure than p_A. Note that the pressure is a minimum at the throat, where the area is a minimum, beyond which it rises again, but with discharge pressures p_A and p_B being lower than the initial pressure. In the wholly subsonic region, the mass flow is controlled by the ratios p_A/p_0 and p_B/p_0.

As the receiver pressure is lowered, eventually the *critical* pressure ratio is reached at the throat, where M = 1, following which the flow becomes subsonic and the pressure rises to the receiver value, p_C. This process is represented by line C.

If the receiver pressure is again lowered, there is only one value, p_D, at which isentropic flow can take place in a nozzle of fixed dimensions. The fluid accelerates to M = 1 at the throat, and then the flow becomes supersonic, with decreasing pressure, as indicated by line D.

It is seen that for the given nozzle there is no isentropic solution between receiver pressures p_C and p_D. It is obvious that flow will occur between these limits, but it will not be reversible. These circumstances will also require investigation later. Between lines C and D, the mass flow is constant, because the flow is choked. This flow can be calculated very simply. From

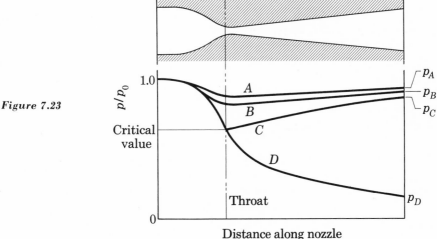

Figure 7.23

Distance along nozzle

the continuity equation,

$$\dot{m} = A_t \rho_t V_t$$

which, on substitution of $p/RT = \rho$ and $V = M \sqrt{g_c k R T}$, gives

$$\dot{m} = \frac{A_t p_t}{R T_t} \sqrt{g_c k R T_t} = \frac{A_t p_t}{\sqrt{T_t}} \sqrt{\frac{g_c k}{R}}$$

Substituting stagnation values from the critical pressure and temperature conditions, Eqs. 7.50 and 7.51, yields

$$p_t = p_0 \left(\frac{2}{k+1}\right)^{k/(k-1)} \quad \text{and} \quad T_t = T_0 \left(\frac{2}{k+1}\right)$$

This becomes

$$\dot{m} = \frac{A_t p_0}{\sqrt{T_0}} \left(\frac{2}{k+1}\right)^{(k+1)/[2(k-1)]} \left(\frac{g_c k}{R}\right)^{\frac{1}{2}} \qquad [7.52]$$

Thus the choking mass flow for a given fluid is a function only of throat area and stagnation pressure and temperature. For air at normal temperature, with $k = 1.4$, A_t in square inches, p_0 in pounds per square inch absolute, and T_0 in degrees Rankine, Eq. 7.52 reduces to

$$\dot{m} = 0.53 A_t \frac{p_0}{\sqrt{T_0}} \qquad [7.53]$$

known as *Fliegner's equation*.

If a nozzle is convergent only, the throat becomes the discharge area. With a pressure difference across the nozzle, flow will commence, increasing as the difference increases up to the point where the critical pressure ratio occurs. If the upstream pressure is increased still further, the mass flow will increase in direct proportion, according to Eq. 7.53. However, if p_0 is held constant and the *receiver* pressure is lowered, the mass flow will remain constant, because the nozzle is choked. If p_0 is above the minimum value required to attain the critical pressure at discharge, then the nozzle-throat (discharge) pressure will be above that of the receiver, and so beyond the nozzle there will be a sudden expansion. This process is irreversible and cannot be analyzed in the terms of the present discussion.

7.20   *One-dimensional isentropic compressible-flow functions*

Means have been given for calculating the necessary quantities for isentropic compressible flow with varying area. Although the basic analytic procedure should be fully understood, it is also desirable to have tables of functions available to facilitate computation. For such tables a reference point or datum is required to which all quantities can be referred, so that a change of state or ratio between any two states 1 and 2 can be evaluated from a ratio of each to the reference point; e.g., to find the ratio of two areas, A_2/A_1, we can write

$$\frac{A_2}{A_1} = \frac{A_2}{A_r} \frac{A_r}{A_1}$$

where A_r is the fixed reference point for each area. For isentropic flow, there are two convenient reference states: (1) the stagnation state, since both T_0 and p_0 are constant; and (2) the sonic state, where $V = a$ and $M = 1$. The independent parameter is taken as the Mach number, and ratios of other variables are determined as functions of Mach number, with either a stagnation state or the state where $M = 1$ as the datum. The state where $M = 1$ is written with the superscript * ("star").

Temperature, pressure, and density are all expressed as ratios of static values to stagnation values as functions of Mach number, as explained in Sect. 4.28. Thus, for temperature,

$$\frac{T}{T_0} = \frac{1}{1 + [(k - 1)/2]M^2} \qquad [\textbf{4.65}]$$

For pressure,

$$\frac{p}{p_0} = \left(\frac{T}{T_0}\right)^{k/(k-1)} = \frac{1}{\{1 + [(k - 1)/2]M^2\}^{k/(k-1)}} \qquad [\textbf{4.66}]$$

For density,

$$\frac{\rho}{\rho_0} = \frac{p}{p_0}\frac{T_0}{T} = \frac{1}{\{1 + [(k - 1)/2]M^2\}^{1/(k-1)}} \qquad [\textbf{7.54}]$$

For area, the ratio of the required area at any point to the area where $M = 1$ can be shown to be a function of Mach number only. Starting off with the ratio of any two states 1 and 2, from continuity we have

$$\dot{m} = A_1\rho_1V_1 = A_2\rho_2V_2$$

Substituting $\rho = p/RT$ and $V = M\sqrt{g_ckRT}$, we obtain

$$\frac{A_1}{A_2} = \frac{\rho_2V_2}{\rho_1V_1} = \frac{\rho_2}{\rho_1}\frac{T_1}{T_2}\frac{M_2}{M_1}\frac{\sqrt{T_2}}{\sqrt{T_1}}$$

assuming constant specific heat ($k = $ constant). Substituting

$$\left(\frac{T_2}{T_1}\right)^{k/(k-1)} = \frac{p_2}{p_1}$$

yields

$$\frac{A_1}{A_2} = \frac{M_2}{M_1}\left(\frac{T_2}{T_1}\right)^{(k+1)/[2(k-1)]}$$

Now

$$\frac{T_2}{T_1} = \frac{T_2}{T_0}\frac{T_0}{T_1} = \frac{1 + [(k - 1)/2]M_1^2}{1 + [(k - 1)/2]M_2^2} = \frac{2 + (k - 1)M_1^2}{2 + (k - 1)M_2^2}$$

Therefore,

$$\frac{A_1}{A_2} = \frac{M_2}{M_1}\left[\frac{2 + (k - 1)M_1^2}{2 + (k - 1)M_2^2}\right]^{(k+1)/[2(k-1)]}$$

Let state 2 be the reference state where M = 1 and state 1 be any other state; i.e., $A_2 = A^*$ where $M_2 = 1$, and $A_1 = A$ where $M_1 = M$. Then

$$\frac{A}{A^*} = \frac{1}{M} \left[\frac{2 + (k-1)M^2}{k+1} \right]^{(k+1)/[2(k-1)]} \qquad [7.55]$$

Tabulated values of T/T_0, p/p_0, ρ/ρ_0, and A/A^* appear in the Keenan and Kaye *Gas Tables*, Tables 30 to 35, for k = 1.4, 1.0, 1.1, 1.2, 1.3, and 1.67. These tables provide a rapid method for establishing duct design for reversible, adiabatic, compressible flow. Suppose, for instance, that the throat and discharge areas are to be determined for a nozzle to pass $\dot{m}$ lb/sec and to have a discharge Mach number, M_2, at a given discharge back pressure, p_2, the initial total temperature being T_0. For M_2, the tables can be read for values of p_2/p_0, T_2/T_0, and A_2/A^*. From these values, p_0 and T_2 can be computed. As the discharge Mach number has a supersonic value, the nozzle must be convergent-divergent and have a throat. The throat is choked, and so the throat area can be calculated from the relationship given before, Eq. 7.52 (in general, from the continuity equation). Since $A_t = A^*$, then A_2 can be found from A_2/A^*.

The isentropic-flow tables in the *Gas Tables* also list values of functions entitled M^*, F/F^*, and $(A/A^*)(p/p_0)$, which have not yet acquired meaning from this discussion.

In M^*, the star does not have the same significance as in the other limit values. M^* stands for the ratio of the velocity at any point to the velocity where M = 1; i.e., $M^* = V/V^*$. To obtain a function of M^* in terms of the local Mach number, M, we write

$$M^* = \frac{V}{V^*} = \frac{V}{a} \frac{a}{V^*} = M \frac{a}{V^*}$$

where a is acoustic velocity.

Since

$$\frac{a}{V^*} = \frac{\sqrt{g_c k R T}}{\sqrt{g_c k R T^*}} = \sqrt{\frac{T}{T^*}}$$

and

$$\frac{T}{T^*} = \frac{T}{T_0} \frac{T_0}{T^*} = \frac{1}{1 + [(k-1)/2]M^2} \frac{k+1}{2} = \frac{k+1}{2 + (k-1)M^2}$$

we have

$$M^* = M \left[\frac{k+1}{2 + (k-1)M^2} \right]^{1/2} \qquad [7.56]$$

The F function is called the *thrust* or *impulse* function and defined as

$$F = pA + \frac{\dot{m}V}{g_c}$$

It is seen to be the sum of the force due to pressure on an area and the force due to rate of change of momentum. The difference of impulse function

$(F_2 - F_1)$ is the net thrust produced by a stream of fluid between stations 1 and 2. By substituting $A\rho V$ for $\dot{m}$, p/RT for ρ, and M^2 for $V^2/g_c kRT$, we obtain

$$F = pA(1 + k\mathrm{M}^2)$$

and
$$F^* = p^*A^*(1 + k)$$

so that
$$\frac{F}{F^*} = \frac{p}{p^*}\frac{A}{A^*}\frac{1 + k\mathrm{M}^2}{1 + k}$$

On substitution of $p/p^* = (p/p_0)(p_0/p^*)$, with the right-hand side in terms of Mach number as previously developed, and with A/A^* in terms of Mach number, there finally results

$$\frac{F}{F^*} = \frac{1 + k\mathrm{M}^2}{\mathrm{M}(2(k + 1)\{1 + [(k - 1)/2]\mathrm{M}^2\})^{\frac{1}{2}}} \qquad [7.57]$$

The function $(A/A^*)(p/p_0)$ is made up of previously defined quantities and is given in the tables as a convenience for certain calculations.

As all this development is for reversible, adiabatic flow, it may well be asked whether it is valid for actual flow conditions, where friction is always present. For practical use, the areas and velocities obtained are modified by coefficients of "discharge" and "velocity." Such modifying factors are usually small, and the flow is close to ideal for the design conditions. The actual values of the coefficients are rather closely related to the type of nozzle, e.g., whether for turbines or rockets, and reference should be made to the detailed literature in each case.

7.21 *Plane normal shock*

For flow in a given convergent-divergent nozzle, it was demonstrated that there is no solution for isentropic conditions between a receiver pressure, p_C, giving $\mathrm{M} = 1$ at the throat followed by subsonic diffusion and a receiver pressure, p_D, giving $\mathrm{M} = 1$ at the throat followed by supersonic flow and decreasing pressure down to p_D at nozzle discharge. As flow does take place for a receiver pressure $p_D > p > p_C$, some process and change of state occurs in the divergent part of the nozzle, even in the absence of friction, and the preceding analysis does not account for it. It is therefore necessary to resort to experiment, measuring temperatures and pressures along the duct. This shows that there is a sudden rise of pressure at some point in the divergent cone, so abrupt, in fact, that it represents a discontinuity. The density change is so sharp that it can be seen visually by means of a suitable arrangement of a light source and a screen, owing to the differing refraction of light by fluids of different density. Qualitative

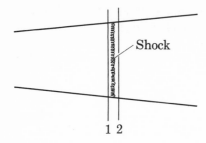

Figure 7.24

observation is possible with a simple shadow arrangement, but for precise work the *schlieren* method is preferable.*

The discontinuity takes place normal to the flow axis in an extremely small length of path, of the order of a few thousandths of an inch, and the supersonic flow changes to subsonic flow with a considerable rise of pressure and temperature across the discontinuity. Such a discontinuity is known as a *plane normal shock wave*, or simply as a *normal shock*. With this picture in mind, we can apply some basic relationships for a simple analysis, using energy, momentum, and continuity as before. Fig. 7.24 shows the idealized arrangement, with stations 1 and 2 before and after the shock, respectively.

For energy, we have Eq. 4.64,

$$c_p T_0 = c_p T + \frac{V^2}{2g_c} = \text{constant} \qquad [\textbf{4.64}]$$

because the flow is still adiabatic and there is no shaft work.

For momentum, we have Eq. 4.34b, because, as the shock occurs instantaneously, $A_1 = A_2 = A$, and there are no external shear or body forces. Thus

$$(p_2 - p_1)A = \frac{\dot{m}}{g_c}(V_1 - V_2) \qquad [\textbf{7.58}]$$

For continuity, with $A_1 = A_2 = A$, we have

$$\rho_1 V_1 = \rho_2 V_2 \qquad [\textbf{7.59}]$$

These governing equations, together with the equation of state, $p = \rho RT$, and the definition of Mach number as $V^2 = M^2 g_c k RT$, are combined to give convenient expressions. Note that we cannot use differential forms because the shock is considered as a discontinuity and finite derivatives do not exist.

* See, e.g., H. W. Liepmann and A. Roshko, *Elements of Gas Dynamics*, Wiley, New York, 1957.

From the momentum relationship (Eq. 7.58), with substitution for $\dot{m} = A\rho_1 V_1 = A\rho_2 V_2$, then

$$p_2 - p_1 = \frac{\rho_1 V_1{}^2 - \rho_2 V_2{}^2}{g_c}$$

which, on substitution of $\rho = p/RT$ and $V^2 = \mathrm{M}^2 g_c k R T$, yields

$$p_2 - p_1 = k p_1 \mathrm{M}_1{}^2 - k p_2 \mathrm{M}_2{}^2$$

Thus

$$\frac{p_2}{p_1} = \frac{1 + k\mathrm{M}_1{}^2}{1 + k\mathrm{M}_2{}^2} \qquad [7.60]$$

For temperature,

$$\frac{T_2}{T_1} = \frac{T_2}{T_0}\frac{T_0}{T_1} = \frac{1 + [(k-1)/2]\mathrm{M}_1{}^2}{1 + [(k-1)/2]\mathrm{M}_2{}^2} \qquad [7.61]$$

(Note that we cannot write $T_2/T_1 = (p_2/p_1)^{(k-1)/k}$ because the process is *not* reversible, although it is adiabatic.)

For stagnation pressure,

$$\frac{p_{0_2}}{p_{0_1}} = \frac{p_{0_2}}{p_2}\frac{p_2}{p_1}\frac{p_1}{p_{0_1}} = \frac{\{1 + [(k-1)/2]\mathrm{M}_2{}^2\}^{k/(k-1)}}{\{1 + [(k-1)/2]\mathrm{M}_1{}^2\}^{k/(k-1)}}\frac{1 + k\mathrm{M}_1{}^2}{1 + k\mathrm{M}_2{}^2} \qquad [7.62]$$

Eqs. 7.60, 7.61, and 7.62, are in terms of M_1 and M_2. It is worthwhile to see whether there is a relationship between M_1 and M_2 so that all the various ratios can become functions only of the initial Mach number.

Beginning with the continuity relation (Eq. 7.59) and substituting $\rho = p/RT$ and $V = \mathrm{M}\sqrt{g_c k R T}$, we obtain

$$\frac{p_1}{RT_1}\mathrm{M}_1\sqrt{g_c k R T_1} = \frac{p_2}{RT_2}\mathrm{M}_2\sqrt{g_c k R T_2}$$

With k as constant,

$$\frac{\mathrm{M}_2}{\mathrm{M}_1} = \frac{p_1}{p_2}\sqrt{\frac{T_2}{T_1}}$$

We can use Eqs. 7.60 and 7.61, for p_2/p_1 and T_2/T_1, to obtain an equation in M_1 and M_2 only. On rearranging the resulting expression, we get

$$\mathrm{M}_2{}^2 = \frac{\mathrm{M}_1{}^2 + 2/(k-1)}{[2k/(k-1)]\mathrm{M}_1{}^2 - 1} \qquad [7.63]$$

Thus, across a shock wave, there is a unique dependence of the Mach number after the shock on the Mach number before the shock. Utilizing Eq. 7.63 for substitution into Eqs. 7.60, 7.61, and 7.62, together with new relationships of ρ_2/ρ_1 and p_0/p_1 formed in similar manner to these equations, gives us the one-dimensional shock functions as follows:

$$M_2{}^2 = \frac{M_1{}^2 + 2/(k-1)}{[2k/(k-1)]M_1{}^2 - 1} \qquad [7.64]$$

$$\frac{p_2}{p_1} = \frac{2k}{k+1}\,M_1{}^2 - \frac{k-1}{k+1} \qquad [7.65]$$

$$\frac{T_2}{T_1} = \frac{\{1 + [(k-1)/2]M_1{}^2\}\{[2k/(k-1)]M_1{}^2 - 1\}}{\{(k+1)^2/[2(k-1)]\}M_1{}^2} \qquad [7.66]$$

$$\frac{\rho_2}{\rho_1} = \frac{p_2}{p_1}\frac{T_1}{T_2} \qquad [7.67]$$

$$\frac{p_{0_2}}{p_{0_1}} = \left\{\frac{[(k+1)/2]M_1{}^2}{1 + [(k-1)/2]M_1{}^2}\right\}^{k/(k-1)} \left(\frac{2k}{k+1}\,M_1{}^2 - \frac{k-1}{k+1}\right)^{1/(1-k)} \qquad [7.68]$$

$$\frac{p_{0_2}}{p_1} = \left(\frac{k+1}{2}\,M_1{}^2\right)^{k/(k-1)} \left(\frac{2k}{k+1}\,M_1{}^2 - \frac{k-1}{k+1}\right)^{1/(1-k)} \qquad [7.69]$$

These shock functions for various values of k appear in Tables 48 to 52 of *Gas Tables*, with subscripts x and y in place of 1 and 2.

This discussion started with the assumption from observation that an originally supersonic stream is reduced to a subsonic stream across a normal shock. This can be demonstrated analytically with the same relationships of energy, continuity, momentum, and state.

From the energy equation,

$$c_p T_1 + \frac{V_1{}^2}{2g_c} = c_p T_0 = c_p T_2 + \frac{V_2{}^2}{2g_c}$$

Substituting $T = p/\rho R$ and $c_p/R = k/(k-1)$ yields

$$\frac{p_1}{\rho_1} + \frac{k-1}{k}\frac{V_1{}^2}{2g_c} = \frac{p_0}{\rho_0} = \frac{p_2}{\rho_2} + \frac{k-1}{k}\frac{V_2{}^2}{2g_c}$$

or $\qquad \dfrac{p_2}{\rho_2} = \dfrac{p_0}{\rho_0} - \dfrac{k-1}{k}\dfrac{V_2{}^2}{2g_c} \qquad$ and $\qquad \dfrac{p_1}{\rho_1} = \dfrac{p_0}{\rho_0} - \dfrac{k-1}{k}\dfrac{V_1{}^2}{2g_c} \qquad [7.70]$

From the momentum equation,

$$p_2 - p_1 = \frac{\rho_1 V_1{}^2 - \rho_2 V_2{}^2}{g_c}$$

which, on division through by the continuity equation, $\rho V = \rho_1 V_1 = \rho_2 V_2$, becomes

$$\frac{p_2}{\rho_2 V_2} - \frac{p_1}{\rho_1 V_1} = \frac{V_1 - V_2}{g_c} \qquad [7.71]$$

Substituting values from Eq. 7.70 into Eq. 7.71 gives as

$$\frac{1}{V_2}\left(\frac{p_0}{\rho_0} - \frac{k-1}{k}\frac{V_2{}^2}{2g_c}\right) - \frac{1}{V_1}\left(\frac{p_0}{\rho_0} - \frac{k-1}{k}\frac{V_1{}^2}{2g_c}\right) = \frac{V_1 - V_2}{g_c}$$

or
$$\frac{p_0}{\rho_0}\left(\frac{1}{V_2} - \frac{1}{V_1}\right) + \frac{k-1}{k}\frac{1}{2g_c}(V_1 - V_2) = \frac{V_1 - V_2}{g_c} \qquad [7.72]$$

Since $1/V_2 - 1/V_1 = (V_1 - V_2)/V_1V_2$, on dividing through Eq. 7.72 by $V_1 - V_2$, we have

$$\frac{p_0}{\rho_0}\frac{1}{V_1V_2} + \frac{k-1}{k}\frac{1}{2g_c} = \frac{1}{g_c}$$

Substituting $RT_0 = p_0/\rho_0$ and rearranging result in

$$V_1V_2 = \frac{2k}{k+1}g_cRT_0$$

We now substitute $T^* = T_0/[(k+1)/2]$, i.e., the critical temperature ratio, thus:

$$V_1V_2 = g_ckRT = a^{*2}$$

or
$$\frac{V_1}{a^*}\frac{V_2}{a^*} = 1$$

and
$$M_1{}^*M_2{}^* = 1 \qquad [7.73]$$

This shows that if $M_1{}^* > 1$ (supersonic), then $M_2{}^* < 1$ (subsonic).

There is, however, nothing in any of the preceding analyses to indicate the reverse possibility, i.e., transition from subsonic to supersonic flow through a discontinuity. To demonstrate this, it is necessary to examine the change of entropy.

From Eq. 4.68 we can obtain the relationship of entropy change and stagnation pressure ratio as

$$s_2 - s_1 = -R\ln\frac{p_{0_2}}{p_{0_1}} \qquad [7.74]$$

From Eq. 7.68, p_{0_2}/p_{0_1} can be expressed in terms of M_1. If this is done, it will be found that, for $M_1 > 1$, $p_{0_2}/p_{0_1} < 1$ and $s_2 - s_1$ is positive but, for $M_1 < 1$, $p_{0_2}/p_{0_1} > 1$ and $s_2 - s_1$ is negative. As a decrease of entropy is not possible under the circumstances, it is concluded that only a *compression* shock is possible and that a *rarefaction* shock is not.

If the receiver pressure is higher than that required for reversible expansion in the nozzle down to that pressure, a normal shock will occur. After the shock, the flow will be subsonic, and diffusion will take place. Assuming reversible flow up to the shock, a change of state occurring across the shock in accordance with the relationships developed, and subsequent subsonic isentropic diffusion to the receiver pressure, we see that the location of the

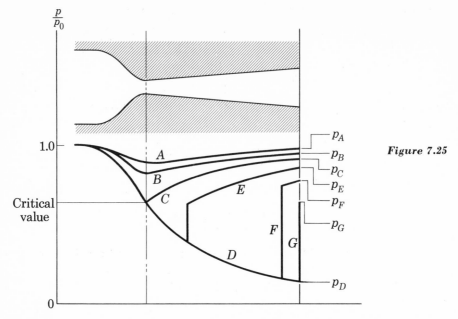

Figure 7.25

shock in the nozzle is governed by the relationships. Although these are idealized conditions, they are useful in building up a picture of the processes in the nozzle. Thus the diagram of Fig. 7.23 may be repeated, with three additional lines, E, F, and G, corresponding to three receiver pressures, p_E, p_F, and p_G, and three shock locations (Fig. 7.25). Line G shows the situation when the normal shock occurs right at the end of the nozzle, the recompression being just sufficient to reach the receiver, at pressure p_G. There is still a gap for conditions between p_G and p_D. Here oblique shocks occur, and they will be dealt with in Chapter 8.

The actual states, as opposed to the ideal states in Fig. 7.25, are modified to the extent that the boundary layer on the nozzle walls exerts a powerful effect. Thus the normal shock may occur not across the whole channel area but only across the central part, being attached to the boundary layer by a complex system of oblique shocks (Fig. 7.26). Following the shock, the flow is not reversible, for the interaction of shock and boundary layer produces separation at the walls. The shock is often unstable in position, as slight irregularities in flow and wall surface cause it to oscillate along the nozzle. Nevertheless, the discontinuity occurs and results in the situation shown in Fig. 7.27, which represents experimental data.

For a receiver pressure below that required for reversible expansion, i.e., $p < p_D$, the nozzle flow is wholly supersonic to the nozzle discharge, where the fluid suffers a free expansion to the lower pressure. The result is a series of external standing waves in the receiver fluid. For a receiver pressure just

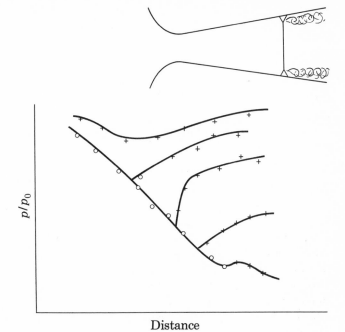

Figure 7.26

Figure 7.27

p/p_0

Distance

above the nozzle-exit pressure, i.e., $p_D < p < p_G$, the fluid is slightly compressed after discharge, and a standing-wave pattern again results, yielding the "shock diamonds" characteristic of supersonic exhausts, which will be discussed in Chapter 8.

Nozzles that operate with the fluid discharging at a nozzle-exit pressure higher than the receiver pressure are said to be *underexpanded*, whereas those in which the pressure falls to a value lower than the receiver pressure are said to be *overexpanded*. Underexpansion gives rise to less loss than overexpansion, because the latter may have normal shock. Loss of available energy across a shock may be estimated by the ratio p_{0_2}/p_{0_1} for the idealized case; p_{0_2}/p_{0_1} as a function of Mach number, from Eq. 7.62, is shown in Fig. 7.28.

For M_1 up to about 1.5, the loss is not too great theoretically, but in practice it is larger because of the flow separation. The figure emphasizes the desirability of avoiding normal shock at high Mach numbers and of operating a convergent-divergent nozzle only at or close to design conditions. Operation at off-design conditions requires careful checking of the actual states.

This development of nozzle flow has all been based on the flow of a perfect gas. One of the uses of nozzles is in steam turbines, where the fluid is not a perfect gas. Even in the high *superheat* region, it is customary to refer to the steam tables, with actual values of enthalpy replacing specific heat and

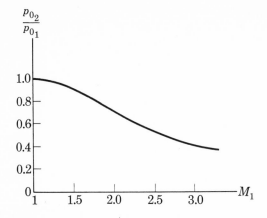

Figure 7.28

temperature. Qualitatively the nozzle behaves for steam as it does for air, but for quantitative work it is necessary to substitute individual enthalpy and kinetic-energy quantities for stagnation temperature. Thus, for a given entry state and pressure ratio, we find the specific volume and the enthalpy difference at constant entropy from the tables and charts and calculate the velocities in order to determine the areas. Steam differs from a perfect gas in one major respect: it is possible to have "wet steam," i.e., a mixture of vapor and liquid. The fluid may change from all vapor to a mixture during the nozzle expansion, and complex phenomena may ensue, leading to difficulty in calculating the processes and in determining whether or when the change of phase takes place. The expansion may occur so rapidly that the vapor is below its saturation temperature; then it is said to be *subcooled*.

7.22   *Adiabatic compressible flow with friction at constant area*

The general problem of flow with friction in a duct of varying area is complicated, and only very limited analytical solutions are possible. However, adiabatic flow in a constant-area duct is amenable to a straightforward analysis and is important in practice. At high Mach number, frictional effects may produce very rapid changes of state in compressible fluids. Since these effects are usually undesirable, it is necessary to be able to estimate their magnitude.

For adiabatic compressible flow, there are available the relationships of energy, momentum, and continuity, the equation of state, and the definition of Mach number. Note that, as the flow is irreversible, the isentropic relationships cannot be used.

For energy, we have

$$h + \frac{V^2}{2g_cJ} = h_0 = \text{constant} \qquad [7.75a]$$

For the time being, enthalpy is left in general terms so that it is applicable to all fluids as well as to perfect gases.

For momentum, the frictional effects could be introduced in a force-momentum relationship by means of the shear stress, but initially loss will be measured in general terms by change of entropy. For a pure substance, entropy is a function of any other two properties, these properties being chosen for convenience.

For continuity, as the area is constant, we have

$$\rho V = \text{constant} = G \qquad [7.76]$$

where the symbol G, used for convenience, has units of *specific* mass flow rate, pounds per second per square foot.

From Eq. 7.75a, on substitution of $G^2/\rho^2 = V^2$, there results

$$h + \frac{G^2}{2g_cJ\rho^2} = \text{constant} \qquad [7.77]$$

This equation contains two variables, h and ρ, and therefore, for a given flow rate, G, with the initial state of the fluid known, the relationship can be plotted. It is convenient, however, to introduce entropy. As stated earlier, for any pure substance we may write $\rho = \rho(h, s)$ and then obtain an equation in enthalpy and entropy. The development involves either rather cumbersome expressions or successive calculations of states in terms of pressure and temperature and eventually h and s. Leaving $\rho = \rho(h, s)$ as a general equation, we must accept the fact that the relationship of enthalpy and entropy leads to a plot as shown in Fig. 7.29, where each curve represents a particular value of G. Such curves, whether for h and s, or h and ρ, etc., are known as

Figure 7.29

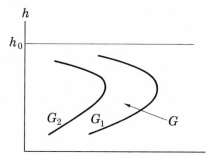

Fanno lines.* The point to emphasize is that entropy has a maximum value or, in other words, that at a certain state $ds = 0$. This state requires analysis and may be determined in the following manner.

From Eq. 7.75a, we obtain

$$dh + \frac{V\,dV}{g_cJ} = 0 \qquad [7.75b]$$

Likewise, from continuity, $\rho V = $ constant, we obtain

$$dV = -\,V\frac{d\rho}{\rho}$$

which, substituted in Eq. 7.75b, gives

$$dh - \frac{V^2\,d\rho}{g_cJ\,\rho} = 0 \qquad [7.78]$$

From thermodynamics, we have the relationship between states, Eq. 1.21,

$$T\,ds = dh - \frac{v\,dp}{J} = dh - \frac{dp}{\rho J} \qquad [1.21]$$

Substituting for dh from Eq. 1.21 into Eq. 7.78 yields

$$T\,ds + \frac{dp}{\rho J} - \frac{V^2\,d\rho}{g_cJ\,\rho} = 0$$

For the limit state where $ds = 0$, then

$$\frac{dp}{\rho J} - \frac{V^2\,d\rho}{g_cJ\,\rho} = 0$$

or

$$V^2 = \frac{dp}{d\rho}\,g_c \qquad [7.79]$$

At this particular limit where $ds = 0$, there is constant entropy in an adiabatic process, and it was shown previously that for this condition $\sqrt{g_c\,dp/d\rho}$ was the velocity of propagation of a wave in a compressible medium, i.e., the acoustic velocity, a; hence $V^2 = a^2$, and $V = a$.

It is possible to make an analysis to show some of the general features of a Fanno line for a perfect gas, and this will be done, as it will also show how primary relationships in gas flow can be manipulated to produce a desired formulation.

We wish to obtain a relationship in differential form for enthalpy and entropy, with Mach number as the parameter to indicate subsonic and supersonic regimes. We immediately change enthalpy, h, to temperature, T, since for a perfect gas $h = c_pT$, making the simplifying assumption that the specific

---

* It should be noted that although Fanno lines are shown here as solid lines, the process is *irreversible*.

ι.eat is constant. This allows us to use the equation of state, $p = \rho RT$, and the acoustic velocity, $a = \sqrt{g_c k RT}$.

We have available a general expression for entropy,

$$ds = c_p \frac{dT}{T} - R \frac{dp}{p}$$

into which we introduce the relationships governing the Fanno process, i.e., the energy equation for adiabatic flow and the continuity equation,

$$c_p\, dT + \frac{V\, dV}{g_c} = 0 \qquad\qquad [4.51]$$

and, from Eq. 7.76, $\qquad \dfrac{d\rho}{\rho} + \dfrac{dV}{V} = 0$

We then have the equation of state and the Mach-number definition for an ideal gas,

$$\frac{dp}{p} = \frac{d\rho}{\rho} + \frac{dT}{T} \qquad\qquad [7.44]$$

and $\qquad M = \dfrac{V}{\sqrt{g_c k RT}} \qquad$ or $\qquad V^2 = M^2 g_c k RT \qquad [4.63]$

which we can use to try to eliminate pressure, p, and introduce Mach number, M.

Looking at these in general, we see that from Eq. 7.44 we can obtain $p = p(\rho, T)$, from Eq. 7.76 we can obtain $\rho = \rho(V)$, and from Eqs. 4.51 and 4.63 we can obtain V as a function of M and T. Thus a sufficient number of relationships are at hand.

Using Eq. 4.64a, dividing by V^2, and substituting for V^2 from Eq. 4.73, we have

$$\frac{c_p\, dT}{V^2} + \frac{V\, dV}{g_c V^2} = \frac{c_p\, dT}{M^2 g_c k RT} + \frac{dV}{g_c\, dV} = 0$$

whence

$$\frac{dV}{V} = - \frac{c_p}{k R M^2} \frac{dT}{T}$$

From Eq. 7.76, $dV/V = - d\rho/\rho$, and substituting for $d\rho/\rho$ from Eq. 7.44 yields

$$\frac{dV}{V} = - \frac{dp}{p} + \frac{dT}{T}$$

Equating these values of dV/V to obtain a relationship among p, T, and M gives us

$$\frac{dp}{p} = \frac{c_p}{k R M^2} \frac{dT}{T} + \frac{dT}{T} = \frac{dT}{T}\left(1 + \frac{c_p}{k R M^2}\right)$$

which with $R = c_p - c_v$ reduces to

$$\frac{dp}{p} = \frac{dT}{T}\left[1 + \frac{1}{(k-1)\mathrm{M}^2}\right]$$

This value of dp/p can now be introduced into the entropy equation, resulting in

$$ds = c_p\frac{dT}{T} - R\frac{dT}{T}\left[1 + \frac{1}{(k-1)\mathrm{M}^2}\right]$$

which can be manipulated into the simplest possible form,

$$ds = c_v\frac{dT}{T}\left(\frac{\mathrm{M}^2 - 1}{\mathrm{M}^2}\right)$$

or

$$\frac{dT}{ds} = \frac{T}{c_v}\left(\frac{\mathrm{M}^2}{\mathrm{M}^2 - 1}\right) \qquad\qquad [7.80]$$

This is the slope of the curve of temperature versus entropy. When $\mathrm{M} < 1$, the term in parentheses is negative, and, as T and c_v must be positive, the slope is negative. When $\mathrm{M} > 1$, the term is positive, and thus the slope is positive. When $\mathrm{M} = 1$, the slope is infinite. The temperature is lower at a higher Mach number, and so for a given stagnation temperature the supersonic branch of positive slope must be below the subsonic branch. At very small and very large Mach numbers, the slope is very small as an absolute value, increasing as $\mathrm{M} \to 1$ from either side. The curve, then, must have the general shape shown in Fig. 7.29.

From the shape of the Fanno line in the diagram, for the upper portion of the line the enthalpy is initially near the stagnation value, i.e., the velocity is low. For the bottom portion of the line, the enthalpy is small, and thus the velocity is high. We may conclude from this that, for adiabatic flow with friction in a constant-area duct, an initially low (subsonic) velocity increases along the pipe, with the enthalpy (and hence the temperature for a perfect gas) decreasing, until the acoustic velocity is reached, i.e., the Mach number is unity.

The decrease of temperature should be particularly observed, because it is contrary to our usual impression that friction produces heating. It was seen in Sect. 4.22 that, for incompressible flow, the dissipation effect of friction resulted in an increase of internal energy. For compressible flow, however, although there is an immediate local increase of temperature, the density is reduced by it as well as by pressure, and hence the velocity is increased, so that there is an over-all reduction of temperature.

It is impossible, however, to attain supersonic flow by this means, because beyond the point where $\mathrm{M} = 1$, the entropy decreases, contrary to the second law of thermodynamics. Similarly, for the bottom part of the line, an initially high (supersonic) velocity decreases along the pipe, with enthalpy

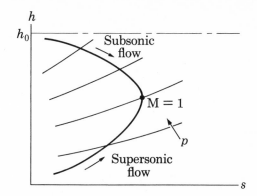

Figure 7.30

(or temperature) increasing until the Mach number is unity. Again this state represents a limit, for decrease to subsonic flow would require decrease of entropy. These processes are pictured in Fig. 7.30.

Since the limit state where $M = 1$ cannot be exceeded, it can only be reached at the end of the pipe. The question then arises as to what happens if, in an existing pipe system, additional resistance causes the limit state to be theoretically exceeded or to be reached in an intermediate part of the system. Because the resistance has not been particularized but has been made general in the form of an entropy increase, it can occur by such means as a valve or an altered setting of some component in the system. The only possible solution is for the mass flow to decrease, i.e., for the process to follow a different Fanno line having a lower value of G, just sufficient to produce $M = 1$ at discharge. Thus resistance in constant-area flow can cause choking or limitation of flow when a Mach number of unity is reached.

The general discussion so far has been valid for any compressible fluid. For a perfect gas, we can form some quantitative relationships and, in particular, develop expressions from which tables can be set up. The reference state is made the limit state where $M = 1$ and is again given the superscript * ("star").

For temperature, since the stagnation temperature is constant,

$$\frac{T_1}{T_2} = \frac{T_1}{T_0}\frac{T_0}{T_2} = \frac{1 + [(k - 1)/2]M_2{}^2}{1 + [(k - 1)/2]M_1{}^2}$$

With $T_1 = T$ where $M_1 = M$ and $T_2 = T^*$ where $M_2 = 1$, then

$$\frac{T}{T^*} = \frac{k + 1}{2 + (k - 1)M^2} \qquad [7.81]$$

For density, we have from continuity

$$\frac{\rho}{\rho^*} = \frac{V^*}{V} = \frac{M^*}{M}\frac{\sqrt{gk_cRT^*}}{\sqrt{g_ckRT}} = \frac{1}{M}\left(\frac{T^*}{T}\right)^{1/2} = \frac{1}{M}\left[\frac{2 + (k - 1)M^2}{k + 1}\right]^{1/2} \qquad [7.82]$$

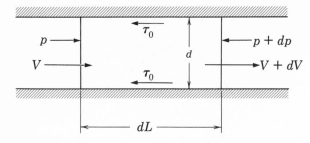

Figure 7.31

For pressure, from $p = \rho RT$,

$$\frac{p}{p^*} = \frac{\rho}{\rho^*}\frac{T}{T^*} = \frac{1}{M}\left[\frac{2 + (k-1)M^2}{k+1}\right]^{1/2}\left[\frac{k+1}{2+(k-1)M^2}\right]^{1/2}$$

$$= \frac{1}{M}\left[\frac{k+1}{2+(k-1)M^2}\right]^{1/2} \quad [7.83]$$

For stagnation pressure (which must decrease for a process with increase of entropy),

$$\frac{p_0}{p_0^*} = \frac{p_0}{p}\frac{p}{p^*}\frac{p^*}{p_0^*} = \left(1 + \frac{k-1}{2}M^2\right)^{k/(k-1)}$$

$$\times \frac{1}{M}\left[\frac{k+1}{2+(k-1)M^2}\right]^{1/2}\left(\frac{2}{k+1}\right)^{k/(k-1)} \quad [7.84]$$

Therefore, $$\frac{p_0}{p_0^*} = \frac{1}{M}\left[\frac{2+(k-1)M^2}{k+1}\right]^{(k+1)/[2(k-1)]}$$

Because pipe friction is the most common resistance in pipe flow, it is desirable to formulate a quantitative expression in terms of the friction factor, f, which can be estimated from the Reynolds number. Fig. 7.31 shows an infinitesimal length of pipe, dL, in which a wall shear stress, τ_0, causes a Fanno effect. Making a force-momentum balance, we obtain

$$pA - (p + dp)A - \tau_0\pi\,dL\,d = \frac{\dot{m}}{g_c}(V + dV) - \frac{\dot{m}V}{g_c}$$

where the nondifferential d represents diameter. With $A = (\pi/4)d^2$ and $\dot{m} = A\rho V$, this reduces to

$$-dp - 4\tau_0\frac{dL}{d} = \frac{\rho V\,dV}{g_c}$$

From the definition of friction factor, $f = 4\tau_0/(\rho V^2/2g_c)$, Eq. 7.4b,

$$dp + f\frac{\rho V^2}{2g_c}\frac{dL}{d} + \frac{\rho V\,dV}{g_c} = 0 \quad [7.85]$$

From the equation of state, $p = p(\rho, T)$, and from continuity, $\rho = \rho(V)$ and $V = V(M, T)$, eventually Eq. 7.85 can be reduced to $f\,dL/d$ as a function of Mach number. The rearrangement will be assumed here as yielding the final result

$$f \frac{dL}{d} = \frac{(1 - M^2) \, d(M^2)}{kM^4\{1 + [(k - 1)/2]M^2\}} \qquad [7.86]$$

(Note that the Mach-number variable is M^2, not M, as M^2 is more convenient for integration and as it represents kinetic energy.)

Before integrating Eq. 7.86 between states 1 and 2, we should note that f is not a constant, since it is a function of $\rho V d/\mu$. However, for constant area, $\rho V = G = $ constant, f is a function of $Gd/\mu \propto 1/\mu$ and μ varies relatively slowly with temperature. Thus a constant average value of $f = \bar{f}$ is usually sufficiently accurate for the process, if it is checked by solution for the final temperature after the first trial. Because f varies only slowly with μ, and μ with T, a close approximation can generally be made quite simply.

The integration can be carried out between states 1 and 2, i.e., between L_1 and L_2 and between M_1 and M_2. If state 2 is taken as the reference state where $L_2 = L^*$ (or $L_{\max}$, since it is the greatest length before choking) and where $M_2 = 1$, and state 1 as any initial state where $L_1 = 0$ and $M_1 = M$, then the integration yields

$$\bar{f} \frac{L^*}{d} = \frac{1 - M^2}{kM^2} + \frac{k + 1}{2k} \ln \frac{(k + 1)M^2}{2 + (k - 1)M^2} \qquad [7.87]$$

For a given size of pipe with a given initial state, so that f can be estimated, then, for the given initial Mach number, M, the maximum length of pipe before choking, L^* or $L_{\max}$, can be calculated.

For finding the length, L_2, where the Mach number is not unity but a lower value, M_2, then

$$\bar{f} \frac{L_2 - L_1}{d} = \left(\frac{\bar{f}L^*}{d} \right)_{M_1} - \left(\frac{\bar{f}L^*}{d} \right)_{M_2} \qquad [7.88]$$

i.e., the choking length is determined for each state, and the length between these states is found by subtraction.

Values of T/T^*, p/p^*, p_0/p_0^*, V/V^*, F/F^* (thrust function), and $4fL_{\max}/D$ for various values of k are given as functions of Mach number in Tables 42 to 47 of the *Gas Tables*. Note that the $4f$ of the tables is equal to our f, because the friction factor used there is one quarter of the value used here; i.e., f is defined from $f = \tau_0/(\rho V^2/2g_c)$. The factor 4 is a matter of convenience only and does not affect the numerical value if used consistently.

The value of $\bar{f}L^*/d$ is large at a low Mach number but decreases rapidly to a very small figure at a high Mach number. Thus with $k = 1.4$, it is 14.533 at $M = 0.2$, 1.06908 at $M = 0.5$, and 0.014513 at $M = 0.9$. With the friction factor taken as 0.015 (equivalent Reynolds number about 2.5×10^5) for all three values and the pipe diameter taken as 1 in., the lengths of pipe necessary to produce choking from the initial Mach number are 80.7 ft, 5.93 ft, and 0.97 in., respectively. The corresponding ratios p_0/p_0^* are 2.9635, 1.3399, and 1.00887, and if the initial p_0 is assumed to be 100 psia in each case, then the stagnation pressures at the limit state are about 33.7 psia, 74.6 psia, and 99.12 psia, respectively. For the last case, it is seen that a loss of stagnation pressure of nearly 1 psi is occasioned in the last inch of path. So at medium and high Mach numbers, it is necessary to check the conditions very carefully, as small changes of one variable can easily lead to choking. Friction factors at high Mach numbers have been found experimentally, showing no significant differences from the values valid for low Mach numbers or incompressible flow in general.

7.23   *Frictionless diabatic compressible flow at constant area*

Up to this point, consideration has been given only to adiabatic flow, but there are many important engineering applications in which *heating* (or cooling) occurs, i.e., in which the flow is *diabatic*. Most of those in which compressibility effects are important involve flow at constant area, e.g., in pipes. Friction is nearly always present, and the problem of combined heating and friction admits no ready solution. Usually, however, the effects due to heating are much greater than those due to friction, and the problem is dealt with as frictionless flow, with estimated correction factors added when necessary to allow for resistance. Heating may take place indirectly by heat transfer, as in heat exchangers of all kinds, notably superheaters in boilers, or directly by internal combustion of fuel, as in ramjets and the combustion chambers of gas turbines.

For analysis we again have the relationships of energy, momentum, and continuity, together with the equation of state and the definition of Mach number where needed. For energy, the steady-flow energy equation gives

$$h_{0_1} + Q = h_{0_2}$$

The stagnation enthalpy (or temperature) is now not constant, and, in fact, the ratio T_{0_1}/T_{0_2} may be used as a measure of the heating effect. For momentum, as the flow is frictionless, we have the Euler equation,

$$\frac{dp}{\rho} + \frac{V\,dV}{g_c} = 0 \qquad\qquad [4.58]$$

For continuity, as the area is constant,

$$\rho V = \text{constant} = G \qquad\qquad [7.76]$$

From this,

$$\rho \, dV - V \, d\rho = -\frac{G \, d\rho}{\rho}$$

Substituting for V and ρ in Eq. 4.58 yields

$$dp - \frac{G^2 \, d\rho}{g_c \rho^2} = 0 \qquad\qquad [7.89]$$

Integrating, we have

$$p + \frac{G^2}{g_c \rho} = \text{constant}$$

or, resubstituting $G = \rho V$,

$$p + \frac{\rho V^2}{g_c} = \text{constant} \qquad\qquad [4.34b]$$

For constant area, this might have been obtained directly from the force-momentum relationship, i.e.,

$$pA + \frac{\dot{m} V}{g_c} = \text{constant} = pA + \frac{(\rho A V) V}{g_c}$$

or
$$p + \frac{\rho V^2}{g_c} = \text{constant}$$

Eq. 4.34b defines the thrust or impulse function, which is constant for constant-area frictionless flow, with or without heating.

To demonstrate the process of constant-area heating, the most significant coordinate system is again that of enthalpy-entropy (or temperature-entropy). For a given initial state and rate of heat transfer, the energy, momentum, continuity, and state relationships, together with entropy as a function of two other properties, will permit determination of the final state. For a given value of specific mass flow rate, G, there results a curve as shown in Fig. 7.32, which is known as a *Rayleigh* line.*

State 1 is the initial state, and, as heat is added, the enthalpy increases to point x and then decreases to point y, the whole process occurring at continually decreasing pressure. Thus there is a limit to the temperature increase by heat addition, represented by state x, and a limit to the entropy increase, represented by state y, which for this process, which is frictionless, also represents maximum heat addition. After state y the entropy decreases, if the process is considered to be continuous from 1 to 2, and this can only occur through the removal of heat, so that y to 2 represents a *cooling* process. In the reverse direction, from 2 to 1, the addition of heat causes the process to move toward y with an increase of temperature and pressure. To proceed

---

* For an ideal gas, an analysis may be made that shows the general form of the Rayleigh line, as was done for a Fanno line. This is left as a problem at the end of the chapter.

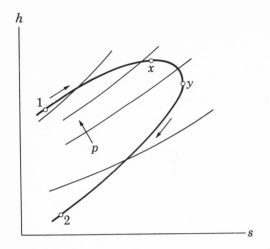

Figure 7.32

past y requires cooling, with the temperature increasing to x and then decreasing while the pressure continues to increase. The limit points x and y must be analyzed, and we shall begin with y.

From Eq. 7.89, we obtain

$$g_c \frac{dp}{d\rho} = \frac{G^2}{\rho^2} = \frac{(\rho V)^2}{\rho^2} = V^2$$

Hence, for any state along a Rayleigh line, $V = \sqrt{g_c\,dp/d\rho}$. For point y, however, $ds = 0$; i.e., instantaneously the process is adiabatic, and as it is also internally reversible, $\sqrt{g_c\,dp/d\rho} = V = a$, the acoustic velocity, at y. Thus state y is one where the Mach number in unity. Evaluation of the Mach number at any state between 1 and y reveals that it is less than unity; i.e., the top portion of the Rayleigh line represents *subsonic* flow. Similarly, it may be shown that the bottom portion represents *supersonic* flow. Theoretically then, a fluid may be accelerated from an initially low velocity to $M = 1$ by the addition of heat and further accelerated to supersonic velocity by cooling. Likewise, an initially supersonic flow may be reduced to subsonic flow without shock by heating to $M = 1$ followed by cooling. In practice these two results cannot be achieved, because of the effect of friction and the impossibility of passing continuously from heating to cooling through state y. However, one important deduction can be made with respect to constant-area flow: heating accelerates a subsonic flow, which seems in line with ordinary experience, whereas cooling accelerates a supersonic flow and heating decelerates it.

Another important deduction from the representation of a Rayleigh line is that an *addition* of heat causes a reduction of pressure in subsonic flow. This is sometimes not appreciated, because superficially we are apt to associate an addition of energy, which may be large, as when fuel is burnt, with an increase of potential, of which pressure can be a manifestation. However, if it is recognized that an addition of heat increases velocity (in subsonic flow) and hence momentum, it will be apparent that an increase of momentum can be acquired only by application of a force, which in this case can only be supplied by a pressure difference, with pressure decreasing in the flow direction.

Turning now to the limit point x, with $dT = 0$, we have as before

$$g_c \frac{dp}{d\rho} = V^2$$

which, on division by kRT, gives

$$\frac{dp}{d\rho} \frac{1}{kRT} = \frac{V^2}{g_c kRT} = \frac{V^2}{a^2} = \mathrm{M}^2$$

Substituting $p/\rho = RT$ yields

$$\frac{dp/p}{d\rho/\rho} \frac{1}{k} = \mathrm{M}^2 \qquad\qquad [7.90]$$

From the equation of state,

$$\frac{dp}{p} = \frac{d\rho}{\rho} + \frac{dT}{T}$$

At state x, $dT = 0$, and so $dp/p = d\rho/\rho$. Thus Eq. 7.90 becomes

$$\mathrm{M}^2 = 1/k$$

i.e., $\mathrm{M} = \sqrt{1/k}$ represents a state of maximum temperature along a Rayleigh line. This again is not obvious, namely, that the addition of heat in constant-area flow does not always cause an increase of temperature. Note that the *stagnation* temperature increases continually up to state y but that beyond state x the velocity increases at a sufficiently high rate that the *static* temperature falls.

State y represents a *choking* state for a heating process in constant-area flow and the point of maximum heat addition for given initial conditions. If more heat is added, the flow rate will decrease; i.e., the process will occur on a different Rayleigh line with a lower value of G. These considerations are important in systems such as ramjets and gas-turbine afterburners, because they imply choking values that limit the amount of fuel (i.e., energy) that can be supplied.

For a perfect gas with constant specific heat, states along a Rayleigh line may be found in terms of Mach number with the choking state, y, as a reference state. For pressure, from the constant-impulse condition,

$$p_1 + \frac{\rho_1 V_1{}^2}{g_c} = p_2 + \frac{\rho_2 V_2{}^2}{g_c}$$

which, with $\rho = p/RT$ and $V^2 = \mathrm{M}^2 g_c kRT$ used as before, gives

$$\frac{p_1}{p_2} = \frac{1 + k\mathrm{M}_2{}^2}{1 + k\mathrm{M}_1{}^2}$$

With $p_2 = p^*$ at $\mathrm{M}_2 = 1$ and $p_1 = p$ at $\mathrm{M}_1 = \mathrm{M}$, then

$$\frac{p}{p^*} = \frac{1 + k}{1 + k\mathrm{M}^2} \qquad [7.91]$$

For temperature, from continuity,

$$\rho_1 V_1 = \rho_2 V_2$$

or

$$\frac{p_1}{RT_1} \mathrm{M}_1 \sqrt{g_c kRT_1} = \frac{p_2}{RT_2} \mathrm{M}_2 \sqrt{g_c kRT_2}$$

and

$$\frac{T_1}{T_2} = \left(\frac{p_1}{p_2}\right)^2 \frac{\mathrm{M}_1{}^2}{\mathrm{M}_2{}^2}$$

which for the reference state becomes

$$\frac{T}{T^*} = \frac{(1 + k)^2 \mathrm{M}^2}{(1 + k\mathrm{M}^2)^2} \qquad [7.92]$$

For stagnation temperature,

$$\frac{T_{0_1}}{T_{0_2}} = \frac{T_{0_1}}{T_1} \frac{T_1}{T_2} \frac{T_2}{T_{0_2}}$$

or

$$\frac{T_{0_1}}{T_{0_2}} = \frac{2 + (k-1)\mathrm{M}_1{}^2}{2 + (k-1)\mathrm{M}_2{}^2} \frac{T_1}{T_2}$$

and

$$\frac{T_0}{T_0{}^*} = [2 + (k-1)\mathrm{M}^2] \frac{(1 + k)\mathrm{M}^2}{(1 + k\mathrm{M}^2)^2} \qquad [7.93]$$

For stagnation pressure,

$$\frac{p_{0_1}}{p_{0_2}} = \frac{p_{0_1}}{p_1} \frac{p_1}{p_2} \frac{p_2}{p_{0_2}} = \left[\frac{2 + (k-1)\mathrm{M}_1{}^2}{2 + (k-1)\mathrm{M}_2{}^2}\right]^{k/(k-1)} \frac{p_1}{p_2}$$

which for the reference condition becomes

$$\frac{p_0}{p_0{}^*} = \left[\frac{2 + (k-1)\mathrm{M}^2}{k + 1}\right]^{k/(k-1)} \left(\frac{1 + k}{1 + k\mathrm{M}^2}\right) \qquad [7.94]$$

For velocity,

$$\frac{v_1}{v_2} = \frac{\rho_2}{\rho_1} = \frac{p_2}{p_1} \frac{T_1}{T_2}$$

$$\frac{V}{V^*} = \frac{p^*}{p} \frac{T}{T^*} = \frac{(1 + k)\mathrm{M}^2}{1 + k\mathrm{M}^2} \qquad [7.95]$$

Values of Rayleigh-line functions, Eqs. 7.91 to 7.95, for various values of k are given in Tables 36 to 41 of the *Gas Tables*.

It was emphasized previously, in reference to static pressure, that heating in subsonic flow causes a reduction of pressure. It is relevant now to consider what happens to the stagnation pressure, the value of which is a measure of the availability of energy for doing useful work. The equation relating p_{0_1} and p_{0_2} preceding Eq. 7.94 can be evaluated and plotted to show that p_{0_2} is always less than p_{0_1}; i.e., the stagnation pressure *always* decreases with heating. This can be demonstrated in direct fashion by an examination of incompressible flow, i.e., flow in which the density is unaffected by change of pressure, although dependent on temperature.

Consider stations 1 and 2 in a constant-area duct with heat transfer taking place. The impulse function is constant; i.e.,

$$p_1 + \frac{\rho_1 V_1^2}{g_c} = p_2 + \frac{\rho_2 V_2^2}{g_c} \qquad [4.34b]$$

The energy relationship may be introduced through the integrated form of the simple Euler equation for incompressible flow (the Bernoulli equation for gases), with a term Δp_0 representing the change of stagnation pressure due to heat transfer (*not* friction), thus:

$$\Delta p_0 = \left(p_1 + \frac{\rho_1 V_1^2}{2g_c} \right) - \left(p_2 + \frac{\rho_2 V_2^2}{2g_c} \right)$$

Eliminating the static pressures p_1 and p_2 in these equations, we obtain

$$\Delta p_0 = \frac{\rho_2 V_2^2}{2g_c} - \frac{\rho_1 V_1^2}{2g_c}$$

From continuity, $\rho_1 V_1 = \rho_2 V_2$; hence

$$\Delta p_0 = \frac{\rho_1 V_1^2}{2g_c} \left(\frac{\rho_1}{\rho_2} - 1 \right) \qquad [7.96]$$

Taking density as constant with pressure and varying with temperature only, we have $\rho \propto 1/T$ and

$$\Delta p_0 \approx \frac{\rho_1 V_1^2}{2g_c} \left(\frac{T_2}{T_1} - 1 \right) \qquad [7.97]$$

Therefore, for heating, $T_2/T_1 > 1$, and there is a loss of stagnation pressure, and vice versa for cooling.

A great many engineering situations involving relatively low velocity may be handled by these equations, for the loss, although important, is small enough to be covered by the incompressible-flow relationship. For the main combustor of a gas turbine, for instance, typical figures might be an inlet pressure of 5 atm at 400°F and a velocity of 50 ft/sec with combustion of fuel to raise the outlet temperature to 1500°F. From Eq. 7.97 the loss of total pressure is 0.08 psi, and from Eq. 4.30 the loss of static pressure is twice this, or 0.16 psi, so that the assumption of incompressible flow is valid. In this example, the loss of total pressure is small, but in equipment with large temperature ratios and low values of other losses, it may be significant. In the afterburners of gas turbines and in ramjets, where velocities and temperature ratios are high, the compressible-flow relationships must be used. It is essential to understand that heating a fluid in subsonic flow always causes a loss of static pressure, sometimes called the "momentum loss," as well as a loss of stagnation pressure.

7.24 *Fanno, Rayleigh, and shock*

It was seen that for a Fanno line, T_0 = constant and ρV = constant, whereas for a Rayleigh line, impulse = constant and ρV = constant. We recall that the conditions for a normal shock are T_0 = constant, ρV = constant, and impulse = constant. Thus a normal shock must satisfy both Fanno and Rayleigh relationships for a given mass flow; i.e., the conditions before and after a normal shock must lie at the intersection of the Fanno and Rayleigh lines for a given value of G, as in Fig. 7.33. This shows diagrammatically the impossibility of a rarefaction shock (subsonic to supersonic), since there cannot be a decrease of entropy and therefore the process can only go from state 1 to state 2 (supersonic to subsonic). As a shock process is adiabatic, the heat added, represented by state 2 to state * on the Rayleigh line, must equal the heat removed from state * to state 1.

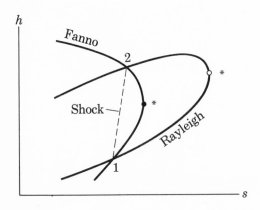

Figure 7.33

7.25   *The recovery factor*

A factor of importance in some instances is the heating of bodies by the stagnation effect, i.e., the rise in local temperature caused by a stream of fluid being stagnated or partially so. This effect takes place everywhere there is a surface, because a boundary layer is a region of reduced velocity and has a temperature close to the stagnation value.

There are two major areas where this effect must be taken into account, one in the measurement of the temperature of a high-velocity gas stream and the other in the design of aircraft and missiles. A body of finite size inserted in a gas stream will experience varying proportions of the dynamic temperature, as the velocity is everywhere different and, furthermore, locally the flow may not be adiabatic.

Fig. 7.34 shows the temperature along an insulated surface parallel to the flow axis. In the body of the fluid stream, the static temperature is T and the dynamic temperature is $T_d = V^2/2g_c c_p J$. The sum, of course, is the stagnation temperature, T_0. In the boundary layer, where the velocity is reduced, the static temperature increases, and the dynamic temperature decreases. If the flow were adiabatic everywhere, $T + T_d$ would always equal T_0, but since T is higher in the boundary layer, heat is transferred out into the main body of the fluid because of the temperature gradient. Consequently, at the wall, where the velocity is zero, the temperature, T_{aw}, is less than T_0. T_{aw} is the *adiabatic-wall temperature*.

For design purposes, the temperature, T_{aw}, of a wall surface is estimated from a knowledge of an experimentally determined *recovery factor*, R_F, defined as

$$R_F = \frac{T_{aw} - T}{T_0 - T} \qquad [7.98]$$

i.e., the ratio of the dynamic temperature at the wall to the full dynamic temperature, $V^2/2g_c c_p J$. This may be put in terms of Mach number,

Figure 7.34

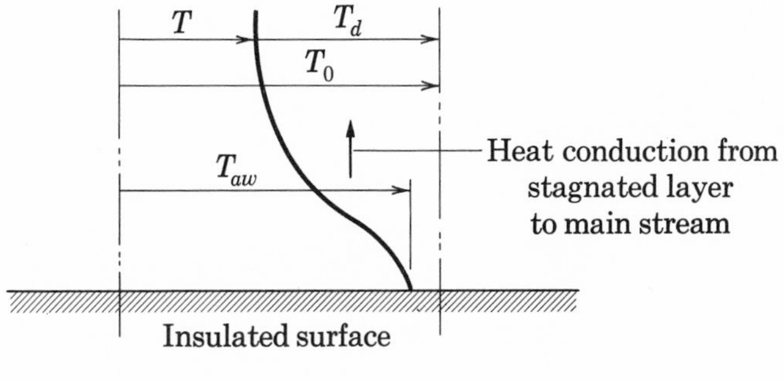

Heat conduction from stagnated layer to main stream

Insulated surface

thus:

$$R_F = \frac{T_{aw} - T}{T_0 - T} = \frac{(T_{aw}/T) - 1}{(T_0/T) - 1} = \frac{(T_{aw}/T) - 1}{\{1 + [(k - 1)/2]M^2 - 1\}}$$

or

$$\frac{T_{aw}}{T} = 1 + R_F\left(\frac{k - 1}{2} M^2\right) \qquad [7.99]$$

Values of R_F for flat surfaces have a slight dependence on Reynolds, Prandtl, and Mach numbers (Prandtl number $= c_p\mu/k$, where k is the thermal conductivity) and range from 0.83 to 0.91. A value of 0.85 is a reasonable average value to assume in the absence of precise data. Values of R_F for surfaces other than flat plates or those in which the velocity is parallel to the surface must be determined empirically for each case. A thermometer, which is essentially a circular cylinder with its axis normal to the flow, has an R_F value of about 0.60. In high-velocity streams, then, a temperature-measuring instrument must be calibrated for the recovery factor, as considerable error is possible.

Airfoil sections, such as those in aircraft and turbomachine blades, act very much like flat plates because the air flow is smooth and parallel to the surface. Therefore, at high velocities the aerodynamic heating effect may be considerable, and it represents a serious problem in high-speed flight. From Eq. 7.99, with an air temperature of $-60°F$ (high altitude) and a recovery factor of 0.9, the adiabatic-wall temperature becomes, in degrees Fahrenheit,

$$T_{aw} = T\left[1 + R_F\left(\frac{k - 1}{2} M^2\right)\right] - 460$$
$$= 400[1 + 0.9(0.2M^2)] - 460 = 72M^2 - 60$$

Results are as follows:

M	T_{aw}, °F
1	12
2	228
3	588
4	1092 (dark red heat)
5	1740 (yellowish red heat)

This table gives the skin temperatures attained at various flight Mach numbers. Aircraft are in regular operation at $M = 2$, and $M = 3$ aircraft are being designed. Missiles represent the extreme case, and the reentry problem of a space vehicle is well known.

7.26   *Isothermal flow with friction at constant area*

At relatively high velocities over short lengths, flow with friction in a constant-area pipe may be considered to be adiabatic. In very long lengths of pipe, however, where the velocities are usually lower, the process more nearly approaches the isothermal condition. This is true, for instance, in natural-gas pipelines, which stretch many hundreds of miles, with booster-pump stations at intervals.

For an analysis of this problem, Eq. 7.85 may be used, since it resulted from a general force-momentum balance in a pipe, thus:

$$dp + f \frac{\rho V^2}{2g_c} \frac{dL}{d} + \frac{\rho V \, dV}{g_c} = 0 \qquad [7.85]$$

V and dV may be eliminated by the continuity relation for constant area, $\rho V = G$, together with its derivative, $dV = - \, G \, d\rho/\rho^2$, so that

$$dp + f \frac{dL}{d} \frac{G^2}{2g_c\rho} - \frac{G^2 \, d\rho}{g_c\rho^2} = 0$$

For isothermal flow, from $p = \rho RT$, then with T constant, $dp/p = d\rho/\rho$, whence

$$dp + f \frac{dL}{d} \frac{G^2 \, RT}{2g_c p} - \frac{G^2 RT \, dp}{g_c p^2} = 0$$

Friction factor f is constant for isothermal flow because $\rho V d/\mu = G d/\mu$ and μ is constant. Multiplying the preceding equation by p and placing constant terms outside the integral sign, we have

$$\int_1^2 p \, dp + \frac{f}{d} \frac{G^2 RT}{2g_c} \int_1^2 dL - \frac{G^2 RT}{g_c} \int_1^2 \frac{dp}{p} = 0$$

This can be integrated readily, giving

$$p_2{}^2 - p_1{}^2 + \frac{f L_{1-2}}{d} \frac{G^2 RT}{g_c} + 2 \frac{G^2 RT}{g_c} \ln \frac{p_1}{p_2} = 0 \qquad [7.100]$$

Eq. 7.100 is a form of the relationship that can be used with p_2 and L_{1-2} as unknowns, but it is an implicit form that must be solved by trial and error. A simpler, but still implicit form, can be obtained in terms of the initial Mach number, M, by substitution of $G = \rho V = (p/RT)(M \sqrt{g_c k RT})$ in Eq. 7.100 and rearrangement, as follows:

$$\frac{f L_{1-2}}{d} = \frac{1}{k M_1{}^2} \left[1 - \left(\frac{p_2}{p_1} \right)^2 \right] - 2 \ln \frac{p_1}{p_2} \qquad [7.101]$$

Adiabatic flow with friction was found to have a limit point at $M = 1$, and isothermal flow can be examined to see whether it has an analogous situation. From Eq. 7.85 we can obtain the pressure gradient along the pipe, dp/dL, in terms of Mach number. Substituting $\rho = p/RT$, $dV = -V \, d\rho/\rho$ (from ρV = constant), and $d\rho/\rho = dp/p$ (from $p \propto \rho$ in an isothermal process) gives us

$$dp + f \frac{dL}{d} \frac{pV^2}{2g_cRT} - \frac{V^2}{g_cRT} dp = 0$$

From the definition of Mach number, $M^2 = V^2/g_ckRT$, then

$$dp + f \frac{dL}{d} \frac{kp}{2} M^2 - kM^2 \, dp = 0$$

and

$$dp(1 - kM^2) + f \frac{dL}{d} \frac{kp}{2} M^2 = 0$$

Therefore,

$$\frac{dp}{dL} = \frac{(f/d)(p/2)M^2}{M^2 - 1/k} \qquad [7.102]$$

In Eq. 7.102, the numerator is always positive, but the denominator is zero when $M = \sqrt{1/k}$ ($= 0.845$ for air with $k = 1.4$). Then dp/dL becomes infinite, and the process cannot proceed beyond this point. Hence this state represents a limit point, where the flow is choked, choking in this case being at $M = \sqrt{1/k}$ and not at $M = 1$ as previously.

Recalling that in adiabatic flow with friction in a pipe (the Fanno process) the temperature decreases in the direction of flow, we realize that to keep the process isothermal requires the addition of heat. Near the critical Mach number of $\sqrt{1/k}$, the state changes rapidly, and the heat-transfer rate has to be very great. Thus in practice, unless heat is added deliberately, the flow becomes more nearly adiabatic, and the theoretical limit is not attained. It is also helpful to recall the process of heat addition at constant area (the Rayleigh process) in this connection. For a transition from state 1 to state 2, the isothermal process may be thought of as a combination of adiabatic flow with friction causing a temperature drop and heat addition causing a temperature rise, the effects balancing to produce isothermal flow. At $M = \sqrt{1/k}$, however, both friction and heat addition cause the temperature to decrease, and so the isothermal process reaches a limit.

As with isentropic-flow and shock processes, isothermal-state functions can be expressed in terms of Mach number with the limit state as a datum. The prime symbol (′) here designates the limit state; i.e., $M' = \sqrt{1/k}$. Starting with Eq. 7.101, with state 1 any initial state where $p_1 = p$, $M_1 = M$, and $L = 0$, and with state 2 as the limit state where $p_2 = p'$, $M_2 = M' =$

$\sqrt{1/k}$, and $L_2 = L'$, then, we have

$$\frac{fL'}{d} = \frac{1}{k\text{M}^2}\left[1 - \left(\frac{p'}{p}\right)^2\right] - \ln\left(\frac{p}{p'}\right)^2 \qquad [7.103]$$

From continuity, $\rho V = \rho'V'$; hence $pV = p'V'$, and with $V = \text{M}\sqrt{g_c k R T}$, then

$$\frac{p}{p'} = \frac{V'}{V} = \frac{\text{M}'}{\text{M}}$$

as T is constant. For the limit state, since $\text{M}' = \sqrt{1/k}$, then

$$\frac{p}{p'} = \frac{\sqrt{1/k}}{\text{M}} \qquad [7.104]$$

Substituting for p/p' in Eq. 7.103 reduces it to

$$f\frac{L'}{d} = \frac{1}{k\text{M}^2}(1 - k\text{M}^2) + \ln k\text{M}^2 \qquad [7.105]$$

Thus fL'/d is a function only of initial Mach number, and, as before, it can be determined from

$$\frac{fL}{d} = \left(\frac{fL'}{d}\right)_{\text{M}_1} - \left(\frac{fL'}{d}\right)_{\text{M}_2}$$

from which L itself can be obtained.

The heat addition is represented by the change in T_0, which can be formulated in terms of the limit state as follows:

$$\frac{T_0}{T_0'} = \frac{T_0}{T}\frac{T}{T'}\frac{T'}{T_0'}$$

Since $T = T'$, this resolves to

$$\frac{T_0}{T_0'} = \frac{1 + [(k-1)/2]\text{M}^2}{1 + [(k-1)/2](1/k)} = \frac{2k}{3k-1}\left(1 + \frac{k-1}{2}\text{M}^2\right) \qquad [7.106]$$

The stagnation-pressure function is

$$\frac{p_0}{p_0'} = \frac{p_0}{p}\frac{p}{p'}\frac{p'}{p_0'} = \left(1 + \frac{k-1}{2}\text{M}^2\right)^{k/(k-1)}\frac{\sqrt{1/k}}{\text{M}}\frac{1}{\{1 + [(k-1)/2](1/k)\}^{k/(k-1)}}$$

$$= \left(\frac{2k}{3k-1}\right)^{k/(k-1)}\frac{\{1 + [(k-1)/2]\text{M}^2\}^{k/(k-1)}}{\sqrt{k}\,\text{M}} \qquad [7.107]$$

Eqs. 7.104 to 7.106 are the functions for isothermal flow with friction at constant area in terms of Mach number. They are not given in the *Gas Tables* and must be calculated.

7.27   *The hydraulic analogy*

Test work with supersonic flow demands high compressor power and precise instrumentation. As an example, just to choke a throat of 1 in.^{2} area with air pumped from the atmosphere requires nearly 30 hp. Furthermore, although the flow can be visualized in certain aspects by optical means relying on the variation of the refractive index of air with density, the technique is not simple. There is, however, an analogy available that is very satisfactory qualitatively and that can be used quantitatively to some extent. It is based on water flow and is thus called the *hydraulic analogy.*

The topic of the flow of water in an open channel, i.e., one with a free surface, is of great interest in the realm of civil engineering, but we shall discuss it here only to make clear the hydraulic analogy.

Consider water, or any liquid, flowing in an open channel of constant cross section. An obstruction in the channel will cause the depth of the water to change. If the flow velocity is less than the *celerity* or velocity of surface-wave propagation (Sect. 4.30), i.e., if the flow is *subcritical*, the presence of the obstruction is signaled upstream, and the flow adjusts itself upstream and around the body as it does in fully confined flow. If, however, the flow velocity is greater than the celerity, i.e., if the flow is *supercritical*, then no message can be transmitted upstream, and the flow must change suddenly at some point. This change is called a *hydraulic jump*, and it can be observed in any stream or gutter during a rainstorm. A typical hydraulic jump is shown in Fig. 7.35(a). The effect is not actually instantaneous, as a rolling, turbulent step occurs.

We can see here the possibility of an analogy with a plane normal shock, which is a discontinuity joining supersonic flow with subsonic flow. However, an analysis is necessary to establish the relationship more firmly.

Fig. 7.35(b) shows the idealized, sudden discontinuity, with liquid at depth y_1 and velocity V_1 changing to depth y_2 and velocity V_2. With an instantaneous change, there is no shear stress due to surface friction, and the

Figure 7.35

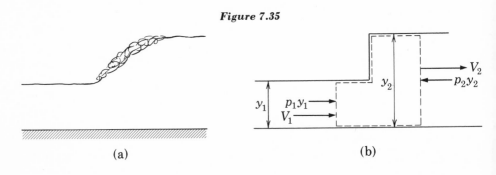

(a)   (b)

only forces are those due to pressure, which, for a unit width of liquid, are p_1y_1 and p_2y_2. Thus the momentum equation for unit width is

$$p_1y_1 - p_2y_2 = \frac{\dot{m}}{g_c}(V_2 - V_1)$$

The pressure forces are those due to hydrostatic pressure, and from Sect. 2.7, these are equivalent to the pressure at the centroid of the area; i.e., $p = \frac{1}{2}\rho g y/g_c$. From continuity, $\dot{m} = y_1 \rho V_1 = y_2 \rho V_2$. With these substitutions and simplification, the momentum equation becomes

$$\frac{y_1^2}{2} - \frac{y_2^2}{2} = \frac{y_1 V_1}{g}(V_2 - V_1) \qquad [7.108]$$

V_2 can be eliminated by means of the continuity relationship $V_2 = V_1 y_1/y_2$; hence

$$y_1^2 - y_2^2 = \frac{2 y_1 V_1^2}{g}\left(\frac{y_1}{y_2} - 1\right) \qquad [7.109]$$

Rearranging and solving for y_2/y_1 yield

$$\frac{y_2}{y_1} = -\frac{1}{2} + \sqrt{\frac{1}{4} + \frac{2 V_1^2}{g y_1}} \qquad [7.110]$$

in which the negative sign in front of the square root has been dropped as giving a physically impossible solution.

Examination of Eq. 7.110 shows that when $V = \sqrt{g y_1}$, the celerity, then $y_2 = y_1$; i.e., there is no change of depth. When $V_1 > \sqrt{g y}$, then $y_2/y_1 > 1$, as was postulated in the beginning. However, the momentum analysis is general in that there is nothing to prevent V_1 from being less than $\sqrt{g y_1}$. If $V_1 < \sqrt{g y_1}$, then $y_2/y_1 < 1$; i.e., there is a decrease of depth. Further investigation will be required to see whether this is possible.

The analysis was based on a momentum relationship with no external shear stress or other force that would immediately lead to the conclusion that energy was being dissipated. However, there may be dissipation of mechanical energy internally, and to determine this, we can use the energy equation with a loss term. From Eq. 4.56,

$$\frac{p_1}{\rho} + \frac{g}{g_c} z_1 + \frac{V_1^2}{2g_c} = \frac{p_2}{\rho} + \frac{g}{g_c} z_2 + \frac{V_2^2}{2g_c} + E_L \qquad [4.56]$$

Rewriting this in the present context as a head-loss equation for h_L, taking points 1 and 2 on the surface where $p_1 = p_2 = 0$ (gage), and substituting y

for z, we have

$$h_L = y_1 - y_2 + \frac{V_1^2 - V_2^2}{2g}$$

From continuity, $V_2^2 = (y_1/y_2)^2/V_1^2$, and V_1^2 can be replaced by its value from Eq. 7.110,

$$\frac{V_1^2}{g} = \frac{y_1 y_2 + y_2^2}{2y_1}$$

With these substitutions,

$$h_L = y_1 - y_2 + \frac{y_1 y_2 + y_2^2}{4y_1}\left(1 - \frac{y_1^2}{y_2^2}\right)$$

which can be rearranged to

$$h_L = \frac{(y_2 - y_1)^3}{4y_1 y_2} \qquad [\textbf{7.111}]$$

Therefore, h_L may have a finite value, but if it does, it must be positive, as a negative value would imply a gain of mechanical energy, which would contravene the second law of thermodynamics. With h_L positive, then $y_2 > y_1$, and so V_1 must be greater than $\sqrt{gy_1}$, or supercritical. A decrease of y_1 with an increase of V_2 is not possible for the conditions of this analysis, a sudden discontinuity. (Note that this does not exclude the possibility of acceleration in a continuous process analogous to nozzle flow for a gas.) We may also note that as $y_2 \to y_1$, $h_L \to 0$; i.e., the hydraulic jump becomes an ideal process as $\Delta y/y \to 0$.

Returning to Eq. 7.109 and dividing it through by $y_1 V_1 = y_2 V_2$, we obtain

$$\frac{y_1^2}{y_1 V_1} - \frac{y_2^2}{y_2 V_2} = \frac{2}{g}(V_2 - V_1)$$

or

$$V_1 V_2 = \frac{g}{2}\frac{y_1 V_2 - y_2 V_1}{V_2 - V_1}$$

With substitution for $V_2 = V_1 y_1/y_2$ on the right-hand side only, this can be reduced to

$$V_1 V_2 = g\frac{y_1 + y_2}{2} = gy_m = c_m^2 \qquad [\textbf{7.112}]$$

i.e., the product of the velocities on either side of the jump is equal to the square of the mean celerity, c_m, equivalent to the mean depth of the two sides.

Replacing V_1 by $V_2 y_2 / y_1$, dividing through by y_2, and rearranging Eq. 7.112 yield

$$\frac{V_2{}^2}{g y_2} = \frac{y_1}{y_2{}^2}\left(\frac{y_1 + y_2}{2}\right)$$

With y_2 replaced by Ky_1, where K must be greater than unity,

$$\frac{V_2{}^2}{g y_2} = \frac{y_1}{K^2 y_1{}^2}\left(\frac{y_1 + Ky_1}{2}\right) = \frac{1}{K^2}\left(\frac{1+K}{2}\right) = \frac{1}{K}\left[\frac{(1/K)+1}{2}\right]$$

With $K > 1$, then both terms on the right-hand side must be less than unity, and hence $V_2{}^2 < g y_2$; i.e., V_2 is less than the celerity. In a hydraulic jump, then, V_1 must be supercritical, and V_2 must be subcritical.

From this analysis and that of Sect. 7.21, it is clear that there is a close qualitative analogy between the *hydraulic jump* and the *plane normal shock*. We may make a comparison thus:

HYDRAULIC JUMP	NORMAL SHOCK
Celerity $c = \sqrt{gy}$	Acoustic velocity $a = \sqrt{g_c k R T}$
Subcritical velocity	Subsonic velocity
Supercritical velocity	Supersonic velocity
Possible only for $V_1 > C_1$	Possible only for $V_1 > a_1$
$V_2 < C_2$	$V_2 < a_2$
$V_1 V_2 = c_m{}^2$	$V_1 V_2 = a^{*2}$
Loss of mechanical energy	Loss of stagnation pressure

This analogy has found considerable use in the representation of supersonic flow and shock by a water flow-table, which consists basically of nothing more than the flow of a shallow sheet of water over an almost horizontal surface. Models placed in the water demonstrate various features of shock waves, both those of normal shock as considered here and those of two-dimensional (oblique) shock as discussed in Chapter 8. A deeper analysis results in a quantitative relationship, but this will not be dealt with here.

It was mentioned previously that the hydraulic jump is common in nature, but it is also invoked intentionally to reduce the velocity of water in a channel. High-velocity flow causes erosion, and supercritical flow may be converted to subcritical flow by suitable obstruction. Thus kinetic energy is transformed into eddies, which are eventually dissipated as internal energy.

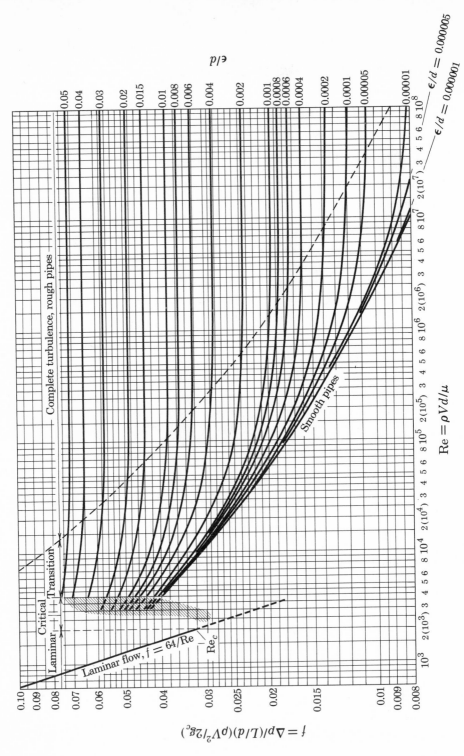

Chart based on the Moody diagram.

312

Problems

7.1. The cross section of a duct is an equilateral triangle of side b. Calculate its equivalent diameter (a) when running full, and (b) when running with liquid to a depth of half the altitude, with one side horizontal in both cases.

7.2. Find the loss of head in ft due to friction for a flow of 1 gal/min of water at 68°F along a 2 in. i.d. smooth pipe 50 ft long.

7.3. Find the maximum rate of flow in gal/min for SAE 30 oil, if the flow must remain laminar, for the following conditions: oil of sp gr 0.90; $\frac{1}{2}$ in. i.d. pipe 6 ft long; allowable pressure loss, 15 in. Hg. Find the corresponding temperature of the oil.

7.4. Find the loss of pressure, in psi and in in. H_2O, due to friction for a flow of 0.3 lb/sec of air at 92°F and 15 psia along a 3 in. i.d. smooth pipe 24 ft long.

7.5. Develop Eq. 7.13a by considering a force balance on an element of fluid.

7.6. Show that for laminar flow between fixed, infinite, parallel plates the average velocity is two-thirds of the maximum velocity.

7.7. Show that for constant-velocity, laminar flow of a liquid down a gradient as in the figure the velocity distribution is given by

$$u = \frac{g}{\nu} \frac{(h^2 - s^2)}{2} \sin \theta$$

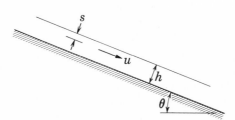

7.8. Show that the velocity distribution for fully developed laminar flow in a horizontal annulus of outer radius r_1 and inner radius r_2 is given by

$$u = -\frac{1}{4\mu_f} \frac{dp}{dx} \left[r_1{}^2 - r^2 - \frac{r_1{}^2 - r_2{}^2}{\ln (r_1/r_2)} \ln \frac{r_1}{r} \right]$$

where x is the flow direction and r is any radius.

7.9. For water at 60°F and for air at the same temperature and atmospheric pressure flowing through a given smooth pipe, what must be the ratio of volume rates of flow in order for the friction factor to be the same?

7.10. If a duct with smooth walls is to be rectangular in cross section and of a given fixed area, find the shape as a ratio of length of the sides a and b in order to give the minimum friction loss per unit length of duct for a given fluid flow rate and state (for laminar flow).

7.11. Calculate the pressure loss for the following conditions, assuming flow is fully developed in all cases:

    a. 45 gal/min of water at 50°F flowing in a smooth 2 in. i.d. pipe 20 ft long. Express answer in ft and psi.

    b. 2 lb/sec of air at 77°F and 1.5 in. Hg flowing in a smooth 3 in. i.d. pipe 8 ft long. Express answer in psi and in. H_2O.

    c. 1500 ft³/min of air at 150°F and 29.2 in. Hg abs flowing in a smooth-walled rectangular duct 15 in. $\times$ 8 in. $\times$ 6 ft long. Express answer in in. oil of sp gr 0.83.

7.12. 50 gal/min of water at 68°F is flowing in a smooth-walled pipe of 2 in. i.d.

    a. Assuming fully developed flow, calculate (a) the thickness of the laminar sublayer, (b) the thickness of the buffer layer, (c) the velocity at the boundary of the laminar sublayer, (d) the velocity at the boundary of the turbulent core, (e) the velocity at the pipe axis, (f) the value of the average velocity, using the friction factor.

    b. Plot to scale the velocity distribution, magnifying the thickness of the laminar sublayer and buffer layer by a factor of 10.

    c. Compare the value of friction factor obtained from the diagram in the text with that computed from an analytical expression.

7.13. For air at atmospheric pressure and at 122°F flowing in a smooth pipe of 1 in. i.d., what must be the flow rate in lb/sec in order for the ratio of average velocity to maximum velocity to have a value of 0.85?

7.14. Find the ratio of the pumping power required for the flow of 6.1 gal/min of water at 60°F for (a) galvanized-iron pipe of 1 in. i.d. and (b) commercial steel pipe of ½ in. i.d.

7.15. Both laminar and turbulent flow are possible in a smooth pipe at a Reynolds number of 3500 under proper conditions. For water at 70°F flowing at this Reynolds number in a smooth pipe of 2 in. i.d. and 40 ft length,

    a. Find the ratio of the average velocity, pressure loss, and wall shear stress in turbulent flow to those in laminar flow.

    b. Find the total pressure loss for turbulent flow.

    c. Find the velocity at the pipe centerline for laminar flow.

7.16. Calculate the momentum and kinetic energy coefficients, k_m and k_e, for laminar flow in a pipe, assuming incompressible flow.

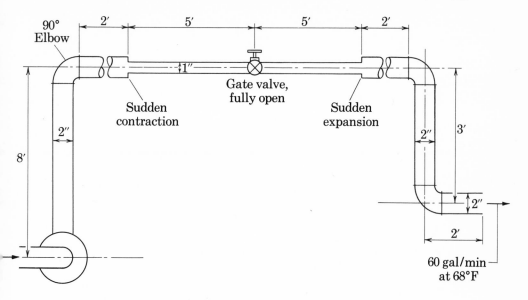

7.17. Calculate the necessary pump total head for the arrangement shown.

7.18. Water flows through the system shown. Neglect all friction losses except those occurring at sections 2 (sudden contraction), 3 (open globe valve), 5 and 6 (90° elbows), and 7 (sudden enlargement). Find pressure p_8.

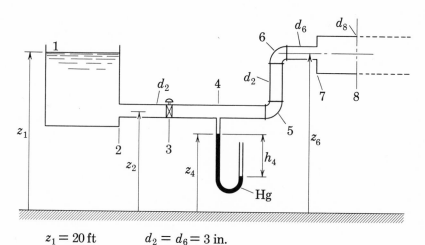

$z_1 = 20$ ft $d_2 = d_6 = 3$ in.
$z_2 = 5$ ft $d_8 = 5$ in.
$z_4 = 2$ ft
$z_6 = 9$ ft $p_1 = p_a = 15$ psia
$h_4 = 0.8$ ft

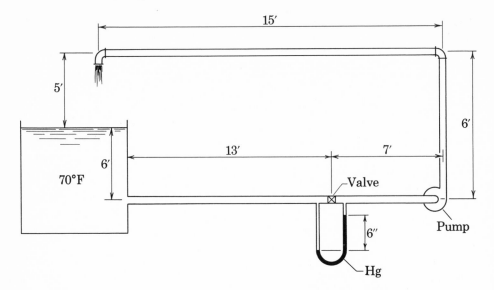

7.19. Water flows from a reservoir through a sharp-edged entry into a piping system as shown. A flow rate of 50 gal/min is maintained by the pump. A new type of valve is being tested for pressure loss, and the mercury-filled manometer indicates 8 in. for its flow rate. The piping is 1 in. i.d. commercial steel.

    a. Find the pressure drop across the valve in feet of water and in psi.
    b. Calculate the loss factor, K, for the valve.
    c. Calculate the static pressure just upstream of the valve.
    d. Find the total head loss through the system neglecting any losses in connection with the pump and, for an ideal pump, compute the necessary power input to the water.

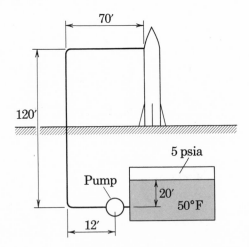

7.20. Gasoline of sp gr 0.7 is pumped from a pressurized underground storage bin to a missile fuel tank as shown. The fuel tank is vented to the atmosphere. A flow rate of 200 gal/min is maintained with a 2 in. flexible line, which is considered as smooth pipe. Compute the total head change across the pump (a) for ideal flow, (b) including the friction loss of the flexible line (assume fully developed flow throughout and neglect minor losses). What is the horsepower required in b if the pump is 70% efficient in transferring energy?

7.21. With p/p_0 as abscissa from 0 to 1.0, plot values of velocity V, Mach number M, density ρ, temperature T, and area A for reversible adiabatic flow in a convergent-divergent nozzle with the following conditions: $t_o = 1350°F$, $p_o = 100$ psia, and unit mass flow rate. Use $k = 1.4$ (it would be about 1.335 for air at this temperature) for convenience in use of tables. Compute the maximum air velocity of the nozzle. Why is it not infinite if $\rho = 0$?

7.22. a. With stations 0–6 as abscissa, plot the pressure p in psia at each station for a pressure $p_6 = 94$ psia.

b. Plot pressure p for the case where $M = 1$ at the throat (station 3), stating values of p_6 and M_6.

c. Compute the mass flow rate for b.

Station	0	1	2	3	4	5	6
Area, in^2	∞	4.00	1.500	1.000	1.2292	1.4583	1.6875

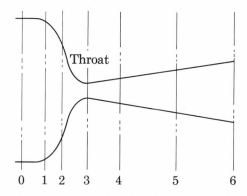

Reversible adiabatic flow of air throughout

Use $c_p = 0.24$ Btu/lb-°F, $p_0 = 100$ psia, $t_0 = 1000$ °R

7.23. Air flows into a pipe at a rate of 2 lb/sec. At station 1 the pressure is 30 psig, the temperature is 1200°F, and the area of the duct is 7 in.^{2}. Taking the flow as reversible and adiabatic, with $c_p = 0.27$ Btu/lb-°F,

a. Find the area of the duct at station 2 if the Mach number required there is 1.2.

b. Find the percentage error involved in calculating the difference between stagnation and static pressures at station 2 as $\rho V^2/2g_c$.

7.24. Steam with stagnation properties of 940°F and 2000 psia is to be supplied to nozzles in the first stage of a large turbine. The total steam flow of 10^6 lb/hr is to be divided among 50 nozzles. The exhaust pressure for the nozzles is to be 800 psia. Assume a reversible adiabatic process. (Steam tables or charts are required for this problem.)

    a. Computing for an adequate number of points, plot p/p_0, T/T_0, and A vs. V in the nozzle.

    b. For the state at the minimum area location, find p/p_0, T/T_0, $\sqrt{kg_cRT}$, and $V\sqrt{kg_cRT}$.

    c. How do the values of p/p_0 and T/T_0 found in b compare with the critical ratios of a perfect gas having the same k?

7.25. A rocket motor has a nozzle that expands 25 lb/sec of combustion gases down to atmospheric pressure (14.7 psia). The gases enter the nozzle with a velocity of 1100 ft/sec, a static temperature of 2940°F, and a static pressure of 105 psia. Assume that flow is isentropic and that the gases have similar properties to those of air at the same conditions. Calculate (a) nozzle entrance area, (b) throat area, (c) discharge area, (d) throat pressure, (e) throat temperature, (f) throat velocity, (g) discharge velocity, and (h) discharge Mach number.

7.26. For a convergent nozzle 2 in. in diameter, at atmospheric pressure (14.7 psia) and atomspheric temperature (65°F),

    a. Calculate the mass flow rate from the nozzle, assuming reversible adiabatic flow.

    b. Calculate the mass flow rate if the pressure in the pipe is reduced to 7 psig, the velocity and temperature remaining the same.

$$\text{Air} \longrightarrow \quad \begin{aligned} t &= 110°F \\ V &= 440 \text{ ft/sec} \\ p &= 28 \text{ psi} \end{aligned}$$

7.27. A new type of torpedo is to be propelled by a rocket motor expanding hot gases through a convergent-divergent nozzle. It is to operate in sea water of sp gr 1.025. To minimize external flow resistance, the exit area of the nozzle is made equal to that of the body. Products of combustion (taken as air) with a total

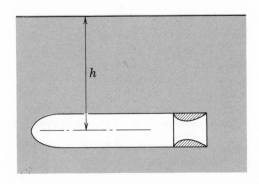

pressure of 200 psia and total temperature of 2000°R flow from the body at a Mach number of 0.4.

    a. For a mass flow rate of 30 lb/sec, calculate the body flow area and the nozzle throat area.

    b. Calculate the operating depth for best performance of the nozzle.

    c. Discuss briefly the essential features of the nozzle flow for operating depths, h, of 15, 50, and 300 ft.

7.28. Plot values of shock functions M_y, p_y/p_x, T_y/T_x, p_{0_y}/p_{0_x} for values of M_x of 1.0, 1.1, 1.2, 1.5, 2.0, 2.5, 3.0, 3.5, and 4.0. Discuss the significance of the characteristics of the values of the pressure functions.

7.29. Show that for the "supersonic Pitot tube" the pressure, p, measured by the tube is given by

$$p = \frac{p_\infty \{[(k+1)/2]M^2\}^{k/(k-1)}}{\{[2k/(k+1)]M^2 - (k-1)/(k+1)\}^{1/(k-1)}}$$

Assume a plane normal shock ahead of the tube, followed by reversible adiabatic flow.

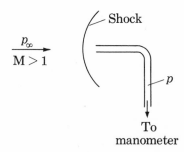

7.30. A flow passage is made up with two successive throats. Air at 100 psia and 540°F flows from a reservoir through the first choked throat of 1 in.² area into an area of 3 in.². Assuming isentropic flow except where shocks exist and assuming that the first throat is *always* choked,

    a. Find the pressure, temperature, velocity, and Mach number here.

    b. What is the area of the second throat if it is to be choked?

    c. If a shock occurs at the 3 in.² point, find the second throat area if it is to be choked.

    d. Find the pressure, temperature, velocity, and Mach number at a point where the area is 3 in.² after the second throat with the shock as in c.

7.31. Air enters a convergent-divergent nozzle from a reservoir in which the pressure is 100 psia and the temperature is 240°F. The exhaust (receiver) pressure initially is 14.7 psia, and the mass flow rate is 5 lb/sec.

    a. Find the nozzle-exit area and Mach number for isentropic flow.

    b. With the same nozzle and flow rate, the receiver pressure is raised until a plane shock occurs at a location where the pressure is 36.09 psia immediately before the shock. Find (a) the Mach number, pressure, and temperature immediately after the shock; (b) the receiver pressure necessary for this state of affairs, assuming isentropic flow to the nozzle exit following the shock; (c) the discharge Mach number.

7.32. For the same nozzle as in Problem 7.31, with the same reservoir conditions and mass flow rate, calculate the Mach number immediately before the shock if the receiver pressure is raised to 80 psia. (Hint: Use a trial-and-error method based on the results of the preceding problem as a guide.)

7.33. Plot values of the Fanno line functions T/T^*, p/p^*, p_0/p_0^*, and fL^*/d for $k = 1.4$ for Mach numbers of 0, 0.1, 0.25, 0.4, 0.5, 0.75, 1.0, 1.2, 1.5, 2.0, and 2.4. Discuss the significance of the forms of the p/p^*, p_0/p_0^*, and fL^*/d curves.

7.34. Air enters a 2 in. diameter smooth pipe at 50 psia and 155°F, with a mass flow rate of 1.75 lb/sec.
    a. Find the Mach number, temperature, and distance from entrance of the section where the pressure is 32 psia, if the process is adiabatic.
    b. Find the maximum length of pipe necessary for a flow of 1.75 lb/sec at the initial conditions.

7.35. Air enters a 3 in. diameter pipe 20 ft long at 3 psig and 80°F, with a velocity of 330 ft/sec.
    a. Calculate the pressure loss due to friction in adiabatic flow, (a) assuming incompressible flow, i.e., constant (inlet) density; (b) assuming incompressible flow but using an arithmetic mean density throughout; (c) using the compressible-flow relationships.
    b. Express the errors in (a) and (b) as percentages of (c).
    c. Evaluate these results for an engineering situation.

7.36. Air flows adiabatically through a ¼ in. diameter smooth brass pipe. At a point where the Mach number is 2, the pressure and temperature are 10 psia and 100°R.
    a. Calculate the length of pipe required for $M = 1$ at exit.
    b. Calculate the length of pipe required for $M = 1$ at exit if a plane normal shock occurs at the $M = 2$ point.
    c. Find the pressure and temperature at exit in a and b.
    d. Sketch accurately both cases on a T-s plane.

7.37. A smooth, open-ended tube of 1 in. diameter and length L is located in and with axis parallel to an airstream flowing at a Mach number of 1.27 with a static pressure of 14.7 psia and a temperature of 60°F. A normal shock occurs right at the entrance to the tube, and the subsonic stream flows through the tube.
    a. Find the length of the tube and the pressure that must be maintained at its downstream end in order to produce choked flow.
    b. Find the Mach number at the downstream end of a tube half the length of that in a.

7.38. For the process of heat transfer to and from air in a duct of constant area without friction, plot values of T_0/T_0^*, T/T^*, p/p^*, and p_0/p_0^* against Mach numbers of 0 to 2.4, choosing suitable scales for each variable.

7.39. The combustion chamber of a ramjet is of constant area, and air enters at a pressure of 64.8 psia, a temperature of 410°F, and a Mach number of 0.25. Fuel is admitted and burnt, the exhaust gas passing from the combustion chamber to a nozzle, where it is expanded to provide thrust. Assuming that the combustion process occurs with $c_p = 0.24$ Btu/lb-°F and $k = 1.4$ throughout, find the maximum temperature to which the air can be heated, the maximum heat addition per lb of air, and the maximum changes in static and stagnation pressures. Neglect friction.

7.40. In a heat exchanger the stagnation temperature of air is raised from 100 to 500°F. The specific mass flow rate is 7.5 lb/sec-ft, and the inlet pressure is 1 atm. Assuming frictionless flow in constant-area tubes, find the initial and final Mach numbers and the pressure drop.

7.41. For the frictionless flow with heat transfer of a perfect gas in a constant-area duct, show that

$$\frac{T_1 - T_2}{T_1} = \frac{(k - 1)^2}{(k + 1)^2}$$

where T_1 is the maximum temperature in the duct and T_2 is the temperature at the condition of maximum entropy.

7.42. For the frictionless flow with heat transfer of an ideal gas in a pipe, show that the ratio of static pressure at the point of maximum static temperature to static pressure at the point of maximum stagnation temperature is $(k + 1)/2$.

7.43. An ideal gas is flowing in a pipe with negligible friction but with heat transfer. For two stations in the pipe at the same temperature, show that $p_1/p_2 = M_2/M_1$.

7.44. Show that for the frictionless flow with heat transfer of an ideal gas with $k = 1.4$ in a pipe the decrease of temperature from the maximum temperature obtainable to the temperature at the choking point is about 2.8% of the maximum temperature.

7.45. Air flows through a frictionless, constant-area duct in which heat may be added or subtracted reversibly. If the air at entrance is at $M = 2$, $p = 10$ psia, and $T = 1000°R$,
    a. Find the maximum heat that may be added.
    b. Find the maximum heat that may be added if the air passes through a plane normal shock before entering the duct.
    c. Calculate the pressure and temperature at the end of the duct for maximum heat addition.
    d. Sketch on a T-s plane.

7.46. A supersonic ramjet has been simplified as follows for analysis. Air flows at 40°F and 10 psia at a Mach number of 4 into a diffuser. A plane normal shock occurs at the entrance. The diffuser has an area ratio of 2. After passing through a combustor, the air has a velocity of 660 ft/sec, a temperature of 2500°F, and a pressure of 60 psia.

a. Find the air pressure, temperature, velocity, and Mach number at the diffuser exit.

b. If the air from the combustor is expanded through a supersonic nozzle, find the exit velocity and mass flow per unit exit area. Assume that $k = 1.4$ and that the flow is frictionless.

7.47. Air at station A in a pipe has a pressure of 40 psig, a temperature of 150°F, and a velocity of 880 ft/sec. It undergoes a series of steady-flow processes as follows: AB, a reversible adiabatic process to a pressure, p_B, of 54 psig; BC, a frictionless, constant-area process to a Mach number of 0.6; CD, an adiabatic, constant-area process with a decrease of temperature of 50°F; DE, a reversible adiabatic process to an atmospheric pressure of 14.7 psia.

a. Sketch the sequence of processes on a T-s diagram.

b. Sketch diagrammatically the apparatus needed to perform the processes.

c. Calculate the discharge Mach number, M_E.

7.48. A ramjet flies at a Mach number of 2.5 through air at $-60°F$ and 3.8 psia as shown in the figure. The nozzle expands the combustion products to freestream pressure. $A_1 = 0.5$ ft², and $A_2 = 1.0$ ft². A normal shock occurs immediately at

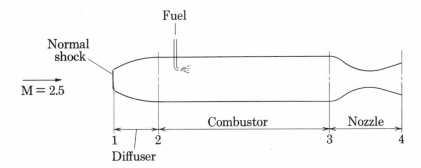

entrance, and the diffuser and nozzle processes are reversible adiabatics. Neglect the mass flow of fuel, and assume that the combustion process is frictionless. The heat added in the combustor is 500 Btu/lb air. Assume $k = 1.4$ and $c_p = 0.24$ throughout. Find (a) temperatures T_2 and T_3, (b) pressures p_2 and p_3, (c) the rate of air induction to the engine, (d) the velocity at the nozzle exit, V_4, and (e) the time rate of change of momentum caused by the engine.

7.49. A ramjet is traveling at a Mach number of 2.5 at an altitude of 50,000 ft. If the recovery factor is taken to be 0.85, calculate the adiabatic-wall temperature for (a) the freestream flow outside the duct and (b) the flow inside the duct at a point where the air has been diffused reversibly and adiabatically to a pressure of 22.6 psia.

7.50. A ramjet flies at sea level with a speed of 1500 mph. At one point in the inlet duct, the air has a Mach number of 0.5. Estimate the temperature indicated by a thermometer at that point, assuming a recovery factor of 0.80.

7.51. An aircraft is flying at a Mach number of 1.3 at 10,000 ft above the earth's surface. The ground-level pressure and temperature are 14.55 psia and 40°F, respectively, and the atmosphere is regarded as isothermal up to 10,000 ft. The aircraft has an entrance duct (leading to the turbojet engine) that diffuses the air reversibly and adiabatically to a Mach number of 0.5 at the inlet to the engine.
  a. Calculate the static pressure at the engine inlet.
  b. Calculate the temperature at the engine inlet as recorded by a thermometer with a recovery factor of 0.9.

7.52. Natural gas, CH_4, is to be pumped through a 60 mile section of 30 in. i.d. standard steel pipe (relative roughness, $\epsilon/d = 0.00015$) at the rate of 7×10^7 std ft^3/day (std ft^3 measured at 70°F and 1 atm). If the gas is to be delivered at 8 psig, find the pressure required at the pump discharge. Assume that flow is isothermal and that CH_4 is a perfect gas with an absolute viscosity at 70°F of 0.027 lb/ft-hr.

7.53. For the isothermal flow of an ideal gas with friction in a pipe, with an initial velocity of flow sufficiently small that the Mach number is negligible, show that the amount of heat added per lb of gas from the initial state at temperature T_i to the choking state is $\frac{1}{2}RT_i$.

7.54. Show by means of an analysis analogous to the Fanno analysis in Sect. 7.22 that the general shape of a Rayleigh process on a T-s diagram is similar to that in Fig. 7.32.

Flow over Immersed Bodies

8.1 *Introduction*

The general characteristics of flow over bodies completely immersed in a
fluid were discussed in Chapter 6, namely, the existence of a *boundary layer*
giving rise to a wake at the rear of a body, and possible large-scale *separation*,
with a much larger wake and greater resistance. We shall now examine these
in some detail, with a view to understanding the behavior and obtaining
quantitative relationships where possible.

For flow in ducts, it was convenient to express the performance in
terms of pressure loss, with friction factor as the variable of interest. For
flow over bodies in an infinite fluid, pressure loss has no meaning, and
although we may be interested in the pressure distribution over a body, the
performance parameter becomes the *force* on the body. The resistance force
is called the *drag* force (or simply the drag), but there may also be a useful
force. In aircraft propulsion, this force supports the body against the action
of gravity and is called the *lift* force (or, again, simply the lift). This same
force can produce mechanical work, as in a turbine, or, when supplied
through mechanical work, give energy to a fluid, as in a pump or compressor.
It may still be called lift in these cases, as it is developed from the same
fluid behavior.

Dimensional analysis provides parameters with which to study such
flow. Assuming that drag, D, and lift, L, are dependent on fluid velocity,
V, a characteristic dimension of the body, d, and the fluid properties of
density, ρ, viscosity, μ, and elasticity, E, then, by the methods of Chapter 5,

we obtain

$$\frac{D \text{ (or } L)}{\rho V^2 d^2} = \phi(\text{Re, M})$$

For flow through ducts, the function of Reynolds number is the friction factor, f. (Note that roughness is not taken into account in this analysis, since it is regarded as having a small-order effect compared to the other quantities.) For flow over bodies, this function, which includes the effect of Mach number as well where applicable, is called the *drag coefficient*, C_D, or *lift coefficient*, C_L. The d^2 in the denominator of the left-hand side of the equation represents area and may be replaced by A. Rearranging the relationships in convenient terms, we may write

$$D = C_D \frac{\rho V^2}{2g_c} A_S \qquad\qquad [8.1]$$

and
$$L = C_L \frac{\rho V^2}{2g_c} A_S \qquad\qquad [8.2]$$

with A_S signifying a surface area, which may be the actual area or a nominal area specified for particular shapes of body. Eqs. 8.1 and 8.2 are the defining equations for drag and lift, with the coefficients C_D and C_L being functions of Reynolds and Mach numbers. The major concern of this chapter is the phenomena associated with C_D and C_L. First the drag process will be discussed, initially for incompressible flow. The results are valid for liquids and for gases at low velocities.

It has been noted that drag may be due to the boundary-layer effect and to separation. That in the former category, due directly to viscous effects and hence tangential stresses, is called the *friction* or *viscous* drag. That in the latter category, although due indirectly to viscosity, is due directly to pressure and hence to normal forces and is called *form* or *pressure* drag. The sum of the two for two-dimensional flow (i.e., with no end effects) is called the *profile* drag. For bodies of revolution, the profile drag is the total drag but for bodies having a finite span, in which end effects occur, the total drag must include another component. Our emphasis will be on profile drag in both its aspects, friction and form. When a body is not one of revolution, we shall nevertheless consider the flow two-dimensional; or, in other words, we shall consider the body as of infinite span except where noted.

It is useful to approach the problem of drag first from the standpoint of purely friction or viscous drag, as exemplified by flow over a flat surface. A flat plate set edgewise and parallel to the flow is subject only to friction drag. This is amenable to an exact analysis, and precise quantitative results can be obtained. The opposite of this is the flow over completely *bluff* bodies, in which the drag is essentially wholly due to pressure. A flat plate

et normal to flow is an example of a bluff body.* Intermediate between
hese extremes are what may be called *rounded* bodies, in which both friction
nd form drag are present, at least over part of the usual range of flow vari-
,bles, although one or the other may be greatly predominant in a certain
egion of flow. Examples of rounded bodies are cylinders and spheres. A
 body having a finite thickness but so shaped as to yield only friction drag
under normal conditions is called a *streamlined* body. We shall begin, then,
vith the boundary layer without separation. Our treatment will be limited
o *incompressible* flow.

8.2   *Boundary-layer thickness*

The term "boundary layer" connotes a layer of relatively small thickness,
but what exactly is the "thickness"? If the boundary layer is envisaged as
, region of retardation of fluid due to viscous effect from the solid surface,
he velocity at the surface is taken as zero (no-slip condition), with suc-
eeding layers outward into the fluid having increasing velocities. Theoreti-
ally the retardation should spread out an infinite distance in a direction
normal to the surface, but actual measurements of velocity show that the
ocal velocity becomes indistinguishable from the freestream velocity in a
very short distance. Nevertheless, some criterion is needed if a definite
limension is required. Commonly, the thickness is defined as the distance
normal to the surface at which the ratio of local velocity to freestream
velocity is some fraction close to unity, e.g., 0.99 to 0.995.

This definition is useful for many practical purposes and for visualizing
he effective thickness of the boundary layer, but it is arbitrary and inconvenient as a parameter for analytical purposes. A unique value for thickness
at a given station is defined by a *displacement thickness*, δ^*, which for incom-
oressible flow is the distance the solid boundary would have to be displaced
f the flow were ideal (no boundary layer) to yield the same total flow rate as
he actual integrated flow rate with a boundary layer. This can be seen
eadily from Fig. 8.1, where U_∞ is the freestream velocity and u is the local
velocity in the boundary layer. δ^* is a distance such that the flow rate given
by the product of the freestream velocity, U_∞, and the distance from δ^*
out to infinity is equal to the integrated flow rate from the solid boundary
o infinity; i.e.,

$$\int_0^\infty u \, dy = \int_{\delta^*}^\infty U_\infty \, dy \qquad [8.3]$$

* The term "bluff bodies" is not exact. It is sometimes applied to bodies that are
ot wholly bluff but that exhibit a considerable separation zone, i.e., what are here
alled "rounded bodies."

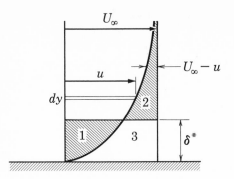

Figure 8.1

The right-hand side of Eq. 8.3 can be written as

$$\int_{\delta^*}^{\infty} U_\infty \, dy = \int_0^\infty U_\infty \, dy - \int_0^{\delta^*} U_\infty \, dy = \int_0^\infty U_\infty \, dy - U\delta^*$$

Thus
$$\int_0^\infty u \, dy = \int_0^\infty U_\infty \, dy - U_\infty \delta^*$$

which on rearrangement becomes

$$U_\infty \delta^* = \int_0^\infty U_\infty \, dy - \int_0^\infty u \, dy = \int_0^\infty (U_\infty - u) \, dy \qquad [8.4]$$

and
$$\delta^* = \frac{1}{U_\infty} \int_0^\infty (U_\infty - u) \, dy = \int_0^\infty \left(1 - \frac{u}{U_\infty}\right) dy \qquad [8.5]$$

Eq. 8.5 is the defining equation for δ^*, which can also be interpreted as the thickness of a stagnated layer that has the same integrated velocity deficit, $U_\infty - u$, as the actual boundary layer; i.e., in Fig. 8.1,

area 1 + area 3 = area 2 + area 3

If u/U_∞ is known as a function of y, Eq. 8.5 can be integrated to give δ^*.

Analogous to the displacement thickness is a *momentum thickness*, θ, associated with the total momentum deficit in the boundary layer. Corresponding to Eq. 8.4 for δ^*, we have

$$U_\infty^2 \theta = \int_0^\infty u(U_\infty - u) \, dy \qquad [8.6]$$

and
$$\theta = \int_0^\infty \frac{u}{U_\infty}\left(1 - \frac{u}{U_\infty}\right) dy \qquad [8.7]$$

It should be noted that in Eq. 8.6, θ is defined in terms of actual flow in the boundary layer ($\int u \, dy$) and the velocity deficit ($U_\infty - u$), whereas the total momentum deficit is equal to the mass-flow deficit ($U_\infty - u$) times the velocity deficit ($U_\infty - u$), i.e., to ($U_\infty - u$)^2. Thus θ is not a distance by which the solid boundary would have to be displaced to yield the same momentum as if the flow were ideal—hence the word "associated" in the sentence introducing θ.

Similarly, an *energy thickness*, δ^{**}, is defined as

$$\delta^{**} = \int_0^\infty \frac{u}{U_\infty}\left(1 - \frac{u^2}{U_\infty{}^2}\right) dy \qquad [8.8]$$

The use of δ^*, θ, and δ^{**} facilitates the formulation of boundary-layer relationships.

8.3 General characteristics of boundary layers

Examination of a boundary layer on a flat surface in a uniform stream of fluid with a very fine Pitot tube or hot-wire anemometer shows that it grows in thickness from the leading edge or starting point, but at a gradual rate, so that only after a very long distance in the flow direction is it thicker than a few inches. For instance, for the flow of atmospheric air along a flat surface at a velocity of 300 mph, the thickness is just under $\frac{1}{4}$ in. at a distance of 1 ft from the leading edge and only about $1\frac{1}{2}$ in. at a distance of 10 ft. This relative thinness, i.e., ratio of thickness normal to the surface to length in the flow direction, is the justification for certain simplifying assumptions made in setting up an analytical expression for boundary-layer behavior.

Because a boundary layer is a flow region in which the effective forces are those due to inertia and viscosity, its behavior and properties are correlated in terms of Reynolds number. The characteristic dimension cannot be a "diameter" as for duct flow but must be a length from the leading edge in the flow direction or in the direction normal to the surface, e.g., δ^* or θ. For the former, Re_x denotes the Reynolds number at distance x from the leading edge, and Re_L signifies the value for the total surface length, L.

The boundary layer grows more slowly in the initial stages than farther along the surface, and there is a small local region between the two regions that is unstable in behavior. The hot-wire anemometer reveals that at first the boundary layer is *laminar* in character even though the main flow may be turbulent, that the unstable region is one of *transition*, and that the boundary layer is *turbulent* from there on downstream.

Because the behavior of the boundary layer, and in particular the value of the drag coefficient, differs so markedly according to whether the flow in the layer is laminar or turbulent, the nature of the transition region is of great interest and importance, although very complex.

The basic problem of transition is one of *stability*, i.e., the growth or decay of an initially small disturbance superposed on laminar flow. At sufficiently low boundary-layer Reynolds numbers, Re_x, a disturbance is damped out very quickly, and the flow continues to be laminar. At high Reynolds numbers, a disturbance causes the boundary layer to be "tripped" to turbulent flow almost instantaneously. In between these values is a region in which the flow at a given location may oscillate between being laminar and being turbulent, the oscillation giving rise to a transition *zone*.

It has been shown that in two-dimensional flat-plate flow, turbulence does not develop along a continuous front. Rather, spots develop in random fashion in space and time, increasing in number downstream and spreading out to form a "fully developed" turbulent boundary layer. In general, this instability is dependent on the previous history of the flow, the degree of turbulence in the approach stream, the geometry of the surface and hence the local pressure gradient, the roughness of the surface, the degree of compressibility (Mach number), heating or cooling of the surface, and so forth. Therefore, it is difficult to predict accurately a *critical* Reynolds number for transition, Re_c. For adiabatic flow over a smooth surface with a negligible pressure gradient, a value of $\mathrm{Re}_c = \rho V x_c/\mu$ of 3×10^5 is reasonable for conditions where turbulence is present, and a value of 3×10^6 is reasonable for exceptionally favorable conditions. Here x_c is the distance from the leading edge to the transition point. Because drag is greater for turbulent flow than for laminar flow, the lower value of Re_c is a conservative one for design work in the absence of exact information. As an example, with atmospheric air at 300 mph, x_c is only a little over 1 in. For the flow of 50°F water at 5 ft/sec, $x_c \approx 10$ in. Remembering that these values are for the lower critical Reynolds number, we see that for a surface of some length the laminar-flow region may or may not be of significance compared with the turbulent-flow region, but it is always necessary to check the critical length before making any calculations.

A schematic picture of boundary-layer flow is given in Fig. 8.2, in which the thickness of the layer has been greatly exaggerated for clarity of presentation. Initially uniform, the stream forms a laminar boundary layer that grows in thickness to the transition region at a nominal distance, x_c, from the leading edge. The thickness increases in this region, beyond which the boundary layer becomes turbulent, growing in thickness more rapidly than in the laminar region.

The problem then is divided into three parts: the laminar layer, the transition zone, and the turbulent layer. Analysis of the laminar layer is most accurate because the physical behavior in it can be precisely stated in terms of a readily calculable shear stress, $\tau = \mu \, du/dy$, although a closed solution for all but simple geometrics may lead to mathematical complications. The transition zone is the most complex, and no attempt will be made to deal with it here. For the turbulent layer, no exact physical picture can be drawn that permits a precise solution, and recourse must be made to empiricism as in the case of pipe flow. Nevertheless, it is possible to develop

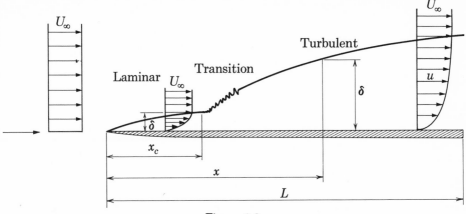

Figure 8.2

engineering solutions that allow design information to be formulated for a number of practical situations. Our greatest gap in knowledge is that to enable us to predict the behavior with severe adverse pressure gradients and to estimate the onset of separation of the boundary layer.

8.4 *Laminar boundary layer—general*

We shall start off the development of relationships for the laminar boundary layer with a very rough estimate of behavior that is useful as a guide to more precise formulations. This will be followed by the exact analysis for a particular case, that of flow over a flat plate with no pressure gradient. Even this presents mathematical difficulties that we shall not pursue in detail, but it is worth doing as a typical example of the class of "exact" solutions and will serve as the standard for a less precise relationship that can be applied more widely. Finally this more general approximate method will be developed and compared with the exact solution for the case of the flat plate. Only *incompressible* flow will be studied, but the results are applicable without great error to gas flow up to medium subsonic Mach numbers, and qualitatively much can be carried over to compressible flow.

For the rough estimate, suppose that the element of fluid shown in Fig. 8.3 is part of a two-dimensional laminar boundary layer. With no pressure gradient, the forces acting on the element are those of viscosity and inertia. For the viscous force, F_v,

$$F_v = \left(\tau + \frac{d\tau}{dy} \Delta y - \tau \right) \Delta x \, \Delta z = \frac{d\tau}{dy} \Delta x \, \Delta y \, \Delta z$$

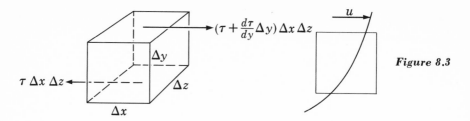

Figure 8.3

and with $\tau = \mu \, du/dy$ and with the assumption of constant viscosity,

$$F_v = \mu \frac{d^2u}{dy^2} \, \Delta x \, \Delta y \, \Delta z$$

For the inertia force, F_i, with steady flow

$$F_i = M a_x = M \frac{Du}{Dt} = M u \frac{du}{dx}$$

and with the mass $M = \rho \, \Delta x \, \Delta y \, \Delta z$,

$$F_i = \rho u \frac{du}{dx} \, \Delta x \, \Delta y \, \Delta z$$

If now we make the assumption that in the boundary layer the viscous and inertia effects are proportional, i.e., $F_v \propto F_i$, then, with volume $\Delta x \, \Delta y \, \Delta z$ canceling out, we have

$$\mu \frac{d^2u}{dy^2} \propto \rho u \frac{du}{dx} \qquad [8.9]$$

It is reasonable to suppose that the velocity gradient across the boundary layer, du/dy, is proportional to the total change of velocity, $U_\infty - 0 = U_\infty$, divided by the total boundary-layer thickness, δ. Hence du/dy is of the order of U_∞/δ, and $d^2u/dy^2 = (d/dy) \, (du/dy)$ is of the order of U_∞/δ^2. Likewise, the velocity gradient in the flow direction, du/dx, is proportional to U_∞/x, where x is the total distance downstream from the leading edge. Hence $u \, du/dx$ is of the order of U_∞^2/x. Substituting these values in Eq. 8.9 gives us

$$\frac{\mu U_\infty}{\delta^2} \propto \frac{\rho U_\infty^2}{x}$$

and

$$\delta \propto \sqrt{\frac{\mu x}{\rho U_\infty}} \qquad [8.10]$$

i.e., for a given fluid and freestream velocity, the boundary-layer thickness increases with the square root of distance from the leading edge. For an ideal fluid ($\mu = 0$), $\delta = 0$, as it should.

Eq. 8.10 may be rearranged as

$$\frac{\delta}{x} \propto \sqrt{\frac{\mu}{\rho U_\infty x}} = \sqrt{\frac{1}{\mathrm{Re}_x}} \qquad [8.11]$$

i.e., the relative thickness, δ/x, is proportional to the reciprocal of the square root of the boundary-layer Reynolds number, Re_x. Although this is obviously a rough estimate, we shall see that the square-root relationship is correct, that the necessary constant for an exact relationship is 5.0, and that this analysis is justified. It is really a dimensional analysis with the added assumption that viscous and inertia effects are approximately equal.*

8.5   *Laminar boundary layer—the exact solution for flat-plate flow*

The starting point for a laminar-flow problem is in general the Navier-Stokes equations (Sect. 4.33). However, we obtained a simplified form applicable to steady, boundary-layer flow in Sect. 6.4, the result being Eq. 6.1,

$$-\frac{1}{\rho}\frac{\partial p}{\partial x} + \frac{\mu}{\rho g_c}\frac{\partial^2 u}{\partial y^2} = \frac{1}{g_c}\left(u\frac{\partial u}{\partial x} + v\frac{\partial u}{\partial y} + \frac{\partial u}{\partial t}\right) \qquad [6.1]$$

This equation expresses the relationship of pressure forces and viscous forces in the x direction to acceleration in the x direction for incompressible flow. For steady flow in the absence of a pressure gradient, which is the case for flow over a semi-infinite flat plate in a uniform stream, the first and last terms disappear, and so

$$u\frac{\partial u}{\partial x} + v\frac{\partial u}{\partial y} = \nu\frac{\partial^2 u}{\partial y^2} \qquad [8.12]$$

Continuity must also be satisfied, and for this case of incompressible flow, the general relationship reduces to

$$\frac{\partial u}{\partial x} + \frac{\partial v}{\partial y} = 0 \qquad [8.13]$$

Eqs. 8.12 and 8.13 then represent the boundary-layer flow. The boundary conditions that must be met are these:

at the surface, $y = 0$ $u = 0$ $v = 0$

at $y = \infty$, $u = U_\infty$ (freestream velocity) $[8.14]$

The problem, then, is the solution of the two simultaneous partial-differential equations, Eqs. 8.12 and 8.13, in conjunction with the boundary

---

* Note that this result can be obtained directly by the method of vector dimensional analysis mentioned in Sect. 5.6, with the δ direction as L_y and the flow direction, x, as L_x.

conditions, Eq. 8.14, one of the equations being nonlinear. The necessary steps are (1) to reduce Eqs. 8.12 and 8.13 to one equation, (2) to reduce the resulting partial-differential equation to an ordinary differential equation, and (3) to solve this equation. We shall discuss the first two steps, because they involve some fluid-flow concepts that we have developed and because they are representative of a method for handling many boundary-layer problems. We shall assume the result of the last step, because the mathematics is lengthy and does not yield a closed solution, so that a numerical procedure is required.

To combine the two equations, which are functions of u, v, x, and y, we utilize the stream function, ψ, which was used in Chapter 3 for just such a simplification of a flow problem. From Eq. 3.11, we have

$$u = \frac{\partial \psi}{\partial y} \qquad \text{and} \qquad v = -\frac{\partial \psi}{\partial x} \qquad\qquad [3.11]$$

Substituting these in Eq. 8.13 and the result in Eq. 8.12 yields

$$\frac{\partial \psi}{\partial y}\frac{\partial^2 \psi}{\partial x \, \partial y} - \frac{\partial \psi}{\partial x}\frac{\partial^2 \psi}{\partial y^2} = \nu \frac{\partial^3 \psi}{\partial y^3} \qquad\qquad [8.15]$$

i.e., introduction of the stream function satisfies Eq. 8.13 by *definition* and reduces the unknowns in Eq. 8.12 by one, since Eq. 8.15 has only ψ, x, and y. However, Eq. 8.15 is a third-order equation.

We now seek to state Eq. 8.15 in terms of a new independent variable, a function of x and y, so that x and y do not appear explicitly but only in the form of this function. To do this, we make the very reasonable assumption that, for a given U_∞, the velocity distributions across the boundary layer at varying values of x are of similar form, i.e., that they can be made identical by means of suitable scale factors for u and y. It was noted in the previous section that scale factors for u and y are U_∞ and δ, respectively, with u giving the same scale factor, U_∞, at all values of x and with y giving a varying factor, δ, that itself increases with x. Thus the similarity of distributions can be expressed as

$$\frac{u}{U_\infty} = \phi_1\left(\frac{y}{\delta}\right) = \phi_1(\zeta)$$

where $\zeta = y/\delta$ and ϕ_1 is an unknown function. Furthermore, in the previous section it was found that $\delta/x \propto 1/\sqrt{\text{Re}}$ or $\delta \propto \sqrt{\nu x/U_\infty}$. Hence

$$\phi_1(\zeta) = \phi_1\left(\frac{y}{\delta}\right) = \phi_2\left(y\sqrt{\frac{U_\infty}{\nu x}}\right) = \phi_2(\eta)$$

where

$$\eta = y\sqrt{\frac{U_\infty}{\nu x}} \qquad\qquad [8.16]$$

For any given flow, U_∞ and ν are fixed, and so the relationship of x and y is $y/\sqrt{x}$. Another way of describing η is to say that it represents the relationship of x and y, with U_∞ and ν included to make a dimensionless group.

Now it is necessary to relate η to the stream function, ψ. Since η is a function of x and y, and ψ is a function of x and y, then ψ is a function of η, but a different one from $\phi_2(\eta)$. It is again convenient to use a dimensionless form, and from inspection (or the method of vector dimensional analysis), we can write for the function of η,

$$\frac{\psi}{\sqrt{\nu x U_\infty}} = f(\eta)$$

or
$$\psi = \sqrt{\nu x U_\infty}\, f(\eta) \qquad [8.17]$$

The various derivatives of ψ can be obtained from Eq. 8.17 and substituted into Eq. 8.15, or, because the formulation in terms of ψ is equivalent to the inclusion of continuity, u and v and their derivatives can be obtained from ψ in Eq. 8.17 and substituted into the original equation, Eq. 8.12.

The values are as follows, with $(d/d\eta)[f(\eta)]$ denoted as $f'(\eta)$, $(d/d\eta)[f'(\eta)]$ as $f''(\eta)$, and $(d/d\eta)[f''(\eta)]$ as $f'''(\eta)$:

$$u = \frac{\partial\psi}{\partial y} = \frac{d\psi}{d\eta}\frac{\partial\eta}{\partial y} = \frac{df(\eta)}{d\eta}\sqrt{\nu x U_\infty}\sqrt{\frac{U_\infty}{\nu x}} = U_\infty f'(\eta) \qquad [1]$$

$$\frac{\partial u}{\partial x} = \frac{\partial^2\psi}{\partial x\,\partial y} = U_\infty\frac{\partial}{\partial x}[f'(\eta)] = U_\infty\frac{df'(\eta)}{d\eta}\frac{\partial\eta}{\partial x} = U_\infty f''(\eta)\frac{\partial\eta}{\partial x} \qquad [2]$$

and
$$\frac{\partial\eta}{\partial x} = y\sqrt{\frac{U_\infty}{\nu}}\left(-\frac{1}{2x\sqrt{x}}\right) = -\frac{1}{2}y\sqrt{\frac{U_\infty}{\nu x}}\left(\frac{1}{x}\right) = -\frac{\eta}{2x}$$

Hence
$$\frac{\partial u}{\partial x} = U_\infty f''(\eta)\left(-\frac{\eta}{2x}\right) = -\frac{U_\infty \eta f''(\eta)}{2x}$$

$$v = -\frac{\partial\psi}{\partial x} = -\frac{\partial}{\partial x}[\sqrt{\nu x U_\infty}\, f(\eta)]$$

$$= -\left[\sqrt{\nu x U_\infty}\frac{df(\eta)}{d\eta}\frac{\partial\eta}{\partial x} + f(\eta)\frac{\partial}{\partial x}\sqrt{\nu x U_\infty}\right]$$

$$= -\left[\sqrt{\nu x U_\infty}\, f'(\eta)\left(-\frac{\eta}{2x}\right) + f(\eta)\frac{1}{2}\sqrt{\frac{\nu U_\infty}{x}}\right]$$

$$= \frac{1}{2}\left[\eta f'(\eta) - f(\eta)\right]\sqrt{\frac{\nu U_\infty}{x}} \qquad [3]$$

$$\frac{\partial u}{\partial y} = \frac{\partial^2\psi}{\partial y^2} = U_\infty\frac{\partial}{\partial y}[f'(\eta)] = U_\infty\frac{df'(\eta)}{d\eta}\frac{\partial\eta}{\partial y} = U_\infty f''(\eta)\sqrt{\frac{U_\infty}{\nu x}} = U_\infty\sqrt{\frac{U_\infty}{\nu x}}f''(\eta) \qquad [4]$$

$$\frac{\partial^2 u}{\partial y^2} = \frac{\partial^3\psi}{\partial y^3} = U_\infty\sqrt{\frac{U_\infty}{\nu x}}\frac{df''(\eta)}{d\eta}\frac{\partial\eta}{\partial y} = U_\infty\sqrt{\frac{U_\infty}{\nu x}}f'''(\eta)\sqrt{\frac{U_\infty}{\nu x}} = \frac{U_\infty{}^2}{\nu x}f'''(\eta) \qquad [5]$$

Substitution of values 1, 2, 3, 4, and 5 into either Eq. 8.12 or Eq. 8.15, cancellation, and rearrangement yield

$$f(\eta)f''(\eta) + 2f'''(\eta) = 0 \qquad [8.18]$$

which is a third-order ordinary differential equation. The boundary conditions of Eq. 8.14 in the new variable, η, are

at $\eta = 0$, $\qquad\qquad f(\eta) = 0 \quad$ and $\quad f'(\eta) = 0$

at $\eta = \infty$, $\qquad\qquad\qquad f'(\eta) = 1 \qquad\qquad [8.19]$

Several workers have solved Eq. 8.18, beginning with Blasius[*] in 1908. The most accurate solution is that of Howarth,[†] in 1938. Some of his values for $f(\eta)$, $f'(\eta)$, and $f''(\eta)$ appear in Table 8.1.

Table 8.1

$\eta = y\sqrt{\dfrac{U_\infty}{\nu x}}$	$f(\eta)$	$f'(\eta) = \dfrac{u}{U_\infty}$	$f''(\eta) = y\,\dfrac{\partial u/\partial y}{\eta U_\infty}$
0	0	0	0.33206
0.4	0.02656	0.13277	0.33147
0.8	0.10611	0.26471	0.32739
1.2	0.23795	0.39378	0.31659
1.6	0.42032	0.51676	0.29667
2.0	0.65003	0.62977	0.26675
2.4	0.92230	0.72899	0.22809
2.8	1.23099	0.81152	0.18401
3.2	1.56911	0.87609	0.13913
3.6	1.92954	0.92333	0.09809
4.0	2.30576	0.95552	0.06424
4.4	2.69238	0.97587	0.03897
4.8	3.08534	0.98779	0.02187
5.0	3.28329	0.99155	0.01591
5.2	3.48189	0.99425	0.01134
5.6	3.88031	0.99784	0.00543
6.0	4.27964	0.99898	0.00240
6.4	4.67938	0.99961	0.00098
6.8	5.07928	0.99987	0.00037
7.2	5.47925	0.99996	0.00013
7.6	5.87924	0.99999	0.00004
8.0	6.27923	1.00000	0.00001
8.4	6.67923	1.00000	0.00000
8.8	7.07923	1.00000	0.00000

[*] H. Blasius, *Z. Math. u. Phys.*, **56** (1), 1 (1908), trans. as *N.A.C.A. Tech. Mem.* No. 1256 (1950).

[†] L. Howarth, *Proc. Roy. Soc. London, Ser. A*, **164,** 547 (1938).

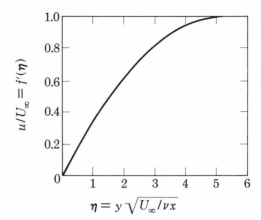

Figure 8.4

From relationship 1 the dimensionless velocity distribution, u/U_∞, is given by $f'(\eta)$. This is plotted against η in Fig. 8.4, which shows the velocity distribution across the boundary layer at any given distance, x, downstream. It is seen that u/U_∞ approaches unity, although it does so asymptotically. Theoretically, the boundary extends to infinity, and thus $u/U_\infty \to 1$ only as $y \to \infty$. However, recalling the discussion in Sect. 8.2, we may arbitrarily define δ at a certain value of u/U_∞ close to unity. A value commonly accepted is $u/U_\infty = 0.99$, for which $\eta \approx 5$. Hence

$$y|_{u/U_\infty = 0.99} = \delta = 5.0\sqrt{\frac{\nu x}{U_\infty}}$$

or
$$\frac{x}{\delta} = \frac{5.0}{\sqrt{U_\infty x / \nu}} = \frac{5.0}{\sqrt{\mathrm{Re}_x}} \qquad [8.20]$$

The more useful displacement thickness, δ^*, can also be computed. Only the result is given here, as

$$\frac{\delta^*}{x} = \frac{1.73}{\sqrt{\mathrm{Re}_x}} \qquad [8.21]$$

The y component of velocity, v, is given by relationship 3,

$$v = \frac{1}{2}\sqrt{\frac{\nu U_\infty}{x}}\,[\eta f'(\eta) - f(\eta)]$$

and can be calculated from Table 8.1. The term in brackets approaches a limit of 1.73 as $\eta \to \infty$, and thus

$$\left.\frac{v}{U_\infty}\right|_{y \to \infty} = \frac{0.865}{\sqrt{\mathrm{Re}_x}} \qquad [8.22]$$

There is, then, a finite value of v at the outer edge of the boundary layer, and this is due to displacement of the fluid outward from the wall as the boundary-layer thickness increases. The edge of the boundary layer as described by Eq. 8.20 is *not* a streamline, for some flow crosses it transversely, although v is very small.

Having obtained a solution for the velocity distribution in the boundary layer, we can now determine the skin friction or drag, because for laminar flow, $\tau = \mu \, du/dy$. The shear stress of the wall is then

$$\tau_0 = \frac{\mu}{g_c} \frac{\partial u}{\partial y} \bigg|_{y=0}$$

From relationship 4,

$$\frac{\partial u}{\partial y} = U_\infty \sqrt{\frac{U_\infty}{\nu x}} f''(\eta)$$

From Table 8.1, the value of $f''(\eta)$ at $y = 0 = \eta$ is 0.332; hence

$$\tau_0 = 0.332 \frac{\mu}{g_c} U_\infty \sqrt{\frac{U_\infty}{\nu x}} \qquad [8.23]$$

Dividing both sides by $\rho U_\infty{}^2/2g_c$ yields a *friction coefficient*, c_f (cf. Eq. 7.4a, for the friction coefficient for pipe flow),

$$c_f = \frac{\tau_0}{\rho U_\infty{}^2/2g_c} = \frac{0.332\mu U_\infty}{\rho U_\infty{}^2/2} \sqrt{\frac{U_\infty}{\nu x}} = 0.664 \sqrt{\frac{\mu}{\rho U_\infty x}} = \frac{0.664}{\sqrt{\mathrm{Re}_x}} \qquad [8.24]$$

c_f is a *local* friction coefficient at a distance x for flow over a flat plate and is inversely proportional to the square root of the boundary-layer Reynolds number in terms of x.

The friction force or drag on the whole plate of length L and unit width is obtained by integration of the shear stress from 0 to L,

$$D = \int_A \tau_0 \, dA = \int_0^L \tau_0 \, dx$$

and substitution for τ_0 from Eq. 8.23,

$$D = 0.332 \frac{\mu}{g_c} U_\infty \sqrt{\frac{U_\infty}{\nu}} \int_0^L \frac{dx}{\sqrt{x}} = 0.664 \frac{U_\infty}{g_c} \sqrt{\rho \mu U_\infty L} \qquad [8.25]$$

From Eq. 8.1, the drag coefficient, C_D, *per unit width* is

$$C_D = \frac{D}{\rho U_\infty{}^2 A/2g_c} = \frac{D}{\rho U_\infty{}^2 L/2g_c} = \frac{0.664 U_\infty \sqrt{\rho \mu U_\infty L}}{\rho U_\infty{}^2 L/2}$$

$$= 1.328 \sqrt{\frac{\mu}{\rho U_\infty L}} = \frac{1.328}{\sqrt{\mathrm{Re}_L}} \qquad [8.26]$$

which is twice the *local* friction coefficient. C_D is the drag coefficient per unit width for *one side* of the flat plate. It may also be called the average friction coefficient for flow over a flat surface and denoted by C_F.

This analysis of the laminar boundary layer over a flat plate with no pressure gradient has yielded the velocity distribution and values of friction coefficient or drag. The calculated results agree very well with experimental results, thus vindicating the assumptions made at the outset. The method may be extended to more difficult cases involving a pressure gradient, but the mathematical solutions become more complex, and there are definite limits to application. Therefore, it is necessary to turn to a less precise but more general method in which wider assumptions are made. One advantage of the exact solution is that it provides a standard with which approximate methods may be compared.

8.6   *The momentum-integral method of boundary-layer analysis*

The momentum-integral method, originated by von Karman, is based on the momentum theorem of fluid mechanics (Sect. 4.12) applied to the boundary layer. It will be derived in a general form applicable to laminar or turbulent flow with a pressure gradient and then adapted for particular situations. The freestream velocity outside the boundary layer is denoted by U_1 rather than U_∞ here, as for the general case with a pressure gradient it may vary with x, i.e., $U_1 = U_1(x)$, whereas earlier U_∞ = constant.

Consider the element of fluid in the boundary layer shown in Fig. 8.5, with the control volume bounded by the surface element AE, the edge of the boundary layer, BC, and two parallel planes, AB and CE, of unit depth (transverse to the diagram) a small distance, Δx, apart. There is no variation

Figure 8.5

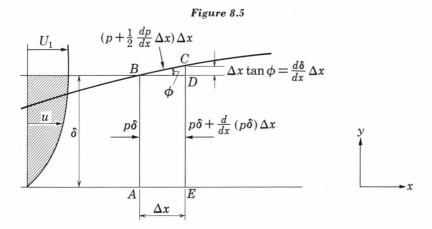

of any quantity in the z direction. The pressure may vary in the flow direction but is considered uniform in any plane in the y direction,

The forces acting on the element in the x direction are due to pressure on AB, CE, and BC and to shear stress along AE. Thus

on AB, $F_x = p\delta$

on CE, $F_x = -\left[p\delta + \dfrac{d}{dx} (p\delta) \, \Delta x \right]$

on BC, $F_x = \left(p + \dfrac{1}{2} \dfrac{dp}{dx} \Delta x \right) \Delta x \sin \phi = \left(p + \dfrac{1}{2} \dfrac{dp}{dx} \Delta x \right) \dfrac{d\delta}{dx} \Delta x$

where $\tan \phi \approx \sin \phi$ and $p + (\frac{1}{2} \, dp/dx) \, \Delta x$ is the average pressure between B and C,

on AE, $F_x = \tau_0 \, \Delta x$

Therefore,

$$\Sigma F_x = p\delta + \left(p + \frac{1}{2} \frac{dp}{dx} \Delta x \right) \frac{d\delta}{dx} \Delta x - \left[p + \frac{d}{dx} (p\delta) \, \Delta x \right] - \tau_0 \, \Delta x$$

$$= \frac{1}{2} \frac{dp}{dx} \frac{d\delta}{dx} (\Delta x)^2 - \delta \frac{dp}{dx} \Delta x - \tau_0 \, \Delta x$$

The first term on the right may be dropped as a second-order term in $(\Delta x)^2$; hence

$$\Sigma F_x = - \left(\tau_0 + \delta \frac{dp}{dx} \right) \Delta x \qquad [8.27]$$

By the momentum theorem, F_x is equal to the rate of change of momentum in the control volume plus the net flux of momentum across the control surface. The former is

$$\frac{d}{dt} \int_R (\rho \, dR) \, u = \frac{d}{dt} \left(\int_0^\delta \rho u \, dy \right) \Delta x \qquad [8.28]$$

The net flux of momentum is the algebraic sum of that across AB, that across CE, and that across BC, thus:

across AB, $\displaystyle \int_0^\delta \rho u^2 \, dy$ $\qquad\qquad\qquad\qquad\qquad\quad\;\; [8.29]$

across CE, $\displaystyle \int_0^\delta \rho u^2 \, dy + \frac{d}{dx} \left(\int_0^\delta \rho u^2 \, dy \right) \Delta x$ $\qquad [8.30]$

across BC,   Here the momentum flux is the product of a certain mass flow rate and the velocity, U_1, since all of the fluid enters from outside the boundary layer. By continuity, the mass rate of flow must be the difference between that leaving CE and that entering AB; i.e.,

$$\frac{d}{dx}\left(\int_0^\delta \rho u\, dy\right)\Delta x$$

Hence, the momentum flux is

$$U_1\frac{d}{dx}\left(\int_0^\delta \rho u\, dy\right)\Delta x \qquad [8.31]$$

Equating the net force, from Eq. 8.27, to the sum of the momentum terms, Eqs. 8.28, 8.29, 8.30, and 8.31, gives us

$$-\left(\tau_0 + \delta\frac{dp}{dx}\right)\Delta x = \frac{d}{dt}\left(\int_0^\delta \rho u\, dy\right)\Delta x + \int_0^\delta \rho u^2\, dy + \frac{d}{dx}\left(\int_0^\delta \rho u^2\, dy\right)\Delta x$$

$$-\int_0^\delta \rho u^2\, dy - U_1\frac{d}{dx}\left(\int_0^\delta \rho u\, dy\right)\Delta x$$

or $\quad -\tau_0 - \delta\frac{dp}{dx} = \frac{d}{dt}\int_0^\delta \rho u\, dy + \frac{d}{dx}\int_0^\delta \rho u^2\, dy - U_1\frac{d}{dx}\int_0^\delta \rho u\, dy \quad [8.32]$

This is a general form of the momentum-integral relation for unsteady, compressible flow in the boundary layer, laminar or turbulent. For steady, incompressible flow (with g_c introduced for our system of units), it reduces to

$$\tau_0 = -\delta\frac{dp}{dx} - \frac{\rho}{g_c}\frac{d}{dx}\int_0^\delta u^2\, dy + \rho\frac{U_1}{g_c}\frac{d}{dx}\int_0^\delta u\, dy \qquad [8.33]$$

The pressure-gradient term can be put in terms of velocity by means of the Euler equation, because the flow outside the boundary layer is considered as ideal. From the Euler equation (with no body force),

$$\frac{dp}{\rho} + \frac{U_1\, dU_1}{g_c} = 0$$

or

$$\frac{dp}{dx} = -\frac{\rho U_1}{g_c}\frac{dU_1}{dx}$$

Integrating with respect to y from 0 to δ (note that dp/dx and hence dU_1/dx are constant with respect to y) yields

$$\int_0^\delta \frac{dp}{dx}\, dy = \delta\frac{dp}{dx} = -\frac{\rho}{g_c}\frac{dU_1}{dx}U_1\int_0^\delta dy$$

The last term of Eq. 8.33 may be written as

$$\rho\frac{U_1}{g_c}\frac{d}{dx}\int_0^\delta u\, dy = \frac{\rho}{g_c}\frac{d}{dx}\left(U_1\int_0^\delta u\, dy\right) - \frac{\rho}{g_c}\frac{dU_1}{dx}\int_0^\delta u\, dy$$

$$= \frac{\rho}{g_c}\frac{d}{dx}\int_0^\delta U_1 u\, dy - \frac{\rho}{g_c}\frac{dU_1}{dx}\int_0^\delta u\, dy$$

Thus Eq. 8.33 becomes

$$\tau_0 = \frac{\rho}{g_c} \frac{dU_1}{dx} \int_0^\delta U_1 \, dy - \frac{\rho}{g_c} \frac{d}{dx} \int_0^\delta u^2 \, dy + \frac{\rho}{g_c} \frac{d}{dx} \int_0^\delta U_1 u \, dy - \frac{\rho}{g_c} \frac{dU_1}{dx} \int_0^\delta u \, dy$$

Grouping terms in d/dx and dU_1/dx, we obtain

$$\tau_0 = \frac{\rho}{g_c} \left[\frac{d}{dx} \int_0^\delta (U_1 u - u^2) \, dy + \frac{dU_1}{dx} \int_0^\delta (U_1 - u) \, dy \right]$$

Recalling the expressions for displacement thickness, δ^* (Eq. 8.5), and momentum thickness, θ (Eq. 8.7), we write this as

$$\tau_0 = \frac{\rho}{g_c} \left[\frac{d}{dx} (U_1^2 \theta) + U_1 \frac{dU_1}{dx} \delta^* \right] \qquad [8.34]$$

(It may be noted that the use of δ^* and θ was occasioned by the two integrals in the preceding equation, which later were interpreted physically; hence the particular form for θ discussed in Sect. 8.2.)

Eq. 8.34 is a compact form of the momentum equation for steady, incompressible flow in the boundary layer, laminar or turbulent, with a pressure gradient in the flow direction. Its usefulness lies in the fact that, if a velocity distribution is known or assumed, then δ^* and θ can be computed, and the wall shear stress found.

8.7 Laminar boundary layer—the momentum-integral equation for flat-plate flow

For flow over a flat plate, i.e., with no pressure gradient, $U_1 = \text{constant} = U_\infty$, $dU_1/dx = 0$, and Eq. 8.34 reduces to

$$\tau_0 = \frac{\rho U_\infty^2}{g_c} \frac{d\theta}{dx} \qquad [8.35]$$

From the definition of the friction coefficient in Eq. 8.24,

$$c_f = \frac{\tau_0}{\rho U_\infty^2 / 2g_c} = 2 \frac{d\theta}{dx}$$

Thus, if the velocity distribution, $u(y)$, is known, θ and du/dy at $y = 0$ can be determined, and the equation solved.

For velocity distribution, we make the same assumption of similitude as for the exact solution; i.e.,

$$\frac{u}{U_\infty} = \phi \left(\frac{y}{\delta} \right)$$

but here we have to *state* the function and use it as an auxiliary equation to solve Eq. 8.35.

The function must satisfy certain *minimum* boundary conditions, $u = 0$ at $y = 0$ and $u = U_\infty$ at $y = \delta$. Note that this last condition makes finding a distribution easier than the formal condition of $u = U_\infty$ at $y = \infty$. It would be desirable also for a more accurate representation to have $du/dy = 0$ and $d^2u/dy^2 = 0$ at $y = \delta$ to provide the smooth transition from the boundary layer to the freestream that we assume to be correct, but these last two conditions are generally not met by simple distributions. A simple distribution is parabolic, which seems reasonable in view of the parabolic profile in duct flow. An expression such as

$$\frac{u}{U_\infty} = 2\frac{y}{\delta} - \left(\frac{y}{\delta}\right)^2 \qquad [8.36]$$

satisfies the boundary conditions $u = 0$ at $y = 0$ and $u = U_\infty$ as well as $du/dy = 0$ at $y = \delta$.

From Eq. 8.36,

$$\tau_0 = \frac{\mu}{g_c}\frac{du}{dy}\bigg|_{y=0} = \frac{\mu}{g_c}U_\infty\left(\frac{2}{\delta} - \frac{2y}{\delta^2}\right)_{y=0} = \frac{2\mu U_\infty}{g_c\delta} \qquad [8.37]$$

and $\quad \theta = \displaystyle\int_0^\delta \frac{u}{U_\infty}\left(1 - \frac{u}{U_\infty}\right)dy = \int_0^\delta\left(2\frac{y}{\delta} - \frac{y^2}{\delta^2}\right)\left(1 - 2\frac{y}{\delta} + \frac{y^2}{\delta^2}\right)dy$

$$= \int_0^\delta\left[2\frac{y}{\delta} - 5\left(\frac{y}{\delta}\right)^2 + 4\left(\frac{y}{\delta}\right)^3 - \left(\frac{y}{\delta}\right)^4 dy\right]$$

$$= \left[\frac{y^2}{\delta} - \frac{5}{3}\frac{y^3}{\delta^2} + \frac{y^4}{\delta^3} - \frac{1}{5}\frac{y^5}{\delta^4}\right]_0^\delta = \left(\delta - \frac{5}{3}\delta + \delta - \frac{1}{5}\delta\right) = \frac{2}{15}\delta$$

and hence

$$\frac{d\theta}{dx} = \frac{2}{15}\frac{d\delta}{dx} \qquad [8.38]$$

Substituting Eqs. 8.37 and 8.38 into Eq. 8.35, we obtain

$$\frac{2\mu U_\infty}{g_c\delta} = \frac{\rho U_\infty^2}{g_c}\frac{2}{15}\frac{d\delta}{dx}$$

Therefore,

$$\int_0^\delta \delta\,d\delta = \frac{15\mu}{\rho U_\infty}\int_0^x dx$$

and

$$\frac{\delta^2}{2} = \frac{15\mu x}{\rho U_\infty}$$

or

$$\frac{\delta}{x} = \sqrt{\frac{30\mu}{\rho U_\infty x}} = \frac{5.48}{\sqrt{\mathrm{Re}_x}} \qquad [8.39]$$

For the local friction coefficient, substituting Eq. 8.37 in the definition of c_f

given in Eq. 8.24 yields

$$c_f = \frac{\tau_0}{\rho U_\infty{}^2/2g_c} = \frac{2\mu U_\infty/g_c\delta}{\rho U_\infty{}^2/2g_c} = \frac{4\mu}{\rho U_\infty \delta}$$

and substituting for δ from Eq. 8.39 yields

$$c_f = \frac{4\mu}{\rho U_\infty} \frac{\sqrt{\mathrm{Re}_x}}{5.48x} = \frac{0.728}{\sqrt{\mathrm{Re}_x}} \qquad [8.40]$$

We can find the average friction coefficient, C_F, or the drag coefficient, C_D, by the same method as in Sect. 8.5. The result is

$$C_F = C_D = \frac{1.456}{\sqrt{\mathrm{Re}_L}} \qquad [8.41]$$

These values of δ, C_F, and C_D are of the same forms as the "exact" values, and the constants are in surprisingly close agreement. Other approximations are possible by means of cubic, quartic, or trigonometric relationships for the velocity distribution. Some of these are given as problems at the end of the chapter.

The reasonable accuracy of the momentum-integral method for laminar flow over a flat plate encourages its use in more complex situations for which an exact method does not allow a solution. Furthermore, if an expression can be assumed for τ_0, it can also be applied to a turbulent boundary layer, for which no exact solution is possible.

8.8   *Turbulent boundary layer—flat-plate flow*

The momentum-integral method is equivalent to neglecting the shear stress at the edge of the boundary layer (refer back to Fig. 8.5 and the momentum equation); i.e.,

$$\int_0^\delta \tau \, dy = \tau(\delta) - \tau(0)$$

and $\tau(\delta) \to 0$. Thus we have only to prescribe the wall shear stress for turbulent flow, i.e., $\tau(0) = \tau_0$.

For the turbulent boundary layer, we have no exact relationship for shear stress comparable to $\mu \, du/dy$; the expression $\overline{u'v'}$ is not helpful directly, as we have seen for pipe flow. It is then necessary to use the momentum-integral equation, and, as we are concerned with τ_0, to make the assumptions that went into the pipe-flow analysis. There the velocity distribution and shear stress were described with good accuracy by logarithmic expressions, but these turn out to be very unwieldy in this instance. However, a relatively simple formulation yielding good results can be obtained from the empirical values of Blasius for friction factor (Eq. 7.16) and of Nikuradse for velocity distribution (Eq. 7.17),

$$f = \frac{0.316}{\text{Re}^{1/4}} \qquad [7.16]$$

and

$$\frac{u}{u_{\max}} = \left(\frac{y}{a}\right)^{1/n} \qquad [7.17]$$

For flow over a flat plate with no pressure gradient, the starting point is again the simple form of the momentum equation, Eq. 8.35,

$$\tau_0 = \frac{\rho U_1^2}{g_c} \frac{d\theta}{dx} \qquad [8.35]$$

It must be noted that Eq. 7.17 is in terms of $u_{\max}$, the pipe center-line velocity, and a, the pipe radius. For flat-plate flow, we can take U_∞, the velocity at the edge of the boundary layer, as equivalent to $u_{\max}$ and δ, the boundary-layer thickness, as equivalent to a. The next consideration is the value of n. This varies with Reynolds number for smooth walls, from 6 at $\text{Re} \approx 4 \times 10^3$ to 10 at $\text{Re} \approx 3.2 \times 10^6$. It was remarked earlier that a value of 7, for $\text{Re} \approx 1.1 \times 10^5$, giving the seventh-root law, was regarded as typical, and this we shall use here. It is consistent with the Blasius friction expression, which is accurate up to a Reynolds number of about 10^5. Thus we have

$$\theta = \int_0^\delta \frac{u}{U_\infty}\left(1 - \frac{u}{U_\infty}\right) dy = \int_0^\delta \left(\frac{y}{\delta}\right)^{1/7}\left[1 - \left(\frac{y}{\delta}\right)^{1/7}\right] dy$$

For convenience in manipulation, we shall substitute the symbol ζ for y/δ. Hence $dy = \delta \, d\zeta$, and the limits of integration become 0 and 1, so that

$$\theta = \delta \int_0^1 \zeta^{1/7}(1 - \zeta^{1/7}) \, d\zeta$$

Integration of this yields

$$\theta = \delta \left[\frac{7}{8}\zeta^{8/7} - \frac{7}{9}\zeta^{9/7}\right]_0^1 = \frac{7}{72}\delta \qquad [8.42]$$

For the shear stress, we have the Blasius friction factor, defined with respect to *pipe flow* as

$$\frac{\tau_0}{\rho V^2/2g_c} = \frac{f}{4} = \frac{0.316}{4\text{Re}^{1/4}} = 0.079\left(\frac{\mu}{\rho V d}\right)^{1/4}$$

and

$$\tau_0 = 0.079 \frac{\rho V^2}{2g_c}\left(\frac{\mu}{\rho V d}\right)^{1/4} \qquad [8.43]$$

τ_0 is in terms of the *average* velocity, V, whereas we require it here (Eq. 8.35) in terms of the freestream velocity, U_∞. The length dimension in the Reynolds number is also in terms of pipe diameter, d, consistent with average velocity, whereas we want it in terms of $\delta = d/2$, consistent with the maximum or freestream velocity at the edge of the boundary layer.

To find U_∞ in terms of V, we follow the procedure of Sect. 7.4; i.e., $V = \int u \, dA/A$ with $u = U_\infty(y/\delta)^{1/7}$, $A = \pi a^2$, and $dA = 2\pi r \, dr$, where $r = a - y$. As a result, $V = 0.817 U_1$, and, on substitution into Eq. 8.43, together with $d = 2\delta$,

$$\tau_0 = 0.079 \frac{\rho U_\infty^2}{2g_c} \left(\frac{\mu}{\rho U \delta}\right)^{1/4} \frac{(0.817)^{7/4}}{(2)^{1/4}} = 0.0233 \frac{\rho U_\infty^2}{g_c} \left(\frac{\mu}{\rho U_\infty \delta}\right)^{1/4} \quad [8.44]$$

With Eqs. 8.43 and 8.44 for Eq. 8.35,

$$0.0233 \frac{\rho U_\infty^2}{g_c} \left(\frac{\mu}{\rho U_\infty \delta}\right)^{1/4} = \frac{7}{72} \frac{\rho U_\infty^2}{g_c} \frac{d\delta}{dx}$$

Separating variables and reducing, we have

$$0.24 \left(\frac{\mu}{\rho U_\infty}\right)^{1/4} \int_0^x dx = \int_0^\delta \delta^{1/4} \, d\delta$$

from which

$$\frac{4}{5} \delta^{5/4} = 0.24 \left(\frac{\mu}{\rho U_\infty}\right)^{1/4} x$$

and

$$\frac{\delta}{x} = 0.381 \left(\frac{\mu}{\rho U_\infty x}\right)^{1/5} = \frac{0.381}{\mathrm{Re}^{1/5}} \quad [8.45]$$

From the expression for τ_0, Eq. 8.24, we obtain the local friction coefficient as before,

$$c_f = \frac{0.0592}{\mathrm{Re}_x^{1/5}} \quad [8.46]$$

and likewise the average coefficient,

$$C_F = C_D = \frac{0.074}{\mathrm{Re}_L^{1/5}} \quad [8.47]$$

In spite of the assumptions made in the derivation, these values of δ/x, c_f, and C_D are in excellent agreement with experimental values. For a Reynolds number above that for which the Blasius relation is accurate, an analysis based on the logarithmic velocity distribution gives C_F as

$$C_F = \frac{0.455}{(\log_{10} \mathrm{Re}_L)^{2.58}} \quad [8.48]$$

This is known as the *Prandtl-Schlichting skin-friction formula for a flat plate* and is valid for the whole range of the turbulent boundary layer. It agrees with Eq. 8.46 up to $\mathrm{Re} \approx 10^7$.

A comparison of these results with those for the laminar boundary layer shows that for the laminar case $\delta \propto x^{1/2}$ and $D \propto U^{3/2}$ and $L^{1/2}$, whereas for the turbulent case $\delta \propto x^{4/5}$ and $D \propto U^{9/5}$ and $L^{4/5}$. The turbulent boundary layer increases in thickness at a faster rate than the laminar one, and for minimum drag a laminar layer is preferable to a turbulent layer.

The question arises as to the drag for an actual boundary layer that is laminar to transition and then becomes turbulent, because the expression for turbulent friction assumes turbulent flow from the leading edge. It is found that accurate estimates result from calculating the drag due to a turbulent boundary layer over the whole length, subtracting that due to a turbulent layer from the leading edge to the point of transition, and adding that due to a laminar layer for the same length; i.e., with $\mathrm{Re}_c = \rho U x_c / \mu$ the Reynolds number at the transition distance, x_c,

$$D_{0-L} = D_{\text{turbulent},0-L} - D_{\text{turbulent},0-x_c} + D_{\text{laminar},0-x_c}$$

or, for unit width of plate,

$$D_{\text{total}} = \frac{\rho U_\infty^2}{2g_c} \left(\frac{0.455L}{(\log_{10} \mathrm{Re}_L)^{2.58}} - \frac{0.074x_c}{\mathrm{Re}_c^{\frac{1}{5}}} + \frac{1.328x_c}{\mathrm{Re}_c^{\frac{1}{2}}} \right) \qquad [8.49]$$

8.9   Drag of a bluff body—flat plate normal to stream

The extreme example of a bluff body is a flat plate set normal to the free-stream. The *ideal-* or potential-flow pattern is shown in Fig. 8.6(a). The streamlines are symmetrical on either side of the plate, with a stagnation streamline along the mid-axis. Owing to the symmetry of flow and therefore the same pressure distribution on both sides, the drag would be zero for ideal flow. At the edges of the plate, the fluid has to make a sharp turn, and for ideal flow the velocity right at the corners is infinite. For actual flow, we know that the fluid cannot make a sharp turn, as it leads to a large negative pressure gradient. Except at the very lowest Reynolds numbers, the fluid *separates* at the edges, forming an eddy, with a confused turbulent motion on the back surface (Fig. 8.6(b)). There is an almost total lack of stagnation pressure on the back surface, and so the drag is wholly *form drag* due to the

Figure 8.6

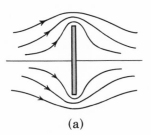

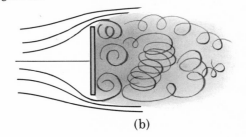

(a)   (b)

pressure difference between the upstream and downstream sides. The pressure is similar to that produced by flow meeting the front side of an infinite flat surface and being deflected through 90° (cf. Problem 4.5). The force due to change of momentum is $\dot{m}U_\infty/g_c = \rho A U_\infty^2/g_c$, and thus the drag coefficient is $C_D = F/(\rho A U_\infty^2/2g_c) = 2$. Experimentally, C_D is about 1.95, very slightly lower than the force due to pure impulse, indicating a very small pressure recovery on the back side. This value is valid only for plates of infinite length (aspect ratio). C_D is considerably reduced for finite lengths because of flow around the ends of the plate. Some C_D values are given in Sect. 8.13.

8.10   *Drag of a rounded body—cylinder*

For flow over rounded bodies, a cylinder will serve as an example, since, as a preeminent structural shape, it is most widely used and has received much attention. Potential flow around a cylinder was studied in Chapters 3 and 4. The flow pattern and pressure distribution are as shown in Fig. 8.7.

At $\theta = \pi/2$ and $3\pi/2$, i.e., along the y axis, the pressure coefficient $C_p = (p - p_\infty)/(\rho U_\infty^2/2g_c) = -3$, its minimum value. For points on the cylinder to the right of the y axis, i.e., downstream from the line of symmetry, the pressure increases, and so again there would be an adverse pressure gradient. However, actual flow over a cylinder exhibits several different phenomena, and these we shall discuss in terms of increasing Reynolds number.

Figure 8.7

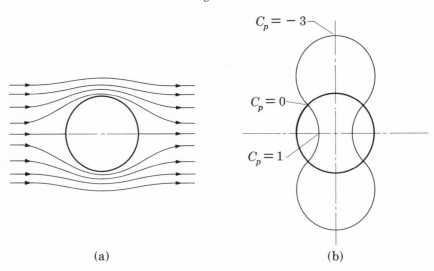

(a)   (b)

At very low Reynolds numbers (<1), the viscous effects so outweigh the inertia effects that the latter can be dropped from the Navier-Stokes equations, which then yield only pressure terms and viscous terms; i.e., for incompressible flow with no body force, Eqs. 4.89 reduce to

$$\text{grad } p = \mu \nabla^2 \mathbf{V} \qquad [8.50]$$

Such a flow necessarily has very low velocity and hence is called a *creeping motion*, also *Stokes* or *Hele-Shaw flow* from two workers who investigated this area. It occurs very seldom, the most important case being that for a *sphere* (not a cylinder). Solution of Eq. 8.50 gives *Stokes' law* of resistance or drag for a *sphere*,

$$D = 3\pi \frac{\mu}{g_c} U_\infty d \qquad [8.51]$$

Expressed in the form of a drag coefficient, with A the cross-sectional area, this is

$$C_D = \frac{D}{\rho U_\infty^2 A / 2g_c} = \frac{3\pi\mu U_\infty d}{\rho U_\infty^2 (\pi/4) d^2 g_c} = \frac{24\mu}{\rho U_\infty d} = \frac{24}{\text{Re}} \qquad [8.52]$$

where the Reynolds number is based on the diameter. Stokes' law is valid only for a Reynolds number of about 0.5 and under and for a steady velocity. It may be applied to the terminal velocity of very small droplets of liquid falling through a gas as in a fog (not raindrops, which are generally too big), to solid particles in a fluid, or to small gas bubbles rising in a liquid. For a cylinder, it is necessary to introduce acceleration terms, as no solution of Eq. 8.50 is possible in this case. The answer is more complex, and as the problem seldom arises, we shall omit the development.

Returning to the cylinder, the flow at very low Reynolds numbers, below about 40, is laminar, with a wake region over most of the rear half, as in Fig. 8.8(a). A pair of standing vortexes is formed at the rear, with rotations in opposite directions.

Somewhere around a Reynolds number of 40, depending on the turbulence of the main stream, the wake becomes periodic, and the vortexes are shed alternately from the top and bottom of the cylinder in parallel rows as

Figure 8.8

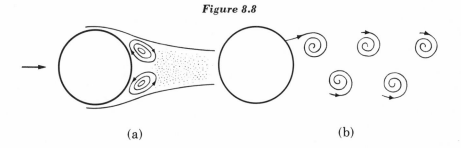

(a)   (b)

Figure 8.9

in Fig. 8.8(b). Von Karman analyzed this flow pattern, showing that for stability the vortexes must be uniformly staggered with a certain fixed ratio of transverse to longitudinal spacing. The pattern of alternate vortexes shed from a bluff or rounded body is known as a *von Karman vortex street* or *trail*. The von Karman analysis assumes potential flow, although the body generates vortexes continually, which is not possible according to the theory of ideal flow. However, the viscous effects are concentrated in the very thin boundary layer next to the surface that produces the vortexes, the flow elsewhere being near enough to nonviscous to permit a potential analysis.

Up to a Reynolds number of about 150, the vortex street is quite stable and regular, and the flow pattern for the ideal case is as shown in Fig. 8.9. Allowing for the effects of viscosity at the boundaries of the vortexes, this pattern is followed very closely for a real fluid.

At Reynolds numbers between 150 and 300,* there is a transition region, with an irregular frequency of vortex shedding. For Re $\approx$ 300, the frequency is more irregular, and the flow pattern is highly fluctuating, with the vortexes being dissipated rapidly into a turbulent wake. This behavior is interpreted as due to *turbulence*, so that there is an analogy with the flat-plate boundary layer in the progression from a laminar regime through transition to a turbulent regime, with vortex shedding continuing up to very high Reynolds numbers. The relationship of shedding frequency, n, velocity, U_∞, and size, d, is incorporated in the *Strouhal number*, $S = nd/U_\infty$. The value of S is a function of the Reynolds number, varying from about 0.12 to 0.21 in the laminar and transition vortex-street range and remaining at about

* A. Roshko, *N.A.C.A. Rept.* No. 1194 (1951).

0.21 up to very high Reynolds numbers. The alternate distribution of the vortexes produces an unbalanced force on the cylinder of a periodic nature, causing a vibration that gives rise to such phenomena as the Aeolian harp, the "singing" of telephone wires, and, in general, the "howling" of winds. When the aerodynamic frequency corresponds to the structural frequency, resonance occurs, which can cause severe damage to the structure. One of the more spectacular manifestations is the oscillation of suspension bridges, where amplitudes large enough to cause failure can be built up, as witness the well-known disaster of the Tacoma Narrows bridge in the state of Washington.

At very low Reynolds numbers, the drag is roughly proportional to the velocity, and hence C_D falls rapidly as Re increases, with a less rapid rate in the stable vortex-street region. Total C_D is the sum of the friction-drag coefficient and the pressure-drag coefficient. The former decreases with increase of Reynolds number, while the latter remains fairly constant, increasing slightly in the vortex-street transition region but staying approximately the same thereafter; above Re $\approx 10^4$, the friction drag becomes negligible compared with the pressure drag. The over-all values of C_D are shown in Fig. 8.10.

Examination of the flow pattern in the range of Reynolds number from the stable vortex street upward to about 10^5 shows that the front half behaves very much like that in ideal flow, but with a laminar boundary layer extending nearly to the vertical axis (Fig. 8.11(a)). This boundary

Figure 8.10

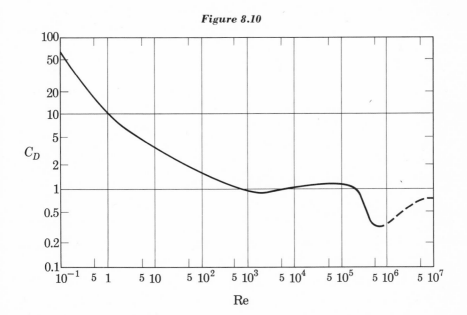

Re

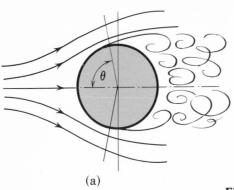

(a)

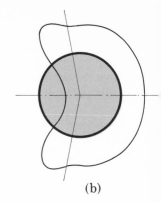

(b)

Figure 8.11

layer separates at a point where $\theta \approx 80°$ (θ is the angle measured from the forward stagnation point), giving rise to the double, alternating eddy at the rear of the cylinder that becomes the turbulent wake previously described. This pattern explains why the drag is almost all pressure drag, as the region of viscous drag is small and there is little pressure recovery in the rear, separated region. Fig. 8.11(b) shows the distribution of pressure around the cylinder in the form of the pressure coefficient, C_p. The minimum pressure is at $\theta \approx 70°$, after which C_p increases somewhat. The adverse pressure gradient thus produced leads quickly to separation. Following this, C_p is approximately constant, with a negative value of about -1, to $\theta = 180°$. The physical reason for the drag coefficient is therefore apparent.

Reference to Fig. 8.10, however, reveals that at a Reynolds number somewhat above 10^5, the drag coefficient is sharply reduced from a value of about 1.2 to about 0.3. This must indicate a sudden change of flow pattern, and it is found that the laminar boundary layer changes to a turbulent boundary layer before separation occurs. The latter has more kinetic energy than the former and resists separation for a greater distance around the cylinder, the separation point being at $\theta \approx 105°$. The pattern is shown in Fig. 8.12, together with a polar plot of C_p. Although the turbulence causes a slight increase in friction drag, this is negligible compared with the decrease in pressure drag due to the postponement of separation. The smaller region of separation results in a less negative coefficient over the rear half of the cylinder and hence lower drag; or, looked at in another way, the region of turbulent eddies is smaller, so that there is less dissipation of ordered kinetic energy.

For a cylinder, the region of laminar boundary layer with forward separation is called *subcritical* flow, and that of turbulent boundary layer with rearward separation is called *supercritical* flow. The Reynolds number at which the transition occurs depends on the turbulence of the freestream

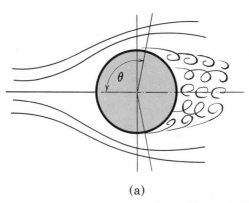
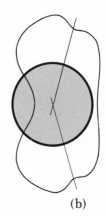

(a)   (b)

Figure 8.12

and the condition of the surface of the cylinder. For smooth surfaces, the critical Reynolds number is about 2×10^5, with the transition region extending to about 4×10^5. Early transition can be brought about by roughening the surface ahead of the normal separation point or placing a wire to "trip" the boundary layer.

Flow above a Reynolds number of 10^6 has not been explored very extensively, as few wind tunnels are adequate. Recent investigations by Roshko[*] show that C_D tends to increase again up to a value of about 0.7 at Re $\approx 10^7$, which is the limit of present experiment. The flow pattern is not quite clear, but a tentative explanation is that the separation point moves forward, with an increase of wake width and an increase of loss.

The behavior of a cylinder through the Reynolds-number range is qualitatively characteristic also of spheres and of rounded bodies generally (ellipses, ovals, rounded rectangles, etc.), with the cylinder and sphere having most importance as the most widely used shapes. Eddy formation, leading to a vortex street and to turbulent shedding, is also characteristic of bluff bodies (e.g., normal flat plates), but the separation point is always fixed at the sharp edge, and there is no subsequent boundary-layer mechanism to cause supercritical flow.

8.11   *Drag of a streamlined body*

For a body of finite thickness, we deduce from the foregoing discussion that we can obtain the minimum drag by designing for low rates of change of curvature to avoid separation and by trying to preserve a laminar boundary

[*] A. Roshko, *J. Fluid Mech.*, **3**, 315 (1961).

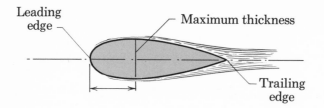

Leading edge — Maximum thickness

Trailing edge

Figure 8.13

layer as far along the body as possible. Both these criteria are met by the avoidance of steep adverse pressure gradients and can be attained by a *streamlined* body, a long slender shape with no sharp changes of curvature save at the trailing edge, as shown in Fig. 8.13. At the leading edge, the radius of curvature is necessarily rather small, but it increases rapidly to a position of maximum thickness some distance downstream. Beyond this point the body gradually thins, so that a small adverse pressure gradient is produced. The trailing edge ideally is a cusp but in practice must have a finite radius of curvature for structural reasons. A well-designed, symmetrical streamlined body at zero angle of attack (i.e., with its longitudinal axis in the direction of the freestream) has a boundary layer that is laminar over the front region and that becomes turbulent without separation, moving smoothly to the rear to form a thin wake.

To obtain a maximum length of laminar boundary layer entails shaping a body so that a favorable pressure gradient is maintained as far back as possible. This means having the maximum thickness well back, followed by a relatively rapid reduction of thickness to the trailing edge. If the body is carefully designed within certain limits of change of curvature, a long laminar boundary layer changes to a turbulent layer after the section of maximum thickness, the greater kinetic energy of the turbulent layer preventing separation. This is the basis of the laminar-flow airfoil, which has a very low drag coefficient, little more than that for a flat plate. It has, however, a disadvantage in that the low drag holds only for a small range of angles of attack, i.e., attitudes of the airfoil with respect to the freestream. Outside this range, the transition point may shift forward rather suddenly, increasing the drag and possibly leading to difficulty of control as an aircraft wing.

8.12   *Boundary-layer suction*

In addition to controlling the boundary layer by means of body shape, we can promote stability by external means. The object is to energize the layer of slow-moving fluid near the wall, either by "blowing," i.e., directing fluid of higher kinetic energy into the layer, or by suction, i.e., removing the "tired" air and reducing the thickness of the layer. Suction is the method most generally used, and it is particularly valuable when a severe adverse pressure gradient occurs in the normal flow pattern. This idea of removal of fluid through the surface, or *boundary-layer suction*, is an old one, but it has yet to be applied successfully as a routine procedure for aircraft. It has regular application in experimental apparatus, such as wind tunnels, in which a uniform flow to simulate a freestream is necessary and in which the provision of the essential means and auxiliary equipment is not difficult.

The aim is to remove enough slow-moving air to prevent separation of either a laminar or a turbulent boundary layer. The suction may be applied continuously, through a surface of porous material behind which a lower pressure is maintained, or at certain points, through small slots. Power is required for the suction process, although it is usually small in comparison with the drag reduction obtained, but the chief problems involve arrangements for the suction to be effective within the confines of a structurally sound wing section, the weight and size of the exhaust equipment, and the possibility of eventual blockage of the suction surface (particularly if the suction is continuous through a porous material with very small voids). Nevertheless, the gains promised are sufficiently great that efforts are continually being made to develop an efficient suction method for full-scale aircraft.

8.13   *Drag coefficients—general*

Bodies that suffer drag due to pressure, i.e., those in which separation occurs, have to be tested in a wind tunnel for drag coefficient, as theory can lead only to an approximation. Table 8.2 presents some collected data for C_D for a number of shapes, obtained mostly from Hoerner's book,* which is a very comprehensive survey of drag of all kinds.

It should be noted that the drag coefficients of three-dimensional bodies are always less than those of corresponding two-dimensional shapes, e.g., rectangular plates normal to flow. The end effects are such as to allow fluid to enter the zone of separated flow and thus increase the pressure on the rear surface. In addition, flow around the ends reduces the loss due to interaction of the vortex streets, which are characteristic of bluff and rounded bodies.

The drag coefficients quoted are typical or average values. Most rounded

* S. F. Hoerner, *Fluid-Dynamic Drag*, publ. by author, Midland Park, N.J., 1958.

Table 8.2

FORM OF BODY	$d*$	REYNOLDS-NUMBER RANGE	C_D	REMARKS
Flat plate—edgewise	L	Laminar B.L Turbulent B.L: $<10^7$ $>10^7$	$1.328/\sqrt{Re_L}$ $0.074/Re^{1/5}$ $0.455/\log_{10}(Re_L)^{2.58}$	Based on one side only.
Flat plate—normal	d	$>10^3$	L/d 1 1.18 5 1.2 10 1.3 20 1.5 30 1.6 ∞ 1.95	Note great effect of finite length; e.g., at $L/d = 10$, C_D is only about $\frac{2}{3}$ its value at $L/d = \infty$.
Circular disk—normal	d	$>10^3$	1.17	
Sphere	d	<1 10^3 to 3×10^5 $>3 \times 10^5$	$24/Re$ 0.47 0.2	Re_c depending on turbulence. Based on projected area.
Airfoil	c	$>10^6$	0.007	Typical value for angle of attack for minimum C_D. Based on projected area $c \times s$.
Hollow hemishpere	d d	10^4 to 10^6 10^4 to 10^6	0.38 1.42	Based on projected area $\pi d^2/4$.
Solid hemisphere	d d	10^4 to 10^6 10^4 to 10^6	0.42 1.17	Based on projected area $\pi d^2/4$.

Table 8.2 Continued

FORM OF BODY	d^*	REYNOLDS-NUMBER RANGE	C_D		REMARKS
Semicircle	d d	10^4 to 10^6 10^4 to 10^6	1.2 2.3		Based on projected area $d \times L$.
Cylinder	d	10^3 to 10^5	L/d 1 5 10 20 30 ∞	0.63 0.8 0.83 0.93 1.0 1.2	Based on projected area $d \times L$. See Fig. 8.10 for $L/d = \infty$ over wide range of Re.

* This is the characteristic linear dimension for use in the Reynolds number, $\rho U_\infty d/\mu$.

bodies exhibit curves like that for a cylinder, with variation of C_D with Re. The single values given are mean values for a useful range of Reynolds number in which C_D is essentially constant.

8.14   Lift

The preceding analysis dealt with the component of force parallel to the flow direction, i.e., the drag, when the flow pattern is symmetrical with respect to the longitudinal axis. An unsymmetrical flow pattern produces a net force whose direction makes an angle with the flow direction, and by resolving this force into components parallel to and perpendicular to the flow direction, we obtain respectively the drag and the *lift*. The lift is the useful component, as discussed previously, while the drag is undesirable and must be minimized.

Lift was examined for the case of ideal flow around a cylinder with circulation (Sect. 4.10). It was found to be $\rho U_\infty \Gamma/g_c$ per unit length of cylinder, where Γ is the circulation. The value of Γ was left unspecified earlier, and it is the purpose here to see how it can be utilized in the analysis of lift and airfoils. The concept of lift in terms of circulation is a theoretical one, but nevertheless of the greatest importance, for it promotes qualitative understanding of flow behavior and makes possible quantitative analyses of ideal-flow behavior.

The physical nature of lift is made apparent by consideration of the

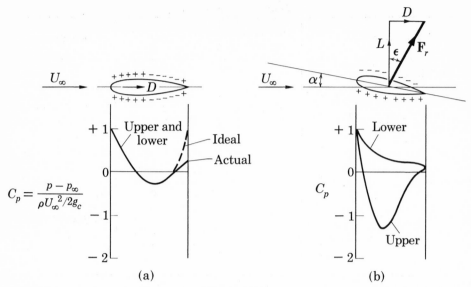

Figure 8.14

pressure distribution around an immersed body. A symmetrical, streamlined body, the airfoil of Fig. 8.14(a), produces only drag when placed in a flow with zero angle of attack.

The diagram below the airfoil sketch shows the pressure distribution as the pressure coefficient, $C_p = (p - p_\infty)/(\rho U_\infty^2/2g_c)$. The leading edge is a stagnation point; hence $C_p = 1$. At the trailing edge, the pressure would again rise to the stagnation pressure (cf. Fig. 3.29) for ideal flow, as indicated by the dashed line, but owing to the boundary-layer friction loss, it rises only to some fraction of this, as indicated by the solid line. The pressure distribution for both surfaces (upper and lower) is the same.

For the same airfoil with an angle of attack α (Fig. 8.14(b)), the fluid accelerates very rapidly from the leading edge over the upper surface, the result being a large *negative* pressure coefficient. The fluid then decelerates with increasing C_p to the trailing edge. Over the lower surface, the fluid first accelerates but then, at this particular angle of attack, flows at a roughly constant rate to the trailing edge. Thus there is a lift force, L, produced by excess pressure on the lower surface and by suction pressure on the upper surface, with the latter having the greater effect. L is proportional to the net area enclosed by the pressure lines. The resultant force, $\mathbf{F}_r$, has the components L and D. The angle $\epsilon = \tan^{-1} D/L$ is called the *glide angle*, because it is the angle for steady gliding flight. The object of aerodynamic design is to maximize the *lift-drag ratio*, L/D.

Before treating the actual behavior of airfoils in more detail, we shall return to the circulation theory.

8.15 *Lift and circulation—the Kutta-Joukowsky theorem*

It was shown in Sect. 4.10 that the lift force on a circular cylinder in ideal flow is $\rho U_\infty \Gamma / g_c$, and it was stated that this is true of any right cylinder. This situation will now be demonstrated from the momentum relation.

Consider an airfoil cascade (or grid or lattice) consisting of an infinite number of similar shapes, parallel to each other and a distance s apart, as shown in Fig. 8.15. The control surface is $ABDCA$, formed by two similar streamlines, AC and BD, and two lines, AB and CD, parallel to the cascade or y axis. It includes the airfoil, and the momentum equation will therefore give the force on the airfoil. The velocity components in the x and y directions, u and v, are considered uniform over AB and CD, as AB and CD are far removed from the cascade. Since AC and BD are similar streamlines, the momentum equations for the directions x and y are

$$F_x + p_1 s - p_2 s = \frac{\dot{m}}{g_c}(u_2 - u_1)$$

or

$$F_x = \frac{\dot{m}}{g_c}(u_2 - u_1) + (p_2 - p_1)s$$

$$F_y = \frac{\dot{m}}{g_c}[-v_2 - (-v_1)]$$

or

$$F_y = \frac{\dot{m}}{g_c}(v_1 - v_2)$$

From continuity, $\dot{m} = \rho u_1 s = \rho u_2 s$; i.e., $u_1 = u_2 = u$. Hence the momentum term disappears in the x equation. Because the flow is assumed ideal,

Figure 8.15

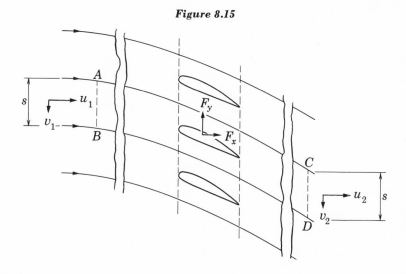

Bernoulli's equation applies between 1 and 2; i.e.,

$$p_2 - p_1 = \frac{\rho}{2g_c}[(u_1{}^2 + v_1{}^2) - (u_2{}^2 + v_2{}^2)] = \frac{\rho}{2g_c}(v_1{}^2 - v_2{}^2)$$

since $u_1 = u_2$. Thus

$$F_x = \frac{\rho s}{2g_c}(v_1{}^2 - v_2{}^2)$$

and

$$F_y = \frac{\rho u s}{g_e}(v_1 - v_2)$$

From the standpoint of circulation around an airfoil, this is the line integral around a closed path, and for $ACDBA$ (clockwise circulation),

$$\Gamma = s(v_1 - v_2)$$

since the contributions along the streamline sections AC and DB cancel each other out. Substituting in the momentum equations, we obtain

$$F_x = \frac{\rho s}{2g_c}(v_1{}^2 - v_2{}^2) = \frac{\rho s}{2g_c}(v_1 + v_2)(v_1 - v_2) = \frac{\rho \Gamma}{2g_c}(v_1 + v_2)$$

and

$$F_y = \frac{\rho u s}{g_c}(v_1 - v_2) = \frac{\rho u \Gamma}{g_c}$$

Now let the cascade spacing $s \to \infty$. In the circulation relationship, $\Gamma = s(v_1 - v_2)$, Γ must remain finite, and so $v_1 - v_2 \to 0$; i.e., $v_1 = v_2$ in the limit. With $v_1 = v_2$ and $u_1 = u_2$, then as AB and CD are far removed from the airfoil, and with the flow at this distance considered to have the direction of the x axis, $v_1 = v_2 = 0$, and $u_1 - u_2 = U_\infty$; hence

$$F_x = 0$$

and

$$F_y = \frac{\rho U_\infty \Gamma}{g_c} \qquad [8.53]$$

These two relations show that for *ideal* flow there is no force in the direction of flow (i.e., no drag) but there is a transverse or y-direction force with circulation. With U positive and Γ clockwise, F_y is positive (upward) and is therefore *lift*. Eq. 8.53 is known as the *Kutta-Joukowsky theorem*.*

8.16 *Circulation and flow around an airfoil*

The Kutta-Joukowsky theorem is of great value because it shows that in the analysis of lift an airfoil can be replaced by a vortex of such strength as to give the circulation Γ and thus make possible the formulation of mathemat-

---

* It was developed independently by W. Kutta in 1902 and N. Joukowsky in 1906.

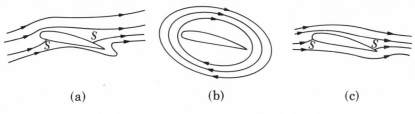

Figure 8.16

ical relationships. It should, however, be noted that in a consideration of an airfoil as a wing or turbomachine blade traveling through a fluid, this vortex is attached to the airfoil rather than being the fixed collection of fluid particles constituting a true vortex. It is called a *bound* vortex but otherwise has the same properties as a true vortex.

Although the Kutta-Joukowsky theorem simplifies analysis, the problem remains of specifying the value of the circulation, as the body itself and the boundary conditions are not sufficient to determine the flow. A further contribution of Kutta and Joukowsky demonstrated how we may specify Γ for ideal flow.

The streamlines for flow around an airfoil *without* circulation are shown in Fig. 8.16(a), those for a vortex alone are shown in Fig. 8.16(b), and those for a combination of the two are shown in Fig. 8.16(c). The result of imposing a circulation is to move the stagnation streamlines and stagnation points, S. Note that for flow from left to right with a clockwise circulation, the rear stagnation point is moved downstream toward the trailing edge (cf. Sect. 3.18 for flow around a cylinder with circulation). Various arbitrary values of circulation displace the stagnation points to various locations.

The figure shows that the streamlines near the lower surface have to turn a sharp corner at the trailing edge, and for a real fluid even a small viscous effect of the boundary layer would make this impossible. The boundary layer would separate, and fluid would be induced to flow from the stagnation point on the upper surface. Therefore, with a real fluid, the flow over upper and lower surfaces meets at the trailing edge, which is the stagnation point. This real-flow condition can be met in the potential-flow theory by adjustment of the circulation so that the rear stagnation point is at the trailing edge. For a given airfoil in a stream of given velocity, *the value of Γ is such as to meet this condition.*

This is the last link in the development of the flow pattern to simulate flow around an airfoil. It was seen in Chapter 3 that a suitable combination of sources and sinks in uniform flow could depict any arbitrary shape,* i.e.,

* For two-dimensional flow, the shape is described much more conveniently mathematically by the method of conformal transformation, involving the use of functions of a complex variable. However, the underlying principle is the same in both procedures.

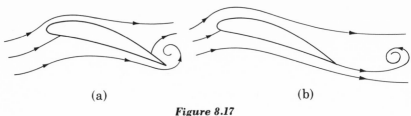

(a)   (b)

Figure 8.17

a given airfoil. If a circulation is added of such strength as to move the rear stagnation point to the trailing edge, then the whole flow field is defined. Pressure, velocity distribution, and the value of lift can be calculated. Real flow introduces a boundary layer that can be estimated from the previous relationships, modified by the pressure gradient imposed by the ideal-flow field.

The bound vortex around the airfoil is not a reality, but there is a rather startling correspondence between this concept and the behavior of the fluid when the body is set in motion or comes to rest. Prandtl took motion pictures of the movement, making the flow pattern visible by scattering aluminum dust on the surface of water and then towing the model through the water.

In the first moment after starting, before any significant boundary layer has a chance to build up, the fluid actually flows around the trailing edge at high velocity. Almost immediately, however, a boundary layer develops, and the slow-moving fluid on the lower surface has insufficient energy to move from the high-velocity, low-pressure region at the trailing edge toward the high-pressure stagnation region of S on the upper surface. Thus it separates, and a counterclockwise vortex is formed as shown in Fig. 8.17(a). The stagnation point moves rearward, giving the pattern shown in Fig. 8.17(b).

Now there is an important theorem, known as *Kelvin's theorem*, which states that for nonviscous flow circulation must remain constant in a flow field. This cannot be strictly true for a viscous fluid, but if the fluid has a relatively low viscosity and is nonturbulent, its behavior tends toward constant circulation. In the case of the starting body, the circulation is initially zero, since everything is at rest. The trailing-edge eddy, or *starting vortex*, has counterclockwise circulation, and so, to satisfy Kelvin's theorem, there must be an equal and opposite circulation within the flow field. Accordingly, the *bound vortex* of the airfoil has clockwise circulation. The actions of the bound vortex and the starting vortex increase until they reach a value such that the flows from upper and lower surfaces join smoothly at the trailing edge. The starting vortex provides circulation and hence lift on the airfoil. In ideal flow, the starting vortex remains unchanged downstream, thus satisfying Kelvin's theorem of constant circulation. In a real fluid, it is dissipated by viscous action, but this has no effect on the flow immediately

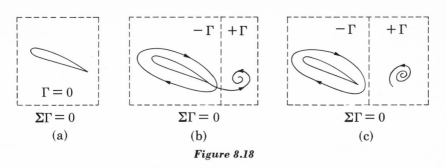

$$\Sigma\Gamma = 0 \qquad \Sigma\Gamma = 0 \qquad \Sigma\Gamma = 0$$

(a)   (b)   (c)

Figure 8.18

adjacent to the airfoil, which continues to experience lift. This picture of starting flow is summarized by Fig. 8.18.

Figure 8.19

When the airfoil is stopped, an analogous situation occurs. The circulation of the bound vortex is shed at the trailing edge, and simultaneously a *stopping* vortex of opposite rotation is formed as shown in Fig. 8.19, the two vortexes, of zero net circulation, moving downward by virtue of their induced effects on each other.

8.17   *Airfoil of finite span—wing behavior*

The foregoing discussion relates to two-dimensional flow, i.e., a body of infinite length or span. An airfoil of finite span introduces three-dimensional problems due to the end effects. Two major questions immediately become apparent. What happens to the bound vortex at the end of the airfoil (wing), and how can we explain the fact that the lift must decrease to zero at the end because the pressures on the upper and lower surfaces must approach equality?

It seems reasonable to suppose that a vortex filament cannot just end in an ideal fluid where there is no dissipation effect, and it can be proved (by the Helmholtz laws) that a vortex filament must either extend to the boundaries of the fluid or form a closed path (e.g., a smoke ring). The physical explanation of lift was that it is produced by a higher pressure on the lower surface and a lower pressure on the upper surface. Hence, at the

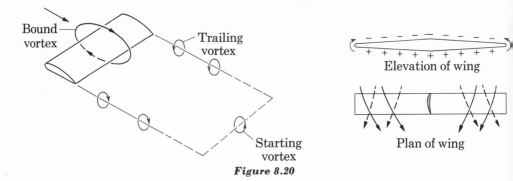

Figure 8.20

wing tip, there must be a flow of fluid around the edge from bottom to top, and this spanwise flow must extend inward, from continuity considerations. The tip flow causes a surface of discontinuity in the fluid, which gives rise to a vortex rearward from the tip. This vortex is the continuation of the bound vortex around the body of the wing. Thus we have the *horseshoe* vortex, as shown in Fig. 8.20. The closed vortex path according to Helmholtz is included, although in real flow it is quickly dissipated, as indeed are the *trailing* vortexes some distance behind the wing.

These trailing vortexes from the wing tips are a reality, as evidenced by the vapor trails left by a high-flying aircraft and seen in a clear sky at certain levels of temperature and humidity. The characteristic of a free vortex is increase of velocity with decrease of radius—hence decrease of pressure and temperature, producing condensation.

The two-dimensional picture of a circulation of constant strength along a whole span can be modified for a finite span of varying lift if it is assumed that the circulation is made up of an infinite number of bound vortexes of varying length, each with its trailing vortexes. This situation is shown diagrammatically for a finite number of vortexes in Fig. 8.21.

In this manner, Figs. 8.20 and 8.21 illustrate how the finite wing can be

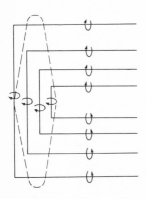

Figure 8.21

represented to conform to circulation theory and allow quantitative formulation of behavior.

The concept of the closed vortex as shown in Fig. 8.20 entails modification of the flow around the wing. Within the loop formed by this closed vortex, there must be an induced velocity directed downward, as on the inside of the loop the velocities of the vortexes are all directed downward. This downward component of velocity, or *downwash*, w, is in addition to the freestream velocity, U_∞, experienced by the airfoil, as shown in Fig. 8.22.

The resultant induced velocity is U_i, inclined at an angle $\alpha_i = \tan^{-1} w/U_\infty$, and the resultant induced lift is L_i, composed of two components, the lift from the bound vortex, $L = \rho U_\infty \Gamma/g_c$, and the force from the downwash, $F_i = \rho w \Gamma/g_c$. L is normal to U_∞, F_i is normal to w, and L_i is normal to U_i. The force, F_i, from the downwash is directed oppositely to the direction of motion and is thus a drag force. Hence it is called the *induced* drag, D_i. In addition to regarding induced drag as a component of the redirected lift force, we may think of it as due to the kinetic energy necessary for the trailing vortexes. For a finite span, then, an inherent drag, which is present in ideal flow and has nothing to do with friction drag, is introduced.

The value of w is associated with the degree of circulation, and therefore the induced drag increases as lift increases. It can be demonstrated that the induced-drag coefficient, C_{D_i}, has a value of $C_L^2/(\pi s/c)$, where s/c is the *aspect*, or *span-chord*, *ratio*. Thus the total drag of a finite wing is the sum of the profile drag and the induced drag, or, in terms of drag coefficient,

$$C_{D_0} = C_{D_p} + C_{D^i} = C_{D_p} + \frac{C_L^2}{s/c} \qquad [8.54]$$

The expression for C_{D_i} shows that an increasing penalty is paid in drag as lift increases and that it may be minimized by a large aspect ratio, i.e., long slender wings. A detailed analysis also shows that, for a given span, an

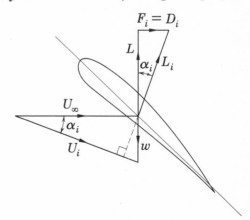

Figure 8.22

elliptical distribution of lift yields a minimum total induced drag. These are valuable results from a consideration of wing performance in terms of the circulation theory of lift.

8.18   *Performance of airfoil sections*

Returning to the infinite airfoil, or two-dimensional flow, we note that both lift and drag are dependent on the orientation or angle of attack, α, of the airfoil. α is defined as the angle between the direction of the freestream and the chord line of the airfoil (Fig. 8.23). Drag was previously studied only for symmetrical flow patterns, but it has now been seen that an unsymmetrical flow pattern, and hence an unsymmetrical pressure distribution, is required for lift. However, an unsymmetrical body is not essential. A flat plate produces lift when placed at an angle of attack.

If an airfoil section is tested in a wind tunnel, with measurements made of lift and drag, plots of the corresponding coefficients against angle of attack are curves like those in Fig. 8.24. The curve for C_L is linear over a large part of the range of α shown, with α being positive or negative. At a certain angle of attack, α_0, the "zero angle of attack," $C_L = 0$. As α increases in a positive direction, C_L increases but at a decreasing rate. It eventually reaches a maximum, and then it decreases.

The curve for C_D is much flatter (when drawn to the same scale), as $C_D \ll C_L$ for a usable airfoil, showing a minimum at a low angle of attack (in this case, a negative value) and a rapid rise as α increases to large positive values. This rapid increase of C_D and corresponding decrease of C_L are due to the onset of *stall*, in which ordered flow breaks down over a large part of the high-velocity, low-pressure upper surface, as shown in Fig. 8.25.

As α increases, the fluid has to accelerate and decelerate more rapidly over the upper surface. The result is an adverse pressure gradient, which moves the transition point for the laminar boundary layer forward, thus increasing the drag. Further increase of α causes separation of the turbulent boundary layer at the rear of the airfoil, the separation point moving forward

Figure 8.23

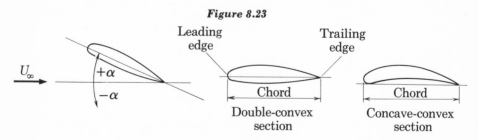

| Leading edge | | Trailing edge |

Double-convex section

Concave-convex section

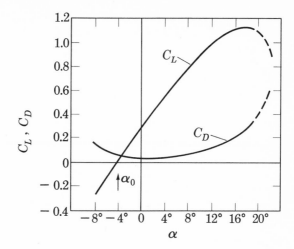

Figure 8.24

until, at a sufficiently large value of α, most of the upper surface is a region of separated flow. The lift decreases, the drag increases, and the airfoil stalls. Depending on the actual airfoil, stalling may occur gradually, as shown in Fig. 8.24, or suddenly, indicating separation before transition from a laminar to a turbulent boundary layer.

A convenient way of representing airfoil data is by means of a "polar diagram," Fig. 8.26, with C_L plotted against C_D and values of α given at intervals. As the induced drag, C_{D_i}, is a function of lift for a given airfoil, it can also be shown, in the so-called *drag parabola* ($C_{D_i} \propto C_L^2$). The tangent to the C_L-C_D curve drawn from the origin of coordinates gives the maximum lift-drag ratio, with the corresponding value of α being capable of interpolation.

The analysis of lift and drag of immersed bodies has been made largely in connection with airfoils for wings, but airfoils are also used for blades of turbomachines, such as fans, compressors, pumps, and turbines of all kinds.

Figure 8.25

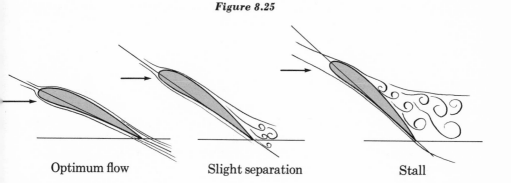

Optimum flow   Slight separation   Stall

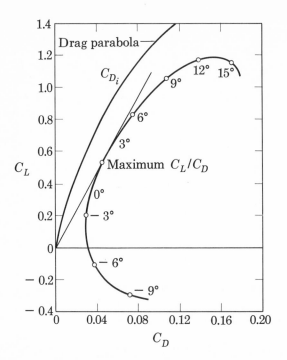

Figure 8.26

A number of adjacent blades and confinement by casings introduce some complications, but the basic characteristics noted for flow over wings apply in essence to flow through blades as well, and performance analyses are treated in the same terms. It must be remembered that airfoil lift and drag have been discussed in terms of dimensionless coefficients, C_L, C_D, etc., and that these coefficients are functions of Reynolds number for any real fluid. Thus any particular set of data is valid only for the Reynolds number, or small range of Reynolds number, for which the data were obtained. The effects of Reynolds number, although very important for exact design, are usually relatively small, modifying but not changing the essential behavior outlined here. For a compressible fluid, however, the effects of Mach number are considerable, changing the whole flow pattern.

8.19 *Effect of compressibility on flow over immersed bodies*

The preceding material has assumed incompressible flow. It is therefore valid quantitatively for flow in liquids and for flow at relatively low velocities in gases (cf. Sect. 4.29). It remains qualitatively true as long as flow is *subsonic* everywhere, requiring modification only with variation of density, which calls for the "compressible-flow" Bernoulli equation or its equivalent. This introduces some difficulties in exact analysis, but the fundamental phenomena (compressible and incompressible flow over immersed bodies) are similar.

However, when the flow, or any part of the flow, becomes supersonic, the picture is radically changed, as has been seen in Chapter 7. Even if the freestream Mach number is well below unity, the acceleration around an immersed body may produce supersonic flow locally. Thus, for a cylinder, it was shown that at the 90° point the ideal local velocity, V, is twice the freestream velocity, U_∞ (Sect. 3.17). For a compressible fluid, an increase of velocity is accompanied by a decrease of temperature and density; hence the local Mach number increases to a greater relative extent over the regions of higher local velocity and exceeds unity for quite low freestream Mach numbers. The analysis of flow through ducts of variable area demonstrated that there was no difficulty in passing through $M = 1$ smoothly with little or no loss, and this is equally true of freestream flow. However, it is known from duct flow that when the flow must decelerate, the relationship of pressure and area ratio is critical; otherwise, a discontinuity or *shock* wave is formed to adjust the pressure.

The same state of affairs holds for an immersed body. One may visualize the body as an obstruction in a duct, producing a convergent-divergent channel with, in this case, the duct walls being parallel streamlines some distance from the body. Theoretically the fluid in the freestream can be pushed laterally to infinity, but in practice the effect of the body is not felt to a very great distance from the surface. The result is that for some subsonic freestream Mach number the fluid is supersonic near the point of maximum velocity, and in the subsequent deceleration or recompression a shock wave is formed.

This is shown in Fig. 8.27(a). It will be noted that (1) the shock wave is not normal to the surface but is inclined at an angle and (2) it is somewhat curved. The region of supersonic flow is confined to the upper surface, over which the velocity is highest, but extends only a finite distance from the airfoil, as the streamlines straighten out and become less affected by the

Figure 8.27

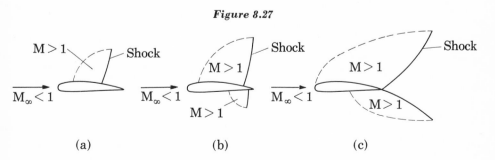

(a)   (b)   (c)

presence of the body. This reduction of velocity transverse to the surface is one reason for the curvature of the shock.

At still higher, but still subsonic, M_∞, the supersonic region is extended, the upper shock moves rearward, and at the same time a shock appears on the lower surface (Fig. 8.27(b)), as the flow there is now locally supersonic. Finally, as M_∞ increases still further, both upper and lower shocks move rearward until they form at the trailing edge (Fig. 8.27(c)).

This is the regime of *transonic* flow, in which both subsonic and supersonic flows appear in the same flow pattern. It has great complexity analytically and in practice leads to problems of aircraft stability. It will be appreciated at this time, although we have not discussed freestream two-dimensional shocks, that a shock wave is accompanied by a sudden increase of pressure. If we think of lift in terms of pressure forces on the airfoil, the pressure configurations in Fig. 8.27 indicate that the forces and accompanying moments vary a great deal once a shock has formed, causing difficulties of control.

Continuing the description of phenomena as Mach number increases, we see that the next stage is when $M_\infty > 1$. The flow pattern here depends very much on the shape of the airfoil. If it has a rounded, relatively thick, leading edge, then a curved shock wave appears in front of it, as shown in Fig. 8.28(a). This is called a *detached shock* or *bow shock*, and behind it the flow may be subsonic in part and supersonic in part.

If the leading edge of the airfoil is sharp, the shock may be attached and linear until it becomes attenuated some distance out from the surface (Fig. 8.28(b)). Behind this shock the flow may be, and usually is for wings, supersonic over the whole airfoil. In this case, the whole regime is of *supersonic* flow, and a different analysis is required.

As the Mach number increases still further, the shock lines are inclined at very small angles to the surface, and somewhere about $M_\infty = 5$ we enter the *hypersonic* region. Here the flow pattern changes but little with Mach

Figure 8.28

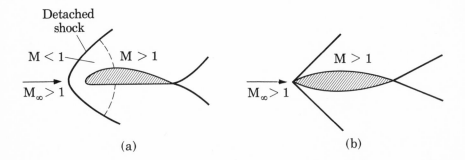

(a)   (b)

number, and major changes are due to temperature distribution. The temperature change across shocks of high Mach number is large, and the gas may become reactive. Because very high speeds are possible only at high altitudes, the situation may be complicated by an air density so low that continuum flow as defined in Chapter 1 is no longer a valid hypothesis. With a very low density, the molecular structure is significant, and the domain is one of *slip* flow, as the no-slip condition postulated previously no longer holds. At lower pressures still, individual molecules become important, and the domain is one of *free-molecule* flow. For an understanding of the features of high-speed flow as shown in Figs. 8.27 and 8.28, it will be necessary to analyze two-dimensional supersonic flow to supplement the one-dimensional treatment for flow in ducts.

8.20   *Two-dimensional supersonic flow*

The ideas of wave-propagation velocity, a, flow velocity, V, and their ratio, $V/a = \mathrm{M}$, the Mach number, will be recalled from Sects. 4.27 and 4.28. Consider now a very small particle traveling with velocity V in a straight line in still air, initially with $V < a$, i.e., $\mathrm{M} < 1$. We call it a "particle" for convenience only, as formally it should be designated a "point source" of no magnitude. The disturbance or infinitesimal pressure impulse caused by the particle is propagated radially outward at velocity a. We shall confine ourselves to two-dimensional flow; i.e., a diagram gives a representative cross section of the flow pattern.

Consider successive constant intervals of time, Δt, with the body successively at points A, B, C, and D, so that the time interval between A and D is $3\,\Delta t$ (Fig. 8.29(a)). When the particle is at D, the pressure pulse initiated at A has spread to a circle of radius $3a\,\Delta t$. Two time intervals previously, the particle was at B, and the disturbance from B has traveled out to a circle of radius $2a\,\Delta t$. Likewise, one interval previously, the particle was at C, and the disturbance initiated at C has traveled a radial distance $a\,\Delta t$. Because the pulse is traveling faster than the particle, it always stays "ahead" of the particle itself; i.e., the presence of the particle is communicated everywhere, and the streamlines adjust themselves as we have assumed implicitly in all the previous discussions for flow around bodies. The figure shows a finite number of stations, and for an infinite number of infinitesimal time intervals, the whole system is in a state of continuous change. As $V \rightarrow a$, the loci of pulses at successive equal time increments crowd together on the left-hand side, and when $V = a$, the picture of Fig. 8.29(b) is obtained, with the pressure pulse from the particle traveling at the same speed as the particle,

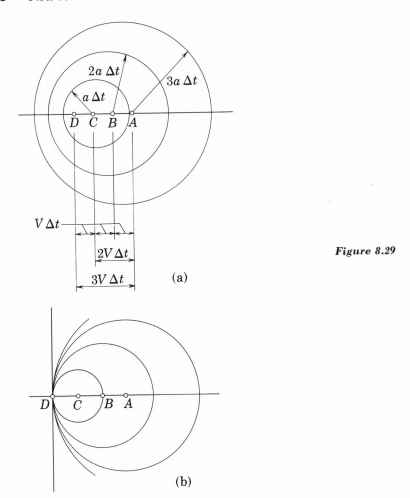

Figure 8.29

(a)

(b)

giving a plane front to the loci of disturbances. To the left of this front, i.e., ahead of the particle, no advance notice has been given of the travel of the particle, and so this area of fluid is undisturbed, all changes taking place to the right.

Now consider the particle (point source) having $V > a$, as shown in Fig. 8.30(a). In this case, the particle is out ahead of the corresponding disturbance circle for a given time interval, and the region in which any change has been communicated lies within the wedge formed by the lines tangent to the circles. Any part of the field outside this wedge has not been made aware of the presence of the particle. These two regions have been called by von Karman the "zone of action" and "zone of silence," respectively.

From Fig. 8.30(b), the semi-angle of the wedge, μ, is related to the propagation and particle velocities, since, from the geometry,

$$\sin \mu = \frac{a \, \Delta t}{V \, \Delta t} = \frac{a}{V} = \frac{1}{V/a} = \frac{1}{M} \qquad [8.55a]$$

or
$$\mu = \sin^{-1} \frac{1}{M} \qquad [8.55b]$$

The angle μ is called the *Mach angle,* and the lines of the wedge boundary are called *Mach lines.*

The same situation arises if the particle is *fixed* in space and the fluid flows from left to right with velocity V. This is equivalent to imposing velocity V on the whole system. One might regard the "signals" from the particle when encountered by the fluid as swept downstream at a higher velocity than they are transmitted transversely, thus leading to the line of state change, the Mach line.

It should be carefully noted that the foregoing discussion concerns an infinitesimal particle or, in the limit, a "point," and so the Mach line is a characteristic line associated with the Mach number, its inclination being given by Eq. 8.55. A Mach line can be drawn from a point in a supersonic flow field even though there is no actual disturbance at the point. A very small finite disturbance causes a very small finite change, and this is propagated as a *Mach wave.*

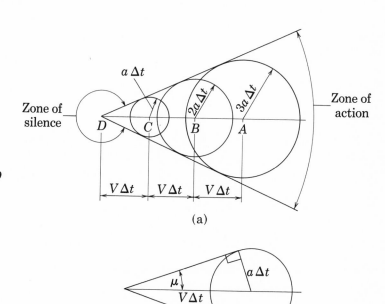

Figure 8.30

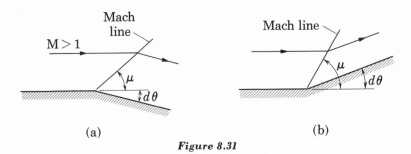

Figure 8.31

8.21   *Supersonic flow with deflection*

Now consider a flow that is initially parallel to a surface and that encounters an *infinitesimally small* change of direction of the surface. The two possibilities are shown in Fig. 8.31, one for an exterior (convex) corner or deflection away from the flow (a) and the other for an interior (concave) corner or deflection into the flow (b). In the diagram the turn angle, $d\theta$, is exaggerated for clarity, but it must be regarded as infinitesimal. With the corner, which represents an infinitesimal disturbance, the Mach line makes a Mach angle, μ, corresponding to the approach Mach number and with respect to the approach streamline direction. Since the approach flow is uniform and the Mach line is linear, the flow behind the line must be uniform and parallel to the new direction. The conditions governing this flow around a corner will now be examined, with the exterior corner as the example.

8.22   *Supersonic flow around a corner—Prandtl-Meyer flow*

Fig. 8.32 shows a flow of uniform supersonic velocity, V, approaching an infinitesimal turn, $d\theta$, making the Mach angle μ with the initial direction. No change of state occurs *along* the Mach line, since this is the locus of the points resulting from the propagation of the disturbance (the corner) into the approach flow, and all changes must occur normal to it. The velocity after the Mach line is crossed is $V + dV$ parallel to the new direction of the surface. The velocities are resolved into normal components (V_n) and tangential components (V_t). The process is governed by continuity and momentum and is taken to be reversibly adiabatic, since the changes are infinitesimal and shear is excluded.

First, from continuity,

$$\rho V_n = (\rho + d\rho)(V_n + dV_n)$$

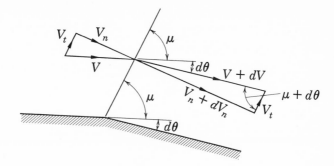

Figure 8.32

from which

$$dV_n = -V_n \frac{d\rho}{\rho} \qquad [8.56]$$

For momentum *along* the Mach line, with no pressure change,

$$\Sigma F = \frac{\Delta(\dot{m}V)}{g_c}$$

and

$$0 = (\rho + d\rho)(V_n + dV_n)(V_t + dV_t) - \rho V_n V_t$$

With ρV_n substituted for the mass flow in the first right-hand expression, this reduces to

$$0 = V_t + dV_t - V_t$$

and $dV_t = 0$ as we expect.

For momentum *across* the Mach line, we can use the simple Euler equation, since the flow is ideal; hence

$$\frac{dp}{\rho} + \frac{V_n \, dV_n}{g_c} = 0$$

or

$$dV_n = -\frac{g_c}{V_n} \frac{dp}{\rho}$$

Substituting for dV_n from the continuity relationship, Eq. 8.56, we obtain

$$-V_n \frac{d\rho}{\rho} = -\frac{g_c}{V_n} \frac{dp}{\rho}$$

and

$$V_n{}^2 = g_c \frac{dp}{d\rho} = a^2$$

where a is the acoustic velocity. Thus the normal component of flow velocity is the propagation velocity, again as we might expect from the definition of Mach line.

We want to find the velocity change, dV, as a function of the change of direction, $d\theta$. Looking at the two velocity triangles in Fig. 8.32 and noting the geometry for the angles, we see that

$$V_t = V \cos \mu = (V + dV) \cos (\mu + d\theta)$$

Expanding $\cos (\mu + d\theta)$ yields

$$V \cos \mu = (V + dV)(\cos \mu \cos d\theta - \sin \mu \sin d\theta)$$

Now $d\theta$ is infinitesimal, and in the limit $\cos d\theta \to 1$, and $\sin d\theta \to d\theta$. Hence

$$V \cos \mu = (V + dV)(\cos \mu - \sin \mu \, d\theta)$$

Dividing through by $\sin \mu$ and simplifying, we have

$$dV \cot \mu = (V + dV) \, d\theta$$

and dropping the second-order differential, $dV \, d\theta$, we have

$$d\theta = \frac{dV}{V} \cot \mu$$

From the definition of $\mu = \sin^{-1} (1/M)$, then $\cot \mu = \sqrt{M^2 - 1}$, and so

$$d\theta = \sqrt{M^2 - 1} \frac{dV}{V} \qquad [8.57]$$

The infinitesimal turn angle $d\theta$ has been taken as positive in this analysis, so that an increase of angle implies an increase of velocity, i.e., an expansion. Substituting from the Euler equation gives us

$$d\theta = \sqrt{M^2 - 1} \left(- g_c \frac{dp}{\rho V^2} \right) = - \frac{\sqrt{M^2 - 1}}{kM^2} \frac{dp}{p} \qquad [8.58]$$

i.e., for $M > 1$, an increase of $d\theta$ is accompanied by a decrease of pressure, or an expansion.

Concomitant with this result, a negative $d\theta$, or interior turn, must be accompanied by a *compression* and a *reduction* of velocity. This flow regime at supersonic velocity is known as *Prandtl-Meyer flow around a corner*.

8.23   *Supersonic flow around a finite corner*

The foregoing discussion dealt with an infinitesimal turn, and we can conceive of a number of infinitesimal turns in series, as shown in Fig. 8.33. Fig. 8.33(a) shows an exterior turn. Since each turn is an *expansion*, the Mach number increases, and the corresponding value of μ decreases; i.e., succeeding Mach lines make increasingly smaller angles with the flow direc-

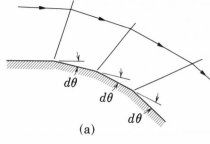

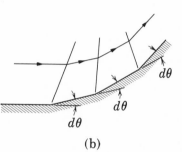

Figure 8.33

(a)

(b)

tion. Therefore, the Mach lines diverge and do not interfere with one another. Exactly the opposite holds for an interior turn (Fig. 8.33(b)), in which the Mach lines *converge*.

Any finite turn, no matter how small, is made up of an infinite number of infinitesimal turns, and so for a sharp, finite turn, we get the picture of Fig. 8.34. For an exterior, expansion turn, Fig. 8.34(a), the result is a "fan" of Mach lines radiating from the corner, with an infinite number of infinitesimal turns and expansions between the initial and final Mach lines, which have Mach angles μ_1 and μ_2, respectively. It is possible to integrate Eq. 8.58, converting velocity, V, into Mach numbers and a finite turn, θ. The resulting expression is known as the *Prandtl-Meyer equation* and may be used for quantitative analysis. However, we shall not go into it, as our purpose is a qualitative understanding.

For an interior, compression turn, Fig. 8.34(b), we have the theoretical result depicted, with increasing values of μ and with Mach lines for succeeding points being in front of each other. Since this situation is clearly impossible, the rays are shown as broken lines. What actually happens is outlined in Fig. 8.34(c); the Mach lines of the first few points (in exaggerated scale) coalesce into a finite compression wave. For a very small turn, the individual Mach lines are separate, but in a very short distance from the surface, they combine to form the finite change. This coalescence of small state changes creates a discontinuity, an *oblique shock wave*. For this case, the preceding analysis is no longer valid, as the change is not infinitesimal

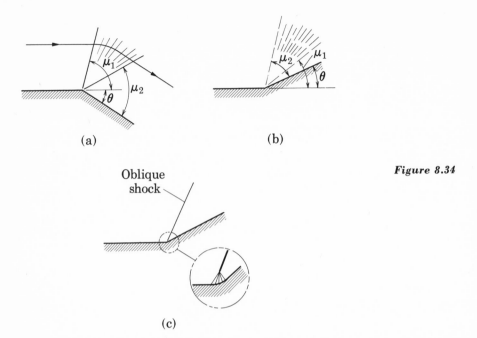

(a)   (b)

(c)

Figure 8.34

or reversible, and a new analysis is necessary, which will be presented in the next section.

In summary, then, supersonic flow around an exterior turn involves a series of reversible expansion processes, producing increases of velocity and Mach number. Supersonic flow around an interior turn involves a single compressive process, yielding an oblique shock wave, and the discontinuous state change is not necessarily reversible.

8.24   *Oblique shock waves*

The diagram for an oblique shock wave, Fig. 8.35, is very similar to that for Prandtl-Meyer flow. However, the change across the shock is finite, with the shock angle, β, being unknown. The deflection angle, θ, is finite, and the velocity changes are not infinitesimal. Again all state changes occur normal to the shock, and V_t is constant.

As before, the equations of continuity and momentum are invoked, but an integrated form of the latter must be used instead of the Euler equation, which is valid only in terms of infinitesimal changes. The flow is adiabatic but not necessarily reversible, for although no wall shear stress is assumed,

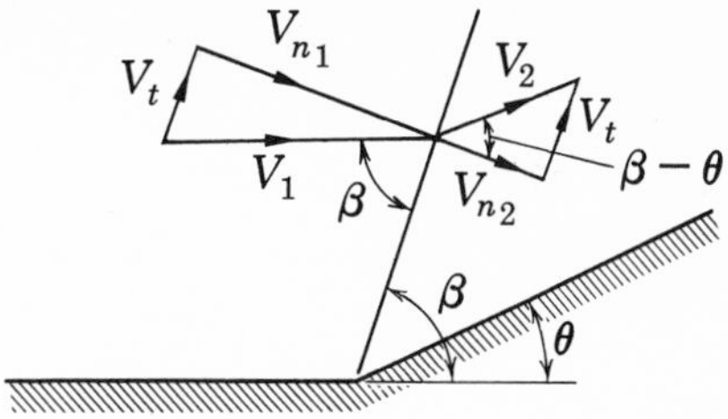

Figure 8.35

there may be an internal irreversibility. The energy equation also provides convenient relationships.

From the continuity equation,

$$\rho_1 V_{n_1} = \rho_2 V_{n_2} \qquad\qquad [8.59]$$

From the momentum equation,

for the tangential direction, $V_{t_1} = V_{t_2} = V_t \qquad\qquad [8.60]$

for the normal direction, $p_1 - p_2 = \dfrac{\rho_2 V_{n_2}{}^2 - \rho_1 V_{n_1}{}^2}{g_c} \qquad\qquad [8.61]$

From the energy equation (with T_0 constant),

$$c_p(T_1 - T_2) = \frac{V_2{}^2 - V_1{}^2}{2g_c}$$

and with $p = \rho RT$, $c_p/R = k/(k-1)$, and $V^2 = V_n{}^2 + V_t{}^2$,

$$\frac{k}{k-1}\left(\frac{p_2}{\rho_2} - \frac{p_1}{\rho_1}\right) = \frac{V_{n_1}{}^2 V_{n_2}{}^2}{2g_c} \qquad\qquad [8.62]$$

When the upstream or initial condition is known, Eqs. 8.59 to 8.62 are sufficient for solving for the four unknowns, p_2, ρ_2, V_{n_2}, and V_t. There are two more parameters, the shock angle, β, and the turn or wedge angle, θ. Since $V_2{}^2 = V_n{}^2 + V_t{}^2$, we can solve in terms of p_2, ρ_2, and V_2 (or M_2 via the equation of state) and a choice of β or θ.

We shall not develop these relationships, but it should be noted that $M_{n_1} = M_1 \sin \beta$ and $M_{n_2} = \sin(\beta - \theta)$. The M_n components are *normal shock* components, and their equations, together with $V_{t_1} = V_{t_2} = V_t$, lead to solutions for many problems.

When we have solved Eqs. 8.59 to 8.62, we can plot β vs. θ, with M_1 as parameter. The result is shown in Fig. 8.36. The following points can be observed:

1. For any given M_1 and θ (less than θ_{max}), there are two possible values of β. The locus of values of θ_{max} is shown as a solid line across the figure.

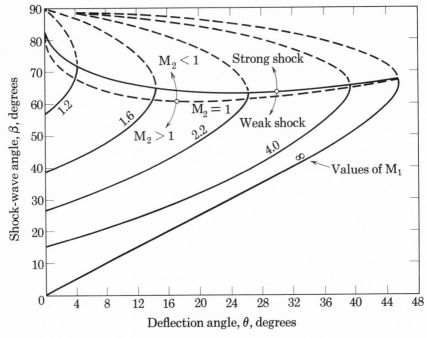

Figure 8.36

The larger value of β is known as the *strong* shock, and the smaller value as the *weak* shock. The dashed line across the figure is the locus of points of downstream Mach number of unity; above this line M_2 is subsonic, and below it M_2 is supersonic. Thus it is possible for the flow to be supersonic following an oblique shock. This is reasonable, in as much as the shock process is dependent on the normal components, V_n, as pointed out previously, and the total velocity, V_2, is the vector sum of V_{n_2} and V_t, which can be supersonic even if V_{n_2} is necessarily subsonic. The two lines of θ_{max} and $M_2 = 1$ are very close, and hence for strong shock the flow nearly always becomes subsonic. For weak shock the flow remains supersonic except for a very small range of θ, since $\theta_{max} - \theta$ for a given Mach number is less than half a degree all the way along the curves.

It is observed that in freestream flow, the *weak* shock nearly always occurs, and thus the flow continues to be supersonic. The reasons for this are not entirely clear but have to be connected with the pressures upstream as in normal shock in a nozzle.

2. It has already been implied that for any M_1 there is a maximum value of θ above which the shock equations yield no analytical answer. In a situation where θ is greater than θ_{max} for a given M_1, the shock becomes detached, as indicated in Fig. 8.28(a). The underlying reason for this is that

continuity must be preserved, and its preservation requires subsonic flow
as achieved through the normal shock region of the bow wave.

It should also be noted that the normal shock is a special case of the
oblique shock; i.e., $\theta = 0°$, and $\beta = 90°$. In this case, the rather cumbersome
expressions for the oblique shock are replaced by the simpler ones of Sect.
7.21. From the latter, it was found that there is a loss of useful energy across
a shock, measured as a decrease of stagnation pressure (although the total
energy as T_0 remains constant). Again without developing the relationships
explicitly, we see that there is a similar loss across an oblique shock. For a
given M_1, this loss is less than in the corresponding normal shock, because
only the normal component, $M_{n_1} = M_1 \cos \beta$, is effective. We may make use
of this circumstance in achieving subsonic flow from originally supersonic
flow, causing a succession of oblique shocks to occur rather than a single
normal shock. If the number of such weak shocks is very large, the flow
approaches the condition of Prandtl-Meyer flow for compression, i.e., reversible flow across Mach lines as shown in Fig. 8.31.

8.25 *Supersonic flow over wings—wave drag*

The analysis of expansion and compression turning of a supersonic flow leads
to a reasonable comprehension of the major aspects of supersonic flight.

In the first place, the leading edge of a wing should be pointed, with a
small wedge angle, so that an oblique shock is obtained rather than a
detached, almost normal, shock of greater loss. This small wedge angle
requires, for a given chord, that the wing must be thin. We may depict a
supersonic airfoil as a symmetrical double wedge or diamond shape for
clarity, as in Fig. 8.37(a).

At the leading edge, there is a shock wave caused by the interior turn,
yielding the weak solution, so that although the flow is decelerated and

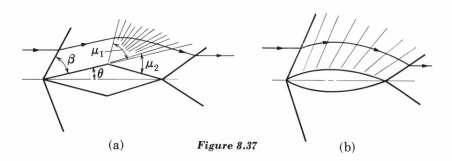

(a)   *Figure 8.37*   (b)

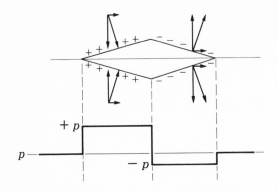

Figure 8.38

compressed, it is still supersonic. The flow remains uniform until the exterior turn at the mid-section is encountered, when the fluid is again deflected but this time accelerated and expanded. The flows from both sides of the rear surface meet, and the line of symmetry is equivalent to a solid surface, so that the effect is one of an interior turn, producing trailing-edge shocks. A biconvex airfoil, as shown in Fig. 8.37(b), is similar in principle, but expansion occurs continually from front to rear, and the possible intersection of Mach lines with shocks could produce a more complex pattern.

The compression and expansion over the surfaces of a wing produce the pressure pattern shown below the profile in Fig. 8.38. This profile is symmetrical and is placed at zero angle of attack. The leading-edge shock produces a rise of pressure and thus an inwardly directed force normal to the front surfaces. The expansion produces a drop of pressure below that of the freestream and thus an outwardly directed force normal to the rear surfaces. The trailing-edge shocks produce no effect on the airfoil itself. Resolving these forces into components normal and parallel to the freestream, we see that the normal components cancel out and thus produce no lift, which is what we might expect from a symmetrical airfoil with a zero angle of attack. The parallel components, however, all act in a *rearward* direction, thus producing a drag force. This drag is called *wave drag* and is inherent in supersonic flow. It has no connection with boundary-layer and viscous effects, which are additional.

Wave drag is minimized by a small wedge angle, as the rearward component of the normal force is reduced. This reinforces the necessity for thin wings in supersonic flow. Although the mechanisms are completely different, one may note that wave drag is another kind of "induced" drag, analogous to the inherent induced drag of finite airfoils in subsonic flow.

Wave drag is decreased if the leading edge is inclined spanwise to the freestream. This arrangement is shown in Fig. 8.39 and is called *sweepback*. The freestream velocity has two components with respect to the wing, a spanwise component, $U_\infty \sin \sigma$, and a normal component, $U_\infty \cos \sigma$. The

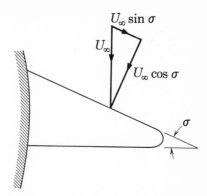

Figure 8.39

former has no effect on the ideal flow (although it does influence the boundary layer). If the normal component, $U_\infty \cos \sigma$, is less than the acoustic velocity, then the wing behaves as if in a subsonic flow, and wave drag is absent.

8.26   *Supersonic flow over wings—lift and drag*

A symmetrical airfoil at zero angle of attack has no lift, as is shown by the pressure distribution of Fig. 8.36. Lift is produced by a finite angle of attack and by a nonsymmetrical airfoil. Since the equations of motion for compressible flow, even without viscous effects, are intractable for general solution, simplifying assumptions must be made to *linearize* them, but even so solutions are not simple. Nevertheless, we shall have to content ourselves here with such a linearized solution for the symmetrical, wedge-shaped airfoil of Figs. 8.37 and 8.38, for which it can be demonstrated that

$$C_L \approx \frac{4\alpha}{\sqrt{M_\infty{}^2 - 1}} \qquad [8.63]$$

and

$$C_D \approx -\frac{4\alpha^2}{\sqrt{M_\infty{}^2 - 1}} + \frac{4}{\sqrt{M_\infty{}^2 - 1}}\left(\frac{t}{c}\right)^2 \qquad [8.64]$$

where α is the angle of attack and t/c is the thickness ratio. These relationships do not apply when $M_\infty \to 1$, i.e., in the transonic regime, and obviously are not valid when $M = 1$. For simple supersonic flow, however, Eq. 8.63 shows that the lift coefficient is directly proportional to the angle of attack and decreases as M_∞ increases. Eq. 8.64 for the drag coefficient has two terms, the first being due to the angle of attack and the second being dependent only on thickness, in line with the discussions of Sect. 8.25. If the thickness component is relatively small, then $C_L/C_D \approx 1/\alpha$. Therefore, for optimum performance, a supersonic wing should operate at a small angle of attack and have a small relative thickness.

8.27   *Drag of miscellaneous shapes in high-speed flow*

As might be expected, the drag of miscellaneous shapes covers a considerable range of behavior. Because of the influence of the wedge angle on the flow pattern, it is more important to streamline the forepart of a body than the rear part (as for low-speed flow). In fact, the trailing edge can be blunt at high Mach numbers, because it approaches a minimum of zero pressure and then streamlining has no effect.

Fig. 8.40 shows qualitatively the difference in behavior between a sharp-nosed body and a blunt-nosed body over a range of Mach number. C_D for both bodies increases rapidly in the transonic range, and that for the blunt-nosed body continues to increase, as a detached shock is always present. That for the sharp-nosed body exhibits a maximum at a Mach number slightly greater than unity, but then decreases gradually, more or less following the relationship of Eq. 8.64.

Maximum C_D for thin sections occurs in the transonic region $0.8 < M < 1.2$, and this led to the idea of the "sonic barrier," particularly for wing sections having a very low C_D at low speeds, as they are well streamlined, but having a very rapidly increasing C_D at transonic speeds. A theoretical expression for drag due to subsonic compressibility shows that $C_D \propto 1/\sqrt{1 - M_\infty^2}$, and Eq. 8.64 for supersonic flow shows that $C_D \propto 1/\sqrt{M_\infty^2 - 1}$. Both relationships point to infinite C_D at $M_\infty = 1$; but it was known in the days before supersonic flight of aircraft that projectiles pass

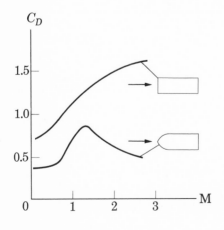

Figure 8.40

through the "sound barrier," and it was apparent that C_D is finite at M $= 1$ and sufficiently low to allow supersonic flight. The advent of the turbojet engine permitted the concentration of great power in a much smaller compass, and a detailed study of the central problem enables supersonic flight to become routine.

8.28   *Supersonic flow of nozzles*

The one-dimensional analysis of shock in Chapter 7 was quite satisfactory for flow in nozzles when the normal shock occurred inside the nozzle itself. Recalling the general behavior, Fig. 8.41 shows the pressure distribution for several situations: wholly subsonic flow, line A; M $= 1$ at the throat followed by subsonic flow, line B; supersonic flow beyond the throat and then shock, followed by subsonic flow, line C; supersonic flow with a normal shock at exit, line D; and supersonic flow throughout, line E.

   For back pressures p_A, p_B, p_C, and p_D, the nozzle-exit pressure is such that the exit flow is subsonic. The exit flow mixes with the surrounding fluid, dissipating its kinetic energy by turbulence and finally by viscous action. This analysis leaves unsolved the problems of the behavior of the flow with a back pressure between p_D and p_E and the behavior of the supersonic flow at pressure p_E and, in particular, pressures below p_E. The two-dimensional theory helps to provide solutions to these problems.

Figure 8.41

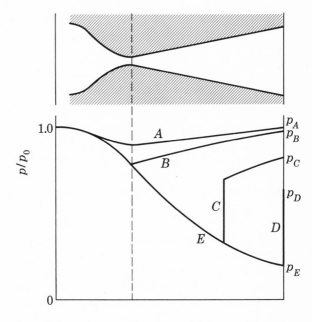

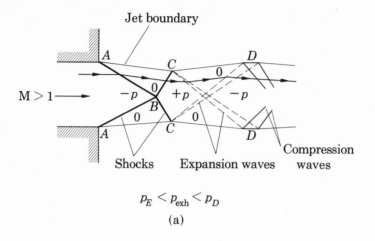

$$p_E < p_{exh} < p_D$$

(a)

Figure 8.42

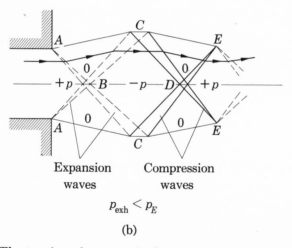

$$p_{exh} < p_E$$

(b)

The turning of supersonic flow with compression or expansion was analyzed by means of a disturbance due to a solid surface. The effect is propagated out into the flow along Mach lines, which if convergent yield a finite shock. A disturbance can occur as a change of pressure without the presence of a solid surface. Such an instance is that of a gas, flowing supersonically in a nozzle at some pressure controlled by the cross-sectional area of the containing surface, that suddenly enters a region of different pressure. For the nozzle-flow regime of Fig. 8.41, the gas right at the nozzle exit is at pressure p_E, and the receiver or exhaust pressure is at some higher value between p_E and p_D. A normal shock yields p_D only, and some lower value of recompression is necessary. On the other hand, if the exhaust pressure is lower than p_E, expansion is required.

In the former case, the initial adjustment is via oblique shock waves from the exit of the nozzle, as shown in Fig. 8.42(a). The boundary of the flow, AC, must be one of constant (exhaust) pressure, and the shock waves, AB, are of such strength as to provide this. For a given nozzle-exit Mach number and pressure, then, the shock angle and flow direction are fixed. Waves AB cross at B, and thus the flow passes through another shock, BC, of such strength as to produce flow parallel to the axis. However, having traversed another shock, it is again at a higher pressure than the ambient pressure. Shock waves BC meet the flow boundary at C, where the pressure has to be the ambient pressure, and are "reflected" as *expansion* waves, CD. The flow passes through waves CD and is expanded to ambient pressure. Waves CD meet at D and, because the pressure at D is the ambient pressure, are reflected as *compression* waves. From then on, all further reflections at the boundaries are expansion of compression waves and the process is repeated cyclically in ideal flow. In practice, viscous action at the jet boundaries slows down the fluid, and only a few "shock diamonds" are obtained. This case of nozzle-exit pressure *lower* than exhaust pressure is called *overexpansion*.

The opposite case of *underexpansion*, with exhaust pressure lower than nozzle-exit pressure, is shown in Fig. 8.42(b). Here the fluid must expand and does so through a series of Mach lines originating at the nozzle exit, of which only the initial and final lines appear in the figure. The flow is expanded to the ambient pressure through AB but is again expanded to a lower pressure through the continuation lines, BC. The expansion fan is reflected from the constant-pressure boundary as compression waves, and the fluid is compressed in crossing lines CD and recompressed in crossing lines DE. These lines are reflected as expansion waves at E, and from then on the process is ideally cyclic. Again viscosity acts as a damping influence, and in addition the compression waves from C tend to coalesce and form finite shocks, which break up the pattern.

Problems

8.1. Find the ratio of δ/δ^* for a boundary layer that is (a) linear as given by $u/U_\infty = y/\delta$, and (b) parabolic as given by $u/U_\infty = 2(y/\delta) - (y/\delta)^2$. (Hint: Replace y/δ by ζ, and obtain a finite limit of integration.)

8.2. Estimate the ratio of the laminar boundary-layer thickness at a given distance from the leading edge for *air* at 100 ft/sec and standard atmospheric density to that for *water* at 5 ft/sec and 70°F.

8.3. A thin plate 2 ft long and 1 ft wide is suspended in a uniform stream of water moving at a velocity of 2 ft/sec and having a temperature of 50°F. The angle of incidence is zero.

    a. Will the entire boundary layer on the plate be laminar?

    b. What are the minimum and maximum boundary-layer thicknesses, and where are they found?

    c. Find the force component parallel to the direction of water flow necessary to hold the plate in position.

    d. Plot the shear stress at the plate surface against x/L.

    e. Plot v at $y = \delta/2$ and $y = \infty$ against x/L.

8.4. For a given plate of length L, find the ratio of the total drag force in water to that in air at atmospheric pressure, if the plate Reynolds number is the same in both fluids. Take temperatures of 59°F for water and 77°F for air.

8.5. Which of the following velocity distributions, u/U_∞, satisfy the *minimum* boundary conditions for flow along a flat plate ($\zeta = y/\delta$)? (a) e^ζ, (b) $\sin(\pi\zeta/2)$, (c) $\zeta - \zeta^2$, (d) $2\zeta - \zeta^3$, (e) $2\zeta - 2\zeta^3 + \zeta^4$.

8.6. Find the boundary-layer thickness and local drag coefficients for a flat plate with a laminar boundary layer, assuming a linear velocity distribution, $u/U_\infty = y/\delta$. Compare the results with those for the exact solution and for the assumed parabolic distribution of Sect. 8.7.

8.7. Repeat Problem 8.6 for $u/U_\infty = \frac{3}{2}(y/\delta) - \frac{1}{2}(y/\delta)^3$.

8.8. For flow around an immersed body under conditions in which inertia, surface-tension, gravitational, and compressibility effects are negligible, show by means of dimensional analysis and the definition of drag coefficient, C_D, that C_D must be inversely proportional to the Reynolds number.

8.9. Derive a relationship for the thickness of a turbulent boundary layer as δ/x, assuming a "sixth-root" law ($n = 6$) and a friction factor, $f = 0.216/\mathrm{Re}^{0.2}$.

8.10. A thin rectangular plate is towed through water at 70°F at a velocity of 20 ft/sec. Assuming that the boundary layer is turbulent from the leading edge,

    a. What is the thickness of the boundary layer 3 ft from the leading edge?

    b. In the section where $x = 3$ ft, what is the velocity at a point where $y = \delta/2$?

8.11. A very thin, smooth, flat plate is set parallel to an air stream having a velocity of 200 ft/sec, a pressure of 15.2 psia, and a temperature of 77°F. The plate has a dimension of 5 ft in the flow direction and is 12 ft wide (span).

    a. Assuming that a laminar boundary layer exists over the whole plate, calculate the thickness of the boundary layer at the trailing edge and the total drag on the plate.

    b. Repeat a, assuming that the boundary layer is wholly turbulent.

c. Find the total drag, assuming that transition occurs at a Reynolds number of 3×10^5.

8.12. An automobile with a projected area of 20 ft^2 has a drag coefficient of 0.3. What is the horsepower required to overcome air friction at 70 mph in still air at 60°F?

8.13. If the vertical component of the landing velocity of a parachute is equal to that acquired during a free fall of 6 ft, find the diameter of the open parachute (hollow hemisphere), assuming a total weight of 250 lb and an air density of 2.4×10^{-3} slug/ft^3.

8.14. Find the ratio of the velocities of a 0.20 in. diameter spherical drop of water falling at constant velocity through air and a 0.20 in. diameter spherical bubble rising at constant velocity through water. Assume air at 50°F and 29.92 in. Hg and water at the same temperature.

8.15. Several types of furnaces burning pulverized solid fuel are based on what is called the "cyclone" principle (see the diagram). Fuel particles and air enter the

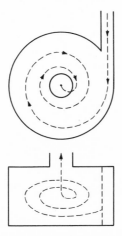

chamber tangentially, and the particles are ignited. A particle loses mass as it pursues an inward spiral course, ideally being completely burnt as it nears the center so that only combustion gases pass up the central tube. Considering a particle as spherical and whirling in a horizontal plane, calculate the inward radial velocity component of the air at entry necessary for the particle to be in equilibrium, if at entry the tangential velocity, V_u, is 150 ft/sec, the radius, r, is 9 in., the particle density, ρ_p, is 79 lb/ft^3, and the particle diameter is 0.0002 in. The air at entry is at 15 psia and 200°C. (Note: The radial velocity is very low, of the order of a few ft/sec.)

8.16. Find the steady-state rotational speed in rpm of the two-cup anemometer in the diagram for a wind velocity of 30 mph. Consider only the position shown, with the arm normal to the wind direction. Assume standard atmospheric conditions and zero mechanical friction.

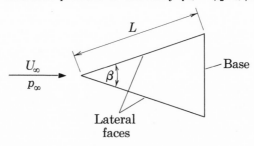

8.17. Find the force exerted by a 90 mph wind blowing at right angles to a billboard measuring 12 ft × 35 ft with the bottom edge 8 ft above the ground (i.e., assume no ground effect).

8.18. A long, wedge-shaped strut is immersed in a subsonic fluid stream as shown. Assume that the base-area pressure is uniformly $p_\infty - \frac{1}{2}U_\infty^2/2g_c$ and that the

surface pressure elsewhere is uniformly p_∞. Using the frictional-drag characteristics of a laminar boundary layer on a flat plate for the lateral faces of the wedge,

a. Derive an expression for the total drag force per unit strut length.

b. Find the strut drag coefficient referred to the base area of the strut.

8.19. If an edgewise flat plate with a laminar boundary layer is porous and fluid is sucked into the plate so as to induce a normal velocity component, U_S, at the surface, with U_S small compared to U_∞, show that

$$\frac{\tau_0}{\rho U_\infty^2/g_c} = \frac{U_S}{U} + \frac{d\delta}{dx}\int_0^1 f(\zeta)[1 - f(\zeta)]\, d\zeta$$

where $\zeta = y/\delta$.

8.20. The effective lift coefficient for an aircraft is 0.47. The wing area applicable to this lift coefficient is 750 ft². Find the maximum weight of aircraft that can be flown at a uniform forward speed of 480 mph at ground-level conditions. What must be the lift coefficient for a forward speed of 600 mph at an altitude of 50,000 ft? For the sea-level case, if the effective drag coefficient is 0.042 relative to an effective area of 267 ft², find the necessary engine thrust.

8.21. For an oblique shock with an angle of 80° for a wedge half-angle of 10° in freestream flow, calculate the value of the initial Mach number by using the normal-shock components.

9

Propulsion

9.1 *Introduction*

The momentum theorem of fluid mechanics studied in Chapter 4 showed that a net force could be developed on a duct as the resultant of the pressure forces and rate of change of fluid momentum. This net force can be used for the *propulsion* of bodies through fluids, giving steady motion when it is just equal to the external resistance or drag due to the fluid and giving acceleration when it is greater than the drag.

It is customary to classify two means of fluid propulsion, one by means of a *propeller* and one by means of *jet propulsion*. In the former, an independent power supply is used to turn a set of blades, which accelerates the ambient fluid in freestream flow, thus creating an equal and opposite force for motion. In the latter, a stream of ducted fluid of high velocity is ejected rearward, this fluid often being the working fluid of the power-supply unit itself. The distinction is not clear-cut, as both mechanisms depend on the momentum principle, and different methods differ only in the treatment of the propelling fluid. In practice, jet propulsion may be further divided into *air-breathing thermal jets* and *rockets*.

Propellers, or *screws*, are used for ships universally and for a large number of aircraft. Their characteristic is that their power supply may be any shaft-power engine of suitable speed, such as a reciprocating gasoline or diesel engine, a steam or gas turbine, or an electric motor. The propulsive fluid is the ambient fluid and is entirely independent of the working fluid of the power supply. We might note here one of the difficulties of classification: a marine craft may have an independent power supply, such as an internal combustion engine, which delivers its energy to a pump, which in turn takes in the ambient fluid (water) and delivers it rearward with a high velocity through a nozzle. In this case, the pump operates as an enclosed propeller, and its action is most easily analyzed in terms of "jet propulsion." Air-breathing thermal jets use the ambient fluid as the working fluid of the power plant, taking in air, passing it through a heat-engine cycle, and delivering it at high velocity. Such units, then, are wholly dependent on the fluid in which they are propelled. The most familiar example is the *turbojet*, now fast becoming standard for aircraft propulsion. In the turbojet, a compressor gives the air a high pressure before delivering it to a combustor, where fuel is burnt to give the air a high temperature. The hot gases are then partially expanded through a turbine to supply the necessary compressor power, the remaining expansion being through a nozzle to give the useful propulsive power. In the *ramjet*, the pressure necessary for the cycle is produced by *ram compression*, i.e., the deceleration of the ambient air from the high velocity relative to the vehicle. The ramjet, then, is ideally a fluid-propulsion device with no moving parts, but it has a reasonable efficiency only at high speeds, where a high stagnation pressure is possible, and thus must first be accelerated to such speeds by other means. Rockets are characterized by the fact that they carry with them their own propulsive fluid and to this extent are independent of their environment. Therefore, they constitute the only possible means of propulsion outside the atmosphere, but they are limited as to duration of flight unless of very large size.

We shall analyze the propulsive effects of these various types of units in terms of the momentum theorem. In every case, we may either regard the unit as traveling forward into still fluid and use the symbol U for the vehicle velocity or regard the vehicle as stationary with the fluid having approach velocity U. This principle of superposition will make no difference to the result, provided that we are careful to define the fluid velocities with respect to a given coordinate system.

9.2   *Momentum analysis for fluid propulsion*

The general momentum equation for a control volume having a linear acceleration is

$$\Sigma \mathbf{F} = \frac{1}{g_c} \left(M \frac{d\mathbf{U}}{dt} + \frac{d}{dt} \int_R \rho \mathbf{V}_r \, dR + \int_S (\rho \mathbf{V}_r) \mathbf{V}_r \cdot d\mathbf{S} \right) \qquad [4.29]$$

Fig. 9.1 shows a typical propulsive duct, which can include any one of the various types of propulsion units mentioned. At the intake, station 1, the fluid velocity relative to the duct is $\mathbf{U}$ (or the duct moves to the left into fluid at rest with velocity $\mathbf{U}$). At the discharge, station 2, the fluid or

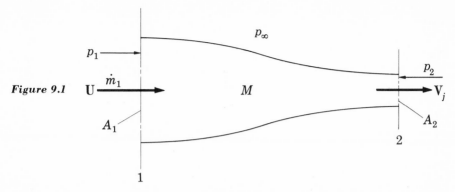

Figure 9.1

jet velocity is V_j *relative* to the duct. Absolute pressure p_1 acts on entry area A_1, through which the mass flow rate is $\dot{m}_1$. Similarly, at discharge, there is absolute pressure p_2 on area A_2 with flow rate $\dot{m}_2$. We shall consider only *steady* flow, so that the time rate of change of momentum within the control volume is zero. We shall also consider that the velocities, densities, and pressures are uniform and normal over areas A_1 and A_2, with the fluid velocity along the axis of the flight velocity. With these conditions, we drop the vector notation, and Eq. 4.29 for the force on the duct yields

$$F_d + p_1 A_1 - p_2 A_2 = \frac{1}{g_c} \left(M \frac{dU}{dt} + \dot{m}_2 V_j - \dot{m}_1 U \right)$$

or
$$F_d = p_2 A_2 - p_1 A_1 + \frac{1}{g_c} \left(M \frac{dU}{dt} + \dot{m}_2 V_j - \dot{m}_1 U \right)$$

F_d represents the external force on the moving duct, which in general is comprised of pressure forces, shear forces, and body forces. For the particular, but common, case where the ambient pressure is uniform and atmospheric, the pressure component of F_d is $- p_\infty (A_1 - A_2)$, and the expression becomes (see Sect. 4.12)

$$F_d = (p_2 - p_\infty) A_2 - (p_1 - p_\infty) A_1 + \frac{1}{g_c} \left(M \frac{dU}{dt} + \dot{m}_2 V_j - \dot{m}_1 U \right) \quad [\textbf{9.1}]$$

For a propulsive duct, then, F_d is the external shear force or friction drag of the duct, plus any body force (commonly gravity). We shall now look at some cases of special interest.

9.3   *Propellers*

The propeller is a very special case, because it is unenclosed; i.e., there is no solid duct. The propeller itself, consisting of a few large blades, commonly four, draws ambient fluid from the front, giving this fluid an increment of

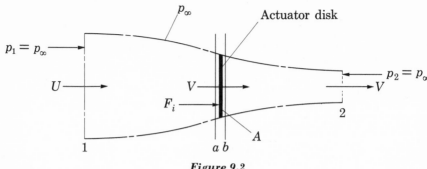

Figure 9.2

pressure as it passes through the blades. The fluid is then discharged rearward at a higher velocity. An exact analysis of propeller action is complex, but the main propulsive features are elucidated if the propeller is simulated by an *actuator disk* and assumptions are made with respect to the flow pattern.

Fig. 9.2 shows the idealized analytical picture. The propeller moves forward at velocity U, through undisturbed fluid, but it is convenient to use the principle of superposition as before and to consider the propeller stationary in a flow field of uniform velocity U. The assumption of incompressible ideal flow is made, together with that of uniform velocity and pressure across any plane normal to the axis. The control surface is formed by streamlines bounding the whole flow through the actuator disk simulating the propeller and thus constituting a large streamtube called the *slipstream*. The entry and exit sections, 1 and 2, are sufficiently far upstream and downstream that the pressure is ambient; i.e., $p_1 = p_2 = p_\infty$. The fluid is accelerated from 1 by the suction action of the actuator disk, undergoing a decrease of pressure to p_a at the front of the disk. Across the disk, the velocity is continuous and is denoted by V, but the pressure undergoes a discontinuous increment to p_b. Following passage through the disk, the fluid expands down to ambient pressure p_∞ again, accelerating to a velocity V_j There is a velocity discontinuity at the lateral boundary, but as the flow is considered ideal, there is no shear stress. Likewise, the pressure on the lateral boundary is taken as p_∞, which is again an idealization that can be justified by a detailed analysis.

With no net pressure force on the control surface given by planes 1 and 2 and the lateral boundary, the only force acting on the fluid is that due to the actuator disk, and this force must be to the right because the fluid acelerates between 1 and 2. It is designated as F_i in the figure, in accordance with the nomenclature in the discussion of momentum in Chapter 4 (e.g., Eq. 4.24). The external force, the force on the actuator disk (propeller), is equal and opposite and is the thrust, F_d, given to the disk by the driving engine. This force is equal to the pressure difference across the disk, $(p_b - p_a)A$; hence, for constant velocity, Eq. 9.1 becomes

$$F_d = (p_b - p_a)A = \frac{\dot{m}}{g_c}(V_j - U) \qquad [9.2]$$

With $\dot{m} = \rho V A$, this reduces to

$$p_b - p_a = \frac{\rho V}{g_c}(V_j - U) \qquad [9.3]$$

p_a and p_b can be expressed in terms of velocities by means of the Bernoulli equation. This can be written between stations 1 and a and between stations b and 2, because the flows in these regions are ideal and there is no work. Thus

$$p_1 + \frac{\rho U^2}{2g_c} = p_a + \frac{\rho V^2}{2g_c}$$

and

$$p_b + \frac{\rho V^2}{2g_c} = p_2 + \frac{\rho V_j^2}{2g_c}$$

From this pair of equations, noting that $p_1 = p_2$, we obtain

$$p_b - p_a = \frac{\rho}{2g_c}(V_j^2 - U^2) \qquad [9.4]$$

Equating Eqs. 9.4 and 9.3 to eliminate $p_b - p_a$ yields

$$\frac{\rho V}{g_c}(V_j - U) = \frac{\rho}{2g_c}(V_j^2 - U^2)$$

and so

$$V = \frac{V_j + U}{2} \qquad [9.5]$$

The fluid velocity at the disk is therefore the simple mean of the approach and discharge velocities, or, we can state that one-half of the velocity increment occurs before the disk and one-half after the disk.

The efficiency of the propeller as a propulsive device is defined as the ratio of the useful propulsive effect per unit time, E_u, to the rate at which energy is supplied, E_s. E_u is the product of the thrust of the propeller, F_d, and the forward velocity of the vehicle, U. The rate of energy supply is the product of the thrust, F_d, and the rate at which the fluid is given this thrust, namely, V, so that $E_s = F_d V$. Hence the propulsive efficiency, η_p, is

$$\eta_p = \frac{E_u}{E_s} = \frac{F_d U}{F_d V} = \frac{U}{V}$$

On substitution for V from Eq. 9.5, this becomes

$$\eta_p = \frac{2U}{U + V_j} \qquad [9.6]$$

Writing $V_j = U + \Delta V$, with ΔV the increment in velocity through the propeller, we obtain

$$\eta_p = \frac{2U}{2U + \Delta V}$$

from which we see that for maximum propulsive efficiency the velocity increment, ΔV, should be as small as possible. Thus the propeller is an efficient propulsive device when it provides a given mass of fluid with a small velocity increase, $V = V_j - U$. However, from Eq. 9.2, the result is a small thrust. To increase the thrust, either the efficiency must be lowered or the mass flow must be large, i.e., through a large area, A, meaning a large-diameter propeller. We shall return to the problem of propulsive efficiency in a more general manner later. This ideal analysis is modified for the flow of a real fluid, but the main conclusions are valid.

9.4   *Turbojets and ramjets*

Although turbojets and ramjets have to accelerate and decelerate, their performance characteristic of major interest is in level flight at constant velocity. In this case, $\dot{m}\, dU/dt = 0$, and the body force of gravity is also zero. Moreover, if only subsonic flight is considered, $p_1 = p_\infty$, and so the $(p_1 - p_\infty)A_1$ term disappears, too. However, if the nozzle is convergent only, it is possible for it to choke under certain conditions. Therefore, with the exit-pressure term retained, Eq. 9.1 becomes

$$F_d = \frac{\dot{m}_2 V_j}{g_c} - \frac{\dot{m}_1 U}{g_c} + (p_j - p_\infty)A_j \qquad [9.7]$$

For *complete expansion*, the pressure term disappears. The effect of incomplete expansion, as compared to that of complete expansion to p_∞, is to reduce the thrust, as V_j is reduced, but the loss is often relatively small. For simple analytical purposes, the inclusion of the pressure term is inconvenient, but it is very helpful to define an *equivalent jet velocity*, V_{je}. The fluid is regarded as completely expanded to p_∞ but giving only the effective jet velocity V_{je}, so that the thrust is the same as that actually given by incomplete expansion to velocity V_j and pressure p_j; i.e.,

$$F_d = \frac{\dot{m}_2 V_{je}}{g_c} - \frac{\dot{m}_1 U}{g_c} = \frac{\dot{m}_2 V_j}{g_c} + (p_j - p_\infty)A_j - \frac{\dot{m}_1 U}{g_c} \qquad [9.8]$$

from which

$$V_{je} = V_j + \frac{g_c(p_j - p_\infty)A}{\dot{m}_2} \qquad [9.9]$$

The use of V_{je} allows the thrust to be expressed in terms of rate of change of momentum only.

For turbojets, the difference between $\dot{m}_1$ and $\dot{m}_2$ is usually very small; $\dot{m}_2$ is greater than $\dot{m}_1$ by virtue of the fuel added for combustion, and this has a maximum value of about 2% of the air flow. It is quite common to "bleed" a quantity of air from the compressor to act as a coolant for the bearings and turbine disk, and this again is usually only 1% or so of the total air. The upshot is that, for all but a detailed analysis of a particular engine, $\dot{m}_1$ and $\dot{m}_2$ may be considered as equal, and thus we write $\dot{m}_1 = \dot{m}_2 = \dot{m}$.

For turbojets, then, we may summarize cases of especial interest as follows, remembering the conditions of subsonic, unaccelerated flight:

1a. Turbojet, constant forward speed, incomplete expansion,

$$F_d = \frac{\dot{m}}{g_c} (V_j - U) + (p_j - p_\infty)A_j = \frac{\dot{m}}{g_c} (V_{je} - U) \qquad [9.10a]$$

1b. Turbojet, constant forward speed, complete expansion,

$$F_d = \frac{\dot{m}}{g_c} (V_j - U) \qquad [9.10b]$$

2. Turbojet, stationary, complete expansion,

$$F_d = \frac{\dot{m} V_j}{g_c} \qquad [9.10c]$$

We may note from these relationships that the effect of forward speed is to *decrease* the thrust for a given mass flow and that the thrust goes to zero when the forward velocity equals the jet velocity. Hence an air-breathing thermal jet cannot travel at a velocity higher than its jet velocity. The "rating" of a turbojet given as some specified thrust in pounds is generally that of the stationary case, $\dot{m} V_j/g_c$, Eq. 9.10c, with possibly another, smaller, value being given for cruising speed at a certain altitude. We should also note that although case 1a for incomplete expansion includes an additional term due to pressure, the thrust is less than that for complete expansion, case 1b, as the jet velocity is lower. Although some turbojets do have a convergent-divergent nozzle for complete expansion, a simple convergent type is more common. One reason is that although full expansion is more efficient at the design condition, any over-expansion at off-design operation may lead to shock and loss of stagnation pressure (Sect. 7.21).

For ramjets, the fuel added for combustion may amount to the stoichiometric value, as there is no turbine to limit maximum temperature. This added fuel may be of the order of 5% of the air flow, and allowance must be made for it. If the ratio of mass flow rate of fuel to air is denoted by f, then $\dot{m}_2 = (1 + f)\dot{m}_1$.

Particular cases of the ramjet are then as follows:

1a. Ramjet, constant forward speed, incomplete expansion,

$$F_d = \frac{\dot{m}_1}{g_c}[(1+f)V_j - U] + (p_j - p_\infty)A_j \qquad [9.11a]$$

1b. Ramjet, constant forward speed, complete expansion,

$$F_d = \frac{\dot{m}_1}{g_c}[(1+f)V_j - U] \qquad [9.11b]$$

The stationary case is meaningless, because the ramjet must have forward speed to provide a "ram" pressure for the heat-engine cycle, this pressure being produced by the compressor in the turbojet.

These relationships for the ramjet are, of course, also applicable as more precise equations for the turbojet, as they take into account the addition of fuel.

9.5   *Rockets*

In a rocket, the propulsive fluid or *propellant* is carried by the vehicle itself and expelled rearward, so that no fluid crosses station 1. Hence $\dot{m}_1 = 0$, and $A_1 = 0$. The mass, M, continually decreases as propellant is used, and in general the vehicle is seldom in uniform motion. Thus the basic equation, Eq. 9.1, becomes, with $m_2 = \dot{m}_p$, the mass flow rate of propellant,

$$F_d = \frac{\dot{m}_p V_j}{g_c} + (p_j - p_\infty)A_j - \frac{M}{g_c}\frac{dU}{dt} \qquad [9.12]$$

F_d is the total external force on the rocket vehicle, consisting of fluid drag and body forces.

The major use of rockets is for missions outside the earth's atmosphere, and the time taken for travel in the atmosphere is very small. Solving the motion for travel in the atmosphere is a very complex problem, as the air density and the vehicle velocity vary continually. Hence the Reynolds and Mach numbers also change, and the drag calculation becomes a step-by-step process. Furthermore, the gravitational force of the earth is reduced significantly for the altitudes attained by rockets ($g \approx 29.1$ ft/sec^2 at a height of 200 miles, about 90% of the standard value), so that body force may be variable.

We shall confine ourselves here to the case of *linear motion* in *field-free space*, i.e., journeys outside the earth's atmosphere and outside any gravitational field. In this case, $F_d = 0$, and the whole thrust of the rocket is directly available for acceleration.

For a rocket operating in space, $p_\infty = 0$, but there will *always* be a $p_j A_j$ term, because the nozzle-area ratio, A_j/A^*, must be finite, whereas the pressure ratio for complete expansion, p_j/p_∞, is infinite. Thus it is convenient to use the equivalent jet velocity, V_{je}, defined previously, i.e., to regard the propellant as fully expanded to V_{je}, with V_{je} the velocity producing the actual thrust obtained with incomplete expansion. In rocket technology, this velocity is usually given the symbol c. In conformity with this usage, the gross thrust developed by the rocket is

$$\frac{\dot{m}_p c}{g_c} \equiv \frac{\dot{m}_p V_j}{g_c} + (p_j - p_\infty)A_j$$

For linear motion in field-free space, Eq. 9.12 then becomes

$$0 = \frac{\dot{m}_p c}{g_c} - \frac{M}{g_c}\frac{dU}{dt}$$

or

$$M\frac{dU}{dt} = \dot{m}_p c \qquad \textbf{[9.13]}$$

In Eq. 9.13, M is the instantaneous mass of the vehicle, which decreases continuously with time as propellant is used. If a constant propellant rate, $\dot{m}_p$, is assumed, then, with M_0 the initial mass of the rocket at time $t = 0$, the instantaneous mass after time t is

$$M = M_0 - \dot{m}_p t$$

Substituting for M in Eq. 9.11 yields

$$(M_0 - \dot{m}_p t)\frac{dU}{dt} = \dot{m}_p c \qquad \textbf{[9.14]}$$

Velocity c is usually constant for constant back pressure, as a programed combustion process is not yet common for rockets. Thus Eq. 9.14 can be integrated between limits of time $t = 0$ when $U = U_0$, an initial velocity, and time $t = t_b$, the *burning* time, when $U = U$. Thus

$$\int_{U_0}^{U} dU = \dot{m}_p c \int_0^{t_b} \frac{dt}{M_0 - \dot{m}_p t}$$

On integration,

$$U - U_0 = \Delta U = -c\left[\ln(M_0 - \dot{m}_p t_b) - \ln M_0\right] = -c\ln\frac{M_0 - \dot{m}_p t_b}{M_0}$$

If the burning time, t_b, is the total time for consumption of all the propellant, then $\dot{m}_p t_b = M_p$, the total propellant mass at $t = 0$. Hence

$$\Delta U = -c\ln\frac{M_0 - M_p}{M_0} = -c\ln(1 - \lambda) = c\ln\frac{1}{1-\lambda} \qquad \textbf{[9.15]}$$

where $\lambda = M_p/M_0$, the *propellant fraction*. Again, $M_0 - M_p$, the initial mass minus the propellant mass consumed, is the final mass of the rocket, M_t. Thus

$$\Delta U = -c \ln \frac{M_t}{M_0} = c \ln \frac{M_0}{M_t} = c \ln M_r \qquad [9.16]$$

where $M_r = M_0/M_t$, the *mass ratio* of the rocket.

Eq. 9.16 is the *simple, basic rocket equation*, and it is seen that the final velocity achieved is directly proportional to the effective exhaust velocity and to the *logarithm* of the mass ratio. For maximum rocket velocity, and hence distance, the mass ratio must be high; i.e., the propellant fraction must be large. The remainder of the mass, $M_0 - M_p = M_t$, consists of the *structure* mass (casing, tanks, etc.) and the *payload* mass. With the need for a large propellant fraction and an inescapable minimum of fixed structural mass, then the payload is necessarily small. Therefore, a very large rocket is needed to carry a relatively small payload.

The thrust of the rocket is $\dot{m}_p c/g_c$, and the ratio of thrust to rate of propellant flow is called the *specific impulse*, I_s. Thus

$$I_s = \frac{F_d}{\dot{m}_p} = \frac{\dot{m}_p c}{\dot{m}_p g_c} = \frac{c}{g_c} \qquad [9.17a]$$

or
$$c = g_c I_s \qquad [9.17b]$$

The units of I_s are pounds force per pound mass per second (lb_f-sec/lb_m), which are commonly reduced to "seconds." As $\Delta U \propto c \propto I_s$, there is

Figure 9.3

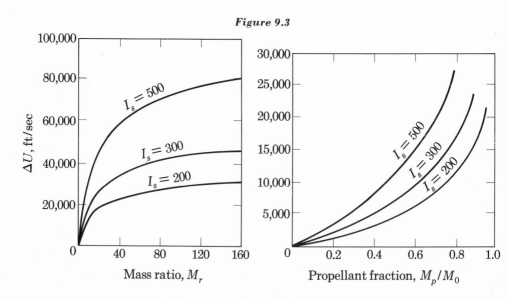

a constant search for propellants of high specific impulse. At the present time, solid propellants have $I_s \approx 180$ to 250 sec, and liquid propellants such as hydrocarbon–liquid oxygen (Lox) have $I_s \approx 240$ to 300 sec. One of the best realizable combinations is liquid hydrogen–Lox, with $I_s \approx 350$ to 420 sec.

The effects of mass ratio and propellant fraction are shown in Fig. 9.3, with M_r and M_p/M_0 plotted against the velocity increment, ΔU, for various values of specific impulse.

For long journeys into space, I_s values for chemical propellants like those mentioned are too low, and so other propulsive means must be considered, such as nuclear-power plants with hydrogen as propellant, electromagnetic methods utilizing ions, or plasmas. Some alleviation of the effect of mass ratio can be achieved by the discarding of part of the structure at intervals, i.e., by the use of several rocket *stages* rather than one large single stage. This is the usual practice for placing satellites into orbit and for lunar and interplanetary probes.

9.6 *Propulsive efficiency*

For a propulsive duct, useful work is done at a rate equal to the thrust, F_d, times the velocity of the duct, U. The useful energy is supplied by the expenditure of fuel or propellant, but some of it is dissipated in the power-plant process, e.g., a heat-engine cycle, before it becomes available for propulsion. In turn, some of the available propulsive energy is used to provide thrust, but some is wasted as kinetic energy corresponding to the *absolute* velocity of the ejected fluid. The over-all efficiency, then, would be the ratio of useful propulsive effect, F_dU, to the total energy supplied, calculated from some arbitrary datum (the heating value of a fuel, for instance). The power-cycle losses are the province of thermodynamics, and we shall consider here only the *propulsive efficiency*, η_p, which is defined as the ratio of useful propulsive effect to the *propulsive* energy supplied.

We shall first take the case of an air-breathing thermal jet with $F_d = m(V_{je} - U)/g_c$, where V_{je} is the effective exhaust velocity allowing for incomplete expansion. The *available* propulsive energy is the increase of kinetic energy, $\Delta(E_K)$, given to the working fluid by the power plant, $\dot{m}(V_{je}^2 - U^2)/2g_c$. Thus

$$
\eta_p = \frac{F_dU}{\Delta(E_K)} = \frac{\dot{m}(V_{je} - U)U/g_c}{\dot{m}(V_{je}^2 - U^2)/2g_c} = \frac{2(V_{je} - U)U}{V_{je}^2 - U^2}
$$

$$
= \frac{2(V_{je} - U)U}{(V_{je} - U)(V_{je} + U)} = \frac{2U}{U + V_{je}} \qquad [\textbf{9.18}]
$$

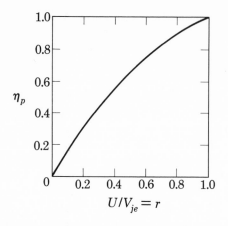

Figure 9.4

This is similar to Eq. 9.6 for the propulsive efficiency of a propeller, as it should be, with $V_{je} = V_j$ for a propeller. It is helpful to note that the same expression can be obtained if the efficiency is defined as the ratio of useful propulsive effect to useful propulsive effect plus propulsive loss, The propulsive loss is the absolute kinetic energy of the exhaust fluid; i.e., $\dot{m}(V_{je} - U)^2/2g_c$, and so

$$
\eta_p = \frac{\dot{m}(V_{je} - U)U/g_c}{\dot{m}(V_{je} - U)U/g_c + \dot{m}(V_{je} - U)^2/2g_c}
$$
$$
= \frac{2U(V_{je} - U)}{2U(V_{je} - U) + V_{je}^2 - 2UV_{je} + U^2}
$$
$$
= \frac{2U(V_{je} - U)}{V_{je}^2 - U^2} = \frac{2U}{U + V_{je}} = \frac{2U/V_{je}}{1 + U/V_{je}} = \frac{2r}{1 + r} \qquad [\textbf{9.19}]
$$

where $r = U/V_{je}$.

From this analysis of propulsive efficiency for an air-breathing jet, we see that the efficiency approaches unity only as $V_{je} \to U$. Fig. 9.4 shows η_p plotted against the velocity ratio, $U/V_{je} = r$.

For positive thrust, the forward speed, U, can never exceed V_{je}, and when $U \to V_{je}$, the thrust, which is proportional to $V_{je} - U$, is very small. A turbojet or ramjet passes all the propulsive fluid through the power plant, so that high thrust is obtained with a relatively low flow rate and a high exhaust velocity. Thus these types of propulsion units give reasonable propulsive efficiencies only for high forward speeds. If the forward speed is low, V_{je} should be low for a reasonable efficiency, and the propeller is the best means of propulsion. Although an economic analysis of propulsion includes many factors, such as fuel consumption, distance of mission, and altitude, the simple propulsive-efficiency expression illustrates the value of the propeller for low-speed flight and the value of the turbojet for high-speed flights. It also explains the increasing use of what is called the *turbofan* for commercial aircraft. With $V_{je} \approx 1850$ ft/sec as the choked value for hot exhaust gases, η_p is only about 0.6 for an aircraft speed of 550 mph. If part of the energy of the gas available for expansion to the exhaust velocity is first used in a turbine to drive a *ducted fan* with a separate air intake and discharge, then a larger mass of gas is ejected at a lower discharge velocity. The thrust is, therefore, not reduced (in fact, it is increased somewhat, as $\dot{m}$ increases more rapidly than U decreases), and the propulsive efficiency is increased. The ducted fan is really equivalent to a propeller with a very large number of small blades. In this way, the advantages of a gas-turbine power plant and a jet are combined with the lower-speed advantages of a propeller.

Turning now to the propulsive efficiency for a rocket, we see that the thrust is $\dot{m}_p V_{je}/g_c$ and the propulsive loss is $\dot{m}_p(V_{je} - U)^2/2g_c$; hence

$$\eta_p = \frac{\dot{m}_p V_{je} U/g_c}{\dot{m}_p V_{je} U/g_c + \dot{m}_p(V_{je} - U)^2/2g_c} = \frac{2V_{je}U}{2V_{je}U + (V_{je} - U)^2}$$
$$= \frac{2V_{je}U}{V_{je}^2 + U^2} = \frac{2U/V_{je}}{1 + (U/V_{je})^2} = \frac{2r}{1 + r^2} \qquad [\mathbf{9.20}]$$

Because the thrust is proportional to V_{je} (not $V_{je} - U$, as for turbojets), $r = U/V_{je}$ can exceed unity; i.e., the rocket can travel faster than the jet velocity. The value of η_p is again unity for $r = 1$ and decreases for larger values of r, but at a lesser rate than for $r < 1$, as shown in Fig. 9.5.

Propulsive efficiency, η_p, is a parameter for estimating the most useful range of application for a propulsive vehicle. It is seldom used quantitatively in design work, as is a component efficiency, for instance; rather it serves as a guide in the initial selection of the appropriate type of propulsive device and in the determination of its limits of operation.

Figure 9.5

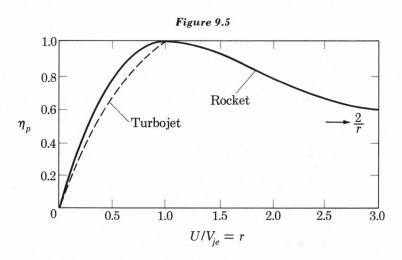

$U/V_{je} = r$

Problems

9.1. The diagram represents a ramjet traveling in level flight at an altitude of 55,000 ft with a constant speed of 1200 mph. The intake conditions have been simplified to represent the formation of a shock wave immediately at the inlet. It may also be assumed that the pressure external to the duct is everywhere that of the ambient atmosphere. The inlet process, 2–3, is one of isentropic diffusion, and the combustion process, 3–4, occurs through the addition of fuel at constant area in a frictionless duct, the stagnation temperature at 4 being 1840°F. Process 4–5

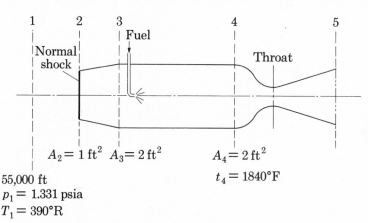

$A_2 = 1 \text{ ft}^2$ $A_3 = 2 \text{ ft}^2$ $A_4 = 2 \text{ ft}^2$

55,000 ft $t_4 = 1840°F$
$p_1 = 1.331$ psia
$T_1 = 390°R$

is one of isentropic expansion. Assume that the air-fuel ratio is 30/1 for g, but elsewhere take the working fluid to be air with $k = 1.4$.

 a. Find the mass flow rate.

 b. Find the throat area at t.

 c. Find the thrust developed by the ramjet if the nozzle expands the gas down to ambient pressure.

 d. Repeat c for a convergent nozzle.

 e. Find the propulsion efficiency for c.

 f. Find the propulsion efficiency for d.

 g. Find the specific fuel consumption for c in lb fuel per hr/lb thrust.

 h. Find the equivalent over-all drag coefficient of the whole ramjet for c, based on a projected (frontal) area (including control surfaces) of 3 ft².

9.2. A rocket has a convergent-divergent nozzle designed to provide complete expansion of the combustion products when run at ground-level conditions ($p_a = 14.7$

psia). If the rocket is operated at very high altitude where the atmospheric pressure is negligibly small, show that the thrust increases by $(100/k\text{M}^2)\%$, where M is the nozzle-exit Mach number. Assume that the mass flow rate and the combustion pressure and temperature remain the same and that the combustion products are a perfect gas.

9.3. A rocket traveling at 1500 mph expands 10 lb/sec of combustion products (taken as air with $k = 1.3$) from a pressure of 300 psia and a temperature of 3500°R to the atmosphere where the pressure is 7.4 psia. For isentropic flow,

   a. Calculate the net thrust if the expansion is complete.
   b. Calculate the net thrust if a convergent nozzle only is used.
   c. Calculate the propulsive efficiency for a.

9.4. A rocket with a convergent nozzle of 2 in. throat diameter gives a thrust of 700 lb when tested at ground level ($p_a = 14.7$ psia). Find the required nozzle stagnation pressure, assuming that it is greater than 30 psia. Assume ideal flow with air as the fluid.

9.5. A space vehicle traveling in a linear path in field-free space has an initial velocity of 25,000 ft/sec and an initial mass of 10 tons. It is powered by an ion rocket with a constant effective specific impulse of 2000 sec. Find the vehicle velocity when its mass is 50% of its initial value and the propulsive efficiency at the beginning and end of the mission.

10

Turbomachinery

10.1 *Introduction*

We now turn to another of the major applications of fluid mechanics, the transfer of energy between a fluid and a rotor by a dynamic machine. Machines that transfer shaft-power energy to fluid energy are called *pumps* for liquids, and *fans, blowers,* or *compressors* for gases. The latter nomenclature is not precise, but the usual connotation of *fan* is a machine whose main function is to move a gas with only sufficient pressure to overcome flow resistance, as in ventilation. A *compressor*, on the other hand, is a machine for compressing a gas to a high pressure useful for some subsequent process, with velocity being a secondary consideration. The term *blower* is used rather loosely, generally connoting a machine of intermediate pressure. Machines that utilize fluid energy to yield shaft-power energy are called *turbines* and are usually classified by their working medium, i.e., *steam, gas*, or *hydraulic* turbines. (There is also the windmill, which is a freestream turbine analogous to the propeller or open fan.)

The term "dynamic machine" was used earlier, but a more descriptive term is "turbomachine" (Latin, *turbo*, a top or whirlwind). The term *turbomachinery* is inclusive of all machines that transfer energy between a fluid and a rotor by means of *dynamic* action as opposed to *positive displacement*. In a turbomachine, both fluid and rotor must have a significant motion to produce a given effect, whereas in a positive-displacement machine (e.g., piston and cylinder), the motion may be infinitely slow and still produce a required effect. Whereas turbomachines are necessarily rotary machines, a positive-displacement machine can be linear (reciprocating) or rotary. Thus a gear pump, a Roots blower, and a vane pump are rotary machines but not turbomachines, since they change the state of the fluid by positive displacement, i.e., change pressure by means of a sealed containment space with one or more moving boundaries. Another method of differentiating between positive-displacement and turbomachines is to consider what happens when they are stopped. In the former, if there is no fluid leakage through seals and no heat transfer, the contained fluid remains indefinitely at its instantaneous state. In the latter, where the fluid is not positively contained, at the cessation of motion the fluid passes to some other state controlled by the surroundings.

Turbomachines will be discussed here as generally as possible because the basic relationships apply to all forms, whether pump, compressor, or turbine. Then the different major types will be analyzed for their particular characteristics.

10.2   *The Euler turbine equation*

The basic design relationship was developed in Chapter 4 as Eq. 4.35, which equates the sum of the moments of the external forces acting on a fluid in a control volume to the rate of change of moment of momentum of the fluid. Eq. 4.35 for a fixed control surface was a general vector relationship including unsteady flow. We are confining ourselves here to the case of steady, constant-velocity flow. Although unsteady flow can be important, e.g., in starting, stopping, and during changes of load, it requires detailed study beyond our scope.

Again referring to Chapter 4, we saw that turbomachines could be studied by means of a single, scalar equation with rotation about an axis rather than about a point. The result is Eq. 4.37,

$$\Sigma T = \frac{\dot{m}}{g_c} \left(r_2 V_{u_2} - r_1 V_{u_1} \right) \qquad [4.37]$$

where T is the torque acting on the fluid, $\dot{m}$ is the mass flow rate, r is the mean radius of rotation of the fluid, and V_u is the tangential or whirl component of fluid velocity in the plane of rotation. For linear momentum, velocities and forces are given positive or negative signs in relation to an arbitrary coordinate system. The same is done for angular momentum, with the direction of rotation of the rotor taken as positive. The torque on the rotor is equal and opposite to the torque on the fluid. If the control surface is taken to include the rotor and to cut the shaft, then the external torque is again ΣT, equal to and in the same direction as the torque acting on the fluid. Thus an increase in the angular momentum of the fluid requires an external torque to be supplied in the direction of rotation. This is the case of the pump or compressor. A decrease of angular momentum of the fluid requires an external torque for equilibrium, this case yielding a turbine.

Now ΣT is the total external torque, in general comprising shaft torque, T_s, and torque due to fluid pressure and shear at the entry and exit sections of the control surface. As noted in Chapter 4, for nearly all turbomachines the control surface can be taken so that the shear effect will be negligible and the pressure effect will yield no net torque due to circumferential symmetry. Likewise, in the absence of electromagnetic effects, body forces will be negligible. Hence, in the great majority of applications, ΣT is simply the shaft torque, T_s. However, a torque can arise in the case of a pressure discontinuity across the control surface, similar to the force due to pressure discontinuity at the exit of a choked nozzle in a propulsive duct. For instance, helicopter rotor blades may be driven by a small combustion chamber and nozzle mounted tangentially at the tips of the blades, with fuel fed up through the hollow blade. If the nozzle is choked, a pressure torque will arise.

Such a pressure torque, T_p, is the product of the pressure difference, Δp, across the control surface, and the radius, r, at which it acts, together with the area, A_u, normal to the tangential direction; i.e., $T_p = \Sigma \Delta p \, r A_u$. If this torque acts on the fluid in the direction of rotation, its value is positive. Thus Eq. 4.37 becomes

$$\Sigma T = T_s + T_p = T_s + \Sigma \Delta p \, r A_u = \frac{\dot{m}}{g_c} (r_2 V_{u_2} - r_1 V_{u_1})$$

yielding $$T_s = \frac{\dot{m}}{g_c} (r_2 V_{u_2} - r_1 V_{u_1}) - \Sigma \Delta p \, r A_u \qquad [10.1]$$

Because cases of pressure torque are infrequent, for simplicity we shall omit the pressure term in subsequent development, remembering that it is necessary in every unfamiliar case to check the control surface to see that there is no special effect unaccounted for in the simple formulation. Therefore, we shall state the simple torque relation for turbomachines as

$$T = \frac{\dot{m}}{g_c} (r_2 V_{u_2} - r_1 V_{u_1}) \qquad [10.2]$$

with T the shaft torque.

Let us look at Fig. 10.1, which represents a generalized turbomachine rotor. This shows a view of a rotor in a casing with axis OO and with fluid entering through area A_1 and leaving through area A_2. The velocity vectors, V_1 and V_2, are three-dimensional, and any path may be followed in the rotor. The velocity vectors may be resolved into three mutually perpendicular components as in the figure, one parallel to the axis of rotation, giving an axial component, V_a, one directed radially through the axis of rotation, giving a radial component, V_m, and one giving a tangential component, V_u.

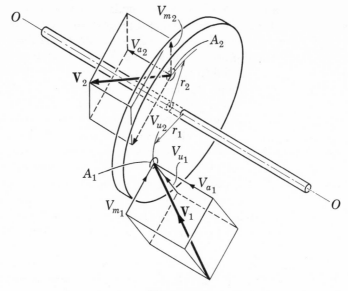

Figure 10.1

The flow is steady in the thermodynamic sense that (1) the mass rate of flow is constant (no storage or addition of fluid in the rotor), so that $\dot{m}_1 = \dot{m}_2 = \dot{m}$, (2) the states of the fluid at 1 and 2 are constant, and (3) the rates of heat and work passing in or out of the rotor are constant. This implies that there is no leakage loss, i.e., that all the fluid is undergoing the same process. The control surface is defined by the outer boundary of the rotor, a section of shaft, and the entry and exit areas, A_1 and A_2. Now Eq. 4.37 can be applied under the simplified conditions stated.

For the *axial* direction, there is a net torque due to the V_a components, but it contributes nothing to the angular rotation. It gives rise, however, to a couple that is resisted by a thrust bearing and is transferred to the stationary rotor casing. For the *radial* direction, there is no torque, because the direction of the velocity is through the axis, but there is a radial force that is communicated via a journal bearing to the casing. For the *tangential* direction, there is a net torque about the axis equal to the net outflow of moment of momentum, $\Delta \dot{m} r V_u$, in accordance with Eq. 10.2.

As a rule, velocities in the direction of rotation are deemed positive. V_{u_1} and V_{u_2} in Eq. 10.2 are scalar and must have a sign in accordance with this convention. Given the fluid velocities, the resultant sign of the right-hand side of the equation indicates whether the torque is acting on the fluid or is produced by the fluid. If rotor torque is acting on the fluid, thereby increasing its angular momentum, and the turbomachine is acting as a pump or compressor, then the sign is positive. If the fluid angular momentum is decreasing, giving rise to rotor torque, as in a turbine, then the sign is negative. Thus in Fig. 10.1, if the rotor rotation is clockwise, V_{u_2} is negative, V_{u_1} is positive, and $T \propto -r_2 V_{u_2} - r_1 V_{u_1}$. The resultant is negative, and there is turbine action. If the rotor rotation is counterclockwise, V_{u_2} is positive, V_{u_1} is negative, and $T \propto r_2 V_{u_2} - r_1(-V_{u_1})$. The resultant is positive, and there is pump action. In the case of counterclockwise rotation, both rV_u terms contribute angular momentum in the same direction for a given machine. In some instances, either pump or turbine, the terms may have opposite signs, and then the criterion of torque direction is the relative value of the resultant $\Sigma r V_u$, *not* V_u alone. This point is emphasized because there are many types of turbomachines, and it is possible that with varying fluid angles, a machine will operate as either a pump or a turbine. Generally, of course, it is perfectly clear whether a machine is a pump or a turbine. When it is clear, common practice is to use positive torque for both pump and turbine and positive values of $\Sigma \dot{m} r V_u$. Thus for turbines, which should have negative values of $\Sigma r V_u$ according to the convention, the order of terms is inverted to give a positive value in subsequent transformations; i.e., $T \propto r_1 V_u - r_2 V_{u_2}$. This avoids continually dealing with negative values in known situations. If this seems complicated, it will soon become clear with practice.

Although Eq. 10.2 in terms of torque and angular momentum is basic, in application we are usually more interested in rate of energy transfer (i.e., power) or in specific energy transfer (i.e., energy per unit mass of fluid). For a rotor operating at a steady angular velocity ω rad/sec, then the total rate of energy transfer E_0 is the product of this velocity and the total torque, i.e., ωT. Thus multiplying through Eq. 10.2 by ω yields

$$E_0 = \omega T = \frac{\dot{m}}{g_c}(\omega r_2 V_{u_2} - \omega r_1 V_{u_1})$$

The product ωr is the linear speed of the rotor at radius r. Denoting this by U, we obtain

$$E_0 = \frac{\dot{m}}{g_c}(U_2 V_{u_2} - U_1 V_{u_1}) \qquad [10.3]$$

Eq. 10.3 gives the total rate of energy transfer between a fluid and a rotor in terms of rotor linear velocity and fluid tangential velocity. With linear velocities in feet per second and flow rate in pounds per second, the units of E_0 are foot-pounds force per second (ft-lb$_f$/sec).

It is most generally useful to work with *specific rate* of energy transfer, i.e., with unit mass flow rate, so that when $\dot{m} = 1$ lb/sec, and E is rate of energy transfer per unit flow rate, still with units of foot-pounds force per second,

$$E = \frac{1}{g_c}(U_2 V_{u_2} - U_1 V_{u_1}) \qquad [10.4a]$$

Now for specific energy transfer, i.e., foot-pounds force per pound mass (ft-lb$_f$/lb$_m$) of fluid, we can divide Eq. 10.3 by the flow rate $\dot{m}$, obtaining

$$H = \frac{E_0}{\dot{m}} = \frac{1}{g_c} (U_2 V_{u_2} - U_1 V_{u_1}) \qquad [10.4b]$$

The symbol H is given to this specific energy with the connotation of head. For hydraulic machines, the difference between pounds force and pounds mass is usually ignored, and thus Eq. 10.4b is given in units of feet. The equation represents the increase of total head given to a fluid in a pump (and by extension of use, in a compressor) and the decrease of total head in a turbine.

Given this customary use of head as meaning specific energy, it is necessary to emphasize that E and H represent the transfer of energy between a fluid and a rotor, with energy in *all its forms*. Hence for a pump the value of $\Delta(UV_u)$ represents the energy given to the fluid, but this energy may not be the useful head increase as measured by static head, dynamic head, and elevation head. Some of the energy in an actual pump of less than 100% efficiency will have gone to losses from eddies, separation, and skin friction, which eventually appear as internal energy (see Sect. 4.22). Thus the actual change of UV_u represents the *runner* or *rotor* head. Likewise, for a turbine, an available head of fluid may not all be converted to runner head, i.e., transferred from the fluid to the rotor, as fluid losses again occur. It is important to realize this fact, because in the analysis of various kinds of turbomachines, we make extensive use of velocity diagrams to calculate energy transfer as $\Delta(UV_u)$. If in practice the fluid does not realize the design V_u values, then the energy is *not* transferred, regardless of the efficiency of conversion as useful energy output.

Eq. 10.2 and the modified Eqs. 10.3 and 10.4 are forms of the *Euler turbine equation*, so called because Euler is credited with its formulation. We shall use Eq. 10.4 most generally and refer to it here as the Euler turbine equation. It is a basic relationship from which we shall develop many different formulations convenient for particular situations. It is well to remember that, no matter what special forms are given for a particular turbomachine, its performance is always given by the Euler turbine equation.

10.3 *Classification of turbomachines*

It is useful to divide the various types of turbomachines into a number of classes, each of which has certain broad features and performance even though within a given class there are many individual differences. The Euler turbine equation gives logically the clue to one important division, i.e., machines *absorbing* mechanical energy and machines *producing* mechanical energy.

The former comprise those machines called fans, blowers, compressors, and pumps, hereafter usually given the generic title *compressors*. The machines in the latter group are invariably called *turbines*. Note that in each class are included, because they have many features in common, machines that use both compressible and incompressible fluids. Compressible-flow machines are the more general, and sometimes introduce features that disappear and simplify the problem of incompressible flow. It should also be noted that in many instances problems will be discussed that relate only to machines designed for high performance, problems that do not appear in some machines of more modest design. For instance, the problems of high Mach number will be discussed because they represent the limitations of high-speed, high–pressure ratio compressors, although in the ordinary commercial blower, the velocities are seldom high enough to produce such Mach-number effects.

The other important division is into *radial-flow* machines and *axial-flow* machines. The latter have no significant change of radius of flow. However, some important types of compressors and turbines have what might be called full radial flow and are called, respectively, *centrifugal* and *centripetal* machines. There are others in which the change of radius is small; these are usually called *mixed-flow* machines but are included under the general head, ing of radial-flow machines. Some sketches of typical configurations are given in Fig. 10.2.

The compressors of turbojet engines and steam turbines are representative of axial-flow types as shown in Fig. 10.2(a). The fluid flows parallel to the axis in concentric cylinders, with a change of tangential velocity in each row of moving blades, and so exchanges energy with the rotor. Between the rows of moving blades and attached to the outer casing, there is a row of fixed blades that, although they change the velocity of the fluid, transfer no energy because they are stationary. Such *multistage* machines are necessary when high pressure ratios or high heads are in question, because each stage, i.e.,

Figure 10.2

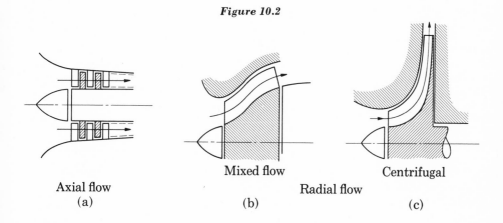

Axial flow
(a)

Mixed flow
Radial flow
(b)

Centrifugal
(c)

each double row of fixed and moving blades, has a limiting value of efficient energy transfer. A single axial stage in the limit is a fan or a propeller turbine, usually with a few large vanes.

The radial-flow type in Fig. 10.2(c) is capable of a greater transfer of energy with a single rotor than is a single axial-flow stage and is used for medium pressure ratios or heads. The single *impeller* is less expensive and more rugged than the multibladed axial-flow rotor. The mixed-flow type in Fig. 10.2(b) transfers energy mainly by axial flow, but may have a varying measure of radial flow to suit particular circumstances. It is used mainly for pumps.

The behavior of these different types of machines and the reasons for their use are the subjects of analysis in this chapter. The student is urged to examine engineering laboratories and industrial buildings, as well as the house where he lives, in order to acquire some familiarity with turbomachines. Pumps, fans, and blowers are ubiquitous as the movement of air and water is a necessary part of our everyday existence.

10.4   *Velocity diagrams*

Use of the Euler turbine equation is based on the velocity diagrams for the turbomachine. These were discussed in Sec. 3.3, with the formulation $\mathbf{U} + \mathbf{V}_r = \mathbf{V}$, or $\mathbf{V}_r = \mathbf{V} - \mathbf{U}$. We shall find it useful to form velocity components in various directions, both for the absolute velocity $\mathbf{V}$ and the relative velocity $\mathbf{V}_r$. Such diagrams must be well understood, as the detailed analyses are based upon them.

It is necessary to have a mental picture of the rotor so that an appropriate viewing plane can be chosen. Remember that in the Euler turbine equation we are concerned with the tangential velocity component V_u and the rotor velocity U. Further, we find it convenient to delineate a "through-flow" velocity component of the absolute fluid velocity V, termed V_m for radial-flow machines and V_a for axial-flow machines. Thus the V_u components yield the energy transfer and the V_m or V_a components yield the flow rate, the two important parameters in the behavior of the turbomachine. The relative velocity, V_r, is identified with the setting of the blade, or angle of the vane or blade, because generally the fluid path must match the blade direction at entry and follows closely the blade direction at exit. For the time being, we shall assume that the angles made by the relative velocity of the fluid are the same as the geometrical angles of the blade, i.e., the fluid angle and the blade angle are the same.

In presenting velocity diagrams, we must choose a plane which shows the true magnitude and direction of the velocities. Thus for an axial-flow machine, Fig. 10.2(a), in which the fluid follows cylindrical surfaces parallel

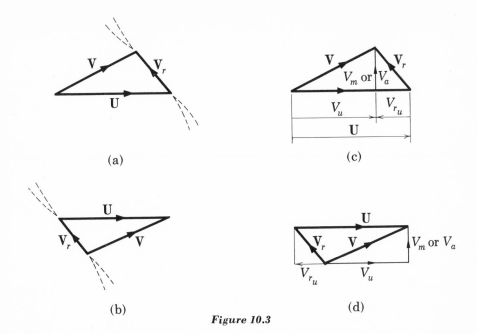

Figure 10.3

to the axis, we view the blades on a cylindrical surface, developed into a flat linear surface. The blades are then seen in cross section. For the radial-flow machine, Fig. 10.2(c), we do the same thing for the entry flow, since this is axial. For the discharge, however, we use a plane normal to the axis because the fluid discharges in radial planes. Here again, the student is urged to study the turbomachines in use around him in order to become familiar with them and so understand their velocity diagrams. Fig. 10.3 demonstrates the construction of velocity diagrams for turbomachines. The triangles (a) and (b) show the principal velocities $\mathbf{U}$, $\mathbf{V}$, and $\mathbf{V}_r$ as alternative representations, the choice of which is dictated by preference. The blade leading and trailing edges drawn in dotted lines indicate how entry and exit conditions are represented. Parts (c) and (d) of Fig. 10.3 show the absolute velocity, $\mathbf{V}$, resolved into components V_u and V_m or V_a, and the relative velocity $\mathbf{V}_r$ with its tangential component V_{r_u}. In general, velocity triangles will not be shown with vectors, as equations are given in scalar form.

10.5   *Energy components of the Euler turbine equation*

Energy transfer between a fluid and a rotor by means of the Euler turbine equation in the form of Eq. 10.4a, $E \propto \Delta(UV_u)$, is fundamental as derived from rate of change of angular momentum. However, the quantity UV_u is

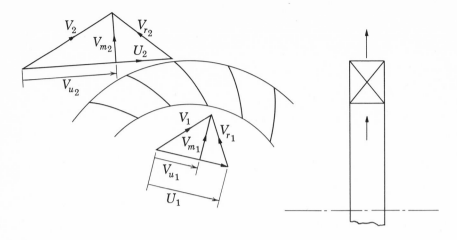

Figure 10.4

difficult to conceive as a physical entity, and it is enlightening and useful to transform it into more familiar terms of energy quantities.

Fig. 10.4 shows a simple radial-flow rotor in which all velocities are in the plane of the rotor; i.e., absolute fluid velocity V has components only of tangential velocity V_u and radial velocity V_m. The velocity triangles at inlet and outlet are shown in terms of absolute velocities, V and U, and relative velocities, V_r, with V resolved into V_u and V_m. It is desired that the UV_u quantities be formulated in terms of the fluid and rotor velocities themselves. Thus for the outlet triangle, from the geometry

$$V_2{}^2 = V_{m_2}{}^2 + V_{u_2}{}^2$$
$$V_{r_2}{}^2 = V_{m_2}{}^2 + (U_2 - V_{u_2})^2$$

Eliminating $V_{m_2}{}^2$ from these two equations,

$$V_2{}^2 - V_{r_2}{}^2 = V_{u_2}{}^2 - (U_2 - V_{u_2})^2$$

from which

$$U_2 V_{u_2} = \tfrac{1}{2}(V_2{}^2 + U_2{}^2 - V_{r_2}{}^2)$$

Similarly, for the inlet triangle

$$U_1 V_{u_1} = \tfrac{1}{2}(V_1{}^2 + U_1{}^2 - V_{r_1}{}^2)$$

Substitution of these values of UV_u into the basic Eq. 10.4a or 10.4b yields

$$E \text{ or } H = \frac{1}{2g_c}[(V_2{}^2 - V_1{}^2) + (U_2{}^2 - U_1{}^2) + (V_{r_1}{}^2 - V_{r_2}{}^2)] \quad [10.5]$$

The pairs of terms in parentheses are energy quantities and the total energy transfer is the sum of these three terms. (Note that the first two terms are outlet minus inlet quantities, while the third term is inlet minus outlet. This reversal of sign is made in order to obtain E as the *sum* of these pairs of quantities.)

The first term is $(V_2{}^2 - V_1{}^2)/2g_c$, the change of *absolute* kinetic energy of the fluid as it passes through the rotor. The second term is $(U_2{}^2 - U_1{}^2)/2g_c$, the energy transfer due to change of *centrifugal effect* or *centrifugal head* of the fluid as it passes through the rotor. It is useful here to refer back to Sect. 2.6, in which it was shown that the pressure in a fluid rotating with constant angular velocity is given

$$p = \frac{\rho}{g_c}\left(\frac{\omega^2 r^2}{2} - gz\right) + C \qquad [2.11]$$

From this, with $\omega r = U$ and neglecting the small effect of z as a very secondary effect in a turbomachine rotor, then the change of head due to rotation is seen to be proportional to $(U_2{}^2 - U_1{}^2)/2g_c$. The fluid in a turbomachine rotor is forced to travel with the rotor and thus a forced vortex exists, giving rise to the head component $\Delta U^2/2g_c$ which is called a centrifugal head.

The third term is $(V_{r_1}{}^2 - V_{r_2}{}^2)/2g_c$, the change of kinetic energy due to the *relative* velocity. To an observer traveling with the rotor, the flow of fluid through it is similar to flow through a stationary duct, and again omitting change of elevation head as negligible, change of velocity head $V_r{}^2$ is evinced as change of pressure head, p. Thus the change of relative kinetic energy appears as a change of pressure.

Of the three terms in Eq. 10.5, the first represents a change of absolute kinetic energy or dynamic pressure of the fluid and the last two represent a change of static pressure of the fluid. This physical representation is useful not only in visualizing the energy transfer process, but in classifying types of turbomachines and their behavior with respect to the methods by which they effect energy transfer.

10.6   *Impulse and reaction*

The relative proportions of energy transfer obtained by change of static pressure and by change of dynamic pressure are important factors with respect to classifying turbomachines, because for a given class of machine this proportion inevitably leads to a particular type of design with certain inherent characteristics. The parameter used to describe this relation is the *degree of reaction*, or simply *reaction*, defined as the ratio of the energy transfer by means of, or resulting in, a change of static pressure in the rotor, to the

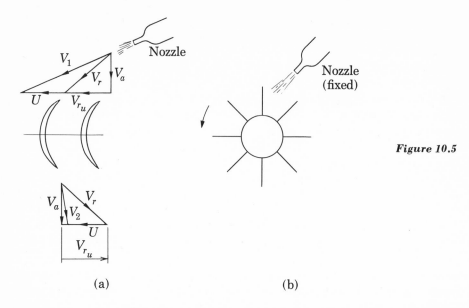

Figure 10.5

(a)   (b)

total energy transfer in the rotor. In terms of the factors in energy transfer analyzed in the previous section, with the reaction given the symbol R,

$$R = \frac{(1/2g_c)[(U_2{}^2 - U_1{}^2) + (V_{r_1}{}^2 - V_{r_2}{}^2)]}{E} \qquad [10.6]$$

where E can be given in the terms of Eq. 10.4 or Eq. 10.5. The reaction R can have any value for a given machine, including negative values, zero, and values greater than unity.

Zero reaction is an important value and characterizes a particular design of many types of turbomachines. If $R = 0$, there is no change of static head or pressure in the rotor. This is characteristic of an *impulse* machine. It should be noted that in the general case where the fluid enters and leaves the rotor at different radii, an impulse machine may result from the occurrence of a change of static head in one direction contributed by the centrifugal effect, and an equal change of static head in the other direction contributed by the change of relative velocity. For the large class of machines known as axial-flow machines, there is no change of radius, and so $U_1 = U_2 = U$ and any change of static head is caused by a change of relative velocity only. Thus an impulse machine of the axial-flow type has $V_{r_1} = V_{r_2}$, and the energy transfer is derived wholly from a change of absolute velocity.

Pure impulse action is most easily visualized in a machine of this last type. Fig. 10.5(a) shows the blade section of a simple axial-flow impulse turbine. With no change of static pressure, $V_{r_2} = V_{r_1}$, and with $U_2 = U_1 = U$, the force on the blade is due to change of the absolute velocity from V_1 to V_2.

With constant blade-passage area and no change of pressure, continuity requires that the axial velocity component, V_a, must also be constant from inlet to outlet. With $V_{r_1} = V_{r_2}$ and V_a constant, the tangential component of the relative velocity, V_{r_u}, must be constant; i.e., $V_{r_{u_1}} = V_{r_{u_2}}$. Using the Euler relationship in the form of Eq. 10.4, we obtain

$$E = \frac{U}{g_c}\,(V_{u_2} - V_{u_1}) = \frac{U}{g_c}\,[(U - V_{r_u}) - (U + V_{r_u})] = -\,\frac{2UV_{r_u}}{g_c}$$

Using the Euler relationship in the form of Eq. 10.5, we obtain

$$E = \frac{1}{2g_c}\,(V_2{}^2 - V_1{}^2) = \frac{1}{2g_c}\,\{[(U - V_{r_u})^2 + V_a{}^2] - [(V_{r_u} + U)^2 + V_a{}^2]\}$$
$$= -\,\frac{2UV_{r_u}}{g_c}$$

Energy transfer shown by the two Euler equations is of course similar, but use of the first equation demonstrates the transfer as effected by a force wholly due to change of the tangential component of absolute velocity, while use of the second equation demonstrates the transfer as a change only of absolute kinetic energy. This latter type of energy transfer is characteristic of impulse action in an axial-flow machine. With no change of static pressure, the rotor can be "open," i.e., the velocity V_1 can represent an open jet of fluid with no connection with the rotor, and the rotor need have no casing. A very simple example of an impulse machine is a paddle wheel rotated by the impingement of water from a stationary nozzle (Fig. 10.5(b)).

A machine with a reaction of any degree other than zero must have the rotor enclosed, in order to prevent the fluid from expanding freely in all directions. A machine with reaction is exemplified by the familiar lawn sprinkler from which water, passing through the rotor, issues at high velocity in a tangential direction. The essential feature of the rotor is that water enters at a high pressure or under high head, and the pressure energy is transformed into velocity energy in a nozzle which is part of the rotor itself (Fig. 10.6). The relationship of this type of machine to that described in the example of impulse action should be noted: in the first machine, the nozzle is stationary, and its function is only to *transform* pressure energy into kinetic energy that is then *transferred* to the rotor by pure impulse action. The change of momentum of the fluid in the nozzle gives rise to a reaction force, but as the nozzle is stationary, no energy is transferred by it. In the second machine, the nozzle is part of the rotor and is free to move, although constrained to a circular path, and it rotates owing to the *reaction* force caused by the change of momentum. These two cases will be analyzed in more detail later.

Many machines are part impulse and part reaction, and for exact classification the amount or degree of reaction should be explicitly stated.

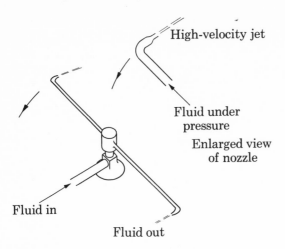

High-velocity jet

Fluid under
pressure

Enlarged view
of nozzle

Figure 10.6

Fluid in

Fluid out

In general, however, the term "reaction" alone is used whenever a machine is not purely impulse, but for the special case of steam turbines it has come to imply 50% or *half-degree* reaction. A velocity diagram for such a case is given in Fig. 10.7(a), in which there is a change of relative velocity but reaction is only 50% and hence the other half of the energy transfer is by impulse action.

It may not be apparent how a machine can have a degree of reaction greater than unity. It can be achieved by a machine similar to that shown in Fig. 10.7(b), which represents a compressor having fixed vanes preceding the rotor. Generally a compressor has *diffusing* action throughout the stage, i.e., a decrease of relative velocity in fixed and moving vanes, with the object of converting velocity energy to static pressure. In this special case, however, the fixed vanes act as a nozzle and accelerate the fluid. Since this acceleration reduces the static pressure, there must be a large reduction of relative velocity in the rotor for the discharge to be higher than the initial pressure at entry to the fixed vanes, so as to have compressor action. Again, it is possible to have negative reaction, impulse action, and positive reaction all in the same machine. This can occur in an axial-flow turbine with a particular design of rotor blading; part of it may diffuse the relative flow and part of it accelerate it, while at a point between there is impulse action with no change of relative velocity.

In radial-flow machines, the centrifugal action is a very important factor in the degree of reaction, sometimes predominantly so, but the above effects are more difficult to demonstrate in simple fashion. However, the reaction can always be calculated from Eq. 10.6 even if the processes leading to it cannot always be clearly pictured. It will now be appreciated how a certain amount of reaction in a given machine immediately gives some important

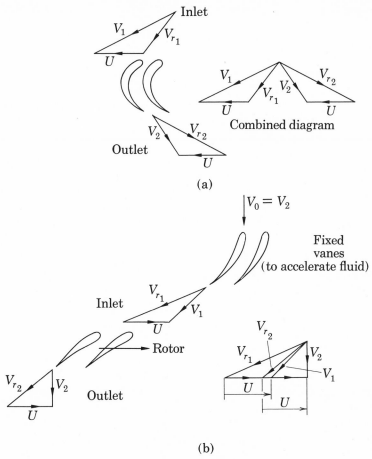

(a)

(b)

Figure 10.7

information, such as open or closed rotor and shape of flow passages, on the
type of machine it is. Other details will become apparent when turbomachines
are discussed in detail.

10.7 *Energy transfer in compressible flow*

The Euler turbine equation expresses the energy transfer in kinematic
terms, $\Delta(UV_u)$, considered as E, the rate of energy transfer for unit mass
flow rate, foot-pounds force per second, or as H, the specific energy transfer
per unit mass in foot-pounds force per pound mass. The latter is convenient

for incompressible flow, where the "head" considered as the height of a column of liquid is meaningful. For compressible flow, pressure is more convenient than head and the problem is usually stated in thermodynamic terms. Thus heat-engine cycles invariably have compression and expansion processes and the amounts of work are calculated from pressure and temperature relations. When these processes are carried out by turbomachines, the steady-flow energy equation provides the link with the Euler turbine equation. The steady-flow equation, Eq. 4.52, with enthalpy $h = u + p/\rho$, gives

$$h_1 + \frac{V_1^2}{2g_c J} + \frac{g}{g_c} \frac{z_1}{J} + q = h_2 + \frac{V_2^2}{2g_c J} + \frac{g}{g_c} \frac{z_2}{J} + w_s$$

For gases, the change of potential energy due to height above a datum is usually negligible and is omitted. The sum of enthalpy and kinetic energy is the stagnation or total enthalpy, thus:

$$h_{0_1} + q = h_{0_2} + w_s$$

For gases, $h = c_p T$, and hence

$$c_{p_1} T_{0_1} + q = c_{p_2} T_{0_2} + w_s$$

and, with c_p taken as constant,

$$w_s = c_p(T_{0_1} - T_{0_2}) + q$$

w_s is the shaft or mechanical work and is the equivalent of H, the energy transfer from the Euler turbine equation. Heat transfer, represented by q, is attempted only in compression processes, when it is a cooling effect; i.e., the compression is an approach to the isothermal process. Although cooling is sometimes effected by water-jacketing the casing surrounding the rotor of compressors, most turbomachine processes are adiabatic, except for very minor effects due to natural convection and radiation. For adiabatic compression and expansion, then, $q = 0$, and hence

$$w_s = H = c_p(T_{0_1} - T_{0_2}) = -\frac{U_1 V_{u_1} - U_2 V_{u_2}}{g_c J} \qquad [10.7]$$

Note that here we have followed the sign convention for E as originally developed, thus making a negative sign for the $\Delta(UV_u)$ term. For the case of a turbine in which w_s is positive and $T_{0_1} > T_{0_2}$, we usually omit the negative sign for $- \Delta(UV_u)$ (refer to Sect. 10.2). It is important to note that the work is represented by the change of *stagnation* enthalpy or temperature, i.e., the kinetic energy must be included, as found in the second form of the Euler equation. In many cases the kinetic energy is a very significant part of the total energy transfer. As an example, in the centrifugal compressors of superchargers or turbojets, the air velocity leaving the rotor is of the order of 1000 ft/sec or higher, sometimes supersonic, representing about half the total energy transfer or work. Again, although the kinetic-energy change from inlet to outlet of a multistage steam turbine may be relatively small compared with the over-all enthalpy drop, it is very significant in each stage, or row of blades.

10.8   *Efficiency of turbomachines*

Efficiency of a machine or engine has many meanings and many definitions. For turbomachines with incompressible flow (pumps and hydraulic turbines), the general definition is the ratio of useful energy delivered to energy supplied. Thus for a pump, the useful energy is the useful fluid specific energy, i.e., the useful head, H, as foot-pounds force per pound mass. The energy supplied to the rotor is this head plus the losses in the rotor and casing, which appear as random kinetic energy (eddies) or as internal energy (temperature rise), the latter increasing as fluid energy is dissipated by viscous effects and the decay of eddies. It should be noted that efficiency is expressed over the whole machine from inlet to discharge and thus includes losses of energy in both rotor and diffusion casing. After the rotor, no energy can be transferred, but losses in the following fixed casing due to friction and diffusion transform part of the useful energy at rotor discharge into unavailable energy as temperature rise. This energy input to the rotor, expressed as specific energy, is denoted by H_i and sometimes called the runner head. The ratio H/H_i is the hydraulic efficiency, η_h. The quantity H_i is equal to $\Delta(UV_u)/g_c$ of the Euler equation, with V_u the actual tangential velocity of the fluid. Some of the energy supplied to the pump shaft, H_s, is used as bearing friction, sealing-gland friction, etc., and is accounted for by a *mechanical efficiency, η_m.* Thus

$$H = \eta_h H_i = \eta_h \eta_m H_s = \eta H_s \qquad [10.8]$$

so that

$$\eta = \eta_h \eta_m$$

Note that the use of specific energy is correct only if no fluid is lost between inlet and discharge. If there is leakage, then this may be expressed as a leakage or volumetric efficiency, η_v, by which the shaft energy, H_s, is multiplied.

For a hydraulic turbine, the useful effect is the energy delivered at the shaft coupling, H_s. The available energy is H, the total energy of the fluid at inlet referred to a datum of zero energy at the level of the turbine discharge or tail-water level. Not all the available head H is transferred to the rotor; some is dissipated by fluid friction and turbulence and some is thrown away to the tail water as discharge kinetic energy. The ratio of rotor energy H_r

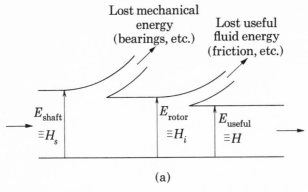

(a)

$$\frac{E_{\text{rotor}}}{E_{\text{shaft}}} = \frac{H_i}{H_s} = \eta_m \qquad \text{(mechanical efficiency)}$$

$$\frac{E_{\text{useful}}}{E_{\text{rotor}}} = \frac{H}{H_i} = \eta_h \qquad \text{(hydraulic efficiency)}$$

$$\frac{E_{\text{useful}}}{E_{\text{shaft}}} = \frac{H}{H_s} = \frac{\eta_h H_i}{H_i/\eta_m} = \eta_m \eta_h = \eta \quad \text{(over-all efficiency)}$$

Figure 10.8

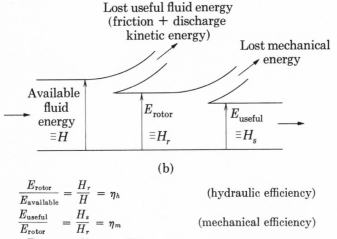

(b)

$$\frac{E_{\text{rotor}}}{E_{\text{available}}} = \frac{H_r}{H} = \eta_h \qquad \text{(hydraulic efficiency)}$$

$$\frac{E_{\text{useful}}}{E_{\text{rotor}}} = \frac{H_s}{H_r} = \eta_m \qquad \text{(mechanical efficiency)}$$

$$\frac{E_{\text{useful}}}{E_{\text{available}}} = \frac{H_s}{H} = \frac{\eta_m H_r}{H_r/\eta_h} = \eta_m \eta_h = \eta \quad \text{(over-all efficiency)}$$

to H is the hydraulic efficiency η_h, where $H_r = \Delta(UV_u)$, again with V_u the actual tangential velocity. Some of the rotor energy is used for bearing friction, etc., and so, with the energy, H_s, delivered at the shaft coupling, then $H_s/H_r = \eta_m$. There results the over-all efficiency, η, with

$$\eta = \frac{H_s}{H} = \frac{\eta_m H_r}{H} = \eta_m \eta_h \qquad \qquad [10.9]$$

It is useful to represent these energy quantities and efficiencies by means of an energy-flow diagram. Fig. 10.8 is such a diagram for a pump or compressor (a) and for a turbine (b), the width of each "channel" showing the relative energy quantitatively if desired.

10.9   *Efficiency of compressible-flow turbomachines*

For compressors the efficiency is expressed more conveniently in somewhat different form. The useful effect is a given pressure ratio, p_r, and the efficiency is defined as the ratio of the work required to attain p_r for the corresponding ideal process to the actual work required. With the analysis restricted to adiabatic compression, the corresponding ideal process is the reversible adiabatic or isentropic process, and so with 1 and 2 representing the initial and final states and superscript prime indicating actual as opposed to ideal, the compression efficiency is

$$\eta_c = \frac{w_s}{w_s'} = \frac{\Delta h_0}{\Delta h_0'} = \frac{c_p(T_{0_2} - T_{0_1})}{c_p'(T_{0_2}' - T_{0_1})} = \frac{c_p T_{0_1}[(p_{0_2}/p_{0_1})^{(k-1)/k} - 1]}{c_p'(T_{0_2}' - T_{0_1})} \qquad [10.10]$$

Note that the temperatures and pressures are stagnation values, in accordance with the result from the energy equation used to find w_s. Because the majority of compressors are used to take air directly from the atmosphere, p_{0_1} and T_{0_1} are usually those of the ambient atmosphere. However, if the machine in question is one of a number of stages or is preceded by another component, e.g., a filter, then to assess properly the compressor performance requires a use of the actual stagnation values at the compressor inlet. At discharge, again the values are often essentially static values because the kinetic energy is negligible, but for some applications the latter quantity may be considerable, as in gas turbines and wind tunnels. Bearing friction is again accounted for by a mechanical efficiency, η_m. Because the variation of specific heats between the actual and ideal values of temperature is usually very small, then with $c_p = c_p'$, η_c becomes the *isentropic temperature efficiency*. Thus

$$\eta = \eta_m \eta_c = \eta_m \frac{T_{0_2} - T_{0_1}}{T_{0_2}' - T_{0_1}} \qquad \text{with } c_p(T_{0_2}' - T_{0_1}) = \Delta(UV_u) \qquad [10.11]$$

For compressible-flow turbines, the usual definition of efficiency is the ratio of actual shaft work produced, w_s', to the work produced by the corresponding ideal process from the initial *stagnation* conditions to the discharge *static* pressure, w_{s_s}. This corresponds to the available head, H, of the hydraulic

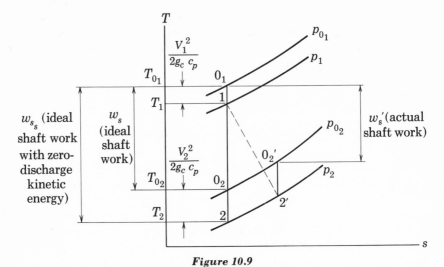

Figure 10.9

turbine. Thus, following the previous analysis,

$$\eta = \eta_m \eta_h = \eta_m \frac{w_s'}{w_{s_s}} = \eta_m \frac{\Delta h_0'}{h_{0_1} - h_2}$$ [**10.12**]

This is the most usual definition for steam turbines in which shaft work is the only output criterion and thus the ideal final state is considered as one with zero velocity. For steam, which is not a perfect gas, the expression has to be left in terms of enthalpy. Again, for most such cases, the initial kinetic energy is a negligible quantity compared with the over-all change of enthalpy from a pressure of several hundreds, or even thousands, of pounds per square inch to the condenser pressure of less than an inch of mercury absolute. Thus the efficiency corresponds effectively to the actual shaft work divided by the work corresponding to the isentropic process between the initial and final (static) states.

For turbines in which the working medium can be considered as a perfect gas,

$$\eta = \eta_m \frac{\Delta h_0'}{h_{0_1} - h_2} = \eta_m \frac{c_p'(T_{0_1} - T_{0_2}')}{c_p(T_{0_1} - T_2)} = \eta_m \frac{c_p'(T_{0_1} - T_{0_2}')}{c_p T_{0_1}[1 - (p_2/p_{0_1})^{k/(1-k)}]}$$ [**10.13**]

with $c_p' \approx c_p$ for the corresponding temperature efficiency.

However, for the gas turbines of turbojets, the turbine is required to deliver only enough work to drive the compressor, the discharge kinetic energy and remaining expansion-pressure energy being in this case the useful output of the turbojet as a whole. Here the efficiency is usually defined as the ratio of the actual shaft work, w_s', to the isentropic work between stagnation states at inlet *and outlet*, i.e.,

$$\eta = \eta_m \frac{w_s{}'}{w_s} = \eta_m \frac{c_p(T_{0_1} - T_{0_2}')}{c_p(T_{0_1} - T_{0_2})} \qquad [10.14]$$

with $T_{0_1} - T_{0_2} = T_{0_1}[1 - (p_{0_2}/p_{0_1})^{(k-1)/k}]$.

These definitions can be visualized more clearly on a T-s diagram showing static and stagnation states, as Fig. 10.9.

10.10   *Dimensional analysis of turbomachines—specific speed*

Before proceeding with further discussion of the various common types of turbomachines, it is useful to consider the methods of dimensional analysis. We seek some relationships between the operating variables, that is, the performance of the machine and the fluid properties. As a first step we may restrict the problem to one of incompressible flow, eliminating as negligible or not applicable, elasticity, surface tension, gravitational, and surface roughness effects. Thus the fluid properties involved are the density, ρ, and the viscosity, μ. The rate of flow of fluid is also obviously important; here we can use either velocity, V, volume flow rate, Q, or mass flow rate, $\dot{m}$. V has previously been used and is certainly the most useful for a fluid-dynamic analysis, but here we are looking for some over-all parameters which will describe performance in the most general terms. For incompressible flow (speaking generally of liquids), the volume rate of flow is most common, hence we choose Q as volume flow per unit time. Since $Q \propto V d^2$ and $\dot{m} = \rho Q$, simple conversions are available. The change of pressure or head in the fluid is desired, and head is usually preferred for incompressible flow. It is necessary to be careful about the dimensions of the head, because although in hydraulics it is convenient to think in terms of "feet of liquid," the dimension of length would not be distinguishable from the linear dimension representing size. We have to remember the fundamental idea of head as *specific energy*, energy per unit mass, with units of foot-pounds force per pound mass. Thus the dimensions of H are $[L(ML/T^2)/M] = [L^2/T^2]$. That this expresses kinetic energy per unit mass (as V^2) can be seen directly, and it may also be considered as $[LL/T^2]$, i.e., length times acceleration, the potential energy of unit mass due to gravitational effect, which is the basic meaning of energy associated with a column of fluid of a certain height. The power, P, of the machine is an important characteristic, as the torque might be. Since power is proportional to the product of torque and speed, and speed as revolutions per minute or radians per second is a necessary variable, ordinarily we do not want both power and torque and choose power. Finally we wish to include the size of the machine as the linear dimension $D \equiv [L]$. Since geometrical similarity is necessary for similitude, only one dimension D is necessary, as scaling implies that *all* linear dimensions will be changed in the same ratio. By this choice of important variable, we then have

$$f(Q, H, P, N, D, \rho, \mu) = 0$$

Note that these choices have been arbitrary to some extent, with exclusions based on the desire to limit the dimensionless groups to a reasonable number, and at the same time to include the most important variables. With seven variables all expressible in the primary dimensions of M, L, and T, four π-terms are necessary. Selecting a kinematic variable, N, a geometric variable, D, and a fluid property, ρ, as three variables that will not themselves form a dimensionless group and combine with the others in turn, the following groups are obtained from the formal dimensional analysis:

$$\pi_1 = \frac{Q}{ND^3} \qquad \pi_2 = \frac{H}{N^2D^2} \qquad \pi_3 = \frac{P}{\rho N^3 D^5} \qquad \pi_4 = \frac{\mu}{\rho ND^2}$$

Note that in this way we arrive at three groups each containing only once the important performance variables of flow rate, head, and power, and that the variable of the special fluid property of viscosity appears in only one group.

The first group, Q/ND^3, is called the *flow* or *capacity coefficient* and represents the dependence of flow rate on speed and size. By putting $Q = $ velocity $\times$ area $\propto VD^2$, we have $\pi_1 \propto V/ND$. With ND, interpreted as the linear speed of the rotor, denoted by U, then $\pi_1 \propto V/U$, the ratio of fluid velocity to rotor velocity. This then is a kinematic condition, or a particular velocity triangle, i.e., similar values of Q/ND^3 imply similar velocity triangles. The second group is called the *head coefficient* and, as earlier, may be thought of as H/U^2 or the ratio of change of fluid head (specific energy) to the kinetic energy of the rotor. By using the reduced form of π_1, V/U, then a group may be formed as $\pi_2/\pi_1 = (H/U^2)/(V/U) = H/UV$, i.e., change of head is proportional to UV (compare the Euler turbine equation). The third group is the *power coefficient*, which is essentially formed of the basic relationship that the product of mass flow rate and head change is proportional to power. The fourth group, which contains the viscosity variable, is, as always, likely to be a form of Reynolds number. We can form this directly by replacing ND with $U \propto V$, and hence obtain $\mu/\rho VD$.

The significance of the groups becomes apparent when one applies the basic principle that a constant value of all the groups implies similar flow conditions regardless of the variation of individual values of the variables. Consider the performance of a given machine at varying speed. As D is constant it can be eliminated; thus Q/N, H/N^2, P/N^3, and $\mu/\rho N$ remain. Further simplification can be made by considering the Reynolds-number effect as negligible, at least when compared with the effect of N on the other three parameters. Then for similar flow conditions, $Q \propto N$, $H \propto N^2$, and $P \propto N^3$. Thus in Fig. 10.10, the top curve represents a *characteristic* curve of head and flow rate of a pump, obtained from a test at constant speed, N_1. At a speed $N_2 = N_1/2$, the dimensionless parameters (in their simple form with D constant in this case) show that for similar conditions, $Q_2 = Q_1/2$ and $H_2 = H_1/4$. Thus any point 1 at speed N_1 is similar to point 2 at speed N_2. Taking a succession of points on line N_1, then similar points can be plotted to give the complete characteristic at speed $N_2 = N_1/2$. Other characteristics can be plotted for all speeds, taking $Q \propto N$ and $H \propto N^2$. Thus a single curve can be used to give information at all other speeds. Similar plots can be made in order to give the power characteristics, i.e., P vs. Q. The size of machine can be taken into account with the D dimension, i.e., at a given speed $Q \propto D^3$, $H \propto D^2$, and $P \propto D^5$. This must mean *geometrically similar* machines of altered size, i.e., the scale ratio is applied to *all* dimensions. Taking changes in both factors, $Q \propto ND^3$; e.g., the flow rate would be 16 times as large in a machine of twice the size and twice the speed.

Similar flow conditions at two different operating points, e.g., 1 and 2 in Fig. 10.10, imply the same value of all dimensionless parameters, of which the efficiency is one. (The efficiency η may be thought of as a ratio of useful output to input.) Then if all the variables which affect the performance have been included in the analysis, similar points will have the same efficiency. In the simple analysis for a given machine, the Reynolds number was neglected and therefore point 2 is not exactly similar to point 1 unless the viscosity is varied directly with N, and so the efficiency would probably not be exactly the same. Some variables may have been omitted in the original analysis, but the use of the simple groups allows estimates to be made of the effects of N, D, etc.; such estimates are usually quite accurate. Note that these estimates are made without specifying the class of machine; that is, they are valid for all types of fans, pumps, and turbines if the flow is essentially incompressible and no large Reynolds-number effects occur.

For fans, compressors, and pumps, the important characteristic is the HQ relationship; hence the parameters Q/ND^3 and H/N^2D^2. Although power is important, the object of the machine is to deliver a given flow rate

Figure 10.10

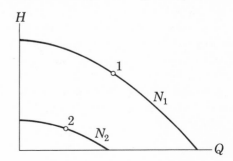

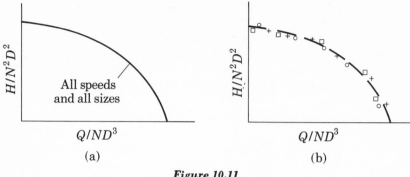

Figure 10.11

at a given head. For turbines, specifically hydraulic turbines since other forms involve compressible flow, the important object is usually to produce a given power with a given head, the flow rate being a concomitant variable. Thus the parameters $P/\rho N^3 D^5$ and $H/N^2 D^2$ are the important ones. Rather than plot two individual variables with a third as parameter, as was done for H and Q, with separate curves for the various values of N, it is possible to plot all the results using the *dimensionless groups* as variables. Thus values of Q/ND^3 plotted against $H/N^2 D^2$ results in a figure as shown in Fig. 10.11(a), which contains all the data pertaining to variation of Q, H, N, and D, so that a single dimensionless H-Q characteristic is given showing the effects of both speed and size changes. Alternatively, a large number of test points of H and Q, for a number of geometrically similar machines of various sizes and differing speeds, can be plotted using the dimensionless groups Q/ND^3 and $H/N^2 D^2$, as shown in Fig. 10.11(b). The points should all fall on a single line or nearly so allowing for experimental inaccuracies, and any points which do not fall on or near a single line indicate that some factor not included in the dimensional analysis is producing an effect. This then is one of the advantages of plotting with dimensionless groups as coordinates, as many of the variables can be included in one two-dimensional plot.

The three parameters of flow, head, and power coefficient resulted from a careful choice in the procedure of dimensional analysis in order to obtain groups in which Q, H, and P appeared separately. Many other dimensionless groups are possible and are correct, but few are so useful in delineating performance. It would be of use, however, to use a group which did not contain D, the linear dimension, as then the parameter would apply to geometrically similar machines of all sizes. Such a parameter can be found by carrying out the formal method to find a large number of π's and then selecting the one which appears most useful. Two that have been found useful and are widely used are

$$\pi_5 = \frac{NQ^{\frac{1}{2}}}{H^{\frac{3}{4}}} \quad \text{and} \quad \pi_6 = \frac{NP^{\frac{1}{2}}}{H^{\frac{5}{4}}}$$

It may be noted that π_5 can be found from π_1 and π_2 by the elimination of D; i.e., $\pi_5 = (\pi_1)^{\frac{1}{2}}/(\pi_2)^{\frac{3}{4}}$. Similarly, $\pi_6 = (\pi_3)^{\frac{1}{2}}/(\pi_2)^{\frac{5}{4}}$ (note that for hydraulic turbines, ρ is usually omitted as a constant, since the fluid is always water). π_5 and π_6 are called *specific speed* parameters, and are denoted by the symbol N_s; the first form is used generally for pumps where H and Q are the effective performance quantities, and the second form is used for turbines, where P and H are more important.

If we use $\pi_5 = NQ^{\frac{1}{2}}/H^{\frac{3}{4}}$ as an example, it can be seen that a certain value of the specific speed parameter then expresses all values of the operational variables N, Q, and H that give similar flow conditions in all sizes of geometrically similar machines. However, if we refer to a typical H-Q characteristic at a given speed, as shown in one of the previous figures, it will be seen that N_s can have any value between zero and infinity, so that a particular value of N_s can be satisfied by any machine with a continuous characteristic (i.e., from $Q = 0$ to $H = 0$). As a practical parameter then, the *specific speed* of a machine is evaluated and given at the *point of maximum efficiency*. Used in this manner, it becomes a parameter of great significance in defining the general type of turbomachine design, because it is found that each different class of machine has its maximum efficiency within a relatively restricted range of specific speed. Looking at Fig. 10.2, which represented three types of machines, we find that the axial-flow machine is adapted to high flow rates because the inlet is unrestricted and its larger area will admit large quantities of fluid without excessively high velocities. On the other hand, each row of blades can transfer only a limited amount of energy with reasonable efficiency. Thus an axial-flow machine will usually have a high Q and a low H, resulting in a high value of $N_s \propto Q^{\frac{1}{2}}/H^{\frac{3}{4}}$. The centrifugal machine has a small inlet because it is at a small radius compared with its over-all diameter, and therefore the flow rate must be small in order to avoid entry velocities which are too high for good efficiency. However, its large outer diameter allows high pressures or heads to be developed at a given speed ($H \propto N^2D^2$). Thus centrifugal machines tend to require a low specific speed in order to have a good efficiency. Experience has provided a considerable amount of data for various types of machines showing ranges of specific speed over which the efficiency is high. Evaluation of N_s from given data for H, Q, and N immediately identifies the type of machine best suited to a particular job. Note that in saying "specific" speed we do not mean that a particular type of machine cannot be made to operate at any given value of N_s, but simply that outside a certain range, satisfactory efficiency is difficult to obtain.

When considering the particular parameter N_s, for pumps, we evaluate N in terms of revolutions per minute, Q in gallons per minute, and H in feet. Thus it is a hopeless confusion of units; they are, nevertheless, convenient units and have come to be used generally where the metric system

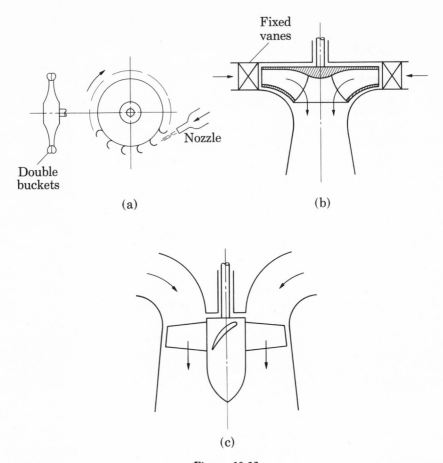

Figure 10.12

does not prevail. Hence specific speed is not a universal parameter as is Reynolds number and the actual units used must be noted.

For turbines, the same remarks apply to the specific speed as $NP^{1/2}/H^{5/4}$. The density, ρ, has already been eliminated so that the parameter cannot be dimensionless. The usual units are revolutions per minute, horsepower, and feet. Water turbines are of three kinds, the *Pelton wheel*, the *Francis turbine*, and the *propeller* or *Kaplan turbine*, shown in Fig. 10.12. The Pelton wheel is wholly an impulse machine, consisting of a double set of hemispherical cups on the circumference of a disk, onto which water is directed from one or two nozzles. The nozzles can deliver water at high velocity and so utilize a high head, but because it is possible to use only a few nozzles, the flow rate is small. Thus a Pelton wheel has a very low specific speed, about 5 to 10 based on $N_s = NP^{1/2}/H^{5/4}$. The Francis turbine is a radial-flow machine of the

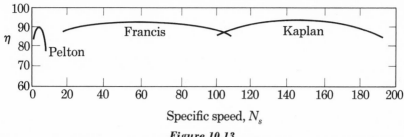

Figure 10.13

mixed-flow type. Water enters all around the periphery of the runner, thus allowing a large flow rate, but as it is a reaction machine, the velocities and consequently the utilizable head are limited. The Francis turbine is best suited for the medium range of specific speed, about 15 to 100. The propeller turbine is an axial-flow machine having a large flow area but utilizing a low head; hence N_s is high, from 100 to 200. The Kaplan turbine is a propeller turbine with adjustable rotor blades. Fig. 10.13 is a graph of efficiency vs. specific speed typical of present-day practice.

10.11 *Compressible-flow parameters*

The previously developed groups are also valid for compressible flow if a Mach-number parameter is included, but it is more convenient to select the variables in different forms. Use of mass flow, $\dot{m}$, is more convenient than volume flow, and use of pressure ratio, p_2/p_1, is more convenient than head for gases. Density is variable for gases, and in conjunction with pressure, introduces temperature that in turn serves, in conjunction with flow rate, to introduce compressibility as Mach number. Thus there are seven variables, $\dot{m}$, p_1, p_2, ρ, N, D, and μ. It is not easy to choose the most useful dimensionless groups except in the case of pressure ratio, p_2/p_1, and Reynolds number, $\dot{m}/\mu D$ ($\equiv \rho V D^2/\mu D = \rho V D/\mu$). There are several groups that may possibly be chosen for flow coefficient, the one most frequently used being $\dot{m}/D^2\sqrt{p_1\rho_1}$, which by means of the equation of state, $p = \rho RT$, becomes $\dot{m}\sqrt{RT}/D^2 p_1$. Choice of some group containing the speed variable is necessary, and the simplest is $ND\sqrt{\rho}/\sqrt{p_1}$ or, again from $p = \rho RT$, $ND/\sqrt{RT}$. By restricting these groups to a single gas, the gas constant R may be dropped, resulting in the four common parameters,

$$\frac{p_2}{p_1} \qquad \frac{\dot{m}\sqrt{T_1}}{D^2 p_1} \qquad \frac{ND}{\sqrt{T}} \qquad \frac{\dot{m}}{\mu D}$$

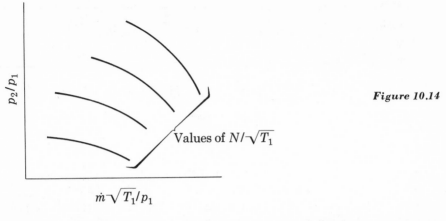

Values of $N/\sqrt{T_1}$

Figure 10.14

$\dot{m}\sqrt{T_1}/p_1$

(Note that the power, P, was not included in the variables this time; when it is included, the usual parameter in which it appears is $P/D^2p_1\sqrt{T}$. Note also that the dimensional analysis was performed with density, whereas the final groups appear with temperature. The analysis was given in the fashion it was in order to avoid ascribing dimensions to temperature, the equation of state being used for conversion.)

These four groups express the change of pressure (corresponding to head coefficient), the mass flow rate (flow coefficient), the speed (as revolutions per minute) and the Reynolds number. No speed parameter as such appeared for incompressible flow, whereas here the absolute speed N in revolutions per minute is connected with temperature. Again neglecting Reynolds number as a secondary influence, the performance of a turbomachine in compressible flow can be expressed in terms of the first three groups. For a given machine, D is constant and thus we have p_2/p_1, $\dot{m}\sqrt{T_1}/p_1$, and $N/\sqrt{T_1}$; similar conditions are then satisfied only by the same values of three groups, with the additional group $N/\sqrt{T}$ signifying that rotational speed by itself is not an absolute variable. The physical significance of p_2/p_1 is obvious but the other two groups require discussion. Taking $\dot{m}\sqrt{T}/D^2p$ and substituting $\dot{m} = A\rho V$, $A \propto D^2$, and $\rho \propto p/T$, there results $V/\sqrt{T}$. The acoustic velocity is proportional to $\sqrt{T}$ so that this parameter signifies *fluid* Mach number (refer to Sect. 5.8). The speed parameter $ND/\sqrt{T}$ may be written as $U/\sqrt{T}$ where U is the linear rotor speed, and thus can be interpreted as *rotor* Mach number. Together the mass flow parameter as $V/\sqrt{T}$ and the speed parameter as $U/\sqrt{T}$ give the kinematic condition of similarity, V/U. The implication of this is that for two flow conditions, not only must the fluid have the same Mach number, but the rotor velocity must have a certain value with respect to the sonic velocity. The indicated speed is thus not the "true" speed, and all variables must be plotted as dimensionless groups in order to correlate the effect of

varying inlet temperature (and pressure). A plot of the performance of a
given compressor or turbine then appears as in Fig. 10.14. It allows turbomachine performance to be correlated over a wide range of inlet gas conditions; this becomes very important for aircraft engines because of the wide
variations of ambient conditions. Although a plot of this nature correctly
correlates performance under varying conditions, often in use a plot is
required that gives mass flow and speed directly. This may be obtained by
the use of "corrected" or "reduced" values, a method that allows performance under the actual ambient conditions to be "corrected" to some standard
condition, i.e., the machine would have given the corrected values of variables if it had been operated at the standard conditions. This means that the
values of the dimensionless groups are the same both for the actual ambient
conditions and the standard conditions. The latter are taken at sea level,
i.e., 14.7 psia and 59°F. For discharge pressure, then,

$$\left(\frac{p_2}{p_1}\right)_{\text{corrected}} = \left(\frac{p_2}{p_1}\right)_{\text{actual}}$$

and, with c and a respectively denoting the corrected and actual conditions,

$$(p_2)_c = \frac{(p_1)_c}{(p_1)_a}(p_2)_a$$

or

$$(p_2)_c = \frac{(p_2)_a}{\delta} \qquad [10.15]$$

where δ = actual ambient pressure/14.7. For the speed parameter,

$$\left(\frac{N}{\sqrt{T_1}}\right)_c = \left(\frac{N}{\sqrt{T_1}}\right)_a$$

and

$$N_c = \frac{(\sqrt{T_1})_c}{(\sqrt{T_1})_a}N = \frac{N_a}{\Theta^{1/2}} \qquad [10.16]$$

where Θ = actual inlet temperature/519. For mass flow, then

$$\left(\frac{\dot{m}\sqrt{T_1}}{p_1}\right)_c = \left(\frac{\dot{m}\sqrt{T_1}}{p_1}\right)_a$$

or

$$\dot{m}_c = \frac{\sqrt{\Theta}}{\delta}\dot{m}_a \qquad [10.17]$$

For instance, a compressor tested at 10,000 rpm on a day when the temperature is 20°F and the barometer reads 28.9 in. Hg yields test data of discharge pressure 48.41 psig and a mass flow rate of 87.3 lb/sec. The pressure
correction factor is

$$\delta = \frac{28.9 \times 0.491}{14.7} = 0.965$$

The temperature correction factor is

$$\theta = \frac{480}{519} = 0.925 \quad \text{and} \quad \theta^{\frac{1}{2}} = 0.962$$

Thus

$$\text{corrected discharge pressure} = \frac{48.41 + (28.9 \times 0.491)}{0.965} = 64.9 \text{ psia}$$

$$= 50.2 \text{ psig}$$

$$\text{corrected speed} = \frac{10,000}{0.962} = 10,400 \text{ rpm}$$

$$\text{corrected mass flow} = \frac{0.962}{0.965} \times 87.3 = 87 \text{ lb/sec}$$

The corrected values are then those that would have resulted if the compressor had been tested at 10,400 rpm on a "standard day" when the ambient pressure was 14.7 psia and the temperature 59°F. If all test data are corrected to standard conditions, then the effect of modifications, etc., can be assessed correctly. If altitude test data are corrected to standard conditions, they will indicate whether any special effects due to the altitude conditions are occurring, e.g., lowered Reynolds number. The effect of a reduced inlet temperature in increasing the corrected speed is very useful for test purposes, as it allows the aerodynamic overspeed performance to be measured without physical overspeed and thus avoids stress problems.

The specific speed parameters may be used for compressible-flow machines but there has been no comprehensive collection of data comparable to that for pumps and hydraulic turbines, so that it is not possible to make a quantitative evaluation of specific speed for immediately identifying a type of machine.

It has been seen, then, that classification of machines into various broad types can be made on the basis of radial or axial flow and that, for identifying incompressible-flow machines specific speed is a very useful parameter. Degree of reaction characteristic of a given classification further defines a machine type. Some of the performance characteristics of the major types of turbomachines will now be discussed in detail, using the energy-transfer equations and the concept of reaction. Convenient classifications are (1) radial-flow pumps and compressors, (2) radial-flow turbines, (3) axial-flow pumps and compressors, and (4) axial-flow turbines.

10.12 *Radial-flow pumps and compressors*

Radial-flow pumps and compressors invariably have outward flow, i.e., from a small radius to a large radius. This is a logical situation for energy transfer, as the second form of the Euler equation shows that for energy transferred *from* the rotor *to* the fluid U_2 should be greater than U_1. Note that this relationship is not essential; the essential criterion is that $U_2 V_{u_2} > U_1 V_{u_1}$, but if the centrifugal effect is utilized in the correct direction, then there is a greater potential for energy transfer. The great majority of such machines have an axial inlet section and a radial discharge section as shown in Fig. 10.15. However, the rotor vanes may be two-dimensional as in Fig. 10.15(a), i.e., the fluid makes the turn from the axial to the radial direction in the open *eye* of the impeller, or the rotor vanes may be three-dimensional as in Fig. 10.15(b), in which case the vanes are bent to receive the fluid at the eye in the axial direction.

The former type is useful for small pumps and for fans and blowers of limited pressure rise, and the latter type is generally used for machines in which velocities are high and good efficiency is important. Because the energy transfer for both types is concerned only with the tangential velocity components, permitting the velocity triangles to be drawn in planes in which these components are apparent, then the velocity triangles are the same for both. Typical inlet and discharge triangles then appear as shown in Fig.

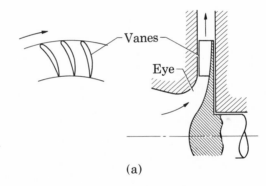

(a)

Figure 10.15

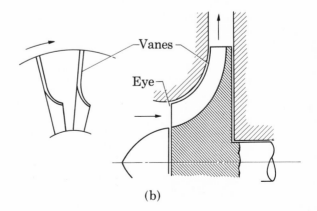

(b)

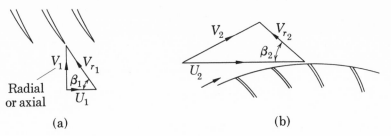

Radial
or axial

(a)

β_2

(b)

Figure 10.16

10.16. The inlet absolute velocity, V_1, is usually radial for two-dimensional vanes and axial for three-dimensional vanes, because the fluid is drawn in from an axial inlet pipe or duct, thus precluding any tangential velocity component at inlet. Fixed blades at or before the eye would be required in order to give the fluid initial angular momentum or whirl, and although they occasionally are used, normally $V_{u_1} = 0$. It is necessary to make the value of inlet vane angle, β_1, such that the fluid flows over the vane smoothly (without "shock," i.e., at small or zero incidence). The angle β_1 is then determined from the absolute velocity, V_1, and the rotor vane linear velocity, U_1. With no inlet whirl, the energy transfer then reduces to $E = U_2 V_{u_2}/g_c$.

At discharge, the fluid leaves with its relative velocity more or less at the discharge vane angle, angle β_2. Vector addition of the relative velocity, V_{r_2}, and the discharge rotor velocity, U_2, then gives the fluid absolute discharge velocity, V_2. Since $E = U_2 V_{u_2}/g_c$, it is the value of the discharge angle, β_2, that controls the energy transfer. Fig. 10.17 shows the absolute velocity, V_2, resolved into two components: V_{m_2}, the *radial* velocity component normal to the circumference, and V_{u_2}, the *tangential* velocity component effective in energy transfer. V_{m_2} is a measure of the flow rate because this velocity multiplied by the discharge area, A_2 (circumference × width), gives the volume flow rate, Q. The Euler equation may be put in terms of V_{m_2} and β_2 rather than V_{u_2}. From the diagram, $V_{u_2} = U_2 - V_{m_2} \cot \beta_2$, and so

$$E \text{ or } H = \frac{U_2 V_{u_2}}{g_c} = \frac{U_2}{g_c} (U_2 - V_{m_2} \cot \beta^2)$$

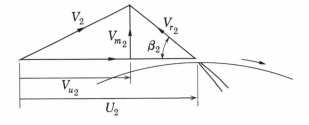

Figure 10.17

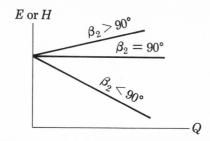

E or H

$\beta_2 > 90°$

$\beta_2 = 90°$

$\beta_2 < 90°$

Q

Figure 10.18

Substituting $Q/A_2 = V_{m_2}$, we then have

$$H = \frac{U_2}{g_c}\left(U_2 - \frac{Q}{A_2}\cot\beta_2\right) \qquad [10.18]$$

For a given machine running at a constant speed, i.e., U_2, A_2, and β_2 fixed, the head, H, is then seen to be a linear function of the flow rate, Q. Eq. 10.18 might be written

$$H = K_1 - K_2Q$$

where $K_1 = U_2^2/g_c$ and $K_2 = U_2\cot\beta_2/g_cA_2$, with K signifying a constant value for a given machine running at a given speed. Now K_2 can be positive or negative, depending on the value of β_2, since U_2 and A_2 necessarily are positive, but $\cot\beta_2$ goes from ∞ to 0 for β_2 from 0 to 90°, and $\cot\beta_2$ goes from 0 to $-\infty$ for β_2 from 90 to 180°. Thus when $\beta_2 < 90°$ the slope of the H-Q characteristic is constant and negative, as shown in Fig. 10.18.

For $\beta_2 = 90°$, $H = K_1$; i.e., the head does not vary with flow rate. For $\beta_2 > 90°$, $\cot\beta_2$ is negative, and the H-Q characteristic has a constant and positive slope. The velocity triangles for *backward-curved* vanes ($\beta_2 < 90°$), *radial* vanes ($\beta_2 = 90°$), and *forward-curved* vanes ($\beta_2 > 90°$) are shown in Fig. 10.19.

Several important conclusions can be drawn from a study of the above two diagrams:

1. The form of head-flow characteristic is controlled by the discharge vane angle, β_2, that is, increase or decrease of head as the flow rate changes. This can be important with respect to the power requirements, since power is proportional to the product of head and flow, and thus a positive H-Q

Figure 10.19

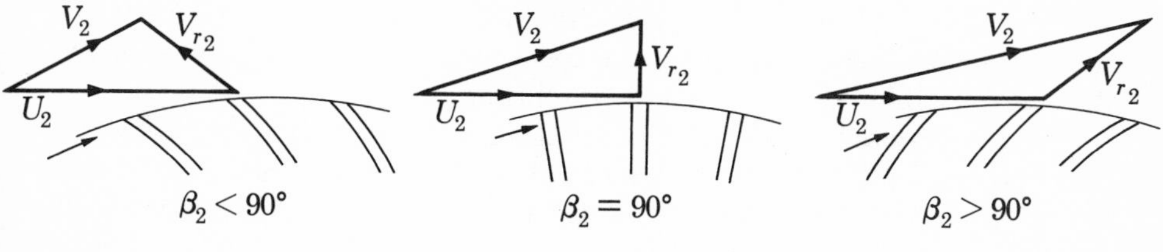

V_2 V_{r_2}

U_2

$\beta_2 < 90°$

V_2 V_{r_2}

U_2

$\beta_2 = 90°$

V_2 V_{r_2}

U_2

$\beta_2 > 90°$

characteristic causes a sharply increasing P-Q relationship. On the other hand, a negative slope characteristic tends to be self-limiting. Therefore, if the "load" should be removed, i.e., the system resistance removed, the driving motor could be overloaded very quickly for a positive characteristic.

2. For a given rotor speed, U_2, and flow rate, Q, forward-curved vanes give the highest head. Thus for a pump of given duty, forward-curved vanes would result in lower blade speed, which can be achieved by a smaller rotor diameter or lower rotational speed.

3. Although forward-curved vanes give the highest head, a considerable portion of this is in the form of kinetic energy, as V_2 is so large. Because it is usually *static* head or pressure which is required, there remains the problem of reducing V_2 in a diffuser casing following the impeller. Efficient diffusion is difficult to achieve without excessive length of duct, and so the machine as a whole either becomes very bulky or has poor over-all efficiency. For compressible-flow machines with a high rotor speed, U_2, the discharge velocity, V_2, may be so high that Mach-number effects occur, i.e., the flow is either transonic or supersonic.

4. At high rotor speeds, either backward- or forward-curved vanes can lead to high stresses because of the bending moments which occur. Radial vanes, on the other hand, impose a direct centrifugal stress of lower magnitude.

As a result of these factors, most centrifugal pumps have a relatively small discharge vane angle, β_2, of about 20 to 30°. This results in a relatively small head for a rotor of a given size, but the discharge velocity is then small and little diffusion is required. Fans and blowers which have a relatively low pressure rise, i.e., expressed in inches of water rather than pounds per square inch, usually have backward-curved vanes to ensure a low discharge velocity. This is not always the case, because with a small increase of total pressure, the velocity may not be very high. Centrifugal compressors having a considerable rise of pressure usually have backward-curved vanes if the unit is a multistage compressor, for the gas must be transferred from the discharge of one rotor to the inlet of the next and high velocities in the transfer duct would cause high losses. Compressors for superchargers, turbo-jets, and gas turbines, however, must have a relatively high pressure ratio and must be compact. Thus a high specific-energy transfer is required, resulting in a high blade speed and hence disk stress. The vanes are invariably radial ($\beta_2 = 90°$) as a compromise between high energy transfer and high exit velocity and because of limits to the disk stress. Also, since rotors are usually of a one-piece forged and machined construction, radial vanes introduce no very difficult manufacturing problems.

In the discussion thus far, the outlet angle, β_2, has been used with the assumption that fluid angle and vane angle are the same. When we consider the energy transfer from the rotor to the fluid, it is the fluid velocity which

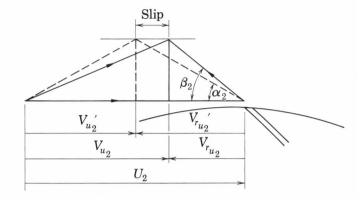

Figure 10.20

is in question. The quantity $U_2 V_{u_2}/g_c$, where V_{u_2} is the tangential velocity of the fluid, then represents both the energy input to the rotor and the energy added to the fluid. Two questions arise: (1) does the fluid follow the vane angle, and if not, what allowances must be made, and (2) how much of the energy actually transferred to the fluid is useful energy, i.e., is useful fluid head, H? It is most important to recognize $H_i = U_2 V_{u_2}/g_c$ as the actual energy transferred and therefore the mechanical energy required in the rotor. It should also be realized that this energy must all appear in the fluid, although a part of it will either appear only as random kinetic energy (i.e., eddies and general turbulence) or it will already have been dissipated from such eddies and changed into internal energy (i.e., rise in temperature).

In examining the first question, it is found that the fluid always leaves the vane in such a manner that the fluid angle, α_2, with respect to the tangential direction is less than the geometric vane angle, β_2, as depicted in Fig. 10.20. For a given radial velocity, V_m (flow rate), this means that the actual fluid tangential velocity, V_{u_2}, is less than the "diagram" fluid velocity, V_{u_2}'. The difference is called the *slip*, and the ratio, V_{u_2}'/V_{u_2}, is called the *slip factor*, μ.

The fundamental reason for the slip can be explained by the theory of circulation about an airfoil with lift, as discussed in Chapter 8. Fig. 10.21 shows the streamlines around the vanes of a turbomachine, these streamlines being relative to the rotor. The vane on the right side shows the ideal streamline pattern with no circulation, similar to the pattern in Fig. 8.16(a). The middle vane shows a circulation streamline; the vane on the left side shows the combined pattern, again similar to that in Fig. 8.16(c) for single airfoils. The Euler turbine equation is based on rate of change of angular momentum in duct flow. From the aspect of channel flow, the effect of circulation is to superpose a component of relative tangential velocity, $\Delta V_{r_{u_2}}$, at discharge in the direction *opposite* to blade rotation, resulting in a reduction of *absolute* tangential velocity by the amount $\Delta V_{u_2} = \Delta V_{r_{u_2}}$.

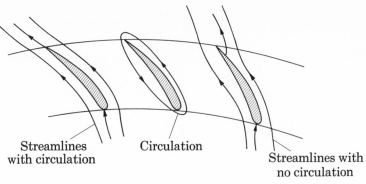

Streamlines
with circulation   Circulation

Streamlines with
no circulation

Figure 10.21

An alternative way of looking at the problem is to consider the inertia effect in the channel, or "relative eddy." In Fig. 10.22, a small body of fluid is just entering the impeller channel and is considered to be oriented with respect to stationary surroundings in the direction of the arrow, as at A. As it travels through the channel, this body of fluid tends to retain its orientation by virtue of its inertia, as at B. On its exit from the channel, it still tends to retain its orientation and thus has rotated *with respect to* the channel, as at C. Thus the fluid has a superimposed circulatory motion or relative eddy, and this results in a velocity component directed tangentially opposite to the direction of rotation. This tangential component is the slip and gives rise to the velocity diagram shown in Fig. 10.20. For design purposes, values of the slip factor, μ, are required. Theories for radial (90°) blades can be derived that may be borne out when tested empirically, but theoretical analysis for $\beta_2 < 90°$ is less satisfactory. The slip decreases as the number of vanes increases, which is reasonably explained either on the basis that there is less relative eddy as the channel width decreases, or by the circulation analysis, i.e., that as the number of blades increases a lower value of lift, and hence less circulation, is required. Consequently, a large number of vanes is desirable for high values of slip factor, but the presence of too many vanes increases the loss by friction and may introduce a serious blockage effect due to the finite vane thickness necessary. It is not possible to give a wide

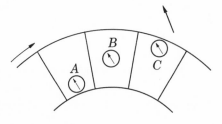

Figure 10.22

range of slip factors, but for radial vanes with the normal number of vanes, $\mu = 0.9$ is a reasonable figure.

Because of slip, the fluid cannot be given the "diagram" value of V_{u_2}, but only V_{u_2}'. Hence only energy proportional to $U_2 V_{u_2}'$ can be transferred and the rotor is not called upon to give any more than this. Thus slip is used only in calculating the energy which can be transferred and has no connotation of efficiency, defined as the ratio of total useful energy produced to total energy supplied. For a given vane angle, the energy input is less than that given in the geometrical velocity diagram by the factor μ; or, alternatively, for a required energy transfer, the vane angle, β_2, must be greater than the necessary fluid angle dependent on the value of μ. The head corresponding to the geometrical blade angle is variously called the "diagram," "virtual," "theoretical," or "Euler" head, and here we will use the last term in order to avoid possible ambiguity, giving it the symbol H_E. The runner head has been denoted by H_i, with subscript i for "input." In ideal flow, this is also the head for the actual velocity diagram, so subscript i may also stand for "ideal." Finally, for flow with losses, the actual fluid head at discharge is symbolized by H. Thus, to summarize,

$$\text{slip factor } \mu = \frac{V_{u_2}'}{V_{u_2}} = \frac{H_i}{H_E}$$
$$\text{hydraulic efficiency } \eta_h = \frac{H}{H_i}$$

Finally, the over-all efficiency of the unit is

$$\eta = \frac{\text{useful head output}}{\text{runner head supplied}} = \frac{H}{H_s}$$

and
$$H = \eta H_s = \eta_m \eta_h H_s$$

with
$$H = \eta_h H_i = \eta_h \mu H_E$$

It must be remembered that, as stated at the outset, these relationships as they stand are valid only for no angular momentum at inlet.

10.13 *Collector casing*

It has been pointed out that although all the energy transfer occurs in the rotor, there still may be the problem of *transforming* the dynamic head or pressure at rotor discharge into static head or pressure. Thus the casing design is concerned only with minimizing loss of useful energy. With low values of vane discharge angle, β_2, the absolute velocity may not require much diffusion and the function of the discharge casing is simply that of a

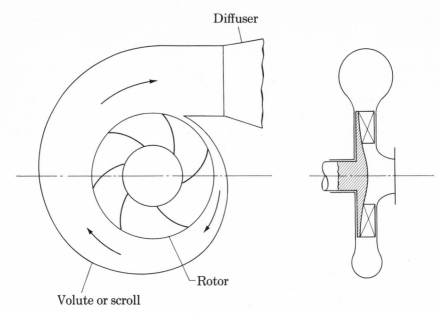

Diffuser

Rotor

Volute or scroll

Figure 10.23

collector. Such a casing is called a *volute* or *scroll* (see Fig. 10.23), with the cross-sectional area increasing from the tongue to the discharge in simple proportion to the angle measured from the tongue. Thus a volute casing is designed for constant average velocity and, therefore, pressure. Any diffusion required is best effected at casing discharge. The casing cross section is usually rounded on the outer diameter, tapering into parallel walls at the impeller tip; but, for low-pressure fans constructed of sheet metal, the cross section is often flat. Sometimes the cross-sectional area is increased to provide some diffusion with collection, but the efficiency is then generally poor.

Where the absolute discharge velocity is high and considerable diffusion is desirable before collection in a volute, the casing walls at impeller tip are continued parallel for a distance, as shown in Fig. 10.24(a). Without vanes, this form is known as a *vaneless casing;* with vanes, as in Fig. 10.24(b), it is a *vaned-diffuser* casing. Diffusion in the first occurs by means of increase of area with radius, and for ideal, incompressible flow this takes place in accordance with the simple law that velocity varies inversely with radius. To demonstrate this, consider Fig. 10.25(a) in which the absolute discharge velocity, V, is regarded as resolved into two components, radial, V_m, and tangential, V_u. For a casing with parallel walls in incompressible flow, continuity gives

$$V_m = \frac{\dot{m}}{A\rho}$$

and $A = 2\pi rb$, which with the width, b, constant gives

$$V_m \propto \frac{1}{r}$$

For the tangential component, $V_u r$ is constant, because from the angular momentum law, torque is proportional to rate of change of angular momentum, i.e., $T \propto \Delta(V_u r)$ and with zero torque, $V_u r$ is constant (zero torque because the fluid has left the rotor, or alternatively, the angular momentum remains constant).

Thus $V_m \propto 1/r$, and $V_u \propto 1/r$; therefore, $V \propto 1/r$. It can be shown

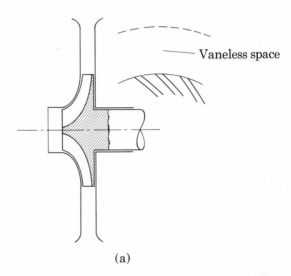

Vaneless space

(a)

Figure 10.24

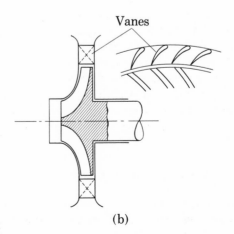

Vanes

(b)

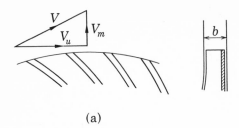

(a)

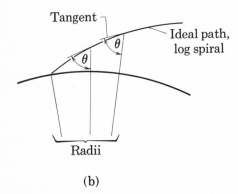

(b)

Figure 10.25

that this ideal path is a logarithmic spiral such that the angle, θ, between the radius and tangent to the path at any point is constant; see Fig. 10.25(b).

When diffuser vanes are used, they cause the fluid to be decelerated in a shorter path by forcing it from the logarithmic spiral. The fluid at exit from either the vaneless or vaned diffuser then suffers a loss due to mixing with the remaining fluid in the volute. Design-point efficiencies are usually higher in a vaned casing, because the path length, and hence friction loss, is less than in a vaneless casing. For off-design flow conditions, however, the efficiency of the vaned diffuser is lower, because the ideal velocity triangle is not obtained and loss occurs due to a sharp angle of attack between fluid and vane. For high-speed compressors of the supercharger or gas-turbine type with radial vanes, approximately half the energy transferred appears as kinetic energy, and thus the casing diffusion process is equally important to the rotor process. Quite often, because space considerations require that diffusion be accomplished in a casing of short length, the impeller efficiency proves higher than the diffuser efficiency.

10.14 *Actual H-Q characteristics*

The ideal H-Q characteristic has been shown, by the Euler equation, to be linear. The losses which occur in a compressor or pump may be considered to be of two types, one due to friction and turbulence, which is proportional

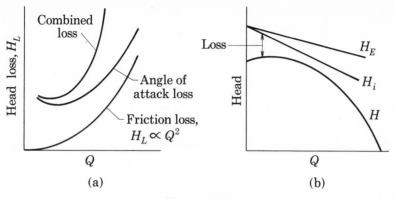

Figure 10.26

to V^2 and hence Q^2, and the other due to angle of attack between the fluid and the rotor vanes and diffuser vanes (if there are any diffuser vanes). Although the second type of loss is proportional to V^2, the loss or drag coefficient itself varies with the angle of attack, which varies with flow rate. The drag coefficient would be a minimum at the design-point flow. Thus the losses would appear separately and combined as in Fig. 10.26(a). In Fig. 10.26(b), H_E represents the Euler head (without slip), H_i the ideal head (and input head), and H the actual head, with $H = H_i$ minus losses.

The actual characteristic curve of H vs. Q is shown as continuous, but for some pumps and compressors under certain conditions, stable flow is possible only over part of the range, owing to the phenomena of *surging*, *choking*, and *cavitation*.

10.15 *Surging*

Fig. 10.27 shows a characteristic with a maximum pressure, together with lines representing various system resistance characteristics (with resistance head approximately proportional to Q^2).

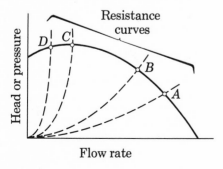

Flow rate

Figure 10.27

Point A is the normal operating condition, i.e., the pressure required for the system is equal to the pressure delivered by the machine. Suppose now that the system resistance is increased (e.g., by partly closing a control valve); then the equilibrium point becomes B, with higher pressure but lower flow rate. This is an operable point. Further system resistance leads to point C, at the maximum pressure of which the machine is capable. This again is a possible, steady running condition. The flow is further reduced by partly closing the control valve. The machine can operate only along its characteristic line; therefore, its delivery pressure is instantaneously reduced to point D. The fluid in the system, however, is at pressure C momentarily higher than D. The machine cannot deliver against a pressure higher than its own delivery pressure, and so flow stops; then momentarily fluid starts to flow backward from the delivery system into the machine. A moment later the fluid pressure in the system has dropped, and the machine starts to deliver fluid again. If the system condition is unaltered, the cycle is repeated again and again. For a low-pressure fan, the instability is mild, resulting in a small oscillation of pressure readings and possibly a "beat" tone from the machine. For high-pressure compressors, the cycle may be almost explosive in character, because the oscillation of energy quantities is large. In compressible-flow machines the phenomenon is called *surging*, although the term *pumping* is sometimes used.

For surging to occur, there must be a body of fluid in which to store a quantity of energy. All compressible fluids will do this, but for liquids, a free surface is necessary, i.e., storage occurs by virtue of potential energy due to position. The degree of surge is dependent on the sharpness of the pressure peak of the characteristic and on the storage capacity of the system. For high-pressure compressors, the effect is sudden and of considerable magnitude, so that the region to the left of the maximum pressure (i.e., of positive slope) is usually inoperable. This results in a *surge line* joining the surge points of all constant speed lines, as shown in Fig. 10.28(a).

Figure 10.28

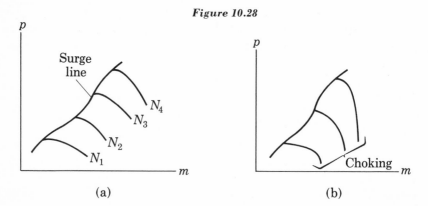

(a)   (b)

Anything that decreases the flow rate may cause surging, e.g., the closing of a valve, the introduction of too much fuel in the combustor of a gas turbine (choking of the turbine), and the flow in the diffusers of the compressor itself (separation). Surging will occur only if a part of the characteristic is of positive slope; hence a low value of β_2 is necessary if surging is to be eliminated.

10.16   *Choking*

A high-speed, high–pressure ratio compressor has high velocities, both of rotor and fluid. Along a characteristic at high rotational speed, as the flow rate increases, the pressure is reduced. For fixed areas, this results in a higher velocity, which may well reach the sonic value at a point of minimum area. Once this *choking* point has been reached, the mass flow cannot increase and thus the characteristic becomes vertical. At high speeds, the characteristic is said to be "steep," and the vertical part of it is useless, as the efficiency becomes very poor. Thus in some cases only the middle portion of the characteristic is useful, being bounded by surging at the lower flow rates and by choking at higher flow rates. The range, i.e., usable range of flow rate, of a high-performance compressor is thus limited. Surging and choking occur only with high-performance machines, the ordinary fan or blower usually having a very flat characteristic and being capable of operation from *shut-off* ($Q = 0$) to zero head.

10.17   *Cavitation*

Pumps may be subject to surging under certain conditions, although usually β_2 is so small that the characteristic is always of negative slope, and, of course, as machines handling liquids, they are not subject to choking. At high flow rates, however, a limiting phenomenon may occur owing to high velocities. This is known as *cavitation*, which occurs when bubbles of vapor appear because the vapor pressure of the fluid has exceeded the local static pressure. Although a pump increases head or pressure, the pressure may be very low at the inlet, particularly if the pump is lifting the fluid, i.e., has a suction lift. It must be realized that the pump can transfer no energy to the fluid until the fluid is in the rotor. Thus the work of raising the fluid from a lower level to the pump inlet is done by the atmosphere, and the absolute pressure at inlet is therefore low.

When cavitation commences, bubbles of vapor appear, usually near the blade surface where the pressure is lowest. Such bubbles interfere with the flow pattern, and by their "blockage" effect increase velocities elsewhere, causing further cavitation. This results in a decrease of useful head and therefore of efficiency. More serious than this, however, is the mechanical effect of cavitation, which is the erosion of the metal surfaces. This effect is not completely understood but it is basically caused by locally very high pressures and very high temperatures, both caused by bubble collapse. A bubble formed at a region of low pressure is carried downstream to a region of higher pressure. The vapor returns to liquid form, and because the collapse is sudden, waves of high pressure are generated that cause an impact effect on the metal surface. The sudden collapse is essentially adiabatic, and locally very high temperatures may be reached, aiding the material breakdown. Considerable research is being done in an attempt to understand the cavitation effect, as it can be very damaging. The very large, high-performance pumps and turbines in use today do not admit the possibility of frequent inspection and maintenance that may be possible with smaller machines, and because machine performance may not indicate that erosion is taking place steadily, it is essential that cavitation be prevented. The problem is particularly acute in the pumps of liquid-fuel rockets. Very high flow rates are required, but the pump weight and size must be minimized, and this requires high speed and very high relative velocity. In small pumps, cavitation is evidenced by noise and is most likely to occur when there is a suction lift, or an inadequately sized inlet pipe, or in pumping hot fluids. For centrifugal pumps, limits of operation have been established that are a guide to estimating the possibility of cavitation. The basis of the analysis follows.

The head on which the cavitation performance might be expected to depend is the difference of the absolute head at inlet and the vapor pressure head. The absolute head is the sum of the atmospheric head, h_a, and the liquid total head, h. With vapor-pressure head denoted by h_v and the net head for the cavitation performance by h_{sv}, then

$$h_{sv} = h_a + h - h_v \qquad [10.19]$$

h_{sv} is usually called the *net positive suction head* (NPSH).

Cavitation may occur locally when the vapor pressure is equal to or less than the local absolute static pressure, i.e., when $h_v = h_a + h_{sl}$, where h_{sl} is the *local static* head at some location in the pump. Just downstream from the nominal pump inlet, i.e., at the inlet flange, the fluid has changed its absolute velocity due to area change, some frictional and turbulence loss h_f has occurred, and locally the fluid has been accelerated (with accompanying decrease of head) around the impeller vanes. Thus the original total head at pump inlet, h, at a given point is now the sum of these energy quantities, i.e.,

$$h = h_f + h_{sl} + \frac{V_i^2}{2g} + \frac{\lambda V_{r_i}^2}{2g} \qquad [10.20]$$

where subscript l indicates a local value and λ is a variable coefficient depending on the actual blade form and speed. For predicting cavitation, the local static pressure, h_{sl}, is required, but this is obviously extremely difficult to obtain from Eq. 10.20 except in isolated instances, as it requires a precise knowledge of the flow at every point. However, rearranging Eq. 10.20, we obtain

$$h_{sl} = h - \left(h_f + \frac{V_l^2}{2g} + \frac{\lambda V_{r_l}^2}{2g}\right)$$

and the cavitation criterion is $h_{sl} = h_v - h_a$. Thus

$$h_v - h_a = h - \left(h_f + \frac{V_l^2}{2g} + \frac{\lambda V_{r_l}^2}{2g}\right)$$

or

$$h_f + \frac{V_l^2}{2g} + \frac{\lambda V_{r_l}^2}{2g} = h_a + h - h_v = h_{sv} \qquad [\boldsymbol{10.21}]$$

The three terms on the left-hand side are all proportional to velocity squared. By dimensional analysis, it was shown that for similar flow conditions fluid velocity is proportional to rotor velocity, i.e., V/U is a dimensionless group, and thus with $U \propto ND$, the three terms are proportional to N^2D^2. Hence the NPSH, $h_{sv} = h_a + h - h_v$, is a characteristic "head" of the pump, varying with N^2D^2 as does the developed head, H. The ratio, h_{sv}/H, is a dimensionless group whose physical significance is representative of cavitation conditions. It is denoted by σ and is called *Thoma's cavitation parameter* or the *Thoma number*. The head, h_{sv}, as $h_a + h - h_v$ is in readily measurable terms. A pump test with varying values of h_{sv} (most readily made by varying the inlet suction lift) can then determine the value of σ at which cavitation appears. As a dimensionless group, this value can then be used to predict the onset of cavitation at other flow rates and speeds. Furthermore, the value is valid for all geometrically similar pumps of various sizes. The critical value of σ has been found to depend on the specific speed of pumps of approximately similar design. Thus for centrifugal pumps with single suction (i.e., inlet on one side only),

$$\sigma = \frac{6.3 N_s^{4/3}}{10^6}$$

is a useful generalized relationship.

10.18   *Energy transfer in turbines*

Before discussing any sort of turbine in detail, it is useful to analyze further the hydraulic efficiency of turbines. It has been pointed out previously that the loss of energy in a turbine is due to fluid friction, etc., and to the amount of kinetic energy at discharge. Thus even for an ideal fluid not all of the energy available can be converted into useful work, because there must be some finite exit velocity, and hence kinetic energy. This ratio of ideal work to energy available is sometimes called the "diagram" efficiency (i.e., the efficiency based on the ideal velocity diagram), but here it will be termed the *utilization factor* and given the symbol ϵ. Thus

$$\epsilon = \frac{\text{energy transfer in ideal flow}}{\text{energy available}} = \frac{E_{\text{ideal}}}{E_{\text{ideal}} + E_{\text{lost}}} = \frac{E_{\text{ideal}}}{E_{\text{ideal}} + V_2{}^2/2g_c}$$

where V_2 is the absolute discharge velocity from the turbine. The amount of energy transferred, E_{ideal}, is given by either form of the Euler equation, with the velocities taken as the ideal values. By inverting the sign in the Euler equation in order to obtain a positive value for convenience, the denominator of the above expression is

$$\begin{aligned}
\text{energy available} &= \frac{U_1 V_{u_1} - U_2 V_{u_2}}{g_c} + \frac{V_2{}^2}{2g_c} \\
&= \frac{(V_1{}^2 - V_2{}^2) + (U_1{}^2 - U_2{}^2) + (V_{r_2}{}^2 - V_{r_1}{}^2)}{2g_c} + \frac{V_2{}^2}{2g_c} \\
&= \frac{V_1{}^2 + (U_1{}^2 - U_2{}^2) + (V_{r_2}{}^2 - V_{r_1}{}^2)}{2g_c}
\end{aligned}$$

From this last expression, the available energy can be seen to be the sum of the initial kinetic energy and the energy from the change of static pressure, the latter represented by the centrifugal and relative velocity components. Thus the hydraulic efficiency, η_h, defined previously as E_r/E, may be further resolved into the product of the utilization factor, ϵ, and an aerodynamic blading efficiency, η_b. Thus

$$\eta_h = \frac{E_r}{E} = \frac{E_{\text{ideal}}}{E} \frac{E_r}{E_{\text{ideal}}} = \epsilon \eta_b$$

The breakdown of η_h into η_b and ϵ is useful, because significant analyses of turbine types are made on the basis of ideal flow, i.e., $\eta_b = 1$. It is of little use to make great efforts to obtain high aerodynamic efficiency if the blade arrangement or flow conditions are such that a considerable amount of energy is lost as discharge kinetic energy, i.e., ϵ is low.

10.19   *Radial-flow turbines*

The second form of the Euler equation shows that if use is made of the centrifugal effect for energy transfer, then U_1 should be larger than U_2; i.e., the flow should be inward from a larger to a smaller radius. Thus most radial-flow turbines are inward-flow, or *centripetal*, turbines.

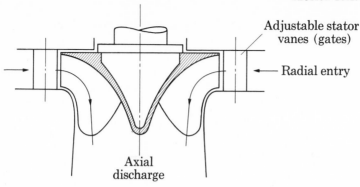

Figure 10.29

The major use of radial-flow turbines has been in hydraulic turbines of the *Francis* type which is shown diagrammatically in Fig. 10.29. Francis turbines are best suited to medium specific speeds and are built in very large sizes (up to 150,000 hp), achieving very high efficiencies (up to 94%). To obtain such efficiencies requires the use of an efficient *draft tube*, which is a diffuser between rotor discharge and tailwater level for reducing kinetic energy at discharge. It must be realized that a reaction turbine can theoretically be placed at any level between reservoir and tailwater levels and have the same head available to it. If placed near the tailwater level, as in Fig. 10.30(a), as seems natural, the turbine operates at a high inlet pressure and at a discharge pressure approximately zero relative to the tailwater. If placed as in Fig. 10.30(b), the inlet pressure is approximately zero, but because the whole flow is enclosed between initial and final levels, and apart from the energy transfer and friction losses, Bernoulli's equation holds in the duct, then the rotor discharge pressure is subatmospheric, i.e., the same pressure or head ratio acts across the turbine wherever it is placed. From practical considerations, such as inspection and maintenance, the turbine is

Figure 10.30

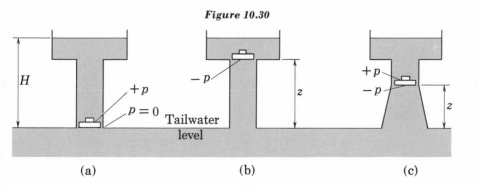

(a)   (b)   (c)

required to be well above the tailwater level, but there is a limit to the height. Even in the ideal case, the distance z cannot exceed that at which the discharge pressure is zero absolute, i.e., about 34 ft. In the actual case, z must be less than this due to frictional losses in the discharge pipe, but more particularly because cavitation would most certainly occur at low absolute pressures. Normally the turbine is placed some 10 to 15 ft above the tailwater level and is fitted with the diverging draft tube as shown in Fig. 10.30(c). The draft tube has two functions: (1) to lower the average velocity in the discharge duct so that friction is minimized; and (2) to lower the velocity at tailwater level so that the minimum energy is lost owing to kinetic energy. The reduction of velocity in the draft tube, and hence regain of static pressure, means that the pressure at rotor discharge is lowered; i.e., there is higher pressure across the rotor and more energy transfer consistent with the low amount of kinetic energy lost at discharge. Thus the hydraulic turbine has a high value of ϵ and, with the relatively low fluid velocities, a high value of η_b.

Inward radial-flow turbines for compressible fluids were seldom used in the past, but they have achieved prominence in the last few years as gas turbines, which are compact, rugged units especially suited to small-output, low-cost machines. In appearance, they are very similar to centrifugal compressors, but with the flow direction reversed and the vane diffusers replaced by nozzles.

A typical schematic diagram with velocity triangles is shown in Fig.

Figure 10.31

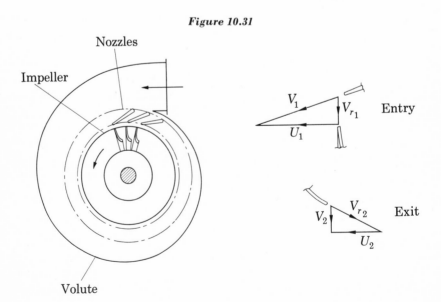

10.31. The hot, high-pressure gas may be admitted from a volute into the nozzle guide vanes. Here it is expanded to a high rotor-entry velocity, V_1. The impeller vanes are usually radial at entry for reasons of stress, and thus V_{r_1} is radial. Through the impeller, the gases expand further, discharging with a high relative velocity, V_{r_2}. Usually the blade angle is made such that the absolute velocity is axial, or nearly so, in order to obtain a high value of ϵ. The radial-flow gas turbine has several advantages when the pressure ratio is not too high. It is a single rotor of rugged construction, contrasted with the several stages with many blades required in the axial-flow type. For small-output turbines, the height of axial-flow blading may be very low, resulting in lowered efficiency due to large relative blade clearance loss and low Reynolds number. The radial-flow turbine suffers a Reynolds-number effect, but it requires less exacting construction in very small sizes. Furthermore, by pivoting them and employing a ring-operating mechanism, it is possible to make the nozzle vanes have variable setting for a wide efficiency range. It is not easy to do this and still maintain small clearances at the high operating temperatures, but it is certainly less difficult than with an axial-flow type. One difficulty with radial-flow turbines is that of providing sufficient discharge area in order to limit exit velocity when a large expansion ratio is necessary. Radial-flow turbines are used not only with hot gases but at the other end of the temperature range as expanders in the field of cryogenics. Here their purpose is to lower the temperature of the working gas and any power they may produce is at best a by-product of their operation. However, high efficiency is required to obtain the lowest possible temperature; 90% efficiency has been attained.

The Ljungstrom steam turbine (Fig. 10.32) is a staged radial-outflow type that has received considerable acceptance in Europe but not in the

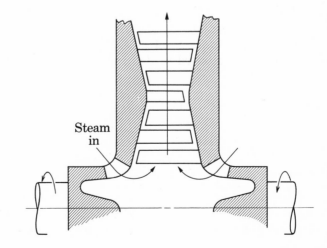

Figure 10.32

Steam
in

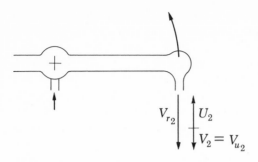

Figure 10.33

U.S. It is necessary to use outward flow, thereby increasing passage area, because of the tremendous increase in the specific volume of steam. Steam is admitted near the axis and flows over two rings of blades, both of them rotating but in opposite directions. The diagram shows a few of the first stages, of which there are many, resulting in a long axial length. The properties of steam in expansion are such that initially the increase in area owing to increased radius is more than enough to accommodate the increased specific volume at a reasonable velocity, and the blade length decreases. Following this, however, the blade length increases through many stages, eventually achieving a length of a few feet. The advantages of the Ljung-strom turbine are (1) contrarotating blade rows, giving a kinematic effect of twice the blade speed, (2) small turbine length for economical use of floor space, (3) possibility of rapid starting from cold, because the rotor disks are of much lower weight, and hence of lower thermal capacity, than are the disks of the equivalent axial-flow turbine.

Finally, in the radial-flow classification is found the "full"-reaction radial-arm type represented by the lawn sprinkler previously mentioned. This type of turbine (Fig. 10.33), by the way, is the earliest known type, exemplified by the Hero turbine (c. 300 B.C.). There is no inlet tangential velocity, and so with $E = (U_1 V_{u_1} - U_2 V_{u_2})/g_c$ for a positive value, the energy transfer becomes $- U_2(- V_{u_2})/g_c$. Note that the sign for V_{u_2} is negative as it is oppositely directed to the rotor velocity, U_2. The utilization factor is

$$\epsilon = \frac{E_{\text{ideal}}}{E_{\text{ideal}} + V_2^2/2g_c} = \frac{U_2 V_{u_2}}{U_2 V_{u_2} + V_2^2/2}$$

Substituting $V_2 = V_{r_2} - U_2$ yields

$$\epsilon = \frac{U_2(V_{r_2} - U_2)}{U_2(V_{r_2} - U_2) + (V_r - U_2)^2/2} = \frac{U_2}{U_2 + (V_{r_2} - U_2)/2} \qquad [10.22]$$

V_{r_2} is the jet velocity or nozzle velocity relative to the rotor. From the expression for utilization factor, it can be seen that $\epsilon = 1$ only when

$V_{r_2} = U_2$. But then $E = 0$, since $E \propto U_2(V_{r_2} - U_2)$; i.e., maximum utilization (and hence maximum efficiency) can be obtained only when the energy transfer is a minimum. For any reasonable degree of energy transfer, either $V_{r_2} \gg U_2$, in which case ϵ is low, or $V_{r_2} \approx U_2$, in which case U_2 must be very high. Thus the "full"-reaction turbine is not used as a prime mover except for simple applications where efficiency is not important, as in the lawn sprinkler. This analysis is comparable with that for jet propulsion (Chapter 9) as the force is obtained by change of momentum of fluid in a moving nozzle. Although here the motion is rotational and not linear, Eq. 10.22 is directly comparable with Eq. 9.15, with $V_{r_2} = V_j$.

10.20   *Axial-flow pumps and compressors*

In an axial-flow machine, $U_1 = U_2 = U$, and thus the Euler equation becomes, from Eq. 10.4a,

$$E = \frac{1}{g_c} U(V_{u_2} - V_{u_1}) = \frac{1}{2g_c} (V_2{}^2 - V_1{}^2) + (V_{r_1}{}^2 - V_{r_2}{}^2)$$

Generally the axial-flow machine has tangential velocity components both at inlet and discharge; the machine having a single stage with axial velocity at inlet $(V_{u_1} = 0)$ is a special case. The second form of the equation shows that the logical method of obtaining energy transfer is a process whereby relative velocity is diffused in the rotor $(V_{r_2} < V_{r_1})$, the rotor increases the absolute velocity $(V_2 > V_1)$, and static pressure is regained in a following stator. In a typical stage where rotor is followed by stator, and where this is one of several similar stages of a multistage machine, we see that the discharge velocity of the preceding stator becomes the entry velocity, V_1, of the succeeding rotor, and V_2 from the rotor becomes the inlet velocity of the succeeding stator. The velocity diagram then appears as shown in Fig. 10.34. For an axial-flow compressor stage (and of course for pumps), the fluid is considered incompressible, so that for constant area the axial velocity is constant. One may also use the Bernoulli equation for ideal flow. Constant axial velocity means that a *combined* velocity diagram, with inlet and outlet diagrams superposed at their apexes, is very useful. Fig. 10.34 shows such a common diagram on the right. It shows fluid deflection directly as the angle between V_{r_1} and V_{r_2}, as well as ΔV_u, which represents the energy transfer for a given blade speed. It also shows clearly the relative values of both absolute and relative velocities.

As with the radial-flow machine, it is useful to transform the Euler equation in terms of $\Delta(UV_u)$ into terms of blade angles and a through-flow velocity, which this time is the axial velocity, V_a. (For radial-flow types,

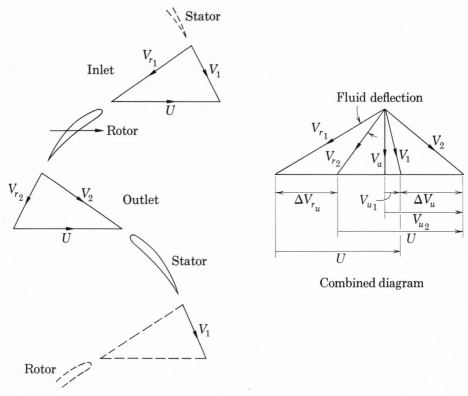

Figure 10.34

the through-flow velocity was represented by V_m, the radial velocity.) In Fig. 10.35, the fluid angles are designated with respect to the *axial* direction, with α_1 and α_2 the fluid angles relative to the rotor, and α_0 and α_4 the fluid angles of the absolute velocity at inlet and outlet. The Euler equation gives

$$E = \frac{U}{g_c}(V_{u_2} - V_{u_1}) = \frac{U}{g_c}(V_a \tan \alpha_4 - V_a \tan \alpha_0)$$

Now, from the geometry,

$$U = V_a \tan \alpha_1 + V_a \tan \alpha_0$$

and
$$U = V_a \tan \alpha_2 + V_a \tan \alpha_4$$

from which
$$\tan \alpha_1 + \tan \alpha_0 = \tan \alpha_2 + \tan \alpha_4$$

or
$$\tan \alpha_4 - \tan \alpha_0 = \tan \alpha_1 - \tan \alpha_2$$

Thus
$$E = \frac{U V_a}{g_c}(\tan \alpha_1 - \tan \alpha_2) \qquad [\boldsymbol{10.23}]$$

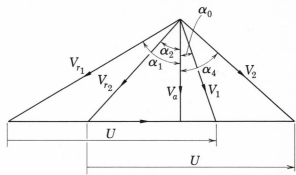

Figure 10.35

This is a convenient formulation, because V_a is a measure of the flow rate ($\dot{m} = A\rho V_a$) and α_1 and α_2 correspond closely to the actual blade angles. This is analogous to the expression for energy transfer in the radial-flow machine in terms of V_m and β_2. It should also be noted from this analysis that

$$\Delta(UV_u) = U(V_{u_2} - V_{u_1}) = U(V_{r_{u_1}} - V_{r_{u_2}}) = \Delta(UV_{r_u})$$

i.e., the change of absolute tangential velocity is equal to the change of relative tangential velocity.

The degree of reaction of an axial-flow stage is

$$R = \frac{(V_{r_1}^2 - V_{r_2}^2)/2g_c}{E} \qquad [\boldsymbol{10.24}]$$

From Fig. 10.35

$$V_{r_1}^2 = V_a^2 + (V_a \tan \alpha_1)^2 = V_a^2(1 + \tan^2 \alpha_1)$$
$$V_{r_2}^2 = V_a^2 + (V_a \tan \alpha_2)^2 = V_a^2(1 + \tan^2 \alpha_2)$$

Substituting these, together with $E = UV_a(\tan \alpha_1 - \tan \alpha_2)/g_c$, we obtain

$$R = \frac{V_a^2(\tan^2 \alpha_1 - \tan^2 \alpha_2)}{2UV_a(\tan \alpha_1 - \tan \alpha_2)} = \frac{V_a(\tan \alpha_1 + \tan \alpha_2)}{2U}$$

Now

$$\frac{V_a(\tan \alpha_1 + \tan \alpha_2)}{2} = \frac{V_{r_{u_1}} + V_{r_{u_2}}}{2} = V_{r_{u_m}}$$

where $V_{r_{u_m}}$ is the mean tangential component of relative velocity, with V_{r_m} the mean relative velocity (Fig. 10.36). Thus

$$R = \frac{V_{r_{u_m}}}{U} \qquad [\boldsymbol{10.25}]$$

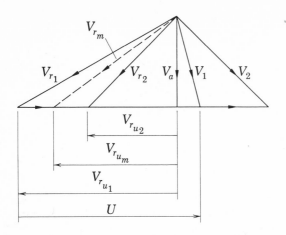

Figure 10.36

This last expression is useful because it can be interpreted graphically in a simple manner. Thus in Fig. 10.36, $V_{r_{u_m}}/U \approx 0.7$; i.e., the reaction is about 70%. It is most useful in a qualitative sense in interpreting various arrangements of blades.

The simplest possible example of an axial-flow machine is that of a rotor alone, with free air intake and discharge, as in a desk fan. If the rotor is enclosed to provide a flow of air or water in a duct, a stator is necessary if inlet and outlet flow are both to be along the axis of the duct. Thus in Fig. 10.37(a) the rotor precedes the stator, so that the air is axial at rotor inlet (i.e., there is direct suction), but has a tangential component at discharge that is removed by the following stator. Alternatively, the stage can be arranged with an inlet stator receiving the air axially and discharging to the rotor so that the change of tangential velocity in the rotor is such that the fluid is discharged axially.

For axial rotor inlet, drawing V_{r_m} as the mean relative velocity shows $V_{r_{u_m}}$ to be less than U; i.e., $1 > R > 0.5$. For axial rotor outlet, $V_{r_{u_m}} > U$; i.e., $R > 1$. For reaction greater than unity, the fluid must be accelerated in the stator, hence the pressure at the inlet to the rotor is actually less than at inlet to the stator, which can be seen from the velocity diagram in that $V_1 > V_2$, and since $V_2 = V_a$, then $V_1 > V_a$, the inlet axial and absolute velocity.

A very common arrangement of blading is 50% reaction; i.e., half the static pressure rise is in the rotor and half is in the stator (Fig. 10.38). This results in a symmetrical diagram with $V_{r_1} = V_2$, $V_{r_2} = V_1$, and $V_{r_{u_m}} = U/2$.

Comparison of the three previous diagrams reveals other features. For the case of $R > 1$, the fluid deflection (i.e., $\alpha_1 - \alpha_2$) is least, i.e., the blade can have the least curvature. However, this case also has the highest velocities, V_{r_1} and V_{r_2}, and thus is not suitable where compressibility or cavitation effects are liable to occur. A comparison of velocity diagrams of this nature can show many features of blade performance. By determining limits of performance from a study of test data from various arrangements of blades, one may choose the arrangement most suitable for given operating conditions.

Figure 10.37

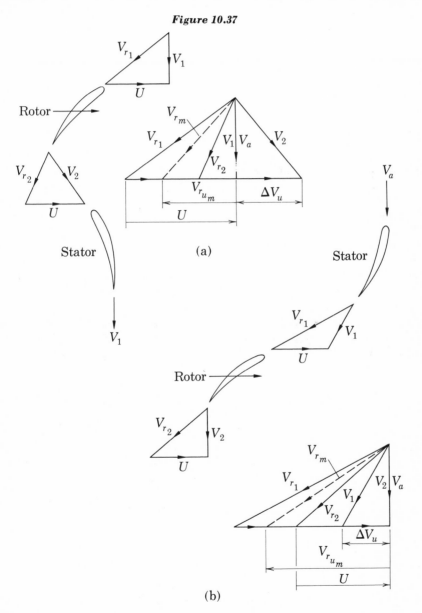

(a)

(b)

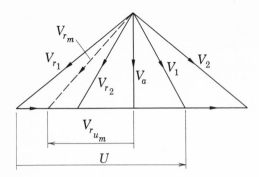

Figure 10.38

10.21   *Efficiency of an axial-flow stage*

The efficiency of a compressor has been defined as the ratio of ideal work or change of enthalpy to the actual work or change of enthalpy. The ideal work can be calculated from measurements of initial temperature and pressure and the final pressure; thus, with the work equal to the change of enthalpy,

$$w_i = \Delta h_i = c_p T_1[(p_2 p_1)^X - 1]$$

where $X = (k - 1)/k$. The actual work can be measured either by torque reaction and speed with a dynamometer or from initial and final temperatures, since $w_a = \Delta h_a = c_p(T_2' - T_1)$. Where the temperature rise is very small, it is more convenient to handle the problem as the ratio of useful specific energy at discharge (i.e., the head) to the specific-energy input. The equivalence for small values of Δp can be seen from the following analysis.

$$w_i = \Delta h_{is} = c_p(T_2 - T_1) = c_p T_1[(p_2/p_1)^X - 1] = c_p T_1\left[\left(\frac{p_1 + \Delta p}{p_1}\right)^X - 1\right]$$

$$= c_p T_1\left[\left(1 + \frac{\Delta p}{p_1}\right)^X - 1\right]$$

where the subscript "is" stands for isentropic. When Δp is small compared with p_1, the term $(1 + \Delta p/p_1)^X$ can be expanded into the series

$$\left[1 + \frac{X\,\Delta p}{p_1} + \frac{X(X - 1)}{2}\left(\frac{\Delta p}{p_1}\right)^2 + \cdots\right]$$

With $\Delta p/p$ very small, $(\Delta p/p_1)^2$ and terms of higher order can be dropped. Thus

$$w_i = c_p T_1 \frac{k - 1}{k}\frac{\Delta p}{p_1}$$

Now $c_p(k - 1)/k = R$ and $RT_1/p_1 = 1/\rho_1$; hence

$$w_i = \frac{\Delta p}{\rho_1} = \Delta H$$

This is then valid within the limits of accuracy obtained by dropping the terms of higher order in the expansion. An accuracy of 1 % results when the pressure rise from normal atmospheric pressure is equivalent to about 12 in. of water or less. This represents a considerable range of industrial compressors which are called fans or blowers. A calculation based on head is usually more accurate than attempting to measure the temperature rise, which is of the order of a few degrees only and subject to radiation and conduction errors.

10.22   *Actual blade performance*

Data on different blade profiles of varying curvature and varying spacing are obtained by mounting a set of such blades in linear, parallel fashion in a wind tunnel and taking measurements of fluid inlet and outlet angles and of loss of total pressure. Such rows of blades are called blade *cascades* or lattices. The angle of attack or *incidence*, i.e., the angle between the geometrical blade-inlet angle and the fluid direction, is important. If it becomes too large, loss increases and eventually complete flow separation occurs and the blade is said to stall. A typical plot of cascade data is shown in Fig. 10.39, which is analogous to Fig. 8.24 of a single, isolated airfoil.

The fluid *deflection* or turning angle ($\alpha_1 - \alpha_2$) increases with angle of attack up to the point where stalling occurs with breakdown of ordered flow. The loss coefficient has a region of minimum value around the design condi-

Figure 10.39

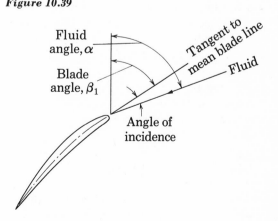

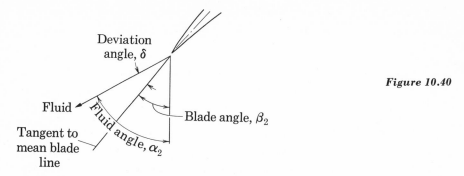

Fluid

Tangent to
mean blade
line

Fluid angle, α_2

Deviation
angle, δ

Blade angle, β_2

Figure 10.40

tion, but rises rapidly as the stall condition is approached. These parameters can be put into terms of lift and drag coefficients as an alternative expression of performance. Data over a range of angle of attack are necessary for two reasons: (1) the blade will experience such a range when operating at part-load conditions; and (2) the maximum efficiency does not necessarily occur when blade angle and fluid angle are the same, i.e., at zero incidence.

Another important phenomenon is that the fluid never leaves the blade at the geometrical blade angle but always at a larger value; i.e., the fluid turning at outlet is always less than the geometrical turning. The difference in angle is called the *deviation*, δ (Fig. 10.40). The effect of deviation is that the total fluid turning angle is less than that given by the blade turning angle. The deviation is analogous to the slip of radial-flow machines and has the same effect, i.e., it does not affect efficiency, as the energy input required is proportional to the actual fluid deflection (ΔV_u). A knowledge of deviation is important for design, in which the problem is to specify a blade arrangement to obtain a given energy transfer (fluid deflection). The amount of fluid deflection possible with compressor blades is limited, because simultaneous diffusion and turning leads to high losses if either is excessive. Fluid deflection angles usually lie within the range 10 to 30°. Deviation angles corresponding to these are approximately 3 to 10°, so that the effect is considerable.

Axial-flow fans and pumps usually have a small number of large blades, consisting of single-stage units of small blade curvature. With large flow area and limited rise of head or pressure, they are high specific-speed units. Axial-flow compressors consist of a number of stages in series capable of giving a relatively high over-all pressure ratio. The number of stages may be as many as 20, although increasing development, particularly for aircraft engines, has led to an increasing stage-pressure ratio, so that seven or eight stages can achieve the same result.

Axial-flow units are subject to Reynolds-number effects qualitatively similar to those studied generally for flow around isolated, immersed bodies. Low values of Reynolds number (based on blade chord as the characteristic dimension) arise with small units, with very viscous fluids, and at high altitude (low density). Pumps are subject to cavitation, which can be a serious matter for the very large units of up to 100,000 hp that are now in use. Mach-number effects are limiting for aircraft gas-turbine compressors, which are designed for maximum fluid and rotor velocities in order to have minimum size and weight. The problem here is that of the transonic regime, i.e., free-stream Mach numbers of 0.75 and above, when local shock waves occur in the regions of high relative velocity around the blade surface. The problem is accentuated by the reduction of air temperature as altitude increases so that a given Mach number increases with altitude even though the fluid and rotor velocities are constant. Thus a Mach number of 0.75 at ground level ($t = 59°F$) becomes 0.865 above the isothermal altitude (at 36,000 ft, $t = -70°F$). Axial-flow compressors can be designed to give efficient operation in the transonic region, but require specialized design skill.

10.23   *Axial-flow turbines*

Axial-flow turbines represent by far the largest group for compressible fluids, both steam and gas, and are frequently employed in hydraulic turbines.

A turbine stage consists of stator blades, usually called *nozzles* because the passage through them invariably accelerates and expands the fluid, and rotor blades, sometimes (but not here) called buckets. Fig. 10.41 is a general diagram. The gas is expanded in the nozzle to a high velocity, V_1. It enters the rotor blades with relative velocity V_{r_1} and in the usual case is expanded further in the rotor so that the exit relative velocity, V_{r_2}, is

Figure 10.41

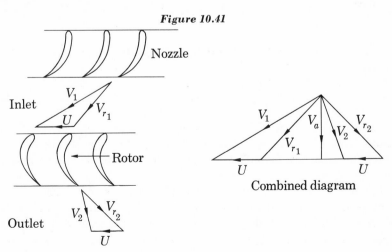

Combined diagram

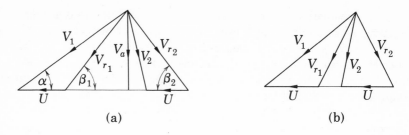

(a)   (b)

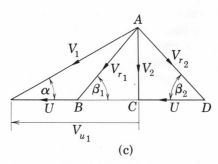

(c)

Figure 10.42

greater than V_{r_1}. The absolute leaving velocity is V_2. If $V_{r_2} > V_{r_1}$, then there is a drop of pressure in the rotor and some finite degree of reaction for the turbine stage. Since $U_1 = U_2 = U$ for an axial-flow machine, the basic relationships are

$$E = \frac{U}{g_c}(V_{u_1} - V_{u_2}) = \frac{1}{2g_c}[(V_1^2 - V_2^2) + (V_{r_2}^2 - V_{r_1}^2)] \quad [10.26a]$$

and
$$R = \frac{(1/2g_c)(V_{r_2}^2 - V_{r_1}^2)}{E} \quad [10.26b]$$

Note that $V_{u_1} - V_{u_2}$ is a vector difference, i.e., in Fig. 10.41, with the sign convention of Sect. 10.3,

$$E = \frac{U}{g_c}[V_{u_1} - V_{u_2}] = \frac{U}{g_c}(V_{u_1} + V_{u_2}) \quad [10.27]$$

Two particular values of reaction are very important, those of $R = 0$ (impulse) and $R = 0.5$ (50% reaction). Practically all steam turbines have either impulse stages or 50%-reaction blading stages or a combination of both.

For $R = 0$, $V_{r_1} = V_{r_2}$, and for ideal flow there is no change of pressure in the rotor, which all takes place in the nozzle and gives a high value of blade inlet absolute velocity V_1. A general impulse-stage velocity diagram appears then as in Fig. 10.42(a). With ideal flow, the only loss is that due to the discharge kinetic energy $V_2^2/2g_c$; i.e., the stage efficiency is equal to the utilization factor, ϵ. Now ϵ has a maximum value when V_2 is a minimum. For a fixed value of U and axial (through-flow) velocity V_a, the nozzle angle, α, and the nozzle discharge velocity, V_1, can vary, and so the discharge velocity, V_2, can be varied. Fig. 10.42(b) is an example. For a minimum value of V_2 for impulse conditions ($V_{r_1} = V_{r_2}$), it is seen that V_2 must be axial, as shown in Fig. 10.42(c). For this condition, $\beta_1 = \beta_2$; i.e., inlet and outlet blade angles are the same, and, from the symmetry of triangles ABC and ADC, then

$$\cos \alpha = \frac{V_{u_1}}{V_1} = \frac{U + U}{V_1} = \frac{2U}{V_1}$$

or
$$\frac{U}{V_1} = \frac{\cos \alpha}{2} \qquad [10.28]$$

Thus for an *ideal impulse* stage, maximum efficiency is achieved for a ratio of blade speed to nozzle velocity equal to $(\cos \alpha)/2$, where α is the nozzle angle. Now

$$\epsilon = \frac{E}{E + V_2^2/2g_c}$$

and for maximum efficiency, V_2 is axial, and $V_{u_2} = 0$; hence $E = UV_{u_1}/g_c$. Thus

$$\epsilon_{\max} = \frac{UV_{u_1}}{UV_{u_1} + V_2^2/2}$$

With $V_{u_1} = V_1 \cos \alpha$ and $V_2 = V_1 \sin \alpha$, then

$$\epsilon_{\max} = \frac{UV_1 \cos \alpha}{UV_1 \cos \alpha + (V_1^2 \sin^2 \alpha)/2}$$

With $U = (V_1 \cos \alpha)/2$, then

$$\epsilon_{\max} = \frac{\cos^2 \alpha}{\cos^2 \alpha + \sin^2 \alpha} = \cos^2 \alpha \qquad [10.29]$$

i.e., the maximum efficiency of an impulse stage is $\cos^2 \alpha$. The maximum value of $\cos^2 \alpha$ is unity, when α must be zero, leading to the ideal "zero-angle" turbine as shown in Fig. 10.43, with $U = V_1/2$. The velocity diagram

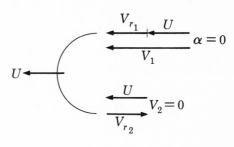

Figure 10.43

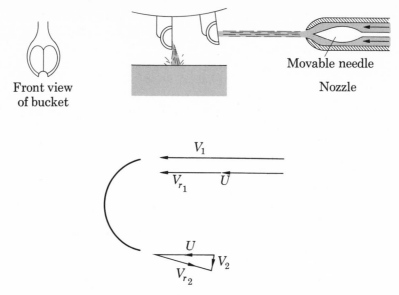

Figure 10.44

demonstrates this, as with $V_1 = 2U$, $V_{r_1} = U = V_{r_2}$, and hence $V_2 = 0$ and $\epsilon = 1$. The zero-angle turbine is an ideal that can never be actually attained for a turbine with continuous admission of fluid, because V_2 must have some finite value to provide a through-flow. Tangential inlet flow is possible only if a small number of nozzles feeds a row of blades around a rotor, as in the Pelton wheel, shown in Fig. 10.44. The velocity diagram shows that V_{r_2} is not quite tangential. This is to give V_2 a finite value so that the following blade does not strike the fluid that is discharging from the preceding blade.

For steam and gas turbines the impulse stage has a finite value of nozzle angle α. Since $E \propto UV_{u_1} = UV_1 \cos \alpha$, small values of α increase the energy transfer and utilization factor. For $\alpha = 20°$, $\cos \alpha = 0.94$, and for maximum utilization, $U/V_1 = (\cos \alpha)/2 = 0.47$, and $\epsilon_{\max} \approx 0.89$. Thus for impulse turbines with the usual low value of α, the approximate rule holds that $U/V_1 \approx \frac{1}{2}$. With the same nozzle angle, ϵ is less than the maximum for any value of U/V_1 other than 0.47. A plot of ϵ vs. U/V_1 is shown in Fig. 10.45. The utilization factor is the efficiency for ideal flow. In practice, friction and turbulence cause losses so that ϵ is modified by an aerodynamic blading efficiency, η_b, and the over-all stage efficiency is reduced, as indicated by the dashed line in Fig. 10.45. The plot of ϵ or η vs. U/V_1 shows what happens when the turbine is run at off-design conditions, e.g., higher values of U/V_1 for constant speed and lower pressure ratio (lower V_1), or for reduced speed and constant pressure ratio.

Losses in steam-turbine blades are measured in terms of a velocity coefficient, C_V, defined as the ratio of actual to ideal discharge velocity for a given pressure ratio. The ideal process is the isentropic process; thus for no initial velocity,

$$C_V = \frac{V_{2_a}}{V_{2_{is}}}$$

From the steady-flow energy equation, with inlet and outlet stations 1 and 2,

$$h_{0_1} = h_2 + \frac{V_2{}^2}{2g_c J}$$

hence
$$V_{2_{is}} = [2g_c J (h_{0_1} - h_2)_{is}]^{\frac{1}{2}}$$

Velocity coefficients are applied to nozzles and rotor blades. Nozzle performance is also expressed as an efficiency, η_n, defined as the ratio of actual discharge kinetic energy to the corresponding isentropic value. Thus

$$\eta_n = \frac{(V_2{}^2)_a}{(V_2{}^2)_{is}} = C_V{}^2$$

Values of C_V for a well-designed nozzle may reach 0.98, as the passage is converging and the only loss is due to skin friction.

From the viewpoint of cost, maximum work per stage is required and thus the highest possible values of blade speed, U, and nozzle velocity, V_1. Values of U are limited by permissible values of stress and these vary widely with temperature, material, and required length of life. Thus a conservatively designed steam turbine expected to have a useful life of at least 20 years may have a limiting blade speed of 800 ft/sec, whereas a turbine for a turbojet may only be expected to have a useful life of a few hundred hours and the blade speed may be 1400 ft/sec or more. The utilization of high blade speeds in conjunction with the optimal impulse relationship, $V_1 = 2U/(\cos \alpha)$, requires convergent-divergent nozzles, the principles of which were studied in Chapter 7. Even if the blade speed is relatively

Figure 10.45

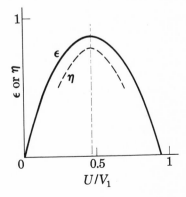

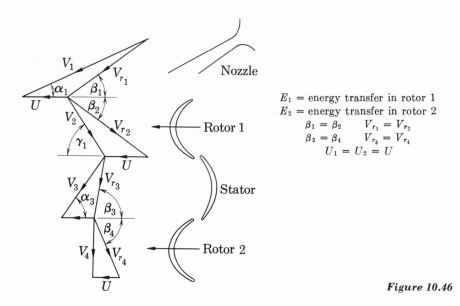

E_1 = energy transfer in rotor 1
E_2 = energy transfer in rotor 2
$\beta_1 = \beta_2$ $V_{r_1} = V_{r_2}$
$\beta_3 = \beta_4$ $V_{r_3} = V_{r_4}$
$U_1 = U_2 = U$

Figure 10.46

low, it is desirable to use high values of V_1 in the first stage or two in order to reduce the pressure and temperature rapidly, and thus minimize the leakage loss due to high pressure and minimize the amount of material subjected to high temperature. A high V_1 and low U can be utilized efficiently by means of *velocity-compounding* in a *Curtis* stage. This is accomplished by a convergent-divergent nozzle and impulse rotor row, followed by a stator row that redirects the fluid, without change of magnitude of the velocity, on to a second rotor row. Thus, in effect, the high nozzle velocity is utilized by two rotor rows in series, and a high utilization factor can be obtained.

An ideal diagram is shown in Fig. 10.46 with the assumed conditions on the right. Thus

$$E_1 = \frac{U}{g_c}(V_{u_1} + V_{u_2}) = \frac{U}{g_c}(V_1 \cos \alpha_1 + V_2 \cos \gamma_1)$$

$$= \frac{U}{g_c}(V_{r_1} \cos \beta_1 + V_{r_2} \cos \beta_2) = \frac{2UV_{r_1} \cos \beta_1}{g_c} = \frac{2U}{g_c}(V_1 \cos \alpha_1 - U)$$

Similarly
$$E_2 = \frac{2U}{g_c}(V_3 \cos \alpha_3 - U)$$

Since
$$V_3 = V_2$$

$$V_3 \cos \alpha_3 = V_2 \cos \gamma_1 = V_{r_2} \cos \beta_2 - U$$

and
$$V_{r_2} \cos \beta_2 - U = V_{r_1} \cos \beta_1 - U = V_1 \cos \alpha_1 - 2U$$

then
$$E_2 = \frac{2U}{g_c}(V_1 \cos \alpha_1 - 3U)$$

The total energy transfer is

$$E = E_1 + E_2 = \frac{2U}{g_c} (2V_1 \cos \alpha_1 - 4U)$$

The energy available, E_{av}, as there is no change of pressure after nozzle discharge, is $V_1{}^2/2g_c$; hence

$$\epsilon = \frac{E}{E_{av}} = \frac{4U}{V_1{}^2} (2V_1 \cos \alpha_1 - 4U) = 8 \frac{U}{V_1} \cos \alpha_1 - 16 \left(\frac{U}{V_1}\right)^2$$

For maximum ϵ, $\partial\epsilon/\partial(U/V_1) = 0$, which yields

$$\frac{U}{V_1} = \frac{\cos \alpha_1}{4} \qquad\qquad [10.30]$$

which is one-half the value for a single impulse stage. Using this value of U/V_1 in the expression for ϵ yields $\epsilon = \cos^2 \alpha_1$, as before. It is also seen that $E_1 = 3E_2$, so that a third rotor row would seldom be very useful because its energy contribution would be small. A Curtis stage is commonly used in steam turbines, but not in gas turbines where the pressures are not sufficiently high to warrant it.

10.24   *50%-reaction stage*

For a 50%-reaction stage, $V_1{}^2 - V_2{}^2 = V_{r_2}^2 - V_{r_1}^2$, and the diagram is symmetrical as in Fig. 10.47(a). Applying the criterion of minimum V_2 for maximum utilization factor as before yields the diagram of Fig. 10.47(b), with V_2 axial and hence coincident with V_{r_1}. It is seen that for ϵ_{max},

$$\frac{U}{V_1} = \cos \alpha \qquad\qquad [10.31]$$

i.e., twice the value for the impulse stage. Thus

$$\epsilon = \frac{UV_{u_1}}{UV_{u_1} + V_2{}^2/2} = \frac{2UV_1 \cos \alpha}{2UV_1 \cos \alpha + V_1{}^2 \sin^2 \alpha}$$

Figure 10.47

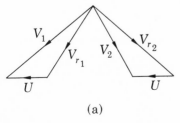

(a)

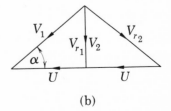

(b)

and, with $U = V_1 \cos \alpha$,

$$\epsilon_{max} = \frac{2 \cos^2 \alpha}{2 \cos^2 \alpha + \sin^2 \alpha} = \frac{2 \cos^2 \alpha}{1 + \cos^2 \alpha} \qquad [10.32]$$

Fig. 10.48 shows the variation of ϵ with U/V_1 for 50% reaction. Fig. 10.48(b) shows ϵ for the two-row Curtis stage (velocity-compounded impulse), the impulse stage, and the 50%-reaction stage, all for a nozzle angle of 20°. Also shown is the relationship for the "full"-reaction Hero turbine analyzed in Sect. 10.19, for which ϵ approaches unity only as the rotor velocity approaches the fluid-discharge velocity.

It must be pointed out here that the definition of reaction as used here is a general one applicable for all forms of turbomachine. For *steam turbines*, 50% reaction is generally defined as *equal enthalpy drop in nozzle and rotor*

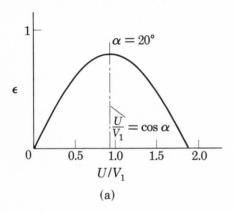

(a)

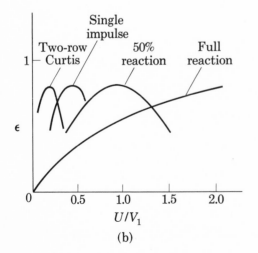

(b)

Figure 10.48

with no initial velocity into the nozzle. Thus

$$\Delta h_{\text{stage}} = \Delta h_{\text{nozzle}} + \Delta h_{\text{rotor}}$$

with $\qquad \Delta h_{\text{nozzle}} = \dfrac{V_1^2}{2g_c} = \Delta h_{\text{rotor}} = \dfrac{V_{r_2}^2 - V_{r_1}^2}{2g_c} = \dfrac{1}{2}\,\Delta h_{\text{stage}}$

This differs from the previous definition in which

$$\frac{V_1^2 - V_2^2}{2g_c} = \frac{V_{r_1}^2 - V_{r_2}^2}{2g_c}$$

Because the absolute velocity leaving the rotor, V_2, is the velocity entering the following nozzle, the steam-turbine definition is equivalent to a disregard of any contribution to energy transfer made by the kinetic energy entering the nozzle. Using this definition of 50% reaction, it can be shown that for maximum utilization, V_2 should again be axial, $U/V_1 = \cos \alpha$ as before, but that the value of $\epsilon_{\max}$ is $\cos^2 \alpha$, similar to that for an impulse turbine, and differing from the previous value, which was $2 \cos^2 \alpha/(1 + \cos^2 \alpha)$. For small values of α, the difference is not large. It is, however, important to recognize the difference in definition, because the steam-turbine definition is of long standing and is often taken as the sole meaning of 50% reaction.

10.25   *Comparison of impulse and 50%-reaction stages*

It has been seen that for maximum utilization factor the rotor velocity–nozzle velocity relationship for these two conditions is

for impulse, $\qquad\qquad \dfrac{U}{V_1} = \dfrac{\cos \alpha}{2}$

for 50% reaction, $\qquad\quad \dfrac{U}{V_1} = \cos \alpha$

For any type of turbine, it is desirable to use the highest allowable blade speed, U, in order to obtain the greatest energy transfer (work) per stage. For maximum utilization, V_2 is axial; thus $V_{u_2} = 0$, and the energy transfer is $U_1 V_{u_1}/g_c = U V_1 \cos \alpha/g_c$. For the impulse turbine, then, for $\epsilon_{\max}$,

$$E_{\text{imp}} = \frac{U V_1 \cos \alpha}{g_c} = \frac{2U^2}{g_c}$$

with $V_1 = 2U/(\cos \alpha)$. For the 50%-reaction turbine, then

$$E_{\text{re}} = \frac{U V_1 \cos \alpha}{g_c} = \frac{U^2}{g_c}$$

with $V_1 = U/(\cos \alpha)$. With U the same for both, then the energy transfer for the impulse stage is twice that of the reaction stage. For the same energy transfer in both, then the blade speed for the reaction stage would have to be $\sqrt{2}$ times that for the impulse stage. Because the impulse stage uses very high velocities and because the rotor blades have no accelerating effect to keep the boundary layer thin, the aerodynamic efficiency of a reaction stage is usually greater than that of the impulse stage. Thus, although a multistage turbine can be made up of a succession of impulse stages, when it is known as a *Rateau* type of turbine, it is more usual to have a few impulse stages initially (of which one may be the Curtis velocity-compounded type) in order to obtain maximum work per stage and rapid lowering of pressure and temperature, followed by a much larger number of reaction stages of higher efficiency.

10.26   *Torque characteristics*

An important feature of a turbine can be the torque it exerts under different conditions. Thus for acceleration when starting under load, as in traction applications (e.g., automotive), the torque-speed relationship may be crucial. A simple analysis of an ideal impulse stage will help to demonstrate these characteristics. Fig. 10.49(a) shows a general velocity diagram for an impulse stage. The torque on the blade has been shown to be proportional

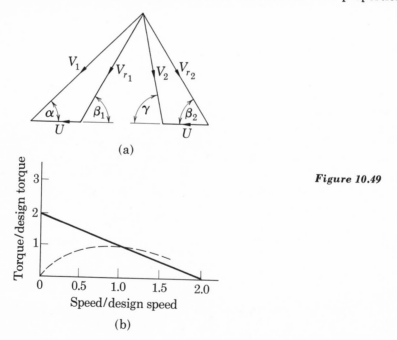

(a)

(b)

Figure 10.49

to the change of tangential velocity, thus

$$T \propto V_1 \cos \alpha + V_2 \cos \gamma = (V_{r_1} \cos \beta_1 + U) + (V_{r_2} \cos \beta_2 - U)$$

For the ideal case with $V_{r_1} = V_{r_2}$ and $\beta_1 = \beta_2$,

$$T \propto 2V_{r_1} \cos \beta_1 = 2(V_1 \cos \alpha - U)$$

Thus for a fixed nozzle angle and nozzle-outlet velocity, the torque is a linear function of blade speed. When $U/V_1 = \cos \alpha$, the torque is zero. When $U/V_1 = (\cos \alpha)/2$, the correct design condition (ϵ_{max}), the torque is proportional to $V_1 \cos \alpha$. When $U/V_1 = 0$, rotor stationary, the torque is proportional to $2V_1 \cos \alpha$. The torque-speed relationship on a ratio basis for a given V_1 then appears as in Fig. 10.49(b). The "stand-still" or stationary torque is thus twice the design-point torque and provides rapid acceleration. The general form of the torque-speed characteristic of a reciprocating engine (e.g., automotive) is shown as a dotted line for the same design torque. The low torque at low speed necessitates either gearing or a torque converter for traction purposes; a turbine can minimize this requirement.

Problems

10.1. A fan has a bladed rotor of 12 in. o.d. and 5 in. i.d. and runs at 1725 rpm. The width of the rotor blades is 1 in. and is constant from inlet to outlet. The flow rate is 230 ft³/min, and the air flows in a purely radial direction at the blade inlet,

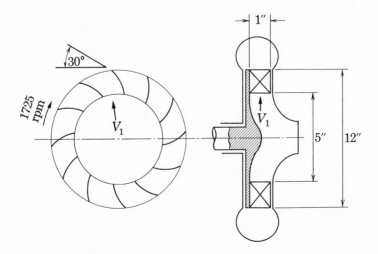

where the pressure is 14.58 psia and the temperature is 70°F. The blades at discharge are inclined at an angle of 30° to the tangential direction at the o.d. Assume ideal, incompressible flow throughout.

    a. Draw the velocity diagram at inlet, and calculate the blade angle at inlet so that the air meets the blade with zero angle of attack ("shockless" entry).

    b. Draw the velocity diagram at outlet, assuming that the angle of the air relative to the blades is zero.

10.2. For the fan of Problem 10.1,

    a. Find the total pressure rise of the air in in. H_2O by means of the basic Euler turbine equation.

    b. Repeat a by means of the second form of the Euler equation, and find the percentages of the total energy transfer contributed by each energy term.

    c. Find the power required.

    d. Find the degree of reaction.

10.3. A radial-outward-flow fan has rotor-vane angles of 45° at inlet and 90° at outlet. The rotor o.d. is twice the rotor i.d., the radial-flow velocity is constant from inlet to outlet, and the inlet angular momentum is zero. Show that the degree of reaction is 0.5.

10.4. A centrifugal water pump is required to operate at a flow rate of 250 ft³/sec, a head of 410 ft, and a speed of 350 rpm. A scale model of this pump is to be tested in a laboratory where a maximum flow rate of 5 ft³/sec and a power supply of 300 hp are available. If model and prototype efficiencies are each assumed to be 100% for a first estimate, calculate the model speed and scale ratio.

10.5. A pump delivers 20 gal/min of water at a head of 40 ft when running at 3600 rpm. The temperature of the water is 50°F. Find the water temperature necessary for complete similitude, if the pump is to be run at 1800 rpm. Find the flow rate, head, and specific speed under the new conditions. Compare specific speeds for the two conditions.

10.6. A hydraulic turbine is designed for a flow rate of 1325 ft³/sec at an available head of 180 ft. Assuming the same efficiency for both, find the linear scale ratings of model and prototype if the model is to be tested in a laboratory where water is available at 15 ft head at a flow rate of 1 ft³/sec.

10.7. A compressor for a turbojet engine, tested at ground level at a barometric pressure of 29.13 in. Hg and an air temperature of 87°F, gives a discharge pressure of 73.4 psi gage and a mass flow rate of 104.7 lb/sec when the actual engine rpm is 9000. For operation in the aircraft at an altitude of 50,000 ft, where the air pressure is 1.68 psia and the temperature is −70°F,

    a. Find the actual rpm necessary for the flow conditions to be similar to those at ground level.

    b. If, at this rpm and altitude, the discharge pressure was measured as 8.65 psig, estimate as closely as possible the anticipated mass flow rate.

10.8. A high-speed axial-flow compressor is designed to run at 10,000 rpm with a flow rate of 75 lb/sec and a pressure ratio of 4. Design conditions assume standard air at inlet. At 35,000 ft a discharge pressure of 10.37 psig and a speed of 8720 rpm are recorded. Estimate the mass rate of flow and justify your answer.

10.9. A centrifugal pump having an impeller diameter of 6 in., an impeller-tip flow width of $\frac{3}{8}$ in., and vanes backward curved at 25° runs at 1725 rpm. The water flow rate is 200 gal/min; the hydraulic efficiency is estimated as 72%, and the slip factor as 0.80. Find the values of (a) Euler head, (b) ideal head, (c) actual head, and (d) input power. Assume no inlet whirl velocity.

10.10. A centrifugal compressor for a gas turbine has to compress air through a total pressure ratio of 4, the inlet conditions being 60°F and 14.7 psia. The impeller has radial vanes ($\beta_2 = 90°$) and a tip diameter of 21 in.; the slip factor is estimated as 0.90 and the isentropic efficiency as 0.78. The radial velocity at impeller discharge is 250 ft/sec. Calculate (a) the necessary speed in rpm, and (b) the absolute Mach number of the air at impeller outlet.

10.11. A centrifugal pump taken from stores has no name plate, but the impeller is measured and found to have a diameter of 5 in., a tip width of $\frac{3}{8}$ in., and blades backward curved at 20°. The pump is to be directly connected to a 3600 rpm motor. If it is assumed that the radial velocity is 10 ft/sec, that the slip factor is 0.7, and that the total head hydraulic efficiency is 75%, calculate the expected delivery total head and flow rate (in gal/min).

10.12. A centrifugal pump delivering 200 gal/min of water has an impeller diameter of 7 in. with vanes backward curved at 30°. Its speed is 1740 rpm, and the radial component of velocity at impeller discharge is 10 ft/sec. The pump is assumed to operate with no inlet whirl and to have a hydraulic efficiency of 0.75, with a loss of 0.25 hp in the bearings and glands. The impeller is assumed to have a slip factor of 0.8.

    a. Find the useful head delivered.

    b. Find the required driving hp.

    c. If a pump of similar design but of different size is to be made, having four times the flow rate and running at twice the speed, estimate the head delivered and the power required at the design point.

10.13. A radial-flow fan test yields the following data:

Speed	2320 rpm
Flow rate	424 ft³/min
Discharge static pressure measured in a 4 in. diameter pipe	6.2 in. H₂O
Power supplied at pump coupling	0.95 hp
Estimated mechanical loss	0.28 hp
Barometric pressure	28.92 in. Hg
Inlet air temperature	73°F
No angular momentum at inlet	

    a. Calculate the efficiency based on incompressible flow.

    b. Calculate the necessary vane angle at discharge if the rotor diameter is 16.5 in. and the rotor width is 1.13 in. (slip factor of unity).

10.14. A centrifugal compressor with radial blades (90°) is running at an impeller-tip speed of 1300 ft/sec. The stagnation pressure ratio is measured as 3.3, and the inlet air temperature is 60°F. If the slip factor is known to be 0.9, calculate the stagnation efficiency of the compressor. Take $c_p = 0.24$ Btu/lb-°R and $k = 1.4$.

10.15. A radial-flow water pump, operating at its maximum efficiency point, delivers 100 gal/min with a useful total pressure rise of 30 psig when running at 3450 rpm. At this condition it absorbs an input power of 2.61 hp.

    a. Find the over-all efficiency of the pump.

    b. Find the hydraulic efficiency if the mechanical losses are estimated to be 0.25 hp.

    c. Estimate the flow rate of a geometrically similar pump of one-half the linear dimensions that is running at the same speed and at its maximum efficiency point.

    d. Find the specific speed of the half-size pump of c. State clearly any assumptions made.

10.16. An ideal radial-inflow turbine has a nozzle angle of 30°. The air leaving the nozzle has a velocity of 1000 ft/sec. The inlet angle to the rotor is 45°. The ratio of inlet to exit diameters of the rotor is 2. If the through-flow velocity of the machine is constant and it is designed for maximum utilization,

    a. Sketch the velocity triangles.

    b. Calculate the specific rate of energy transfer.

    c. Calculate the degree of reaction of the machine.

    d. Find the blade exit angle.

    e. Find the hydraulic efficiency of the turbine.

    f. Find the utilization factor of the turbine.

10.17. An inward-radial-flow turbine has a nozzle angle α and rotor blades that are radial at entry. The radial velocity is constant, and there is no tangential velocity at discharge. Show that the utilization factor is

$$\frac{2 \cos^2 \alpha}{1 + \cos^2 \alpha}$$

10.18. A lawn sprinkler has two arms, each having a nozzle of $\frac{1}{16}$ in. diameter at 6 in. radius, with the nozzles being tangentially opposed. The water enters with zero tangential velocity and leaves the nozzle with an absolute velocity of 20 ft/sec. The sprinkler is rotating at a constant speed of 300 rpm. Assuming the internal flow to be frictionless, find the utilization factor and the hp used in overcoming external resistance.

10.19. A small air turbine is designed on the lines of a Hero turbine as shown. If $\frac{1}{4}$ lb/sec of air is supplied at the axial inlet station at stagnation conditions of 45 psig and 200°F, find the hp output for a design speed of 30,000 rpm. Neglect friction and external drag.

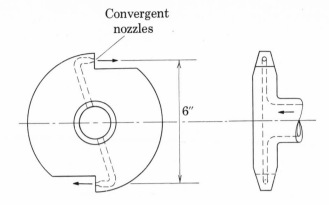

Convergent
nozzles

6″

10.20. Sketch the velocity triangles for an axial-flow fan made as follows: the inlet air flows onto the stator blades at zero incidence and leaves the stators at an angle of 45°; the absolute velocity of the air leaving the rotor is purely axial. If the axial velocity remains constant and equal to the wheel speed of 200 ft/sec, find all blade angles and the total turning angle of the rotor blades. Find the degree of reaction. Calculate the head rise in feet of flowing fluid. Assume ideal flow.

10.21. The first stage of an axial-flow compressor has 50% reaction and a stagnation pressure ratio of 1.13. The axial velocity is 400 ft/sec, and the rotor-blade angles are 45° at inlet and 29° at outlet. Find the necessary blade speed. Assume that the flow is ideal and that fluid angles are the same as blade angles. Take the inlet air condition to be 14.7 psia and 60°F.

10.22. Show that for a 50%-reaction axial-flow compressor stage, with constant axial velocity, the velocity diagram is symmetrical about the axis.

10.23. An axial-flow pump consists of a rotor row followed by a row of stator blades. The water enters the rotor axially with an absolute velocity of 10 ft/sec. The inlet rotor blade angle is 60°, and the outlet angle is 45°. If the flow is considered as ideal, find the change in total head of the water and the correct inlet angle for the stator blades.

10.24. An axial-flow pump has three stages, each with rotor-blade inlet and outlet angles of 45° and 15°, respectively. The flow rate is 735 gal/min, the axial velocity is 4.75 ft/sec, the blade speed is 6.88 ft/sec, and the measured-delivery total head is 17.6 in. H₂O. The water temperature is 50°F.
  a. Draw the velocity diagrams.
  b. Calculate the efficiency and power required, exclusive of mechanical and disk friction losses, assuming the incidence as zero and the deviation angle as 8.8°.
  c. Calculate the power required if this pump uses air as the working medium for conditions similar to those for water, assuming that the air is incompressible under these circumstances. Take the inlet air pressure and temperature as 29.24 in. Hg and 77°F.

10.25. A single-wheel axial-flow impulse turbine has a nozzle angle of 30°. If the wheel speed is 800 ft/sec and the wheel is designed for maximum utilization (assume ideal flow),

   a. Draw the velocity triangles approximately to scale.
   b. Find the values of all velocities.
   c. Find the blade angles for the rotor.
   d. Calculate the specific rate of energy transfer.
   e. Calculate the utilization factor.
   f. What is the hydraulic efficiency of the turbine?

10.26. An axial-flow turbine stage with 50% reaction is operating at maximum utilization and is rotating at 9000 rpm. The turbine diameter at the mean blade height is 24 in. Find the output of the turbine in hp/(lb/sec) of gas.

10.27. An axial-flow impulse-turbine stage using air and operating at maximum utilization has a nozzle-inlet temperature of 1000°R and a blade speed of 1000 ft/sec. It delivers 75 shaft hp when the isentropic stagnation efficiency of the stage is 90%. Find (a) the required stagnation pressure ratio across the stage, and (b) the required mass flow rate.

10.28. Find the necessary blade speed for an axial-flow impulse-turbine stage operating at maximum utilization to deliver 120 hp/(lb/sec) of fluid.

10.29. A turbine having 50% reaction has a nozzle angle of 30° and a blade speed of 1000 ft/sec and is operating at maximum utilization. At nozzle inlet the pressure is 60 psia, the temperature is 1350°F, and the velocity is negligible. Assume isentropic flow with c_p constant at 0.274 Btu/lb$_m$-°R and $R = 53.3$ ft-lb$_f$/lb$_m$-°R. If state 1 is at nozzle inlet, state 2 is between nozzle and rotor, and state 3 is at rotor exit,

   a. Find (a) absolute velocities V_2 and V_3, (b) rotor blade angles β_2 and β_3, (c) static and stagnation temperatures at 2 and 3, (d) static and stagnation pressures at 2 and 3, (e) stagnation pressure ratio between 1 and 3, (f) absolute Mach number at 2, (g) specific rate of energy transfer at hp.
   b. Repeat a for an impulse stage with the same nozzle inlet conditions, nozzle angle, and blade speed, again for maximum utilization.
   c. Tabulate the values for a and b and study the comparison.

10.30. An axial-flow gas-turbine stage has a nozzle angle of 20° and a rotor-blade angle of 60°. The axial gas velocity is 400 ft/sec. If the stage is to operate at maximum utilization, find the degree of reaction. Assume ideal flow.

10.31. An axial-flow turbine stage has a nozzle angle of 30° and a rotor-blade speed of 600 ft/sec. The axial velocity of the air is the same throughout the stage at 600 ft/sec. Assume ideal flow throughout.

   a. Find the rotor-blade angles at inlet and outlet if the reaction of the stage is required to be 0.5.
   b. For the same nozzle angle, axial velocity, and blade speed, find the degree of reaction for maximum utilization.

10.32. The turbine of a turbojet engine delivers shaft power just sufficient to drive the compressor, the remaining expansion energy being available for propulsion, and is to supply a compressor power of 5275 hp when operating at maximum utilization. The nozzle-inlet stagnation conditions are 55 psia and 1500°F, the mass flow rate is 50 lb/sec, and the rotor blade speed is 1100 ft/sec. The axial velocity at rotor outlet is 680 ft/sec. Take $c_p = 0.276$ Btu/lb-°R and $k = 1.333$. Assume a reversible adiabatic process, zero blade incidence and deviation, and constant axial velocity component through the stage. Find (a) the required nozzle angle, (b) the required rotor blade angles at inlet and outlet, (c) the degree of reaction, and (d) the stagnation pressure at rotor outlet.

Appendix: Vector Analysis

Vector quantities possess both magnitude and direction, in contrast to scalar quantities, which have only magnitude. Such quantities as force, momentum, and acceleration are vectors, whereas mass, density, energy, and temperature are scalars. A displacement is a simple example of a vector. This can be represented graphically by a straight line between two fixed points in space. Thus, in Fig. A.1, vector **B**, in bold-face type, is the displacement between points P and Q. The *magnitude* of **B** is a scalar, symbolized by B; or we may say that the *absolute* value of **B** is $|\mathbf{B}|$, the vertical-bar notation standing for absolute (scalar) value or magnitude.

A.1 *Vector addition*

The addition of vectors **B** and **C** is represented geometrically in Fig. A.1 by the line from P to R. Vector **C** is given by line QR. The sum $(\mathbf{B} + \mathbf{C})$ is then given by line PR drawn from the tail of **B** to the head of **C**. It can be

Figure A.1

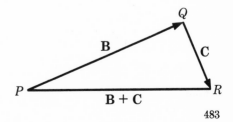

easily seen that the addition of vectors is commutative; i.e., the order of addition is immaterial, so that

$$\mathbf{B} + \mathbf{C} = \mathbf{C} + \mathbf{B}$$

A.2   *Unit vectors*

Representation of a vector in terms of its components with respect to a set of coordinate axes is most conveniently carried out with unit vectors or vectors of unit lengths in the directions of the coordinate axes, together with the magnitudes of the components.

Thus, in Fig. A.2, for Cartesian coordinates,

$$\mathbf{B} = \mathbf{i}B_x + \mathbf{j}B_y$$

The unit vector can be placed either before or behind the magnitude symbol; i.e., $\mathbf{i}B \equiv B\mathbf{i}$. With three dimensions, the unit vector in the z direction is denoted by $\mathbf{k}$. For polar coordinates, we have unit vector $\mathbf{e}_r$ in the radial direction and unit vector $\mathbf{e}_\theta$ perpendicular to it, as in Fig. A.3(a).

The relationship of Cartesian and polar unit vectors can be seen from Fig. A.3(b). Unit vector $\mathbf{e}_r$ is equal to the vector sum of its two components, which have magnitudes $e_r \cos \theta$ and $e_r \sin \theta$ and directions $\mathbf{i}$ and $\mathbf{j}$, respectively. Hence

$$\mathbf{e}_r = |\mathbf{e}_r| \, (\cos \theta) \, \mathbf{i} + |\mathbf{e}_r| \, (\sin \theta) \, \mathbf{j} = e_r \, (\cos \theta) \, \mathbf{i} + e_r \, (\sin \theta) \, \mathbf{j}$$

Since $\mathbf{e}_r$ is a unit vector, the magnitude or absolute value is unity, and so it can be dropped; the result is

$$\mathbf{e}_r = \mathbf{i} \cos \theta + \mathbf{j} \sin \theta \tag{A.1}$$

Similarly, from the diagram,

$$\mathbf{e}_\theta = -\mathbf{i} \sin \theta + \mathbf{j} \cos \theta \tag{A.2}$$

with the minus sign required because $\mathbf{i}$ is defined as positive to the right and the component $e_\theta \sin \theta$ is directed oppositely.

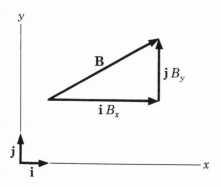

Figure A.2

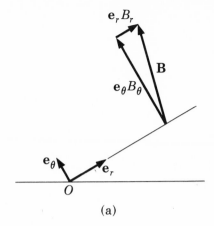

(a)

Figure A.3

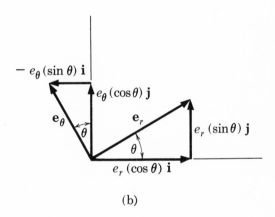

(b)

A.3   *Vector multiplication and the vector product*

Multiplication of vectors can be of three kinds. Simple multiplication of a vector by a positive scalar changes only the magnitude of the vector and not its direction. Therefore, multiplication is distributive; i.e.,

$$a(\mathbf{B} + \mathbf{C}) = a\mathbf{B} + a\mathbf{C}$$

If a is negative, then the direction is reversed. In terms of components in Cartesian coordinates with unit vectors,

$$a(\mathbf{B} + \mathbf{C}) = a(\mathbf{i}B_x + \mathbf{j}B_y + \mathbf{i}C_x + \mathbf{j}C_y) = \mathbf{i}a(B_x + C_x) + \mathbf{j}a(B_y + C_y)$$

The *scalar* product of two vectors, denoted by $\mathbf{B} \cdot \mathbf{C}$ and also known as the "dot" product, is the product of the magnitudes of $\mathbf{B}$ and $\mathbf{C}$, BC, and

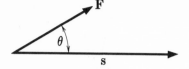

the cosine of the angle θ between them. Thus

$$\mathbf{B} \cdot \mathbf{C} = BC \cos \theta \tag{A.3}$$

This may be regarded as C times the projection of B on C (or as B times the projection of C on B). The product is a scalar. As an example of a scalar product, we may cite work as the result of a force, $\mathbf{F}$, acting through a distance, $\mathbf{s}$, not in the line of action of the force. In Fig. A.4, work $W = \mathbf{F} \cdot \mathbf{s} = Fs \cos \theta$. The scalar product of unit vectors of like kind is unity; e.g.,

$$\mathbf{i} \cdot \mathbf{i} = |\mathbf{i}|\,|\mathbf{i}| \cos \theta = (1)(1) \cos 0° = 1$$

and similarly
$$\mathbf{j} \cdot \mathbf{j} = \mathbf{k} \cdot \mathbf{k} = 1$$

The scalar product of unit vectors of unlike kind is zero; e.g.,

$$\mathbf{i} \cdot \mathbf{j} = |\mathbf{i}|\,|\mathbf{j}| \cos 90° = (1)(1)(0) = 0$$

and similarly
$$\mathbf{j} \cdot \mathbf{k} = \mathbf{k} \cdot \mathbf{i} = 0$$

The scalar product of vectors in component form may be reduced as follows:

$$\mathbf{B} \cdot \mathbf{C} = (\mathbf{i}B_x + \mathbf{j}B_y + \mathbf{k}B_z) \cdot (\mathbf{i}C_x + \mathbf{j}C_y + \mathbf{k}C_z) = B_xC_x + B_yC_y + B_zC_z \tag{A.4}$$

by virtue of the values of the dot products of unit vectors just given.

The *vector*, or "cross," product, denoted by $\mathbf{B} \times \mathbf{C}$, is defined as a vector in a direction perpendicular to the plane containing the two vectors $\mathbf{B}$ and $\mathbf{C}$, with a magnitude equal to the product of the absolute values of the two vectors and the sine of the angle between them, $BC \sin \theta$. The sense of the vector product is given by the right-hand rule; i.e., the direction is that taken by a right-hand screw when turned from the first to the second term of the product. Thus, in Fig. A.5(a), if $\mathbf{B}$ and $\mathbf{C}$ are in the xy plane, the vector product is in the direction normal to the xy plane, i.e., in the z direction. This is indicated by a unit vector, $\mathbf{k}$. Since the right-hand rule applies,

$$\mathbf{B} \times \mathbf{C} = BC\,(\sin \theta)\,\mathbf{k} \tag{A.5}$$

with $\mathbf{k}$ in the positive z direction. For $\mathbf{C} \times \mathbf{B}$ (Fig. A.5(b)), then, by the right-hand rule, the product is in the negative z direction, and hence

$$\mathbf{C} \times \mathbf{B} = -\,\mathbf{B} \times \mathbf{C} \tag{A.6}$$

A simple example of a vector product is the moment of a force around a

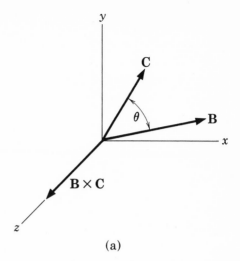

(a)

Figure A.5

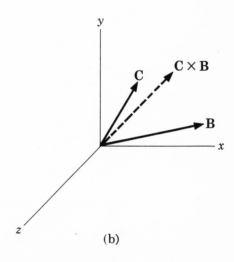

(b)

point. In Fig. A.6, **F** is a force, and **r** is the position vector with respect to any point, P, on the line of action of the force. The moment of **F** about O is the vector product **F** ✕ **r**. If ON is the perpendicular from O to the line of action of **F**, the magnitude of the moment is

$$F(ON) = F(OP \sin \theta) = Fr \sin \theta$$

Division of a vector by a scalar is covered by the multiplication rule, and division of a vector by a vector is not defined.

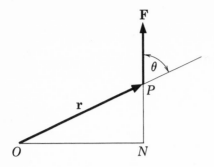

Figure A.6

A.4   Surfaces in vector notation

Very often it is convenient to represent a surface (area) in vector fashion, to give it both magnitude and direction. To do this, we characterize the surface by a vector *normal* to it and directed *outward* from it, as shown in Fig. A.7(a). In terms of a unit vector, we may write $d\mathbf{A} = \mathbf{n}\, dA$.

The components of a surface, $\mathbf{A}$, at some angle, θ, with the x axis are shown in Fig. A.7(b). Because the surface is characterized by an outward normal, the component of $\mathbf{A}$ projected on the y plane is obtained in terms of the normal to the y direction, so that $\mathbf{A}_x = \mathbf{i} A_x$. Similarly, $\mathbf{A}_y = \mathbf{j} A_y$. In scalar terms,

$$A_x = \mathbf{A} \cdot \mathbf{i} = \mathbf{n} A \cdot \mathbf{i} = A \cos (90° - \theta) = A \sin \theta \qquad \text{(A.7a)}$$
$$A_y = \mathbf{A} \cdot \mathbf{j} = \mathbf{n} A \cdot \mathbf{j} = A \cos \theta \qquad\qquad\qquad \text{(A.7b)}$$

Figure A.7

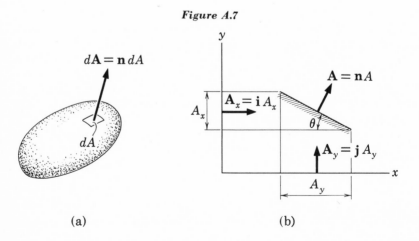

(a)   (b)

A.5 *Vector calculus*

The derivative of a vector is the usual derivative if the vector is a function of a *scalar* quantity. Thus, if $\mathbf{B} = \mathbf{B}(t)$, then

$$\frac{d\mathbf{B}}{dt} = \lim_{\Delta t \to 0} \frac{\mathbf{B}(t + \Delta t) - \mathbf{B}(t)}{\Delta t}$$

For the components of a vector $\mathbf{B} = \mathbf{i}B_x + \mathbf{j}B_y + \mathbf{k}B_z$,

$$\frac{d\mathbf{B}}{dt} = \frac{d}{dt}(\mathbf{i}B_x + \mathbf{j}B_y + \mathbf{k}B_z) = \left(\mathbf{i}\frac{dB_x}{dt} + B_x\frac{d\mathbf{i}}{dt}\right) + \left(\mathbf{j}\frac{dB_y}{dt} + B_y\frac{d\mathbf{j}}{dt}\right)$$
$$+ \left(\mathbf{k}\frac{dB_z}{dt} + B_z\frac{d\mathbf{k}}{dt}\right)$$

The unit vectors $\mathbf{i}$, $\mathbf{j}$, and $\mathbf{k}$ are fixed in magnitude and direction; i.e., they are invariant with t. Hence $d\mathbf{i}/dt$, etc. $= 0$, and so

$$\frac{d\mathbf{B}}{dt} = \mathbf{i}\frac{dB_x}{dt} + \mathbf{j}\frac{dB_y}{dt} + \mathbf{k}\frac{dB_z}{dt} \qquad (A.8)$$

With polar coordinates, the unit vectors $\mathbf{e}_r$ and $\mathbf{e}_\theta$ are not fixed in direction and are functions of the angle θ. From Eqs. A.1 and A.2,

$$\mathbf{e}_r = \mathbf{i}\cos\theta + \mathbf{j}\sin\theta$$

and
$$\mathbf{e}_\theta = -\mathbf{i}\sin\theta + \mathbf{j}\cos\theta$$

Therefore,
$$\frac{d\mathbf{e}_r}{d\theta} = -\mathbf{i}\sin\theta + \mathbf{j}\cos\theta = \mathbf{e}_\theta \qquad (A.9)$$

and
$$\frac{d\mathbf{e}_\theta}{d\theta} = -\mathbf{i}\cos\theta - \mathbf{j}\sin\theta = -\mathbf{e}_r \qquad (A.10)$$

If we have a position vector, $\mathbf{R}$, of the point $P(r, \theta)$ (Fig. A.8), so that $|\mathbf{R}| = r$, then $\mathbf{R} = \mathbf{e}_r r$. Differentiating with respect to a scalar quantity, t, remembering that $\mathbf{e}_r = \mathbf{e}_r(\theta)$, we obtain

$$\frac{d\mathbf{R}}{dt} = \mathbf{e}_r\frac{dr}{dt} + r\frac{d\mathbf{e}_r}{dt} = \mathbf{e}_r\frac{dr}{dt} + r\frac{d\mathbf{e}_r}{d\theta}\frac{d\theta}{dt} = \mathbf{e}_r\frac{dr}{dt} + \mathbf{e}_\theta r\frac{d\theta}{dt} \qquad (A.11)$$

Figure A.8

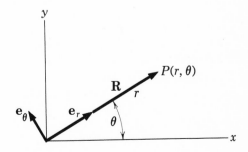

With t as time, $d\mathbf{R}/dt = \mathbf{V}$, the velocity. The components of the velocity are $dr/dt = u_r$ in the $\mathbf{e}_r$ direction and $r\, d\theta/dt = u_\theta$ in the $\mathbf{e}_\theta$ direction.

Integration of a vector is the reverse of differentiation. Thus, if $\mathbf{B} = \mathbf{B}(t)$, and

$$\frac{d\mathbf{B}}{dt} = \mathbf{a}$$

then

$$\int \mathbf{a}\, dt = \mathbf{B} + \mathbf{C} \tag{A.12}$$

where $\mathbf{C}$ is a constant vector.

A.6   *Vector analysis*

There are three important vector operators, the gradient, the divergence, and the curl. They are of great utility in fluid dynamics, both because when applied to a given variable they express certain events commonly occurring and because they provide a short and convenient notation.

The *gradient* of a scalar function $\phi = \phi(x, y, z)$ may be defined geometrically as a vector whose direction is the direction in which ϕ changes most rapidly and whose magnitude is the rate of change of ϕ per unit distance in that direction (a directional derivative). Thus

$$\text{grad } \phi = \mathbf{i}\,\frac{\partial \phi}{\partial x} + \mathbf{j}\,\frac{\partial \phi}{\partial y} + \mathbf{k}\,\frac{\partial \phi}{\partial z} \tag{A.13}$$

The variable ϕ is a scalar, but grad ϕ is a vector, as it expresses the rate of maximum change and also gives the direction of this rate of change.

We may also look at this by considering the differential of ϕ, i.e.,

$$d\phi = \frac{\partial \phi}{\partial x}\, dx + \frac{\partial \phi}{\partial y}\, dy + \frac{\partial \phi}{\partial z}\, dz$$

The terms on the right-hand side are the scalar (dot) product of grad ϕ and a vector, $d\mathbf{s}$, whose three components are dx, dy, and dz. Hence

$$d\phi = d\mathbf{s} \cdot \text{grad } \phi$$

Symbolically, grad ϕ can be denoted by $\nabla\phi$, where ∇ ("del") performs on a scalar quantity ϕ to give the vector $\nabla\phi$. Therefore, we may write in general

$$\nabla \equiv \mathbf{i}\,\frac{\partial}{\partial x} + \mathbf{j}\,\frac{\partial}{\partial y} + \mathbf{k}\,\frac{\partial}{\partial z} \tag{A.14}$$

The term $\nabla\phi$ may be thought of as the simple product of vector ∇ and scalar ϕ. Along these lines we may form the scalar product of ∇ and another vector, **V**. If $\mathbf{V} = \mathbf{V}(x, y, z)$, then

$$\nabla \cdot \mathbf{V} = \frac{\partial V_x}{\partial x} + \frac{\partial V_y}{\partial y} + \frac{\partial V_z}{\partial z} \tag{A.15}$$

This is known as the *divergence* of **V**, or div **V**. Divergence is a scalar quantity, being the dot product of a vector and a vector operator. If **V** has the components V_x, V_y, and V_z in the x, y, and z directions, respectively, then $\mathbf{V} = \mathbf{i}V_x + \mathbf{j}V_y + \mathbf{k}V_z$. Consequently,

$$\text{div } \mathbf{V} = \nabla \cdot \mathbf{V} = \left(\mathbf{i}\frac{\partial}{\partial x} + \mathbf{j}\frac{\partial}{\partial y} + \mathbf{k}\frac{\partial}{\partial z} \right) \cdot (\mathbf{i}V_x + \mathbf{j}V_y + \mathbf{k}V_z)$$

By the rules previously formulated ($\mathbf{i} \cdot \mathbf{i} = 1$, $\mathbf{i} \cdot \mathbf{j} = 0$, etc.), this reduces to

$$\text{div } \mathbf{V} = \nabla \cdot \mathbf{V} = \frac{\partial V_x}{\partial x} + \frac{\partial V_y}{\partial y} + \frac{\partial V_z}{\partial z} \tag{A.16}$$

Similar to gradient as the simple product of ∇ and a scalar and to divergence as the scalar product of ∇ and a vector is the third operator, the *curl*, defined as the vector (cross) product of ∇ and a vector **V**. If $\mathbf{V} = \mathbf{V}(x, y, z)$, then

$$\text{curl } \mathbf{V} = \nabla \times \mathbf{V} = \mathbf{i}\left(\frac{\partial V_z}{\partial y} - \frac{\partial V_y}{\partial z} \right) + \mathbf{j}\left(\frac{\partial V_x}{\partial z} - \frac{\partial V_z}{\partial x} \right) + \mathbf{k}\left(\frac{\partial V_y}{\partial x} - \frac{\partial V_x}{\partial y} \right) \tag{A.17}$$

The result is by definition a vector. The six terms on the right-hand side may be conveniently calculated from the expansion of the third-order determinant, thus:

$$\text{curl } \mathbf{V} = \begin{vmatrix} \mathbf{i} & \mathbf{j} & \mathbf{k} \\ \dfrac{\partial}{\partial x} & \dfrac{\partial}{\partial y} & \dfrac{\partial}{\partial z} \\ V_x & V_y & V_z \end{vmatrix} \tag{A.18}$$

Mathematical definitions of the operators gradient, divergence, and curl are as follows:

$$\text{grad } \phi = \lim_{R \to 0} \frac{\iint_S \phi \, d\mathbf{s}}{R} \tag{A.19}$$

$$\text{div } \mathbf{V} = \lim_{R \to 0} \frac{\iint_S \mathbf{V} \cdot d\mathbf{s}}{R} \tag{A.20}$$

$$\text{curl } \mathbf{V} = \lim_{R \to 0} \frac{\iint_S \mathbf{V} \times d\mathbf{s}}{R} \tag{A.21}$$

where R is a region (volume) in space and S is the surface of the region.

We can obtain the values of the gradient, divergence, and curl as given by Eqs. A.13, A.15, and A.16 by considering a small region as a parallelopiped of sides Δx, Δy, and Δz and performing a simple summation of all six sides in conjunction with unit vectors $\mathbf{i}$, $\mathbf{j}$, and $\mathbf{k}$. This is suggested as an exercise in the use of vector analysis. The body of the text demonstrates that physical meaning can be given to these operations in fluid mechanics.

Index

493

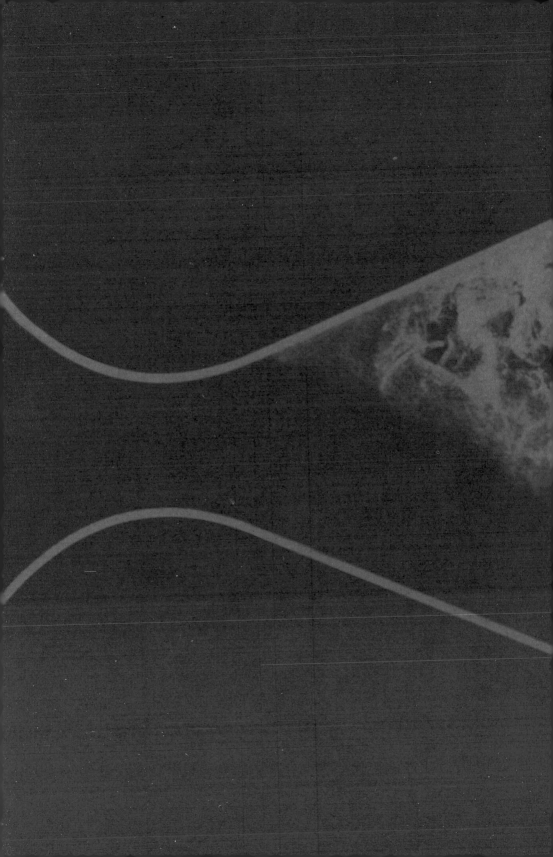